Student Edition

## SpringBoard®

# Mathematics

## Algebra 2

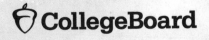
CollegeBoard

## About the College Board

The College Board is a mission-driven not-for-profit organization that connects students to college success and opportunity. Founded in 1900, the College Board was created to expand access to higher education. Today, the membership association is made up of over 6,000 of the world's leading educational institutions and is dedicated to promoting excellence and equity in education. Each year, the College Board helps more than seven million students prepare for a successful transition to college through programs and services in college readiness and college success—including the SAT® and the Advanced Placement Program®. The organization also serves the education community through research and advocacy on behalf of students, educators, and schools.

For further information, visit www.collegeboard.org.

ISBN: 1-4573-0153-9
ISBN: 978-1-4573-0153-7

11 12 13 14 15    22 23 24 25
Printed in the United States of America

# Acknowledgments

The College Board gratefully acknowledges the outstanding work of the classroom teachers and writers who have been integral to the development of this revised program. The end product is testimony to their expertise, understanding of student learning needs, and dedication to rigorous but accessible mathematics instruction.

**Michael Allwood**
Brunswick School
Greenwich, Connecticut

**Bonnie Fenwick**
Atlantic High School
Port Orange, Florida

**Brian Kotz**
Montgomery College
Monrovia, Maryland

**Floyd Bullard**
North Carolina School of Science and Mathematics
Durham, North Carolina

**Kathy Fritz**
Plano Independent School District
Plano, Texas

**Chris Olsen**
Prairie Lutheran School
Cedar Rapids, Iowa

**Marcia Chumas**
East Mecklenburg High School
Charlotte, North Carolina

**Marie Humphrey**
David W. Butler High School
Charlotte, North Carolina

**Dr. Roxy Peck**
California Polytechnic Institute
San Luis Obispo, California

**Wendy DenBesten**
Hoover High School
Fresno, California

**Andrew Kearns**
José Martí MAST 6–12 Academy
Miami, Florida

**Andrea Sukow**
Mathematics Consultant
Nashville, Tennessee

## SpringBoard Mathematics Product Development

**Betty Barnett**
Executive Director
Content Development

**Allen M. D. von Pallandt, Ph.D.**
Senior Director
Mathematics Content Development

**Kimberly Sadler, M.Ed.**
Senior Math Product Manager

**John Nelson**
Mathematics Editor

## Acknowledgments *continued*

### Research and Planning Advisors

We also wish to thank the members of our SpringBoard Advisory Council and the many educators who gave generously of their time and their ideas as we conducted research for both the print and online programs. Your suggestions and reactions to ideas helped immeasurably as we planned the revisions. We gratefully acknowledge the teachers and administrators in the following districts.

ABC Unified
Cerritos, California

Albuquerque Public Schools
Albuquerque, New Mexico

Amarillo School District
Amarillo, Texas

Baltimore County Public Schools
Baltimore, Maryland

Bellevue School District 405
Bellevue, Washington

Charlotte Mecklenburg Schools
Charlotte, North Carolina

Clark County School District
Las Vegas, Nevada

Cypress Fairbanks ISD
Houston, Texas

District School Board of
Collier County
Collier County, Florida

Denver Public Schools
Denver, Colorado

Frisco ISD
Frisco, Texas

Gilbert Unified School District
Gilbert, Arizona

Grand Prairie ISD
Grand Prairie, Texas

Hillsborough County Public
Schools
Tampa, Florida

Houston Independent School
District
Houston, Texas

Hobbs Municipal Schools
Hobbs, New Mexico

Irving Independent School
District
Irving, Texas

Kenton County School District
Fort Wright, Kentucky

Lee County Public Schools
Fort Myers, Florida

Newton County Schools
Covington, Georgia

Noblesville Schools
Noblesville, Indiana

Oakland Unified School District
Oakland, California

Orange County Public Schools
Orlando, Florida

School District of Palm Beach
County
Palm Beach, Florida

Peninsula School District
Gig Harbor, Washington

Polk County Public Schools
Bartow, Florida

Quakertown Community School
District
Quakertown, Pennsylvania

Rio Rancho Public Schools
Rio Rancho, New Mexico

Ronan School District
Ronan, Montana

St. Vrain Valley School District
Longmont, Colorado

Scottsdale Public Schools
Phoenix, Arizona

Seminole County Public Schools
Sanford, Florida

Southwest ISD
San Antonio, Texas

Spokane Public Schools
Spokane, Washington

Volusia County Schools
DeLand, Florida

# Contents

# Contents continued

# UNIT 3   POLYNOMIALS

# UNIT 4   SERIES, EXPONENTIAL AND LOGARITHMIC FUNCTIONS

# Contents *continued*

# Contents continued

# Contents *continued*

# To the Student

Welcome to the SpringBoard program.

This program has been created with you in mind: the content you need to learn, the tools to help you learn, and the critical thinking skills that help you build confidence in your own knowledge of mathematics. The College Board publishes the SpringBoard program. It also publishes the PSAT/NMSQT, the SAT, and the Advanced Placement exams—all exams that you are likely to encounter in your student years. Preparing you to perform well on those exams and to develop the mathematics skills needed for high school success is the primary purpose of this program.

## Standards-Based Mathematics Learning

The SpringBoard program is based on learning standards that identify the mathematics skills and knowledge that you should master to succeed in high school and in future college-level work. In this course, the standards follow these broad areas of mathematics knowledge:

- Mathematical practices
- Number and quantity
- Algebra
- Functions
- Modeling
- Statistics and probability

Mathematical practice standards guide your study of mathematics. They are actions you take to help you understand mathematical concepts rather than just mathematical procedures. For example, the mathematical practice standards state the following:

**MP.1** Make sense of problems and persevere in solving them.

**MP.2** Reason abstractly and quantitatively.

**MP.3** Construct viable arguments and critique the reasoning of others.

**MP.4** Model with mathematics.

**MP.5** Use appropriate tools strategically.

**MP.6** Attend to precision.

**MP.7** Look for and make use of structure.

**MP.8** Look for and express regularity in repeated reasoning.

As you continue your studies from middle school, you will examine expressions, equations, and functions, which will allow you to make comparisons between relations and functions. Expressions and equations connect with functions. Understanding the concept of functions is critical to future success in your study of algebra and the rest of the high school mathematics curriculum.

See pages xiii–xvi for a complete list of the College and Career Readiness Standards for Mathematics for this course.

## Strategies for Learning Mathematics

Some tools to help you learn are built into every activity. At the beginning of each activity, you will see suggested learning strategies. Each of these strategies is explained in full in the Resources section of your book. As you learn to use each strategy, you'll have the opportunity to decide which strategies work best for you. Suggested learning strategies include:

- Reading strategies
- Writing strategies
- Problem-solving strategies
- Collaborative strategies

## Building Mathematics Knowledge and Skills

The SpringBoard program is built around the following.

*Problem Solving* Many of the problems in this book require you to **analyze** the situation and the information in a problem, **make decisions, determine the strategies** you'll use to solve the problem, and **justify** your solution.

*Reasoning and Justification* You will be asked to explain the reasoning behind how you solved problems, the mathematics concepts involved, and why your approach was appropriate.

*Communication* Communicating about mathematics, orally and in writing, with your classmates and teachers helps you organize your learning and explain mathematics concepts.

*Mathematics Connections* As you develop your mathematics knowledge, you will see the many connections between mathematics concepts and between mathematics and your own life.

*Representations* In mathematics, representations can take many forms, such as numeric, verbal, graphic, or symbolic. In this course, you are encouraged to use representations to organize problem information, present possible solutions, and communicate your reasoning.

We hope you enjoy your study of mathematics using the SpringBoard program.

# College and Career Readiness Standards

### HSN-CN The Complex Number System

**HSN-CN.A.1** Know there is a complex number $i$ such that $i^2 = -1$, and every complex number has the form $a + bi$ with $a$ and $b$ real.

**HSN-CN.A.2** Use the relation $i^2 = -1$ and the commutative, associative, and distributive properties to add, subtract, and multiply complex numbers.

**HSN-CN.C.7** Solve quadratic equations with real coefficients that have complex solutions.

**HSN-CN.C.8** (+) Extend polynomial identities to the complex numbers. *For example, rewrite $x^2 + 4$ as $(x + 2i)(x - 2i)$.*

**HSN-CN.C.9** (+) Know the Fundamental Theorem of Algebra; show that it is true for quadratic polynomials.

### HSA-SSE Seeing Structure in Expressions

**HSA-SSE.A.1** Interpret expressions that represent a quantity in terms of its context.*

**HSA-SSE.A.1a** Interpret parts of an expression, such as terms, factors, and coefficients.

**HSA-SSE.A.1b** Interpret complicated expressions by viewing one or more of their parts as a single entity. *For example, interpret $P(1 + r)^n$ as the product of P and a factor not depending on P.*

**HSA-SSE.A.2** Use the structure of an expression to identify ways to rewrite it. *For example, see $x^4 - y^4$ as $(x^2)^2 - (y^2)^2$, thus recognizing it as a difference of squares that can be factored as $(x^2 - y^2)(x^2 + y^2)$.*

**HSA-SSE.B.4** Derive the formula for the sum of a finite geometric series (when the common ratio is not 1), and use the formula to solve problems. *For example, calculate mortgage payments.**

## HSA-APR Arithmetic with Polynomials and Rational Expressions

**HSA-APR.A.1** Understand that polynomials form a system analogous to the integers, namely, they are closed under the operations of addition, subtraction, and multiplication; add, subtract, and multiply polynomials.

**HSA-APR.B.2** Know and apply the Remainder Theorem: For a polynomial $p(x)$ and a number $a$, the remainder on division by $x - a$ is $p(a)$, so $p(a) = 0$ if and only if $(x - a)$ is a factor of $p(x)$.

**HSA-APR.B.3** Identify zeros of polynomials when suitable factorizations are available, and use the zeros to construct a rough graph of the function defined by the polynomial.

**HSA-APR.C.4** Prove polynomial identities and use them to describe numerical relationships. *For example, the polynomial identity $(x^2 + y^2)^2 = (x^2 - y^2)^2 + (2xy)^2$ can be used to generate Pythagorean triples.*

**HSA-APR.C.5** (+) Know and apply the Binomial Theorem for the expansion of $(x + y)^n$ in powers of $x$ and $y$ for a positive integer $n$, where $x$ and $y$ are any numbers, with coefficients determined for example by Pascal's Triangle.

**HSA-APR.D.6** Rewrite simple rational expressions in different forms; write $\dfrac{a(x)}{b(x)}$ in the form $q(x) + \dfrac{r(x)}{b(x)}$, where $a(x)$, $b(x)$, $q(x)$, and $r(x)$ are polynomials with the degree of $r(x)$ less than the degree of $b(x)$, using inspection, long division, or, for the more complicated examples, a computer algebra system.

**HSA-APR.D.7** (+) Understand that rational expressions form a system analogous to the rational numbers, closed under addition, subtraction, multiplication, and division by a nonzero rational expression; add, subtract, multiply, and divide rational expressions.

## HSA-CED Creating Equations

**HSA-CED.A.1** Create equations and inequalities in one variable and use them to solve problems. *Include equations arising from linear and quadratic functions, and simple rational and exponential functions.*

**HSA-CED.A.2** Create equations in two or more variables to represent relationships between quantities; graph equations on coordinate axes with labels and scales.

**HSA-CED.A.3** Represent constraints by equations or inequalities, and by systems of equations and/or inequalities, and interpret solutions as viable or nonviable options in a modeling context. *For example, represent inequalities describing nutritional and cost constraints on combinations of different foods.*

**HSA-CED.A.4** Rearrange formulas to highlight a quantity of interest, using the same reasoning as in solving equations. *For example, rearrange Ohm's law $V = IR$ to highlight resistance R.*

## HSA-REI Reasoning with Equations and Inequalities

**HSA-REI.A.2** Solve simple rational and radical equations in one variable, and give examples showing how extraneous solutions may arise.

**HSA-REI.D.11** Explain why the $x$-coordinates of the points where the graphs of the equations $y = f(x)$ and $y = g(x)$ intersect are the solutions of the equation $f(x) = g(x)$; find the solutions approximately, e.g., using technology to graph the functions, make tables of values, or find successive approximations. Include cases where $f(x)$ and/or $g(x)$ are linear, polynomial, rational, absolute value, exponential, and logarithmic functions.*

## HSF-IF Interpreting Functions

**HSF-IF.B.4** For a function that models a relationship between two quantities, interpret key features of graphs and tables in terms of the quantities, and sketch graphs showing key features given a verbal description of the relationship. *Key features include: intercepts; intervals where the function is increasing, decreasing, positive, or negative; relative maximums and minimums; symmetries; end behavior; and periodicity.*\*

**HSF-IF.B.5** Relate the domain of a function to its graph and, where applicable, to the quantitative relationship it describes. *For example, if the function h(n) gives the number of person-hours it takes to assemble n engines in a factory, then the positive integers would be an appropriate domain for the function.*\*

**HSF-IF.B.6** Calculate and interpret the average rate of change of a function (presented symbolically or as a table) over a specified interval. Estimate the rate of change from a graph.\*

**HSF-IF.C.7** Graph functions expressed symbolically and show key features of the graph, by hand in simple cases and using technology for more complicated cases.\*

> **HSF-IF.C.7b** Graph square root, cube root, and piecewise-defined functions, including step functions and absolute value functions.

> **HSF-IF.C.7c** Graph polynomial functions, identifying zeros when suitable factorizations are available, and showing end behavior.

> **HSF-IF.C.7e** Graph exponential and logarithmic functions, showing intercepts and end behavior, and trigonometric functions, showing period, midline, and amplitude.

**HSF-IF.C.8** Write a function defined by an expression in different but equivalent forms to reveal and explain different properties of the function.

> **HSF-IF.C.8a** Use the process of factoring and completing the square in a quadratic function to show zeros, extreme values, and symmetry of the graph, and interpret these in terms of a context.

> **HSF-IF.C.8b** Use the properties of exponents to interpret expressions for exponential functions. For example, identify percent rate of change in functions such as $y = (1.02)t$, $y = (0.97)t$, $y = (1.01)12t$, $y = (1.2)t/10$, and classify them as representing exponential growth or decay.

**HSF-IF.C.9** Compare properties of two functions each represented in a different way (algebraically, graphically, numerically in tables, or by verbal descriptions). *For example, given a graph of one quadratic function and an algebraic expression for another, say which has the larger maximum.*

## HSF-BF Building Functions

**HSF-BF.A.1** Write a function that describes a relationship between two quantities.\*

> **HSF-BF.A.1b** Combine standard function types using arithmetic operations. *For example, build a function that models the temperature of a cooling body by adding a constant function to a decaying exponential, and relate these functions to the model.*

**HSF-BF.B.3** Identify the effect on the graph of replacing $f(x)$ by $f(x) + k$, $k\,f(x)$, $f(kx)$, and $f(x + k)$ for specific values of $k$ (both positive and negative); find the value of $k$ given the graphs. Experiment with cases and illustrate an explanation of the effects on the graph using technology. Include recognizing even and odd functions from their graphs and algebraic expressions for them.

**HSF-BF.B.4** Find inverse functions.

**HSF-BF.B.4a** Solve an equation of the form $f(x) = c$ for a simple function $f$ that has an inverse and write an expression for the inverse. *For example, $f(x) = 2x^3$ or $f(x) = \dfrac{(x+1)}{(x-1)}$ for $x \neq 1$.*

## HSF-LE Linear, Quadratic, and Exponential Models

**HSF-LE.A.4** For exponential models, express as a logarithm the solution to $ab^{ct} = d$ where $a$, $c$, and $d$ are numbers and the base $b$ is 2, 10, or $e$; evaluate the logarithm using technology.

## HSF-TF Trigonometric Functions

**HSF-TF.A.1** Understand radian measure of an angle as the length of the arc on the unit circle subtended by the angle.

**HSF-TF.A.2** Explain how the unit circle in the coordinate plane enables the extension of trigonometric functions to all real numbers, interpreted as radian measures of angles traversed counterclockwise around the unit circle.

**HSF-TF.B.5** Choose trigonometric functions to model periodic phenomena with specified amplitude, frequency, and midline.*

**HSF-TF.C.8** Prove the Pythagorean identity $\sin^2(\theta) + \cos^2(\theta) = 1$ and use it to find $\sin(\theta)$, $\cos(\theta)$, or $\tan(\theta)$ given $\sin(\theta)$, $\cos(\theta)$, or $\tan(\theta)$ and the quadrant of the angle.

## HSS-ID Interpreting Categorical and Quantitative Data

**HSS-ID.A.4** Use the mean and standard deviation of a data set to fit it to a normal distribution and to estimate population percentages. Recognize that there are data sets for which such a procedure is not appropriate. Use calculators, spreadsheets, and tables to estimate areas under the normal curve.

## HSS-IC Making Inferences and Justifying Conclusions

**HSS-IC.A.1** Understand statistics as a process for making inferences about population parameters based on a random sample from that population.

**HSS-IC.A.2** Decide if a specified model is consistent with results from a given data-generating process, e.g., using simulation. *For example, a model says a spinning coin falls heads up with probability 0.5. Would a result of 5 tails in a row cause you to question the model?*

**HSS-IC.B.3** Recognize the purposes of and differences among sample surveys, experiments, and observational studies; explain how randomization relates to each.

**HSS-IC.B.4** Use data from a sample survey to estimate a population mean or proportion; develop a margin of error through the use of simulation models for random sampling.

**HSS-IC.B.5** Use data from a randomized experiment to compare two treatments; use simulations to decide if differences between parameters are significant.

**HSS-IC.B.6** Evaluate reports based on data.

## HSS-MD Using Probability to Make Decisions

**HSS-MD.B.6** (+) Use probabilities to make fair decisions (e.g., drawing by lots, using a random number generator).

**HSS-MD.B.7** (+) Analyze decisions and strategies using probability concepts (e.g., product testing, medical testing, pulling a hockey goalie at the end of a game).

# Equations, Inequalities, Functions

## Unit Overview

In this unit, you will model real-world situations by using one- and two-variable linear equations. You will extend your knowledge of linear relationships through the study of inverse functions, composite functions, piecewise-defined functions, operations on functions, and systems of linear equations and inequalities.

## Key Terms

As you study this unit, add these and other terms to your math notebook. Include in your notes your prior knowledge of each word, as well as your experiences in using the word in different mathematical examples. If needed, ask for help in pronouncing new words and add information on pronunciation to your math notebook. It is important that you learn new terms and use them correctly in your class discussions and in your problem solutions.

### Academic Vocabulary

- interpret
- compare
- contrast
- feasible
- confirm
- prove

### Math Terms

- absolute value equation
- absolute value inequality
- constraints
- consistent
- inconsistent
- independent
- dependent
- ordered triple
- Gaussian elimination
- matrix
- dimensions of a matrix
- square matrix
- multiplicative identity matrix
- multiplicative inverse matrix
- matrix equation
- coefficient matrix
- variable matrix
- constant matrix
- piecewise-defined function
- step function
- parent function
- composition
- composite function
- inverse function

## ESSENTIAL QUESTIONS

**?** How are linear equations and systems of equations and inequalities used to model and solve real-world problems?

**?** How are composite and inverse functions useful in problem solving?

## EMBEDDED ASSESSMENTS

This unit has two embedded assessments, following Activities 3 and 6. They will give you an opportunity to demonstrate your understanding of equations, inequalities, and functions.

**Embedded Assessment 1:**

Equations, Inequalities, and Systems     p. 55

**Embedded Assessment 2:**

Piecewise-Defined, Composite, and Inverse Functions     p. 99

Write your answers on notebook paper.
Show your work.

1. Given $f(x) = x^2 - 4x + 5$, find each value.
   a. $f(2)$      b. $f(-6)$

2. Find the slope and $y$-intercept.
   a. $y = 3x - 4$      b. $4x - 5y = 15$

3. Graph each equation.
   a. $2x + 3y = 12$      b. $x = 7$

4. Write an equation for each line.
   a. line with slope 3 and $y$-intercept $-2$
   b. line passing through $(2, 5)$ and $(-4, 1)$

5. Write the equation of the line below.

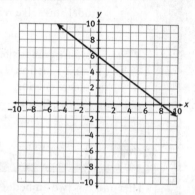

6. Using the whole number 5, define the additive inverse and the multiplicative inverse.

7. Solve $3(x + 2) + 4 = 5x + 7$.

8. What is the absolute value of 2 and of $-2$? Explain your response.

9. Solve the equation for $x$.
   $$\frac{3x + y}{z} = 2$$

10. Which point is a solution to the equation $6x - 5y = 4$? Justify your choice.
    A. $(1, 2)$      B. $(1, -2)$
    C. $(-1, -2)$      D. $(-1, 2)$

11. Find the domain and range of each relation.
    a. $y = 2x + 1$
    b.

    | input | 3 | 7 | 11 |
    |--------|-----|-----|-----|
    | output | −1 | −3 | −5 |

    c.
    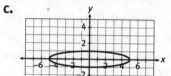

    d.
    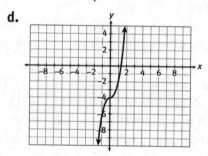

12. How many lines of symmetry exist in the figure shown in Item 11c?

# Creating Equations

One to Two

## Lesson 1-1 One-Variable Equations

**Learning Targets:**
- Create an equation in one variable from a real-world context.
- Solve an equation in one variable.

**SUGGESTED LEARNING STRATEGIES:** Shared Reading, Activating Prior Knowledge, Create Representations, Identify a Subtask, Think-Pair-Share, Close Reading

A new water park called Sapphire Island is about to have its official grand opening. The staff is putting up signs to provide information to customers before the park opens to the general public. As you read the following scenario, mark the text to identify key information and parts of sentences that help you make meaning from the text.

The Penguin, one of the park's tube rides, has two water slides that share a single line of riders. The table presents information about the number of riders and tubes that can use each slide.

**Penguin Water Slides**

| Slide Number | Tube Size | Tube Release Time |
|---|---|---|
| 1 | 2 riders | every 0.75 min |
| 2 | 4 riders | every 1.25 min |

Jaabir places a sign in the waiting line for the Penguin. When a rider reaches the sign, there will be approximately 100 people in front of him or her waiting for either slide. The sign states, "From this point, your wait time is approximately ____ minutes." Jaabir needs to determine the number of minutes to write on the sign. Work with a partner or with your group on Items 1–7.

1. Let the variable $r$ represent the number of riders taking slide 1. Write an *algebraic expression* for the number of tubes this many riders will need, assuming each tube is full.

2. Next, write an expression for the time in minutes it will take $r$ riders to go down slide 1.

3. Assuming that $r$ riders take slide 1 and that there are 100 riders in all, write an expression for the number of riders who will take slide 2.

**MATH TIP**

An *algebraic expression* includes at least one variable. It may also include numbers and operations, such as addition, subtraction, multiplication, and division. It does not include an equal sign.

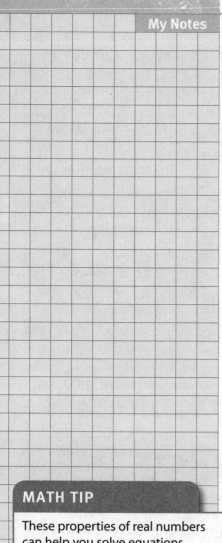

**My Notes**

4. Using the expression you wrote in Item 3, write an expression for the number of tubes the riders taking slide 2 will need, assuming each tube is full.

5. Write an expression for the time in minutes needed for the riders taking slide 2 to go down the slide.

6. Since Jaabir wants to know how long it takes for 100 riders to complete the ride when both slides are in use, the total time for the riders taking slide 1 should equal the total time for the riders taking slide 2. Write an equation that sets your expression from Item 2 (the time for the slide 1 riders) equal to your expression from Item 5 (the time for the slide 2 riders).

7. **Reason abstractly and quantitatively.** Solve your equation from Item 6. Describe each step to justify your solution.

**MATH TIP**

These properties of real numbers can help you solve equations.

**Addition Property of Equality**
If $a = b$, then $a + c = b + c$.

**Subtraction Property of Equality**
If $a = b$, then $a - c = b - c$.

**Multiplication Property of Equality**
If $a = b$, then $ca = cb$.

**Division Property of Equality**
If $a = b$ and $c \neq 0$, then $\dfrac{a}{c} = \dfrac{b}{c}$.

**Distributive Property**
$a(b + c) = ab + ac$

8. **Make sense of problems.** Consider the meaning of the solution from Item 7.
   a. Explain why you should or should not round the value of $r$ to the nearest whole number.

   b. How many people out of the 100 riders will take slide 1?

9. Use the expression you wrote in Item 2 to determine how long it will take the number of riders from Item 8b to go through slide 1.
   a. *Evaluate* the expression for the appropriate value of $r$.

   b. How many minutes will it take the riders to go through slide 1? Round to the nearest minute.

> **MATH TIP**
>
> When you *evaluate* an algebraic expression, you substitute values for the variables and then simplify the expression.

The rest of the 100 riders will go through slide 2 in about the same amount of time. So, your answer to Item 9b gives an estimate of the number of minutes it will take all 100 riders to go down the Penguin slides.

10. Recall that when a rider reaches the sign, there will be approximately 100 people waiting in front of him or her. What number should Jaabir write to complete the statement on the sign?

*From this point, your wait is approximately _____ minutes.*

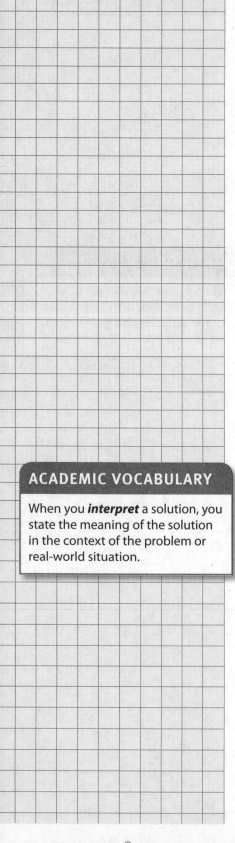

**My Notes**

11. Describe how you could check that your answer to Item 10 is reasonable.

### Check Your Understanding

12. Suppose that Jaabir needs to place a second sign in the waiting line for the Penguin slides. When a rider reaches this sign, there will be approximately 250 people in front of him or her. What number should Jaabir write to complete the statement on this sign? Explain how you determined your answer.

    *From this point, your wait is approximately* _____ *minutes.*

13. Explain the relationships among the terms *variable*, *expression*, and *equation*.

### LESSON 1-1 PRACTICE

Use this information for Items 14–15. When full, one of the pools at Sapphire Island will hold 43,000 gallons of water. The pool currently holds 20,000 gallons of water and is being filled at a rate of 130 gallons per minute.

14. Write an equation that can be used to find $h$, the number of hours it will take to fill the pool from its current level. Explain the steps you used to write your equation.

15. Solve your equation from Item 14, and *interpret* the solution.

Use this information for Items 16–18. Sapphire Island is open 7 days a week. The park has 8 ticket booths, and each booth has a ticket seller from 10:00 a.m. to 5 p.m. On average, ticket sellers work 30 hours per week.

16. **Model with mathematics.** Write an equation that can be used to find $t$, the minimum number of ticket sellers the park needs. Explain the steps you used to write your equation.

17. Solve your equation from Item 16, and interpret the solution.

18. The park plans to hire 20 percent more than the minimum number of ticket sellers needed in order to account for sickness, vacation, and lunch breaks. How many ticket sellers should the park hire? Explain.

### ACADEMIC VOCABULARY

When you *interpret* a solution, you state the meaning of the solution in the context of the problem or real-world situation.

**Learning Targets:**
- Create equations in two variables to represent relationships between quantities.
- Graph two-variable equations.

> **SUGGESTED LEARNING STRATEGIES:** Activating Prior Knowledge, Summarizing, Paraphrasing, Look for a Pattern, Think-Pair-Share, Create Representations, Interactive Word Wall, Identify a Subtask

At Sapphire Island, visitors can rent inner tubes to use in several of the park's rides and pools. Maria works at the rental booth and is preparing materials so that visitors and employees will understand the pricing of the tubes. Renting a tube costs a flat fee of $5 plus an additional $2 per hour.

As you work in groups on Items 1–7, review the above problem scenario carefully and explore together the information provided and how to use it to create potential solutions. Discuss your understanding of the problems and ask peers or your teacher to clarify any areas that are not clear.

1. Maria started making a table that relates the number of hours a tube is rented to the cost of renting the tube. Use the information above to help you complete the table.

**Tube Rentals**

| Hours Rented | Cost ($) |
|:---:|:---:|
| 1 | |
| 2 | |
| 3 | |
| 4 | |
| 5 | |

2. Explain how a customer could use the pattern in the table to determine the cost of renting a tube for 6 hours.

Next, Maria wants to write an equation in two variables, *x* and *y*, that employees can use to calculate the cost of renting a tube for any number of hours.

3. **Reason abstractly.** What does the *independent variable x* represent in this situation? Explain.

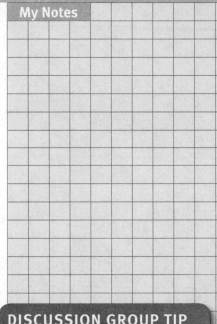

**My Notes**

**DISCUSSION GROUP TIP**

If you need help in describing your ideas during group discussions, make notes about what you want to say. Listen carefully to other group members as they describe their ideas, and ask for clarification of meaning for any words routinely used by group members.

**MATH TIP**

Recall that in a relationship between two variables, the value of the *independent variable* determines the value of the *dependent variable*.

**My Notes**

4. What does the dependent variable *y* represent in this situation? Explain.

5. Write an equation that models the situation.

6. How can you tell whether the equation you wrote in Item 5 correctly models the situation?

7. **Construct viable arguments.** Explain how an employee could use the equation to determine how much to charge a customer.

**MATH TIP**

Before you can graph the equation, you need to determine the coordinates of several points that lie on its graph. One way to do this is by using pairs of corresponding values from the table on the previous page. You can also choose several values of *x* and substitute them into the equation to determine the corresponding values of *y*.

Maria also thinks it would be useful to make a graph of the equation that relates the time in hours a tube is rented and the cost in dollars of renting a tube.

8. List five ordered pairs that lie on the graph of the relationship between *x* and *y*.

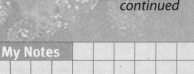

**My Notes**

9. Use the grid below to complete parts a and b.
   a. Write an appropriate title for the graph based on the real-world situation. Also write appropriate titles for the *x*- and *y*-axes.
   b. Graph the ordered pairs you listed in Item 8. Then connect the points with a line or a smooth curve.

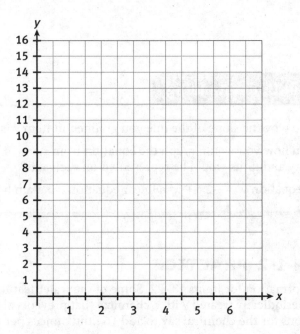

10. Based on the graph, explain how you know whether the equation that models this situation is or is not a *linear equation*.

11. **Reason quantitatively.** Explain why the graph is only the first quadrant.

12. What is the *y-intercept* of the graph? Describe what the *y*-intercept represents in this situation.

13. What is the slope of the graph? Describe what the slope represents in this situation.

**MATH TIP**

Recall that a *linear equation* is an equation whose graph is a line. A linear equation can be written in *standard form* $Ax + By = C$, where $A$, $B$, and $C$ are integers and $A$ is nonnegative.

**MATH TIP**

The *y-intercept* of a graph is the *y*-coordinate of a point where the graph intersects the *y*-axis.

The *slope* of a line is the ratio of the change in *y* to the change in *x* between any two points.

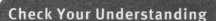

**DISCUSSION GROUP TIP**

Share your description with your group members and list any details you may not have considered before. If you do not know the exact words to describe your ideas, use synonyms or request assistance from group members to help you convey your ideas. Use nonverbal cues such as raising your hand to ask for clarification of others' ideas.

14. Work with your group. Describe a plausible scenario related to the water park that could be modeled by this equation: $y = 40x - 8$. In your description, be sure to use appropriate vocabulary, both real-world and mathematical. Refer to the Word Wall and any notes you may have made to help you choose words for your description.

**Check Your Understanding**

15. Explain why the slope of the line you graphed in Item 9 is positive.

16. Explain how you would graph the equation from Item 14. What quantity and units would be represented on each axis?

17. Is the equation $y = -2x + x^2$ a linear equation? Explain how you know.

## LESSON 1-2 PRACTICE

Use this information for Items 18–22. Some of the water features at Sapphire Island are periodically treated with a chemical that prevents algae growth. The directions for the chemical say to add 16 fluid ounces per 10,000 gallons of water.

18. Make a table that shows how much of the chemical to add for water features that hold 10,000; 20,000; 30,000; 40,000; and 50,000 gallons of water.

19. Write a linear equation in two variables that models the situation. Tell what each variable in the equation represents.

20. Graph the equation. Be sure to include titles and use an appropriate scale on each axis.

21. What are the slope and $y$-intercept of the graph? What do they represent in the situation?

22. **Construct viable arguments.** An employee adds 160 fluid ounces of the chemical to a feature that holds 120,000 gallons of water. Did the employee add the correct amount? Explain.

### Learning Targets:
- Write, solve, and graph absolute value equations.
- Solve and graph absolute value inequalities.

**SUGGESTED LEARNING STRATEGIES:** Marking the Text, Interactive Word Wall, Close Reading, Create Representations, Think-Pair-Share, Identify a Subtask, Quickwrite, Self Revision/Peer Revision

You can use the definition of absolute value to solve *absolute value equations* algebraically.

Since

$$|ax + b| = \begin{cases} -(ax + b) & \text{if } ax + b < 0 \\ ax + b & \text{if } ax + b \geq 0 \end{cases},$$

then the equation $|ax + b| = c$ is equivalent to $-(ax + b) = c$ or $(ax + b) = c$.

Since $-(ax + b) = c$ is equivalent to $ax + b = -c$, the absolute value equation $|ax + b| = c$ is equivalent to $ax + b = -c$ or $ax + b = c$.

**My Notes**

**MATH TERMS**

An **absolute value equation** is an equation involving the absolute value of a variable expression.

**MATH TIP**

Recall that the geometric interpretation of $|x|$ is the distance from the number $x$ to 0 on a number line.

If $|x| = 5$, then $x = -5$ or $x = 5$ because those two values are both 5 units away from 0 on a number line.

### Example A
Solve $2|x - 1| - 5 = 1$. Graph the solutions on a number line.

**Step 1:** Isolate the absolute value expression. Add 5 to both sides and then divide by 2.

$$2|x - 1| - 5 = 1$$
$$2|x - 1| = 6$$
$$|x - 1| = 3$$

**Step 2:** Write and solve two equations using the definition of absolute value.

$$x - 1 = 3 \quad \text{or} \quad x - 1 = -3$$
$$x = 4 \quad \text{or} \quad x = -2$$

**Solution:** There are two solutions: $x = 4$ and $x = -2$

Check to see if both solutions satisfy the original equation. Substitute 4 and $-2$ for $x$ in the original equation.

$$2|4 - 1| - 5 = 1 \qquad 2|-2 - 1| - 5 = 1$$
$$2|3| - 5 = 1 \qquad 2|-3| - 5 = 1$$
$$2(3) - 5 = 1 \qquad 2(3) - 5 = 1$$
$$6 - 5 = 1 \qquad 6 - 5 = 1$$

To graph the solutions, plot points at 4 and $-2$ on a number line.

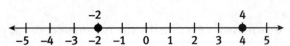

### Try These A
Solve each absolute value equation. Graph the solutions on a number line.

**a.** $|x - 2| = 3$

**b.** $|x + 1| - 4 = -2$

**c.** $|x - 3| + 4 = 4$

**d.** $|x + 2| + 3 = 1$

My Notes

1. **Reason abstractly.** How many solutions are possible for an absolute value equation having the form $|ax + b| = c$, where $a$, $b$, and $c$ are real numbers?

## Example B

The temperature of the wave pool at Sapphire Island can vary up to 4.5°F from the target temperature of 82°F. Write and solve an absolute value equation to find the temperature extremes of the wave pool. (The temperature extremes are the least and greatest possible temperatures.)

Step 1: Write an absolute value equation to represent the situation.

Let $t$ represent the temperature extremes of the wave pool in degrees Fahrenheit.

$$|t - 82| = 4.5$$

Step 2: Use the definition of absolute value to solve for $t$.

$$|t - 82| = 4.5$$
$$t - 82 = 4.5 \quad \text{or} \quad t - 82 = -4.5$$
$$t = 86.5 \quad \text{or} \quad t = 77.5$$

Solution: The greatest possible temperature of the wave pool is 86.5°F, and the least possible temperature is 77.5°F. Both of these temperatures are 4.5°F from the target temperature of 82°F.

### MATH TIP

You know that the distance from $t$ to 82°F on a thermometer is 4.5°F. This distance can be modeled with the absolute value expression $|t - 82|$.

## Try These B

The pH of water is a measure of its acidity. The pH of the water on the Seal Slide can vary up to 0.3 from the target pH of 7.5. Use this information for parts a–c.

a. Write an absolute value equation that can be used to find the extreme pH values of the water on the Seal Slide. Be sure to explain what the variable represents.

b. Solve your equation, and interpret the solutions.

c. **Reason quantitatively.** Justify the reasonableness of your answer to part b.

Solving *absolute value inequalities* algebraically is similar to solving absolute value equations. By the definition of absolute value, $|ax + b| > c$, where $c > 0$, is equivalent to $-(ax + b) > c$ or $ax + b > c$. Multiplying the first inequality by $-1$, and then using a similar method for $|ax + b| < c$, gives these statements:

- $|ax + b| > c$, $c > 0$, is equivalent to $ax + b < -c$ or $ax + b > c$.
- $|ax + b| < c$, $c > 0$, is equivalent to $ax + b < c$ or $ax + b > -c$, which can also be written as $-c < ax + b < c$.

**MATH TERMS**

An **absolute value inequality** is an inequality involving the absolute value of a variable expression.

### Example C

Solve each inequality. Graph the solutions on a number line.

**a.** $|2x + 3| + 1 > 6$

| | | |
|---|---|---|
| **Step 1:** | Isolate the absolute value expression. | $|2x + 3| + 1 > 6$ <br> $|2x + 3| > 5$ |
| **Step 2:** | Write two inequalities. | $2x + 3 > 5$ or $2x + 3 < -5$ |
| **Step 3:** | Solve each inequality. | $x > 1$ or $x < -4$ |
| **Solution:** | | |

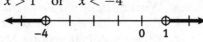

**b.** $|3x - 1| + 5 < 7$

| | | |
|---|---|---|
| **Step 1:** | Isolate the absolute value expression. | $|3x - 1| + 5 < 7$ <br> $|3x - 1| < 2$ |
| **Step 2:** | Write the compound inequality. | $-2 < 3x - 1 < 2$ |
| **Step 3:** | Solve the inequality. | $-\frac{1}{3} < x < 1$ |
| **Solution:** | | |

**MATH TIP**

These properties of real numbers can help you solve inequalities. The properties also apply to inequalities that include $<$, $\geq$, or $\leq$.

**Addition Property of Inequality**
If $a > b$, then $a + c > b + c$.

**Subtraction Property of Inequality**
If $a > b$, then $a - c > b - c$.

**Multiplication Property of Inequality**
If $a > b$ and $c > 0$, then $ca > cb$.
If $a > b$ and $c < 0$, then $ca < cb$.

**Division Property of Inequality**
If $a > b$ and $c > 0$, then $\frac{a}{c} > \frac{b}{c}$.
If $a > b$ and $c < 0$, then $\frac{a}{c} < \frac{b}{c}$.

### Try These C

Solve and graph each absolute value inequality.

**a.** $|x - 2| > 3$

**b.** $|x + 2| - 3 \leq -1$

**c.** $|5x - 2| + 1 \geq 4$

**d.** $|2x + 7| - 4 < 1$

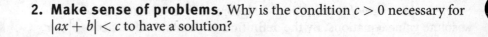

**My Notes**

**ACADEMIC VOCABULARY**

When you **compare** and **contrast** two topics, you describe ways in which they are alike and ways in which they are different.

2. **Make sense of problems.** Why is the condition $c > 0$ necessary for $|ax + b| < c$ to have a solution?

**Check Your Understanding**

3. *Compare* and *contrast* a linear equation having the form $ax + b = c$ with an absolute value equation having the form $|ax + b| = c$.

4. **Critique the reasoning of others.** Paige incorrectly solved an absolute value equation as shown below.

$$-2\,|x + 5| = 8$$
$$-2(x + 5) = 8 \quad \text{or} \quad -2(x + 5) = -8$$
$$-2x - 10 = 8 \quad \text{or} \quad -2x - 10 = -8$$
$$x = -9 \quad \text{or} \quad x = -1$$

   a. What mistake did Paige make?
   b. How could Paige have determined that her solutions are incorrect?
   c. Solve the equation correctly. Explain your steps.

5. Explain how to write the inequality $|5x - 6| \geq 9$ without using an absolute value expression.

**LESSON 1-3 PRACTICE**

Solve each absolute value equation.

   6. $|x - 6| = 5$
   7. $|3x - 7| = 12$
   8. $|2x + 9| - 10 = 5$
   9. $|5x - 3| + 12 = 4$

10. **Model with mathematics.** The flow rate on the Otter River Run can vary up to 90 gallons per minute from the target flow rate of 640 gallons per minute. Write and solve an absolute value equation to find the extreme values of the flow rate on the Otter River Run.

Solve each absolute value inequality. Graph the solutions on a number line.

11. $|x - 7| > 1$
12. $|2x - 5| \leq 9$
13. $|3x - 10| - 5 \geq -1$
14. $|4x + 3| - 9 < 5$

## ACTIVITY 1 PRACTICE
**Write your answers on notebook paper.**
**Show your work.**

### Lesson 1-1

Susan makes and sells purses. The purses cost her $12 each to make, and she sells them for $25. This Saturday, she is renting a booth at a craft fair for $60. Use this information for Items 1–3.

1. Write an equation that can be used to find the number of purses Susan must sell to make a profit of $250 at the fair.

2. Solve the equation, and interpret the solution.

3. If Susan sells 20 purses at the fair, will she meet her profit goal? Explain why or why not.

A medical rescue helicopter is flying at an average speed of 172 miles per hour toward its base hospital. At 2:42 p.m., the helicopter is 80 miles from the hospital. Use this information for Items 4–6.

4. Which equation can be used to determine $m$, the number of minutes it will take the helicopter to reach the hospital?

   **A.** $172(60m) = 80$    **B.** $172\left(\dfrac{m}{60}\right) = 80$

   **C.** $172\left(\dfrac{60}{m}\right) = 80$    **D.** $\dfrac{172}{60m} = 80$

5. Solve the equation, and interpret the solution.

6. An emergency team needs to be on the roof of the hospital 3 minutes before the helicopter arrives. It takes the team 4 minutes to reach the roof. At what time should the team start moving to the roof to meet the helicopter? Explain your reasoning.

Jerome bought a sweater that was on sale for 20 percent off. Jerome paid $25.10 for the sweater, including sales tax of 8.25 percent. Use this information for Items 7–9.

7. Write an equation that can be used to find the original price of the sweater.

8. Solve the equation, and interpret the solution.

9. How much money did Jerome save by buying the sweater on sale? Explain how you determined your answer.

### Lesson 1-2

A taxi company charges an initial fee of $3.50 plus $2.00 per mile. Use this information for Items 10–16.

10. Make a table that shows what it would cost to take a taxi for trips of 1, 2, 3, 4, and 5 miles.

11. Write an equation in two variables that models this situation. Explain what the independent variable and the dependent variable represent.

12. Graph the equation. Be sure to include a title for the graph and for each axis.

13. Describe one advantage of the graph compared to the equation.

14. Is the equation that models this situation a linear equation? Explain why or why not.

15. What are the slope and $y$-intercept of the graph? What do they represent in the situation?

16. Shelley uses her phone to determine that the distance from her apartment to Blue Café is 3.7 miles. How much it will cost Shelley to take a taxi to the café?

**17.** Choose the equation that is *not* linear.

   **A.** $y = \frac{2}{3}x + 6$    **B.** $y = \frac{4}{x} - 1$

   **C.** $3x + 2y = 8$    **D.** $x = -4$

A zoo is building a new large-cat exhibit. Part of the space will be used for lions and part for leopards. The exhibit will house eight large cats in all. Expenses for a lion will be about $8000 per year, and expenses for a leopard will be about $6000 per year. Use this information for Items 18–21.

**18.** Write an equation that can be used to find $y$, the yearly expenses for the eight cats in the exhibit when $x$ of the cats are lions.

**19.** Graph the equation. Be sure to include a title for the graph and for each axis.

**20.** Are all points on the line you graphed solutions in this situation? Explain.

**21.** What would the yearly expenses be if five of the cats in the exhibit are lions and the rest are leopards? Explain how you found your answer.

## Lesson 1-3

**22.** Solve each absolute value equation.

   **a.** $|2x - 3| = 7$

   **b.** $|2x + 5| = 23$

   **c.** $|x - 10| - 11 = 12 - 23$

   **d.** $|7x + 1| - 7 = 3$

   **e.** $|2x| - 3 = -5$

**23.** If the center thickness of a lens varies more than 0.150 millimeter from the target thickness of 5.000 millimeters, the lens cannot be used. Write and solve an absolute value equation to find the extreme acceptable values for the center thickness of the lens.

**24.** Solve the equation $|2x + 4| - 1 = 7$. Then graph the solutions on a number line.

**25.** A thermometer is accurate to within 0.6°F. The thermometer indicates that Zachary's temperature is 101.7°F. Write and solve an absolute value equation to find the extreme possible values of Zachary's actual temperature.

**26.** Solve each absolute value inequality. Graph the solutions on a number line.

   **a.** $|x + 5| < 12$

   **b.** $|5x + 2| \geq 13$

   **c.** $|10x - 12| - 9 \leq -1$

   **d.** $|x - 7| + 3 > 8$

   **e.** $|-2x + 5| + 6 \geq 4$

**27.** Which number line shows the solutions of the inequality $2|x - 1| \geq 4$?

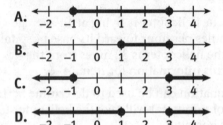

## MATHEMATICAL PRACTICES
### Attend to Precision

**28.** The equation $y = 0.5x + 40$ represents the monthly cost $y$ in dollars of Lesley's cell phone, where $x$ is the number of talk minutes over 750 that Lesley uses.

   **a.** Graph the equation.

   **b.** How did you determine the range of values to show on each axis of your graph?

   **c.** What are the units on each axis of your graph?

   **d.** What are the units of the slope of the linear equation? Explain.

   **e.** Write a different plausible scenario—not related to cell phone costs—that could be modeled using the equation $y = 0.5x + 40$. Be sure to use appropriate vocabulary, both real-world and mathematical.

# Graphing to Find Solutions

## Choices

## Lesson 2-1 Graphing Two-Variable Equations

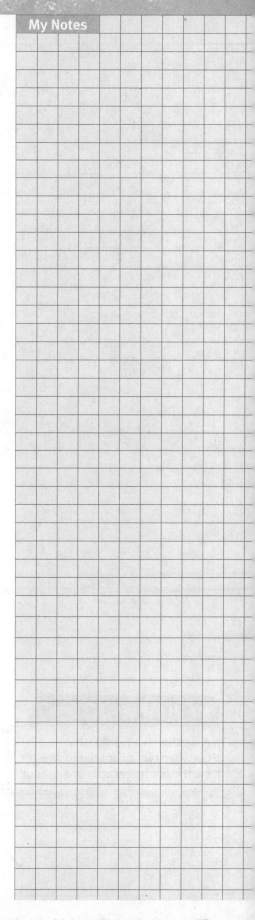

### Learning Targets:
- Write equations in two variables to represent relationships between quantities.
- Graph equations on coordinate axes with labels and scales.

**SUGGESTED LEARNING STRATEGIES:** Shared Reading, Marking the Text, Graphic Organizer, Create Representations, Look for a Pattern, Group Presentation, Activating Prior Knowledge

Roy recently won a trivia contest. The prize was a five-day trip to New York City, including a round-trip airplane ticket and $3000 in cash. The money will pay the cost of a hotel room, meals, entertainment, and incidentals. To prepare for his trip, Roy gathered this information.

- A hotel room in New York City costs $310 per night, and the trip includes staying five nights.
- A taxi between New York City and LaGuardia Airport will cost $45 each way.

Roy must set aside the cash required to pay for his hotel room and for taxi service to and from the airport. Once he has done this, Roy can begin to make plans to enjoy the city with his remaining prize funds.

1. **Reason quantitatively.** How much money will Roy have available to spend on performances, meals, and any other expenses that might arise after paying for his hotel and taxis? Show your work.

During his trip to New York City, Roy wants to spend *only* his winnings from the contest. He wants to focus on two of his favorite pastimes: attending theater or musical performances and dining in restaurants. After surfing the web, Roy determines the following facts:

- On average, a ticket for a performance in New York City costs $100.
- He will spend on average $40 per meal.

My Notes

2. **Model with mathematics.** Roy wants to know how the purchase of each ticket affects his available money. Fill in the table below. Plot the points on the grid.

| Tickets (t) | Money Available (M) |
|---|---|
| 0 | |
| 1 | |
| 2 | |
| 3 | |
| 4 | |
| 5 | |
| 8 | |
| 10 | |
| 13 | |

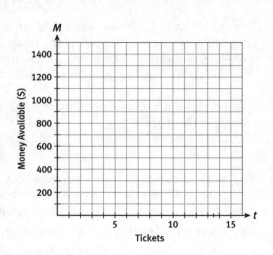

3. What patterns do you notice?

4. Explain how you determined the values for 8, 10, and 13 tickets.

**MATH TIP**

A *function* is a relationship between two quantities in which each input has exactly one output.

5. Write a *function* M(t) that represents the amount of money that Roy has left after purchasing t tickets.

**6.** Use mathematical terminology to explain what −100 and 1360 each represent in your function in Item 5.

**7.** Roy wonders how his meal costs will affect his spending money.
   **a.** Write a function $D(m)$ that represents the amount of money Roy has left after purchasing $m$ number of meals.

   **b.** Graph your function on the grid.

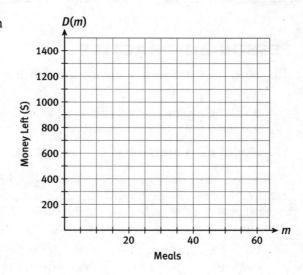

**CONNECT TO TECHNOLOGY**

You can also graph the function by using a graphing calculator. When entering the equation, use $x$ for the independent variable and $y$ for the dependent variable.

**8.** What kind of function is $D(m)$?

**9.** What is the *rate of change* for $D(m)$, including units?

**MATH TIP**

The *rate of change* of a function is the ratio of the amount of change in the dependent variable to the amount of change in the independent variable.

**10. Make sense of problems.** Are all the values for $m$ on your graph valid in this situation, given that $m$ represents the number of meals that Roy can buy? Explain.

My Notes

**Check Your Understanding**

11. What do the $x$- and $y$-intercepts of your graph in Item 7 represent?

12. If you know the coordinates of two points on the graph of a linear function, how can you determine the function's rate of change?

13. What is the relationship between the rate of change of a linear function and the slope of its graph?

14. Using your answers to Items 12 and 13, explain how to write the equation of a line when you are given the coordinates of two points on the line.

## LESSON 2-1 PRACTICE

15. Write the equation of the line with $y$-intercept $-4$ and a slope of $\frac{3}{2}$. Graph the equation.

16. Write the equation of the line that passes through the point $(-2, -3)$ and has a slope of 5. Graph the equation.

17. **Model with mathematics.** Graph the function $f(x) = 3 - \frac{1}{2}(x - 2)$.

Use the following information for Items 18–20. Roy already has 10,368 frequent flyer miles, and he will earn 2832 more miles from his round-trip flight to New York City. In addition, he earns 2 frequent flyer miles for each dollar he charges on his credit card.

18. Write the equation of a function $f(d)$ that represents the total number of frequent flyer miles Roy will have after his trip if he charges $d$ dollars on his credit card.

19. Graph the function, using appropriate scales on the axes.

20. **Reason quantitatively.** How many dollars will Roy need to charge on his credit card to have a total of 15,000 frequent flyer miles? Explain how you determined your answer.

## Learning Targets:
- Represent constraints by equations or inequalities.
- Use a graph to determine solutions of a system of inequalities.

> **SUGGESTED LEARNING STRATEGIES:** Think-Pair-Share, Interactive Word Wall, Create Representations, Work Backward, Discussion Groups, Close Reading, Debriefing, Activating Prior Knowledge

Work with your group on Items 1 through 5. As needed, refer to the Glossary to review translations of key terms. Incorporate your understanding into group discussions to confirm your knowledge and use of key mathematical language.

1. Roy's spending money depends on both the number of tickets *t* and the number of meals *m*. Determine whether each option is *feasible* for Roy and provide a rationale in the table below.

| Tickets (*t*) | Meals (*m*) | Total Cost | Is it feasible? | Rationale |
|---|---|---|---|---|
| 6 | 16 | | | |
| 8 | 14 | | | |
| 10 | 12 | | | |
| 4.5 | 11 | | | |

2. **Construct viable arguments.** For all the ordered pairs (*t*, *m*) that are feasible options, explain why each statement below must be true.
   a. All coordinates in the ordered pairs are integer values.

   b. If graphed in the coordinate plane, all ordered pairs would fall either in the first quadrant or on the positive *m*-axis.

3. Write a *linear inequality* that represents all ordered pairs (*t*, *m*) that are feasible options for Roy.

4. If Roy buys exactly two meals each day, determine the total number of tickets that he could purchase in five days. Show your work.

**My Notes**

### ACADEMIC VOCABULARY
The term *feasible* means that something is possible in a given situation.

### DISCUSSION GROUP TIPS
As you share your ideas, be sure to use mathematical terms and academic vocabulary precisely. Make notes as you listen to group members to help you remember the meaning of new words and how they are used to describe mathematical concepts. Ask and answer questions clearly to aid comprehension and to ensure understanding of all group members' ideas.

### MATH TERMS
A **linear inequality** is an inequality that can be written in one of these forms, where *A* and *B* are not both equal to 0:
$Ax + By < C$, $Ax + By > C$, $Ax + By \leq C$, or $Ax + By \geq C$.

**My Notes**

**MATH TIP**

Recall how to graph linear inequalities. First, graph the corresponding linear equation. Then choose a test point not on the line to determine which half-plane contains the set of solutions to the inequality. Finally, shade the half-plane that contains the solution set.

**5.** If Roy buys exactly one ticket each day, find the maximum number of meals that he could eat in the five days. Show your work.

**6.** To see what the feasible options are, you can use a visual display of the values on a graph.
  **a. Attend to precision.** Graph your inequality from Item 3 on the grid below.

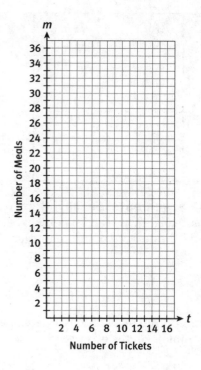

**b.** What is the boundary line of the graph?

**c.** Which half-plane is shaded? How did you decide?

**d.** Write your response for each item as points in the form $(t, m)$.

Item 4                          Item 5

**e.** Are both those points in the shaded region of your graph? Explain.

7. **Use appropriate tools strategically.** Now follow these steps to graph the inequality on a graphing calculator.

**a.** Replace $t$ with $x$, and replace $m$ with $y$. Then solve the inequality for $y$. Enter this inequality into your graphing calculator.

**b.** Use the left arrow key to move the cursor to the far left of the equation you entered. Press [ENTER] until the symbol to the left of Y1 changes to ◣. What does this symbol indicate about the graph?

**c.** Now press [GRAPH]. Depending on your window settings, you may or may not be able to see the boundary line. Press [WINDOW] and adjust the viewing window so that it matches the graph from Item 6. Then press [GRAPH] again.

**d.** Describe the graph.

**TECHNOLOGY TIP**

To enter an equation in a graphing calculator, start with [Y=].

**TECHNOLOGY TIP**

To graph an inequality that includes ≥ or ≤, you would use the symbol ◥ or ◣. You need to indicate whether the half-plane above or below the boundary line will be shaded.

My Notes

**Check Your Understanding**

8. Compare and contrast the two graphs of the linear inequality: the one you made using paper and pencil and the one on your graphing calculator. Describe an advantage of each graph compared to the other.

9. **a.** What part of your graphs represents solutions for which Roy would have *no* money left over? Explain.
   **b.** What part of your graphs represents solutions for which Roy would have money left over? Explain.

10. Explain how you would graph the inequality $2x + 3y < 12$, either by using paper and pencil or by using a graphing calculator.

11. Roy realized that some other conditions or *constraints* apply. Write an inequality for each constraint described below.
    **a.** Roy eats lunch and dinner the first day. On the remaining four days, Roy eats at least one meal each day, but he never eats more than three meals each day.

    **b.** There are only 10 performances playing that Roy actually wants to see while he is in New York City, but he may not be able to attend all of them.

    **c.** Roy wants the number of meals that he eats to be no more than twice the number of performances that he attends.

12. **Model with mathematics.** You can use a graph to organize all the constraints on Roy's trip to New York City.
    **a.** List the inequalities you found in Items 3 and 11.

    **b.** Graph the inequalities from Items 3 and 11 on a single grid.

My Notes

**ACADEMIC VOCABULARY**

When you ***confirm*** a statement, you show that it is true or correct.

13. By looking at your graph, identify two ordered pairs that are feasible options to all of the inequalities. ***Confirm*** that these ordered pairs satisfy the inequalities listed in Item 12.

   a. First ordered pair $(t, m)$:

   b. Second ordered pair $(t, m)$:

14. Label the point $(6, 10)$ on the grid in Item 6.
   a. Interpret the meaning of this point.

   b. **Construct viable arguments.** Is this ordered pair in the solution region common to all of the inequalities? Explain.

15. If Roy uses his prize money to purchase 6 tickets and eat 10 meals, how much money will he have left over for other expenses? Show your work.

**Check Your Understanding**

16. Given the set of constraints described earlier, how many tickets could Roy purchase if he buys 12 meals? Explain.

17. a. If you were Roy, how many meals and how many tickets would you buy during the 5-day trip?
   b. Explain why you made the choices you did, and tell how you know that this combination of meals and tickets is feasible.

18. Explain how you would graph this constraint on a coordinate plane:
   $2 \leq x \leq 5$.

## LESSON 2-2 PRACTICE

19. Graph these inequalities on the same grid, and shade the solution region that is common to all of the inequalities: $y \geq 2$, $x \leq 8$, and $y \leq 2 + \frac{1}{2}x$.

20. Identify two ordered pairs that satisfy the constraints in Item 19 and two ordered pairs that do not satisfy the constraints.

A snack company plans to package a mixture of almonds and peanuts. The table shows information about these types of nuts. The company wants the nuts in each package to have at least 60 grams of protein and to cost no more than $4. Use this information for Items 21–23.

| Nut | Protein (g/oz) | Cost ($/oz) |
|---|---|---|
| Almonds | 6 | 0.30 |
| Peanuts | 8 | 0.20 |

**MATH TIP**

When answering Item 21, remember that the number of ounces of each type of nut cannot be negative.

21. **Model with mathematics.** Write inequalities that model the constraints in this situation. Let $x$ represent the number of ounces of almonds in each package and $y$ represent the number of ounces of peanuts.

22. Graph the constraints. Shade the solution region that is common to all of the inequalities.

23. **a.** Identify two ordered pairs that satisfy the constraints.
    **b. Reason quantitatively.** Which ordered pair represents the more expensive mixture? Which ordered pair represents the mixture with more protein? Explain your answer.

## ACTIVITY 2 PRACTICE
Write your answers on notebook paper.
Show your work.

### Lesson 2-1

1. Write the equation of the line with $y$-intercept 3 and a slope of $-\frac{2}{3}$, and graph it.

2. Write the equation of the line that passes through the point $(-2, 4)$ and has a slope of $-1$. Then graph it.

3. Write the equation of the line in standard form that passes through the points $(2, -3)$ and $(-1, -4)$.

A jeweler is heating a gold bar. It takes 7 joules of heat to raise the temperature of the bar 1°C. The initial temperature of the bar is 25°C. Use this information for Items 4–11.

4. Make a table that shows how many joules of heat would be required to raise the temperature of the gold bar to 26°C, 27°C, 28°C, 29°C, 30°C, and 35°C.

5. Write the equation of a function $h(t)$ that represents the amount of heat in joules required to heat the bar to a temperature of $t$ degrees Celsius.

6. Graph the function. Be sure to label the axes.

7. What is the rate of change of the function, including units?

8. What is the $t$-intercept of the graph of the function? What does it represent in this situation?

9. Explain what the ordered pair $(32, 49)$ represents in this situation.

10. How many joules of heat will be required to heat the gold bar to a temperature of 260°C? Explain how you determined your answer.

11. Explain what a negative value of $h(t)$ represents in this situation.

A college tennis coach needs to purchase tennis balls for the team. A case of 24 cans costs $60, and each can holds 3 balls. Use this information for Items 12–17.

12. Write the equation of a function $c(t)$ that represents the number of cases the coach will need to purchase to have a total of $t$ tennis balls.

13. Graph the function. Be sure to label the axes.

14. What is the slope of the graph?
   **A.** $\frac{1}{72}$   **B.** $\frac{1}{8}$
   **C.** 8   **D.** 72

15. What does the slope represent in this situation?

16. Are all the values for $t$ on your graph valid in this situation, given that the coach can only buy complete cases of tennis balls? Explain.

17. The coach needs to purchase 600 tennis balls.
   **a.** How many cases will the coach need to purchase to have this number of tennis balls? Explain how you determined your answer.
   **b.** What is the actual number of tennis balls the coach will have when he buys this number of cases?
   **c.** The coach has a budget of $500 to buy tennis balls. Is there enough money to buy the number of cases that the coach needs? Explain.

18. Without graphing the equations, explain how you can tell which one represents the steeper line: $y = 5 + 5(x + 4)$ or $y = 2(3x - 2)$.

### Lesson 2-2

**19.** Graph the inequality $y > 2x - 5$.

**20. a.** Graph the inequality $6x - 2y \geq 12$.
   **b.** Did you use a solid or dashed line for the boundary line? Explain your choice.
   **c.** Did you shade above or below the boundary line? Explain your choice.

**21.** Graph the following inequalities on the same grid and shade the solution region that is common to all of the inequalities.
   **a.** $y \geq 6 - \dfrac{2}{3}x$
   **b.** $y \leq 4 + x$
   **c.** $y \leq 11 - 8(x - 7)$

Catelyn has two summer jobs. Each week, she works at least 15 hours at a pet store and at least 6 hours as a nanny. She earns $10 per hour at the pet store and $8 per hour as a nanny. Catelyn wants to work no more than 30 hours and earn at least $250 per week. Use this information for Items 22–25.

**22.** Let $x$ represent the number of hours Catelyn works at the pet store in one week and $y$ represent the number of hours she works as a nanny in one week. Write inequalities that model the four constraints in this situation.

**23.** Graph the constraints. Shade the solution region that is common to all of the inequalities.

**24. a.** Identify two ordered pairs that satisfy the constraints.
   **b.** Which ordered pair represents Catelyn working a greater number of hours? Which ordered pair represents Catelyn earning more money? Explain your answer.

**25. a.** Identify two ordered pairs that do not satisfy the constraints.
   **b.** For each ordered pair, identify the constraint or constraints that it fails to meet.

A tent designer is working on a new tent. The tent will be made from black fabric, which costs $6 per yard, and green fabric, which costs $4 per yard. The designer will need at least 3 yards of black fabric, at least 4 yards of green fabric, and at least 10 yards of fabric overall. The total cost of the fabric used for the tent can be no more than $60. Use this information for Items 26–28.

**26.** Let $x$ represent the number of yards of black fabric and $y$ represent the number of yards of green fabric. Write inequalities that model the four constraints in this situation.

**27.** Graph the constraints. Shade the solution region that is common to all of the inequalities.

**28.** Which ordered pair lies in the solution region that is common to all of the inequalities?
   **A.** $(2, 12)$       **B.** $(4, 7)$
   **C.** $(6, 8)$        **D.** $(10, 3)$

## MATHEMATICAL PRACTICES
### Reason Abstractly and Quantitatively

Look back at the scenario involving the tent designer.

**29. a.** What does the ordered pair you chose in Item 28 represent in the situation?
   **b.** What is the greatest amount of green fabric the designer can use if all of the constraints are met? Explain your answer.
   **c.** What is the least amount of black fabric the designer can use if all of the constraints are met? Explain.

# Systems of Linear Equations
## Monetary Systems Overload
### Lesson 3-1 Solving Systems of Two Equations in Two Variables

**Learning Targets:**

- Use graphing, substitution, and elimination to solve systems of linear equations in two variables.
- Formulate systems of linear equations in two variables to model real-world situations.

> **SUGGESTED LEARNING STRATEGIES:** Shared Reading, Close Reading, Create Representations, Discussion Groups, Role Play, Think-Pair-Share, Quickwrite, Note Taking, Look for a Pattern

Have you ever noticed that when an item is popular and many people want to buy it, the price goes up, but items that no one wants are marked down to a lower price?

The change in an item's price and the quantity available to buy are the basis of the concept of *supply and demand* in economics. *Demand* refers to the quantity that people are willing to buy at a particular price. *Supply* refers to the quantity that the manufacturer is willing to produce at a particular price. The final price that the customer sees is a result of both supply and demand.

Suppose that during a six-month time period, the supply and demand for gasoline has been tracked and approximated by these functions, where $Q$ represents millions of barrels of gasoline and $P$ represents price per gallon in dollars.

- Demand function: $P = -0.7Q + 9.7$
- Supply function: $P = 1.5Q - 10.4$

To find the best balance between market price and quantity of gasoline supplied, find a **solution of a system of two linear equations**. The demand and supply functions for gasoline are graphed below.

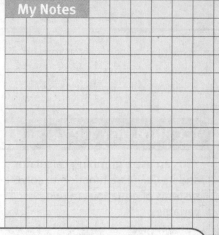

**CONNECT TO ECONOMICS**

The role of the desire for and availability of a good in determining price was described by Muslim scholars as early as the fourteenth century.

The phrase *supply and demand* was first used by eighteenth-century Scottish economists.

**MATH TERMS**

A point, or set of points, is a **solution of a system of equations** in two variables when the coordinates of the points make both equations true.

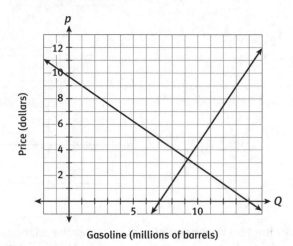

Gasoline (millions of barrels)

1. **Make use of structure.** Find an approximation of the coordinates of the intersection of the supply and demand functions. Explain what the point represents.

My Notes

**MATH TERMS**

Systems of linear equations are classified by the number of solutions.

- Systems with one or many solutions are **consistent**.
- Systems with no solution are **inconsistent**.
- A system with exactly one solution is **independent**.
- A system with infinite solutions is **dependent**.

2. What problem(s) can arise when solving a system of equations by graphing?

3. **Model with mathematics.** For parts a–c, graph each system. Determine the number of solutions.

a. $\begin{cases} y = x + 1 \\ y = -x + 4 \end{cases}$

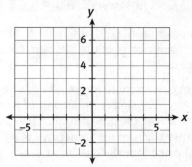

b. $\begin{cases} y = 5 + 2x \\ y = 2x \end{cases}$

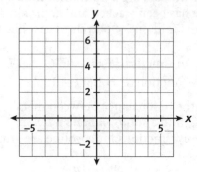

c. $\begin{cases} y = 2x + 1 \\ 2y = 2 + 4x \end{cases}$

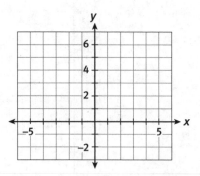

d. Graphing two linear equations illustrates the relationships of the lines. Classify the systems in parts a–c as *consistent* and *independent*, consistent and *dependent*, or *inconsistent*.

### Check Your Understanding

4. Describe how you can tell whether a system of two equations is independent and consistent by looking at its graph.

5. The graph of a system of two equations is a pair of parallel lines. Classify this system. Explain your reasoning.

6. **Make sense of problems.** A system of two linear equations is dependent and consistent. Describe the graph of the system and explain its meaning.

7. Marlon is buying a used car. The dealership offers him two payment plans, as shown in the table.

**Payment Plans**

| Plan | Down Payment ($) | Monthly Payment ($) |
|------|------------------|---------------------|
| 1    | 0                | 300                 |
| 2    | 3600             | 200                 |

Marlon wants to answer this question: How many months will it take for him to have paid the same amount using either plan? Work with your group on parts a through f and determine the answer to Marlon's question.

a. Write an equation that models the amount $y$ Marlon will pay to the dealership after $x$ months if he chooses Plan 1.

b. Write an equation that models the amount $y$ Marlon will pay to the dealership after $x$ months if he chooses Plan 2.

c. Write the equations as a system of equations.

**CONNECT TO PERSONAL FINANCE**

A down payment is an initial payment that a customer makes when buying an expensive item, such as a house or car. The rest of the cost is usually paid in monthly installments.

**DISCUSSION GROUP TIP**

As you work with your group, review the problem scenario carefully and explore together the information provided and how to use it to create a potential solution. Discuss your understanding of the problem and ask peers or your teacher to clarify any areas that are not clear.

© 2015 College Board. All rights reserved.

**My Notes**

**MATH TIP**

When graphing a system of linear equations that represents a real-world situation, it is a good practice to label each line with what it represents. In this case, you can label the lines *Plan 1* and *Plan 2*.

**d.** Graph the system of equations on the coordinate grid.

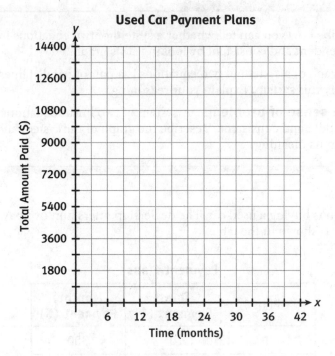

**Used Car Payment Plans**

**e. Reason quantitatively.** What is the solution of the system of equations? What does the solution represent in this situation?

**f.** In how many months will the total costs of the two plans be equal?

**Check Your Understanding**

**8.** How could you check that you solved the system of equations in Item 7 correctly?

**9.** If Marlon plans to keep the used car less than 3 years, which of the payment plans should he choose? Justify your answer.

**10. Construct viable arguments.** Explain how to write a system of two equations that models a real-world situation.

## Lesson 3-1
### Solving Systems of Two Equations in Two Variables

Investors try to control the level of risk in their portfolios by diversifying their investments. You can solve some investment problems by writing and solving systems of equations. One algebraic method for solving a system of linear equations is called **substitution**.

### Example A

During one year, Sara invested $5000 into two separate funds, one earning 2 percent and another earning 5 percent annual interest. The interest Sara earned was $205. How much money did she invest in each fund?

**Step 1:** Let $x =$ money in the first fund and $y =$ money in the second fund.

Write one equation to represent the amount of money invested. Write another equation to represent the interest earned.

$$x + y = 5000 \quad \text{The money invested is \$5000.}$$
$$0.02x + 0.05y = 205 \quad \text{The interest earned is \$205.}$$

**Step 2:** Use substitution to solve this system.

$$x + y = 5000 \quad \text{Solve the first equation for } y.$$
$$y = 5000 - x$$
$$0.02x + 0.05(5000 - x) = 205 \quad \text{Substitute for } y \text{ in the second equation.}$$

$$0.02x + 250 - 0.05x = 205 \quad \text{Solve for } x.$$
$$-0.03x = -45$$
$$x = 1500$$

**Step 3:** Substitute the value of $x$ into one of the original equations to find $y$.

$$x + y = 5000$$
$$1500 + y = 5000 \quad \text{Substitute 1,500 for } x.$$
$$y = 3500$$

**Solution:** Sara invested $1500 in the first fund and $3500 in the second fund.

### Try These A

Write your answers on notebook paper. Show your work.
Solve each system of equations, using substitution.

a. $\begin{cases} x = 25 - 3y \\ 4x + 5y = 9 \end{cases}$   b. $\begin{cases} x + 2y = 14 \\ 2y = x - 10 \end{cases}$   c. $\begin{cases} y - x = 4 \\ 3x + y = 16 \end{cases}$

d. **Model with mathematics.** Eli invested a total of $2000 in two stocks. One stock cost $18.50 per share, and the other cost $10.40 per share. Eli bought a total of 130 shares. Write and solve a system of equations to find how many shares of each stock Eli bought.

**My Notes**

11. When using substitution, how do you decide which variable to isolate and which equation to solve? Explain.

Another algebraic method for solving systems of linear equations is the **elimination method**.

### MATH TERMS

In the **elimination method**, you *eliminate* one variable. Multiply each equation by a number so that the terms for one variable combine to 0 when the equations are added. Then use substitution with that value of the variable to find the value of the other variable. The ordered pair is the *solution* of the system.

The *elimination method* is also called the *addition-elimination method* or the *linear combination method* for solving a system of linear equations.

## Example B

A stack of 20 coins contains only nickels and quarters and has a total value of \$4. How many of each coin are in the stack?

**Step 1:** Let $n$ = number of nickels and $q$ = number of quarters.

Write one equation to represent the number of coins in the stack. Write another equation to represent the total value.

$$n + q = 20 \qquad \text{The number of coins is 20.}$$
$$5n + 25q = 400 \qquad \text{The total value is 400 cents.}$$

**Step 2:** To solve this system of equations, first eliminate the $n$ variable.

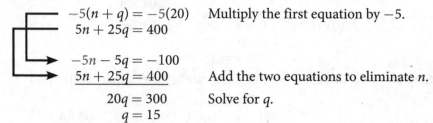

$$-5(n + q) = -5(20) \qquad \text{Multiply the first equation by } -5.$$
$$5n + 25q = 400$$

$$-5n - 5q = -100$$
$$\underline{5n + 25q = 400} \qquad \text{Add the two equations to eliminate } n.$$
$$20q = 300 \qquad \text{Solve for } q.$$
$$q = 15$$

**Step 3:** Find the value of the eliminated variable $n$ by using the original first equation.

$$n + q = 20$$
$$n + 15 = 20 \qquad \text{Substitute 15 for } q.$$
$$n = 5$$

**Step 4:** Check your answers by substituting into the original second equation.

$$5n + 25q = 400$$
$$5(5) + 25(15) = 400 \qquad \text{Substitute 5 for } n \text{ and 15 for } q.$$
$$25 + 375 = 400$$
$$400 = 400$$

**Solution:** There are 5 nickels and 15 quarters in the stack of coins.

### Try These B

Solve each system of equations using elimination. Show your work.

**a.** $\begin{cases} -2x - 3y = 5 \\ -5x + 3y = -40 \end{cases}$

**b.** $\begin{cases} 5x + 6y = -14 \\ x - 2y = 10 \end{cases}$

**c.** $\begin{cases} -3x + 3y = 21 \\ -x - 5y = -17 \end{cases}$

**d.** A karate school offers a package of 12 group lessons and 2 private lessons for $110. It also offers a package of 10 group lessons and 3 private lessons for $125. Write and solve a system of equations to find the cost of a single group lesson and a single private lesson.

### Check Your Understanding

12. Compare and contrast solving systems of equations by using substitution and by using elimination.

13. **Reason abstractly.** Ty is solving the system $\begin{cases} x - 2y = 8 \\ 4x + 6y = 10 \end{cases}$ using substitution. He will start by solving one of the equations for $x$. Which equation should he choose? Explain your reasoning.

14. Explain how you would eliminate one of the variables in this system: $\begin{cases} 2x - 4y = 15 \\ 3x + 2y = 9 \end{cases}$.

## LESSON 3-1 PRACTICE

15. Solve the system by graphing.
$\begin{cases} 2x + 9 = y \\ y = -4x - 3 \end{cases}$

16. Solve the system using substitution.
$\begin{cases} 4y + 19 = x \\ 3y - x = -13 \end{cases}$

17. Solve the system using elimination.
$\begin{cases} 3x + 2y = 17 \\ 4x - 2y = 4 \end{cases}$

18. **Make sense of problems and persevere in solving them.**
At one company, a level I engineer receives a salary of $56,000, and a level II engineer receives a salary of $68,000. The company has 8 level I engineers. Next year, it can afford to pay $472,000 for their salaries. Write and solve a system of equations to find how many of the engineers the company can afford to promote to level II.

19. Which method did you use to solve the system of equations in Item 18? Explain why you chose this method.

## Learning Targets:

- Solve systems of three linear equations in three variables using substitution and Gaussian elimination.
- Formulate systems of three linear equations in three variables to model a real-world situation.

**SUGGESTED LEARNING STRATEGIES:** Close Reading, Vocabulary Organizer, Note Taking, Summarizing, Paraphrasing, Graphic Organizer, Group Presentation, Think Aloud, Identify a Subtask

Sometimes a situation has more than two pieces of information. For these more complex problems, you may need to solve equations that contain three variables.

Read and discuss the material on this page with your group before you move on to Example A on the next page. Use your discussions to clarify the meaning of mathematical concepts and other language used to describe the information. With your group or your teacher, review background information that will be useful in applying concepts to the Example.

In Bisbee, Arizona, an old mining town, you can buy souvenir nuggets of gold, silver, and bronze. For $20, you can buy any of these mixtures of nuggets: 14 gold, 20 silver, and 24 bronze; 20 gold, 15 silver, and 19 bronze; or 30 gold, 5 silver, and 13 bronze. What is the monetary value of each souvenir nugget?

The problem above represents a system of linear equations in three variables. The system can be represented with these equations.

$$\begin{cases} 14g + 20s + 24b = 20 \\ 20g + 15s + 19b = 20 \\ 30g + 5s + 13b = 20 \end{cases}$$

Although it is possible to solve systems of equations in three variables by graphing, it can be difficult.

Just as the ordered pair $(x, y)$ is a solution of a system in two variables, the **ordered triple** $(x, y, z)$ is a solution of a system in three variables. Ordered triples are graphed in three-dimensional coordinate space.

The point $(3, -2, 4)$ is graphed below.

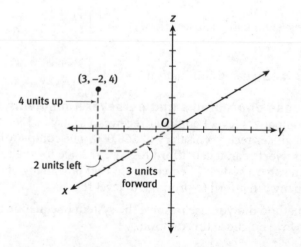

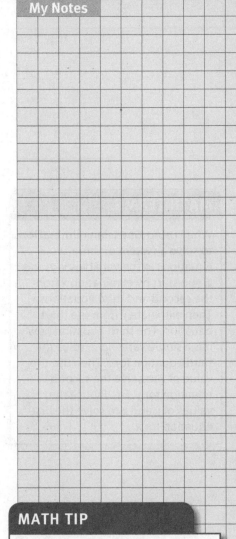

You can use the substitution method to solve systems of equations in three variables.

**Example A**

Solve this system using substitution. $\begin{cases} 2x + 7y + z = -53 \\ -2x + 3y + z = -13 \\ 6x + 3y + z = -45 \end{cases}$

**Step 1:** Solve the first equation for $z$.

$$2x + 7y + z = -53$$
$$z = -2x - 7y - 53$$

**Step 2:** Substitute the expression for $z$ into the second equation. Then solve for $y$.

$$-2x + 3y + z = -13$$
$-2x + 3y + (-2x - 7y - 53) = -13$    Substitute $-2x - 7y - 53$ for $z$.
$-4x - 4y - 53 = -13$    Solve for $y$.
$$-4y = 4x + 40$$
$$y = -x - 10$$

**Step 3:** Use substitution to solve the third equation for $x$.

$$6x + 3y + z = -45$$
$6x + 3y + (-2x - 7y - 53) = -45$    Substitute $-2x - 7y - 53$ for $z$.
$$4x - 4y - 53 = -45$$
$$4x - 4y = 8$$
$4x - 4(-x - 10) = 8$    Substitute $-x - 10$ for $y$.
$4x + 4x + 40 = 8$    Solve for $x$.
$$8x = -32$$
$$x = -4$$

**Step 4:** Solve the last equation from Step 2 for $y$.

$$y = -x - 10$$
$y = -(-4) - 10$    Substitute $-4$ for $x$.
$$y = -6$$

**Step 5:** Solve the last equation from Step 1 for $z$.

$$z = -2x - 7y - 53$$
$z = -2(-4) - 7(-6) - 53$    Substitute $-4$ for $x$ and $-6$ for $y$.
$$z = 8 + 42 - 53$$
$$z = -3$$

**Solution:** The solution of the system is $(-4, -6, -3)$.

**MATH TIP**

As a final step, check your ordered triple solution in one of the original equations to be sure that your solution is correct.

### Try These A

Solve each system of equations using substitution. Show your work.

a. $\begin{cases} x + 4y + z = 3 \\ 2x + y + z = 11 \\ 4x + y + 2z = 23 \end{cases}$

b. $\begin{cases} 3x + y + z = 5 \\ x + 2y - 3z = 15 \\ 2x - y + z = 2 \end{cases}$

Another method of solving a system of three equations in three variables is called ***Gaussian elimination***. This method has two main parts. The first part involves eliminating variables from the equations in the system. The second part involves solving for the variables one at a time.

---

**MATH TERMS**

When using **Gaussian elimination** to solve a system of three equations in the variables $x$, $y$, and $z$, you start by eliminating $x$ from the second and third equations. Then eliminate $y$ from the third equation. The third equation now has a single variable, $z$; solve the third equation for $z$. Then use the value of $z$ to solve the second equation for $y$. Finally, use the values of $y$ and $z$ to solve the first equation for $x$.

---

### Example B

Solve this system using Gaussian elimination. $\begin{cases} 2x + y - z = 4 \\ -2x + y + 2z = 6 \\ x + 2y + z = 11 \end{cases}$

**Step 1:** Use the first equation to eliminate $x$ from the second equation.

$$\begin{array}{r} 2x + y - z = 4 \\ -2x + y + 2z = 6 \\ \hline 2y + z = 10 \end{array}$$

Add the first and second equations.

$\begin{cases} 2x + y - z = 4 \\ 2y + z = 10 \\ x + 2y + z = 11 \end{cases}$

Replace the second equation in the system with $2y + z = 10$.

**Step 2:** Use the first equation to eliminate $x$ from the third equation.

$$\begin{array}{r} 2x + y - z = 4 \\ -2(x + 2y + z) = -2(11) \end{array}$$

Multiply the third equation by $-2$.

$$\begin{array}{r} 2x + y - z = 4 \\ -2x - 4y - 2z = -22 \\ \hline -3y - 3z = -18 \end{array}$$

Add the equations to eliminate $x$.

$\begin{cases} 2x + y - z = 4 \\ 2y + z = 10 \\ -3y - 3z = -18 \end{cases}$

Replace the third equation in the system with $-3y - 3z = -18$.

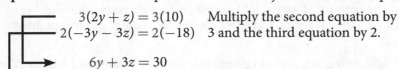

**Step 3:** Use the second equation to eliminate $y$ from the third equation.

$$3(2y + z) = 3(10)$$
$$2(-3y - 3z) = 2(-18)$$

Multiply the second equation by 3 and the third equation by 2.

$$6y + 3z = 30$$
$$\underline{-6y - 6z = -36}$$
$$-3z = -6$$

Add the equations to eliminate $y$.

$$\begin{cases} 2x + y - z = 4 \\ 2y + z = 10 \\ -3z = -6 \end{cases}$$

Replace the third equation in the system with $-3z = -6$.

**Step 4:** Solve the third equation for $z$.

$$-3z = -6$$
$$z = 2$$

**Step 5:** Solve the second equation for $y$.

$$2y + z = 10$$
$$2y + 2 = 10 \qquad \text{Substitute 2 for } z.$$
$$2y = 8$$
$$y = 4$$

**Step 6:** Solve the first equation for $x$.

$$2x + y - z = 4$$
$$2x + 4 - 2 = 4 \qquad \text{Substitute 4 for } y \text{ and 2 for } z.$$
$$2x + 2 = 4$$
$$2x = 2$$
$$x = 1$$

**Solution:** The solution of the system is (1, 4, 2).

## Try These B

**a.** Solve this system of equations using Gaussian elimination. Show your work.

$$\begin{cases} 2x + y - z = -2 \\ x + 2y + z = 11 \\ -2x + y + 2z = 15 \end{cases}$$

1. Work with a partner or with your group. Make a flowchart on notebook paper that summarizes the steps for solving a system of three equations in three variables by using either substitution or Gaussian elimination. As you prepare your flowchart to present to the class, remember to use words and graphics that will help your classmates understand the steps. Also, be careful to communicate mathematical terms correctly to describe the application of mathematical concepts.

**My Notes**

**CONNECT TO MATH HISTORY**

The method of Gaussian elimination is named for the German mathematician Carl Friedrich Gauss (1777–1855), who used a version of it in his calculations. However, the first known use of Gaussian elimination was a version used in a Chinese work called *Nine Chapters of the Mathematical Art*, which was written more than 2000 years ago. It shows how to solve a system of linear equations involving the volume of grain yielded from sheaves of rice.

**My Notes**

A farmer plans to grow corn, soybeans, and wheat on his farm. Let $c$ represent the number of acres planted with corn, $s$ represent the number of acres planted with soybeans, and $w$ represent the number of acres planted with wheat.

2. The farmer has 500 acres to plant with corn, soybeans, and wheat. Write an equation in terms of $c$, $s$, and $w$ that models this information.

3. Growing an acre of corn costs $390, an acre of soybeans costs $190, and an acre of wheat costs $170. The farmer has a budget of $119,000 to spend on growing the crops. Write an equation in terms of $c$, $s$, and $w$ that models this information.

4. The farmer plans to grow twice as many acres of wheat as acres of corn. Write an equation in terms of $c$ and $w$ that models this information.

5. Write your equations from Items 3–5 as a system of equations.

6. **Make sense of problems.** Solve the system of equations. Write the solution as an ordered triple of the form $(c, s, w)$.

**MATH TIP**

Determine the reasonableness of your solution. Does your answer make sense in the context of the problem?

7. Explain what the solution you found in Item 6 represents in the real-world situation.

**Check Your Understanding**

8. Compare and contrast systems of two linear equations in two variables with systems of three linear equations in three variables.

9. Explain how you could use the first equation in this system to eliminate $x$ from the second and third equations in the system:
$$\begin{cases} x + 2y - z = 5 \\ -x - y + 2z = -13. \\ 2x + y - 2z = 14 \end{cases}$$

## LESSON 3-2 PRACTICE

10. Solve the system using substitution.
$$\begin{cases} x - 3y + z = -15 \\ 2x + y - z = -2 \\ x + y + 2z = 1 \end{cases}$$

11. Solve the system using Gaussian elimination.
$$\begin{cases} 3x + y - z = 4 \\ -3x + 2y + 2z = 6 \\ x - y + 2z = 8 \end{cases}$$

Use the table for Items 12–14.

**Frozen Yogurt Sales**

| Time Period | Small Cups Sold | Medium Cups Sold | Large Cups Sold | Sales ($) |
|---|---|---|---|---|
| 1:00–2:00 | 6 | 10 | 8 | 97.60 |
| 2:00–3:00 | 9 | 12 | 5 | 100.80 |
| 3:00–4:00 | 10 | 12 | 4 | 99.20 |

12. Write a system of equations that can be used to determine $s$, $m$, and $l$, the cost in dollars of small, medium, and large cups of frozen yogurt.

13. Solve your equation and explain what the solution means in the context of the situation.

14. **Use appropriate tools strategically.** Which method did you use to solve the system? Explain why you used this method.

### Learning Targets:
- Add, subtract, and multiply matrices.
- Use a graphing calculator to perform operations on matrices.

**SUGGESTED LEARNING STRATEGIES:** Interactive Word Wall, Note Taking, Close Reading, Summarizing, Paraphrasing, Discussion Groups, Work Backward

A *matrix*, such as matrix A below, is a rectangular arrangement of numbers written inside brackets.

$$A = \begin{bmatrix} 2 & 4 & 5 \\ -3 & 8 & -2 \end{bmatrix}$$

The *dimensions of a matrix* give its number of rows and number of columns. A matrix with $m$ rows and $n$ columns has dimensions $m \times n$. Matrix A has 2 rows and 3 columns, so its dimensions are $2 \times 3$.

The numbers in a matrix are called *entries*. The address of an entry gives its location in the matrix. To write the address of an entry, write the lowercase letter used to name the matrix, and then write the row number and column number of the entry as subscripts. The address $a_{12}$ indicates the entry in matrix A in the first row and second column, so $a_{12}$ is 4.

In the next lesson, you will learn how to use matrices to solve systems of equations.

Use these matrices to answer Items 1–3.

$$B = \begin{bmatrix} 3 & -6 \\ 8 & 10 \\ -4 & 0 \end{bmatrix} \qquad C = \begin{bmatrix} 14 & 40 \\ 26 & 30 \end{bmatrix}$$

**1.** What are the dimensions of each matrix?

**2. Make use of structure.** Write the entry indicated by each address.
   **a.** $b_{31}$
   **b.** $b_{12}$
   **c.** $c_{21}$
   **d.** $c_{22}$

**3.** What is the address of the entry 8 in matrix B? Explain.

---

### WRITING MATH

You can name a matrix by using a capital letter.

### READING MATH

To say the dimensions of matrix A, read $2 \times 3$ as "2 by 3."

### MATH TERMS

A **matrix** (plural: matrices) is a rectangular array of numbers arranged in rows and columns inside brackets.

The **dimensions of a matrix** are the number of rows and the number of columns, indicated by $m \times n$, where $m$ is the number of rows and $n$ is the number of columns.

The **entries** of a matrix are the numbers in the matrix.

You can input a matrix into a graphing calculator using the steps below.

**Step 1:** Go to the Matrix menu. To do this, press [2nd], and then press the key with MATRIX printed above it.

**Step 2:** Use the right arrow key to select the Edit submenu.

**Step 3:** Move the cursor next to the name of one of the matrices and press [ENTER] to select it.

**Step 4:** Enter the correct dimensions for the matrix.

**Step 5:** Enter the entries of the matrix. To save the matrix, press [2nd], and then press the key with QUIT printed above it.

> **TECHNOLOGY TIP**
>
> When entering a negative number as an entry in a matrix, be sure to use the negative key to enter the negative sign, not the subtraction key.

4. Input each matrix into a graphing calculator.

   **a.** $A = \begin{bmatrix} 6 & -1 \\ 5 & 4 \end{bmatrix}$

   **b.** $B = \begin{bmatrix} 3 & -2 & 5 \\ 6 & 0 & -4 \end{bmatrix}$

If two matrices have the same dimensions, you can add or subtract them by adding or subtracting their corresponding entries.

### Example A

Find each matrix sum or difference.

$$C = \begin{bmatrix} 2 & 8 & 10 \\ -3 & 1 & -5 \end{bmatrix} \qquad D = \begin{bmatrix} 5 & 0 & -2 \\ 8 & 7 & -4 \end{bmatrix}$$

**a.** Find $C + D$.

$$C + D = \begin{bmatrix} 2+5 & 8+0 & 10+(-2) \\ -3+8 & 1+7 & -5+(-4) \end{bmatrix} = \begin{bmatrix} 7 & 8 & 8 \\ 5 & 8 & -9 \end{bmatrix}$$

**b.** Find $C - D$.

$$C - D = \begin{bmatrix} 2-5 & 8-0 & 10-(-2) \\ -3-8 & 1-7 & -5-(-4) \end{bmatrix} = \begin{bmatrix} -3 & 8 & 12 \\ -11 & -6 & -1 \end{bmatrix}$$

> **TECHNOLOGY TIP**
>
> To add the matrices on a graphing calculator, first input both matrices. Then select [C] from the Names submenu of the Matrix menu. Press [+]. Then select [D] from the Names submenu of the Matrix menu. Your screen should now show [C]+[D]. Press [ENTER] to show the sum.

### Try These A

Find each matrix sum or difference.

$$E = \begin{bmatrix} 6 & -2 \\ 9 & 4 \end{bmatrix} \qquad F = \begin{bmatrix} -1 & 5 \\ 10 & 7 \end{bmatrix}$$

**a.** $E + F$     **b.** $E - F$     **c.** $F - E$

**My Notes**

**MATH TIP**

Recall that the Commutative Property of Addition states that $a + b = b + a$ for any real numbers $a$ and $b$.

**MATH TIP**

The inner dimensions of two matrices indicate whether their product is defined.

$$n \times \qquad \times p$$

The outer dimensions indicate the dimensions of the matrix product.

$$\times m \qquad m \times$$

## Check Your Understanding

5. How is a matrix similar to a table?

6. **Express regularity in repeated reasoning.** Make a conjecture about whether matrix addition is commutative. Then provide an example that supports your conjecture.

7. Explain why you cannot subtract these two matrices.

$$A = \begin{bmatrix} 2 & 3 & 4 \\ -1 & -6 & -8 \end{bmatrix} \qquad B = \begin{bmatrix} 4 & -2 \\ 5 & -6 \\ 6 & -10 \end{bmatrix}$$

8. Two matrices are additive inverses if each entry in their sum is 0. What is the additive inverse of the matrix shown below? Explain how you determined your answer.

$$\begin{bmatrix} 7 & -2 \\ 0 & 4 \end{bmatrix}$$

You can also find the product of two matrices $A$ and $B$ if the number of columns in $A$ is equal to the number of rows in $B$. For example, the dimensions of matrix $A$ below are $3 \times 2$, and the dimensions of matrix $B$ are $2 \times 1$. The matrix product $AB$ is defined because $A$ has 2 columns and $B$ has 2 rows.

$$A = \begin{bmatrix} 2 & 8 \\ -7 & 5 \\ 1 & 3 \end{bmatrix} \qquad B = \begin{bmatrix} 4 \\ -2 \end{bmatrix}$$

The product of an $n \times m$ matrix and an $m \times p$ matrix is an $n \times p$ matrix. Because $A$ above is a $3 \times 2$ matrix and $B$ is a $2 \times 1$ matrix, the product $AB$ is a $3 \times 1$ matrix.

To find the entry in row $i$ and column $j$ of the product $AB$, find the sum of the products of consecutive entries in row $i$ of matrix $A$ and column $j$ of matrix $B$. To see what this means, take a look at the next example.

## Example B

Find the matrix product $AB$.

$$A = \begin{bmatrix} 1 & 5 & -4 \\ 3 & -2 & 2 \end{bmatrix} \qquad B = \begin{bmatrix} 2 & 4 \\ 3 & -1 \\ 0 & -2 \end{bmatrix}$$

**Step 1:** Determine whether $AB$ is defined.

$A$ is a $2 \times 3$ matrix, and $B$ is a $3 \times 2$ matrix, so $AB$ is defined. $A$ has 2 rows and $B$ has 2 columns, so $AB$ is a $2 \times 2$ matrix.

**Step 2:** Find the entry in row 1, column 1 of $AB$.

Use row 1 of $A$ and column 1 of $B$. Multiply the first entries, the second entries, and the third entries. Then add the products.

$$1(2) + 5(3) + (-4)(0) = 17$$

$$AB = \begin{bmatrix} 1 & 5 & -4 \\ 3 & -2 & 2 \end{bmatrix} \begin{bmatrix} 2 & 4 \\ 3 & -1 \\ 0 & -2 \end{bmatrix} = \begin{bmatrix} 17 & - \\ - & - \end{bmatrix}$$

**Step 3:** Find the entry in row 1, column 2 of $AB$.

Use row 1 of $A$ and column 2 of $B$.

$$1(4) + 5(-1) + (-4)(-2) = 7$$

$$AB = \begin{bmatrix} 1 & 5 & -4 \\ 3 & -2 & 2 \end{bmatrix} \begin{bmatrix} 2 & 4 \\ 3 & -1 \\ 0 & -2 \end{bmatrix} = \begin{bmatrix} 17 & 7 \\ - & - \end{bmatrix}$$

**Step 4:** Find the entry in row 2, column 1 of $AB$.

Use row 2 of $A$ and column 1 of $B$.

$$3(2) + (-2)(3) + 2(0) = 0$$

$$AB = \begin{bmatrix} 1 & 5 & -4 \\ 3 & -2 & 2 \end{bmatrix} \begin{bmatrix} 2 & 4 \\ 3 & -1 \\ 0 & -2 \end{bmatrix} = \begin{bmatrix} 17 & 7 \\ 0 & - \end{bmatrix}$$

**Step 5:** Find the entry in row 2, column 2 of $AB$.

Use row 2 of $A$ and column 2 of $B$.

$$3(4) + (-2)(-1) + 2(-2) = 10$$

$$AB = \begin{bmatrix} 1 & 5 & -4 \\ 3 & -2 & 2 \end{bmatrix} \begin{bmatrix} 2 & 4 \\ 3 & -1 \\ 0 & -2 \end{bmatrix} = \begin{bmatrix} 17 & 7 \\ 0 & 10 \end{bmatrix}$$

**Solution:** $AB = \begin{bmatrix} 17 & 7 \\ 0 & 10 \end{bmatrix}$

> **TECHNOLOGY TIP**
>
> To multiply the matrices on a graphing calculator, first input both matrices. Then select [A] from the Names submenu of the Matrix menu. Press $\boxed{x}$. Then select [B] from the Names submenu of the Matrix menu. Your screen should now show [A]*[B]. Press $\boxed{\text{ENTER}}$ to show the product.

### Try These B

Find each matrix product if it is defined.

$$C = \begin{bmatrix} 1 & 4 \\ -7 & 6 \end{bmatrix} \qquad D = \begin{bmatrix} 0 & 8 \\ -4 & -5 \end{bmatrix} \qquad E = \begin{bmatrix} 8 & 5 & -1 \\ -4 & 4 & -9 \end{bmatrix}$$

**a.** $CD$        **b.** $CE$        **c.** $ED$

### Check Your Understanding

9. Is matrix multiplication commutative? Provide an example that supports your answer.

10. The matrix product $RS$ is a $3 \times 4$ matrix. If $R$ is a $3 \times 2$ matrix, what are the dimensions of $S$? Explain your answer.

11. **Critique the reasoning of others.** Rebekah made an error when finding the matrix product $KL$. Her work is shown below. What mistake did Rebekah make? What is the correct matrix product?

$$K = \begin{bmatrix} 2 & 8 \\ -4 & -2 \end{bmatrix} \qquad\qquad L = \begin{bmatrix} 1 & 5 \\ 0 & -3 \end{bmatrix}$$

$$KL = \begin{bmatrix} 2(1) & 8(5) \\ -4(0) & -2(-3) \end{bmatrix} = \begin{bmatrix} 2 & 40 \\ 0 & 6 \end{bmatrix}$$

### LESSON 3-3 PRACTICE

Use these matrices to answer Items 12–17.

$$A = \begin{bmatrix} 3 & -6 & 1 \\ -8 & 2 & 0 \end{bmatrix} \qquad B = \begin{bmatrix} 5 & -7 \\ -3 & 2 \end{bmatrix} \qquad C = \begin{bmatrix} 4 & 10 \\ -1 & -3 \end{bmatrix}$$

12. What are the dimensions of $A$?

13. **Look for and make use of structure.** What is the entry with the address $b_{12}$?

14. Find $B + C$.

15. Find $C - B$.

16. Find $AB$ if it is defined.

17. Find $BC$ if it is defined.

**Learning Targets:**

- Solve systems of two linear equations in two variables by using graphing calculators with matrices.
- Solve systems of three linear equations in three variables by using graphing calculators with matrices.

**SUGGESTED LEARNING STRATEGIES:** Vocabulary Organizer, Note Taking, Discussion Groups, Marking the Text, Debriefing, Identify a Subtask, Create Representations, Look for a Pattern

A *square matrix* is a matrix with the same number of rows and columns. A *multiplicative identity matrix* is a square matrix in which all entries along the main diagonal are 1 and all other entries are 0. The main diagonal of a square matrix is the diagonal from the upper left to the lower right. A multiplicative identity matrix is often called an identity matrix and is usually named $I$.

A $3 \times 3$ identity matrix is shown below. The entries in blue are on the main diagonal.

$$I = \begin{bmatrix} 1 & 0 & 0 \\ 0 & 1 & 0 \\ 0 & 0 & 1 \end{bmatrix}$$

The product of a square matrix and its *multiplicative inverse matrix* is an identity matrix $I$. The multiplicative inverse of matrix $A$ is often called the inverse of $A$ and may be named as $A^{-1}$. So, by definition, $A^{-1}$ is the inverse of $A$ if $A \cdot A^{-1} = I$.

**Check Your Understanding**

1. **Construct viable arguments.** Explain why $\begin{bmatrix} 0 & 1 \\ 1 & 0 \end{bmatrix}$ is *not* an identity matrix.

Use these matrices and a graphing calculator to answer Items 2–4.

$$A = \begin{bmatrix} 2 & 4 \\ 1 & 3 \end{bmatrix} \qquad B = \begin{bmatrix} 1.5 & -2 \\ -0.5 & 1 \end{bmatrix}$$

2. Multiply $A$ by a $2 \times 2$ identity matrix. Describe the relationship between the matrix product $AI$ and $A$.

3. Is $B$ the inverse of $A$? Explain.

4. Is $A$ the inverse of $B$? Explain.

You can use matrices and inverse matrices to solve systems of linear equations.

**My Notes**

### MATH TERMS

A **matrix equation** is an equation of the form $AX = B$.

- $A$ is the **coefficient matrix**, the matrix formed by the coefficients of the system of equations.
- $X$ is the **variable matrix**, a column matrix that represents all the variables of the system of equations.
- $B$ is the **constant matrix**, a column matrix representing all the constants of the systems of equations.

### TECHNOLOGY TIP

If the entries in the inverse matrix are decimals, try converting them to fractions by pressing MATH and selecting 1: ▶ Frac.

The first step in solving a system of linear equations by using matrices is to write the system as a ***matrix equation***. The diagram shows how to write the system $\begin{cases} 2x + 3y = 7 \\ x - 4y = -2 \end{cases}$ as a matrix equation.

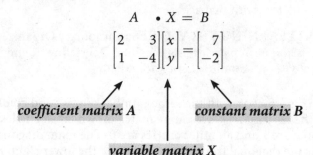

$$A \quad \bullet \, X = B$$
$$\begin{bmatrix} 2 & 3 \\ 1 & -4 \end{bmatrix}\begin{bmatrix} x \\ y \end{bmatrix} = \begin{bmatrix} 7 \\ -2 \end{bmatrix}$$

*coefficient matrix* **A**   *constant matrix* **B**

*variable matrix* **X**

To solve a matrix equation $AX = B$ for $X$, you use a process similar to what you would use when solving the regular equation $ax = b$ for $x$. To solve $ax = b$, you could multiply both sides of the equation by the multiplicative inverse of $a$.

Likewise, to solve the matrix equation $AX = B$, you can multiply both sides of the equation by the multiplicative inverse matrix of $A$. Thus, the solution of $AX = B$ is $X = A^{-1}B$. You can use a graphing calculator to help you find $A^{-1}$.

In Items 5–7, use the matrix equation $\begin{bmatrix} 2 & 3 \\ 1 & -4 \end{bmatrix}\begin{bmatrix} x \\ y \end{bmatrix} = \begin{bmatrix} 7 \\ -2 \end{bmatrix}$.

5. To solve for $X$, you first need to find $A^{-1}$. Input matrix $A$, the coefficient matrix, into a graphing calculator. Then select [A] from the Names submenu of the Matrix menu. Then press $\boxed{x^{-1}}$. Your screen should now show $[A]^{-1}$. Press $\boxed{\text{ENTER}}$ to show the inverse matrix. What is $A^{-1}$?

6. Find the matrix product $A^{-1}B$.

7. **Make sense of problems.** What are the values of $x$ and $y$ in the variable matrix $X$? How do you know?

### Example A

The hourly cost to a police department of using a canine team depends on the hourly cost $x$ in dollars of using a dog and the hourly salary $y$ of a handler. The hourly cost for a team of three dogs and two handlers is $82, and the hourly cost for a team of four dogs and four handlers is $160. The system $\begin{cases} 3x + 2y = 82 \\ 4x + 4y = 160 \end{cases}$ models this situation. Use a matrix equation to solve the system, and explain what the solution means.

**Step 1:** Use the system to write a matrix equation.

$$\begin{bmatrix} 3 & 2 \\ 4 & 4 \end{bmatrix} \begin{bmatrix} x \\ y \end{bmatrix} = \begin{bmatrix} 82 \\ 160 \end{bmatrix}$$

**Step 2:** Enter the coefficient matrix $A$ and the constant matrix $B$ into a graphing calculator.

```
MATRIX[A]  2 × 2
[3      2      ]
[4      4      ]
```

```
MATRIX[B]  2 × 1
[82            ]
[160           ]
```

**Step 3:** Use the calculator to find $A^{-1}B$.

```
[A]⁻¹ * [B]
           [ [2]
             [38] ]
```

**Step 4:** Identify and interpret the solution of the system.

**Solution:** The matrix product $A^{-1}B$ is equal to the variable matrix $X$, so $x = 2$ and $y = 38$. The solution of the system is (2, 38). The solution shows that the hourly cost of using a dog is $2 and the hourly salary of a handler is $38.

### Try These A

Write a matrix equation to model each system. Then use the matrix equation to solve the system.

a. $\begin{cases} 2x + y = 8 \\ 5x + 6y = 13 \end{cases}$   b. $\begin{cases} 6x - 3y = -18 \\ 2x + 4y = 34 \end{cases}$   c. $\begin{cases} x - 2y = -23 \\ 3x + 3y = 21 \end{cases}$

**MATH TIP**

Before you can write a matrix equation to model a system of two linear equations in two variables, each equation in the system must be written in standard form $Ax + By = C$, where $A$, $B$, and $C$ are real numbers.

**My Notes**

8. What is an advantage of using a graphing calculator to solve a system of two linear equations in two variables as opposed to solving the system by making a hand-drawn graph?

You can also use a matrix equation to solve a system of three linear equations in three variables.

Use this information to complete Items 9–15 with your group. Karen makes handmade greeting cards and sells them at a local store. The cards come in packs of 4 for \$11, 6 for \$15, or 10 for \$20. Last month, the store sold 16 packs containing 92 of Karen's cards for a total of \$223. The following system models this situation where $x$ is the number of small packs, $y$ is the number of medium packs, and $z$ is the number of large packs.

$$\begin{cases} x + y + z = 16 \\ 4x + 6y + 10z = 92 \\ 11x + 15y + 20z = 223 \end{cases}$$

9. If you were to model the system with a matrix equation, what would be the dimensions of the coefficient matrix? How do you know?

**DISCUSSION GROUP TIPS**

As you work in groups, review the problem scenario carefully and explore together the information provided and how to use it to create potential solutions. Discuss your understanding of the problem and ask peers or your teacher to clarify any areas that are not clear in order to aid comprehension and to ensure understanding of all group members' ideas.

10. **Model with mathematics.** Write a matrix equation to model the system.

**My Notes**

11. **Use appropriate tools strategically.** Use a graphing calculator to find $A^{-1}$, the inverse of the coefficient matrix.

12. Use a graphing calculator to find $A^{-1}B$.

13. Find the solution of the system of equations and explain the meaning of the solution.

14. How can you check that you found the solution of the system correctly?

15. Work with your group. Compare and contrast using a matrix equation to solve a system of two linear equations in two variables with using a matrix equation to solve a system of three linear equations in three variables.

**DISCUSSION GROUP TIP**

As you listen to the group discussion, take notes to aid comprehension and to help you describe your own ideas to others in your group. Ask questions to clarify ideas and to gain further understanding of key concepts.

## Check Your Understanding

16. A system of equations and the matrix equation that models it are shown below. Find $AX$, the product of the coefficient matrix and the variable matrix of the matrix equation. What is the relationship between $AX$ and the system of equations?

$$\begin{cases} 3x + 2y = 18 \\ 2x + 4y = 20 \end{cases} \qquad \begin{bmatrix} 3 & 2 \\ 2 & 4 \end{bmatrix} \begin{bmatrix} x \\ y \end{bmatrix} = \begin{bmatrix} 18 \\ 20 \end{bmatrix}$$

17. **Critique the reasoning of others.** Doug incorrectly solved the matrix equation in Item 17 by finding the matrix product $\begin{bmatrix} 3 & 2 \\ 2 & 4 \end{bmatrix} \begin{bmatrix} 18 \\ 20 \end{bmatrix}$.

    What mistake did Doug make? What should he have done instead?

18. What happens when you try to solve the system $\begin{cases} 2x + y = 6 \\ 4x + 2y = 16 \end{cases}$

    by writing and solving a matrix equation? What do you think this result indicates about the system? Confirm your answer by graphing the system and using the graph to classify the system.

## LESSON 3-4 PRACTICE

19. Use a graphing calculator to find the inverse of the matrix $\begin{bmatrix} 2 & 8 \\ 5 & 4 \end{bmatrix}$.

For Items 20–21, write a matrix equation to model each system. Then use the matrix equation to solve the system.

20. $\begin{cases} 2x + 4y = 22 \\ -3x + 2y = 7 \end{cases}$

21. $\begin{cases} x + y + z = 11 \\ 2x + 8y + 3z = 80 \\ 4x - 6y + 7z = -62 \end{cases}$

**CONNECT TO ECONOMICS**

The euro is the unit of currency used in many of the nations in the European Union. The British pound is the unit of currency used in the United Kingdom.

22. **Model with mathematics.** Steve has 2 euros and 4 British pounds worth a total of $9.10. Emily has 3 euros and 1 British pound worth a total of $5.55
    a. Write a system of equations to model this situation, where $x$ represents the value of 1 euro in dollars and $y$ represents the value of 1 British pound in dollars.
    b. Write the system of equations as a matrix equation.
    c. Use the matrix equation to solve the system. Then interpret the solution.

23. Which solution method for solving systems of equations do you find easiest to use? Which method do you find most difficult to use? Explain why.

## ACTIVITY 3 PRACTICE
Write your answers on notebook paper.
Show your work.

### Lesson 3-1

1. Solve the system by graphing.
$$\begin{cases} y = -3x + 6 \\ y = -\dfrac{1}{3}x - 2 \end{cases}$$

2. Solve the system using substitution.
$$\begin{cases} 5y - x = -5 \\ 7y - x = -23 \end{cases}$$

3. Solve the system using elimination.
$$\begin{cases} 2x - 5y = 8 \\ x - 3y = -1 \end{cases}$$

4. The system of equations $\begin{cases} 2x + 3y = 7 \\ 10x + cy = 3 \end{cases}$ has solutions for all values of $c$ except:

   **A.** $-15$      **B.** $-3$
   **C.** $10$      **D.** $15$

5. **a.** Graph the system $\begin{cases} y = -2x - 1 \\ 3y = -3 - 6x \end{cases}$.

   **b.** Classify the system, and tell how many solutions it has.

6. Mariana had a $20 gift card to an online music store. She spent the entire amount on songs, which cost $1 each, and music videos, which cost $2 each. Mariana bought five more songs than music videos. Write and solve a system of equations to find the number of songs and the number of music videos Mariana bought.

7. A chemist needs to mix a 2% acid solution and a 10% acid solution to make 600 milliliters of a 5% acid solution. Write and solve a system of equations to find the volume of the 2% solution and the volume of the 10% solution that the chemist will need.

### Lesson 3-2

8. Solve the system using substitution.
$$\begin{cases} x + y + z = 6 \\ 2x + y + 2z = 14 \\ 3x + 3y + z = 8 \end{cases}$$

9. Solve the system using Gaussian elimination.
$$\begin{cases} 2x + 4y + z = 31 \\ -2x + 2y - 3z = -9 \\ x + 3y + 2z = 21 \end{cases}$$

10. A snack company plans to sell a mixture of peanut butter, grape jelly, and granola as a sandwich spread. The table gives information about each ingredient.

| Ingredient | Calories per Ounce | Grams of Fat per Ounce |
|---|---|---|
| Peanut butter | 168 | 14 |
| Grape jelly | 71 | 0 |
| Granola | 132 | 12 |

An 18-ounce jar of the sandwich spread will have a total of 2273 calories and 150 grams of fat. Write and solve a system of equations to find the number of ounces of peanut butter, grape jelly, and granola in each jar.

11. A small furniture factory makes three types of tables: coffee tables, dining tables, and end tables. The factory needs to make 54 tables each day. The number of dining tables made per day should equal the number of coffee tables and end tables combined. The number of coffee tables made each day should be three more than the number of end tables. Write and solve a system of equations to find the number of tables of each type the factory should make each day.

12. Can you solve this system? Explain.
$$\begin{cases} x + 2y + 3z = 8 \\ 3x + 4y + 5z = 10 \end{cases}$$

## Lesson 3-3

Use the given matrices for Items 13–20.

$$A = \begin{bmatrix} 3 & 0 & 1 \\ -1 & 2 & 6 \end{bmatrix} \quad B = \begin{bmatrix} 4 & -2 \\ 1 & 5 \end{bmatrix} \quad C = \begin{bmatrix} 1 & 2 & 3 \\ 3 & 2 & 1 \\ -2 & 4 & 3 \end{bmatrix}$$

$$D = \begin{bmatrix} 3 & -1 & 4 \\ 2 & 3 & 1 \end{bmatrix} \quad E = \begin{bmatrix} 4 & 1 \\ 2 & 3 \end{bmatrix}$$

**13.** What are the dimensions of matrix $A$?

**14.** What is the entry with the address $c_{13}$?

**15.** Find $A + D$.

**16.** Find $B - E$.

**17.** Find $ED$ if it is defined.

**18.** Find $AC$ if it is defined.

**19.** Find $AB$ if it is defined.

**20.** Let $P$ equal the matrix product $BA$. Which expression gives the value of $P_{12}$?
   **A.** $-2(3) + 5(-1)$
   **B.** $1(3) + 5(1)$
   **C.** $4(0) + (-2)(2)$
   **D.** $4(0) + 1(2)$

**21.** Explain how to determine whether the product of two matrices is defined and how to determine the dimensions of a product matrix.

## Lesson 3-4

**22.** Find the inverse of each matrix.
   **a.** $\begin{bmatrix} 3 & 1 \\ 2 & 0 \end{bmatrix}$  **b.** $\begin{bmatrix} -2 & -1 \\ 2 & 3 \end{bmatrix}$

**23.** Are these matrices inverses of each other? Explain.

$$A = \begin{bmatrix} 0 & 4 \\ 1 & 8 \end{bmatrix} \quad B = \begin{bmatrix} -2 & 1 \\ 0.25 & 0 \end{bmatrix}$$

**24.** Write the system of equations represented by the matrix equation below. Then solve the matrix equation.

$$\begin{bmatrix} -3 & -2 \\ 5 & 4 \end{bmatrix} \begin{bmatrix} x \\ y \end{bmatrix} = \begin{bmatrix} 1 \\ -3 \end{bmatrix}$$

**25.** Write a matrix equation to model the system. Then use the matrix equation to solve the system.

$$\begin{cases} 3x + 2y - 7z = -29 \\ 4x - 6y + 5z = -19 \\ 8x + y - 4z = -30 \end{cases}$$

**26.** Guillermo bought ground beef and ground pork for a party. The beef costs \$3.48/lb and the pork costs \$2.64/lb. Guillermo bought 6 pounds of meat for a total of \$19.62. Write a system of equations that can be used to determine how many pounds of each type of meat Guillermo bought. Then use a matrix equation to solve the system.

**27.** Dean, John, and Andrew sold key chains, mugs, and gift wrap for a school fundraiser. The table below shows the number of items that each person sold and the amount of money collected from the sales. Write a matrix equation that can be used to find the price for each item in the table. Then solve the equation to find the prices.

| | Key Chains | Mugs | Gift Wrap | Amount of Sales |
|---|---|---|---|---|
| Dean | 3 | 4 | 5 | \$87.50 |
| John | 1 | 1 | 2 | \$31.50 |
| Andrew | 2 | 0 | 1 | \$17.00 |

## MATHEMATICAL PRACTICES
### Look For and Make Use of Structure

**28.** Compare and contrast solving an equation of the form $ax = b$ for $x$ with solving a matrix equation of the form $AX = B$ for $X$.

# Equations, Inequalities, and Systems

## GAMING SYSTEMS

A gaming manufacturing company is developing a new gaming system. In addition to a game console, the company will also produce an optional accessory called a Jesture that allows users to communicate with the game console by using gestures and voice commands.

Solve the following problems about the gaming system. Show your work.

1. The company plans to sell the video game console at a loss in order to increase its sales. It will make up for the loss from profits made from the sales of games for the system. The company will lose $50 for each console it sells and earn a profit of $15 for each game sold for the system.
   a. Write an equation that can be used to determine $t$, the total amount the company will earn from a customer who buys a console and $g$ games.
   b. Graph the equation on a coordinate grid.
   c. The company predicts that the average customer will buy seven games for the video game console. What is the total amount the company will earn from the average customer who buys a game console and seven games?

2. To produce the new system, the company plans on using resources in two manufacturing plants. The table gives the hours needed for three tasks. For both plants combined, the company has allocated the following resources on a weekly basis: no more than 8500 hours of motherboard production, no more than 9000 hours of technical labor, and no more than 12,000 hours of general manufacturing.

| Resources | Plant 1 (hours per system) | Plant 2 (hours per system) |
|---|---|---|
| Motherboard production | 9 | 1 |
| Technical labor | 9 | 3 |
| General manufacturing | 4 | 8 |

   a. Write inequalities that model the constraints in this situation. Let $x$ represent the number of gaming systems that will be made in Plant 1, and let $y$ represent the number of gaming systems that will be made in Plant 2.
   b. Graph the constraints. Shade the solution region that is common to all of the inequalities.
   c. Identify an ordered pair that satisfies the constraints. Explain what the ordered pair represents in the context of the situation.

3. The Jesture accessory can recognize players when they are within a certain range. The player's distance from the Jesture can vary up to 1.2 meters from the target distance of 2.4 meters.
   a. Write an absolute value equation that can be used to find the extreme distances that a player can stand from the Jesture and still be recognized.
   b. Solve your equation, and interpret the solutions.

4. The Jesture will come with a fitness program. The program allows players to earn fitness points depending on the number of minutes they spend on each activity. The table shows how many minutes three players spent on each activity and the total number of fitness points they earned.

| Play Tester | Yoga (minutes) | Aerobics (minutes) | Jogging (minutes) | Fitness Points |
|---|---|---|---|---|
| Cassie | 30 | 10 | 20 | 130 |
| Clint | 15 | 20 | 10 | 95 |
| Kian | 10 | 25 | 20 | 140 |

a. Write a system of three equations that can be used to determine the number of points a player gets for 1 minute of each activity.
b. Solve your system, and interpret the solution.

| Scoring Guide | Exemplary | Proficient | Emerging | Incomplete |
|---|---|---|---|---|
| | The solution demonstrates these characteristics: | | | |
| **Mathematics Knowledge and Thinking** (Items 2b, 3b, 4b) | • Clear and accurate understanding of solving systems of equations and inequalities, and absolute value equations | • A functional understanding of solving systems of equations and inequalities and absolute value equations | • Partial understanding of solving systems of equations and inequalities and absolute value equations | • Little or no understanding of solving systems of equations and inequalities and absolute value equations |
| **Problem Solving** (Items 1c, 2c, 3b, 4b) | • An appropriate and efficient strategy that results in a correct answer | • A strategy that may include unnecessary steps but results in a correct answer | • A strategy that results in some incorrect answers | • No clear strategy when solving problems |
| **Mathematical Modeling / Representations** (Items 1a, 1b, 2a, 2b, 3a, 4a) | • Fluency in representing real-world scenarios using linear equations, systems of equations and inequalities, and absolute value equations <br>• Clear and accurate understanding of creating graphs of equations and inequalities | • Little difficulty representing real-world scenarios using linear equations, systems of equations and inequalities, and absolute value equations <br>• Mostly accurate creation of graphs of equations and inequalities | • Partial understanding of how to represent real-world scenarios using linear equations, systems of equations and inequalities, and absolute value equations <br>• Partially accurate creation of graphs of equations and inequalities | • Little or no understanding of how to represent real-world scenarios using linear equations, systems of equations and inequalities, and absolute value equations <br>• Inaccurate or incomplete creation of graphs of equations and inequalities |
| **Reasoning and Communication** (Items 2c, 3b, 4b) | • Ease and accuracy in explaining interpreting solutions in the context of a real-world scenario | • Little difficulty in explaining interpreting solutions in the context of a real-world scenario | • Partially correct explanations and interpretations of solutions in the context of a real-world scenario | • Incomplete or inaccurate explanations and interpretations of solutions in the context of a real-world scenario |

# Piecewise-Defined Functions
## Absolutely Piece-ful
### Lesson 4-1 Introduction to Piecewise-Defined Functions

**Learning Targets:**

- Graph piecewise-defined functions.
- Write the domain and range of functions using interval notation, inequalities, and set notation.

**SUGGESTED LEARNING STRATEGIES:** Activating Prior Knowledge, Quickwrite, Create Representations, Interactive Word Wall, Marking the Text, Think-Pair-Share, Discussion Groups

The graphs of both $y = x - 2$ for $x < 3$ and $y = -2x + 7$ for $x \geq 3$ are shown on the same coordinate grid below.

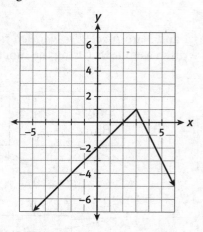

1. Work with your group on this item and on Items 2–4. Describe the graph as completely as possible.

2. **Make use of structure.** Why is the graph a function?

3. Graph $y = x^2 - 3$ for $x \leq 0$ and $y = \frac{1}{4}x + 1$ for $x > 0$ on the same coordinate grid.

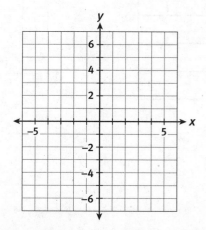

**DISCUSSION GROUP TIP**

As you listen to your group's discussions as you work through Items 1–4, you may hear math terms or other words that you do not know. Use your math notebook to record words that are frequently used. Ask for clarification of their meaning, and make notes to help you remember and use those words in your own communications.

**4.** Describe the graph in Item 3 as completely as possible. Why is the graph a function?

The functions in Items 1 and 3 are ***piecewise-defined functions***. Piecewise-defined functions are written as follows (using the function from Item 3 as an example):

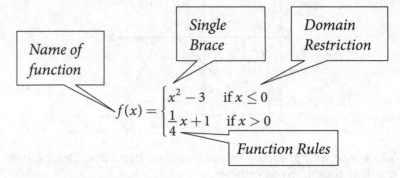

$$f(x) = \begin{cases} x^2 - 3 & \text{if } x \le 0 \\ \frac{1}{4}x + 1 & \text{if } x > 0 \end{cases}$$

*Name of function*  *Single Brace*  *Domain Restriction*  *Function Rules*

**5. Model with mathematics.** Complete the table of values. Then graph the function.

$$g(x) = \begin{cases} -2x - 2 & \text{if } x < -1 \\ x + 3 & \text{if } x \ge -1 \end{cases}$$

| x | g(x) |
|-----|------|
| −4 | |
| −3 | |
| −2 | |
| −1 | |
| 0 | |
| 1 | |
| 2 | |

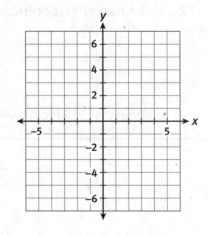

### Check Your Understanding

6. **Critique the reasoning of others.** Look back at Item 5. Esteban says that $g(-1) = 2$. Is Esteban correct? Explain.

7. Explain how to graph a piecewise-defined function.

8. If a piecewise-defined function has a break, how do you know whether to use an open circle or a closed circle for the endpoints of the function's graph?

The *domain* of a piecewise-defined function consists of the union of all the domains of the individual "pieces" of the function. Likewise, the *range* of a piecewise-defined function consists of the union of all the ranges of the individual "pieces" of the function.

You can represent the domain and range of a function by using inequalities. You can also use interval notation and set notation to represent the domain and range.

9. Write the domain and range of $g(x)$ in Item 5 by using:
   **a.** inequalities

   **b.** *interval notation*

   **c.** *set notation.*

10. Graph each function, and write its domain and range using inequalities, interval notation, and set notation. Show your work.

   **a.**
   $$f(x) = \begin{cases} x + 2 & \text{if } x < 0 \\ 2x - 1 & \text{if } x \geq 0 \end{cases}$$

   **b.**
   $$g(x) = \begin{cases} -2x + 2 & \text{if } x < 1 \\ x - 2 & \text{if } x > 1 \end{cases}$$

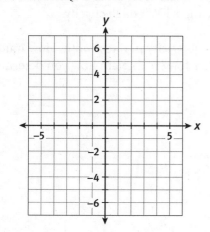

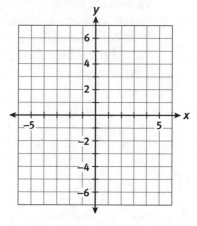

---

**MATH TERMS**

The **domain** of a function is the set of input values for which the function is defined.

The **range** of a function is the set of all possible output values for the function.

---

**MATH TIP**

*Interval notation* is a way of writing an interval as a pair of numbers, which represent the endpoints. For example, $2 < x \leq 6$ is written in interval notation as $(2, 6]$. Use a parenthesis if an endpoint is not included; use a bracket if an endpoint is included. In interval notation, infinity, $\infty$, and negative infinity, $-\infty$, are not included as endpoints.

*Set notation* is a way of describing the numbers that are members, or elements, of a set. For example, $2 < x \leq 6$ is written in set notation as $\{x \mid x \in \mathbb{R}, 2 < x \leq 6\}$, which is read "the set of all numbers $x$ such that $x$ is an element of the real numbers and $2 < x \leq 6$."

### Check Your Understanding

11. The domain of a function is all positive integers. How could you represent this domain using set notation?

12. Explain how to use interval and set notation to represent the range $y \geq 3$.

13. What can you conclude about the graph of a piecewise-defined function whose domain is $\{x \mid x \in \mathbb{R}, x \neq 2\}$?

### LESSON 4-1 PRACTICE

14. Graph each piecewise-defined function. Then write its domain and range using inequalities, interval notation, and set notation.

    **a.** $f(x) = \begin{cases} x^2 & \text{if } x \leq 0 \\ \frac{1}{2}x & \text{if } x > 0 \end{cases}$

    **b.** $f(x) = \begin{cases} 3x & \text{if } x < -1 \\ -x + 2 & \text{if } x \geq -1 \end{cases}$

15. The range of a function is all real numbers greater than or equal to −5 and less than or equal to 5. Write the range of the function using an inequality, interval notation, and set notation.

16. Evaluate the piecewise function for $x = -2$, $x = 0$, and $x = 4$.

    $$g(x) = \begin{cases} -4x & \text{if } x < -2 \\ 3x + 2 & \text{if } -2 \leq x < 4 \\ x + 4 & \text{if } x \geq 4 \end{cases}$$

17. **Model with mathematics.** An electric utility charges residential customers a \$6 monthly fee plus \$0.04 per kilowatt hour (kWh) for the first 500 kWh and \$0.08/kWh for usage over 500 kWh.
    **a.** Write a piecewise function $f(x)$ that can be used to determine a customer's monthly bill for using $x$ kWh of electricity.
    **b.** Graph the piecewise function.
    **c.** A customer uses 613 kWh of electricity in one month. How much should the utility charge the customer? Explain how you determined your answer.

### Learning Targets:
- Graph step functions and absolute value functions.
- Describe the attributes of these functions.

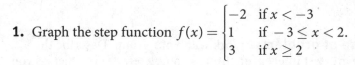

**SUGGESTED LEARNING STRATEGIES:** Activating Prior Knowledge, Interactive Word Wall, Create Representations, Look for a Pattern, Quickwrite, Think-Pair-Share

A *step function* is a piecewise-defined function whose value remains constant throughout each interval of its domain. Work with your group on Items 1–3. Use your group discussions to clarify the meaning of mathematical concepts and other language used to describe problem information. With your group or your teacher, review background information that will be useful in applying concepts and developing reasonable descriptions and explanations.

**MATH TERMS**

A piecewise-defined function with a constant value throughout each interval of its domain is called a **step function**.

1. Graph the step function $f(x) = \begin{cases} -2 & \text{if } x < -3 \\ 1 & \text{if } -3 \leq x < 2 \\ 3 & \text{if } x \geq 2 \end{cases}$.

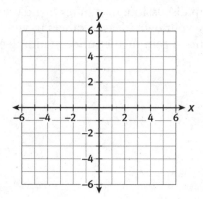

2. Describe the graph in Item 1 as completely as possible.

**DISCUSSION GROUP TIP**

Share your description with your group members and list any details you may not have considered before. If you do not know the exact words to describe your ideas, use synonyms or request assistance from group members to help you convey your ideas. Use nonverbal cues such as raising your hand to ask for clarification of others' ideas.

3. **Reason abstractly.** Why do you think the type of function graphed in Item 1 is called a step function?

One step function is the greatest integer function, written $f(x) = \lfloor x \rfloor$, which yields a value $f(x)$ that is the greatest integer less than or equal to the value of $x$. For example, $f(2.7) = \lfloor 2.7 \rfloor = 2$ because the greatest integer less than or equal to 2.7 is 2; and $f(-3.1) = \lfloor -3.1 \rfloor = -4$ because the greatest integer less than or equal to $-3.1$ is $-4$.

**4.** Graph the greatest integer function on a graphing calculator. To do so, you will need to enter the function as $y = \text{int}(x)$. To locate **int** on the calculator, press [MATH] to reach the Math menu. Then use the right arrow key to access the Number submenu. Finally, select 5: int(.

**TECHNOLOGY TIP**

Before graphing a step function on a graphing calculator, go to the Mode window, highlight Dot, and press [ENTER]. Graphing a step function in dot mode will prevent the calculator from connecting breaks in the graph with line segments.

**5. Make sense of problems.** Work with your group. Describe the graph of the greatest integer function as completely as possible. As you listen to the group discussion, take notes to aid comprehension and to help you describe your own ideas to others in your group. Ask questions to clarify ideas and to gain further understanding of key concepts.

Now take a look at a different type of piecewise-defined function.

**6.** Complete the table and graph the piecewise-defined function.

$$f(x) = \begin{cases} -x & \text{if } x < 0 \\ x & \text{if } x \geq 0 \end{cases}$$

| x | f(x) |
|----|------|
| −3 | |
| −2 | |
| −1 | |
| 0 | |
| 1 | |
| 2 | |
| 3 | |

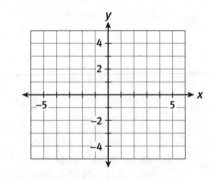

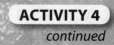

7. **Reason quantitatively.** Look back at the graph of $f(x)$ shown in Item 6.

   **a.** What are the domain and range of the function?

   **b.** Does the function have a minimum or maximum value? If so, what is it?

   **c.** What are the $x$-intercept(s) and $y$-intercept of the function?

   **d.** Describe the symmetry of the graph of the function.

The function $f(x)$ in Item 6 is known as the *absolute value function*. The notation for the function is $f(x) = |x|$. The sharp change in the graph at $x = 0$ is the vertex.

8. Use the piecewise definition of the absolute value function to evaluate each expression.

   **a.** $f(-14) =$          **b.** $f(8) =$

   **c.** $f(0) =$          **d.** $f\left(2 - \sqrt{5}\right) =$

9. Could you have determined the values of the function in Item 8 another way? Explain.

**MATH TIP**

The absolute value function $f(x) = |x|$ is defined by

$$f(x) = \begin{cases} -x & \text{if } x < 0 \\ x & \text{if } x \geq 0 \end{cases}$$

**CONNECT TO AP**

The vertex of an absolute value function is an example of a *cusp* in a graph. A graph has a cusp at a point where there is an abrupt change in direction.

### Check Your Understanding

10. **Construct viable arguments.** Explain why the absolute value function $f(x) = |x|$ is a piecewise-defined function.

11. How is a step function different from other types of piecewise-defined functions?

12. How does the definition of absolute value as a piecewise-defined function relate to the method of solving absolute value equations?

### LESSON 4-2 PRACTICE

13. A step function known as the ceiling function, written $g(x) = \lceil x \rceil$, yields the value $g(x)$ that is the least integer greater than or equal to $x$.
   a. Graph this step function.
   b. Find $g(2.4)$, $g(0.13)$, and $g(-8.7)$.

**Make sense of problems and persevere in solving them.** A day ticket for a ski lift costs $25 for children at least 6 years old and less than 13 years old. A day ticket for students at least 13 years old and less than 19 years old costs $45. A day ticket for adults at least 19 years old costs $60. Use this information for Items 14 and 15.

14. Write the equation of a step function $f(x)$ that can be used to determine the cost in dollars of a day ticket for the ski lift for a person who is $x$ years old.

15. Graph the step function you wrote in Item 14.

Use the absolute value function $h(x) = |x + 2|$ for Items 16−19.

16. Graph the absolute value function.

17. What are the domain and range of the function?

18. What are the coordinates of the vertex of the function's graph?

19. Write the equation for the function using piecewise notation.

**My Notes**

### Learning Targets:

- Identify the effect on the graph of replacing $f(x)$ by $f(x) + k$, $k \cdot f(x)$, $f(kx)$, and $f(x + k)$.
- Find the value of $k$, given these graphs.

**SUGGESTED LEARNING STRATEGIES:** Activating Prior Knowledge, Create Representation, Look for a Pattern, Debriefing, Think-Pair-Share, Identify a Subtask

The absolute value function $f(x) = |x|$ is the parent absolute value function. Recall that a **parent function** is the most basic function of a particular type. *Transformations* may be performed on a parent function to produce a new function.

1. **Model with mathematics.** For each function below, graph the function and identify the transformation of $f(x) = |x|$.

   **a.** $g(x) = |x| + 1$

   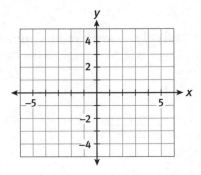

   **b.** $h(x) = |x| - 2$

   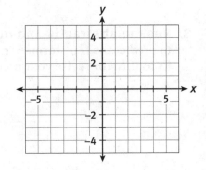

   **c.** $k(x) = 3|x|$

   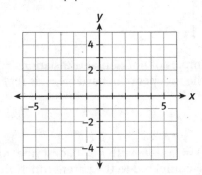

   **d.** $q(x) = -|x|$

   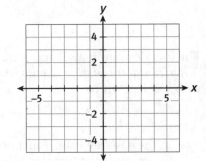

---

**MATH TIP**

*Transformations* include:

- vertical translations, which shift a graph up or down
- horizontal translations, which shift a graph left or right
- reflections, which produce a mirror image of a graph over a line
- vertical stretches or vertical shrinks, which stretch a graph away from the *x*-axis or shrink a graph toward the *x*-axis
- horizontal stretches or horizontal shrinks, which stretch a graph away from the *y*-axis or shrink a graph toward the *y*-axis

---

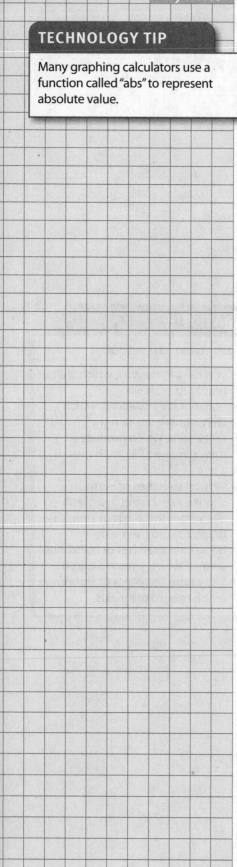

**My Notes**

**TECHNOLOGY TIP**

Many graphing calculators use a function called "abs" to represent absolute value.

2. Use the coordinate grid at the right.
   a. Graph the parent function
      $f(x) = |x|$.

   b. Predict the transformation for
      $g(x) = |x - 3|$ and $h(x) = |-2x|$.

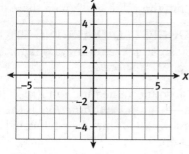

   c. Graph the function
      $g(x) = |x - 3|$ and $h(x) = |-2x|$.

   d. What transformations do your graphs show?

3. **Reason abstractly and quantitatively.** Use the results from Item 2 to predict the transformation of $h(x) = |x + 2|$. Then graph the function to confirm or revise your prediction.

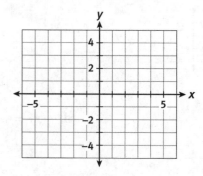

The functions in Items 2 and 3 are examples of horizontal translations. A *horizontal translation* occurs when the independent variable, $x$, is replaced with $x + k$ or with $x - k$.

4. In the absolute value function $f(x) = |x + k|$ with $k > 0$, describe how the graph of the function changes, compared to the parent function.

5. In the absolute value function $f(x) = |x - k|$ with $k > 0$, describe how the graph of the function changes, compared to the parent function.

**My Notes**

6. Graph each function.
   **a.** $f(x) = |x - 4|$                    **b.** $f(x) = |x + 5|$

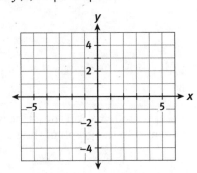     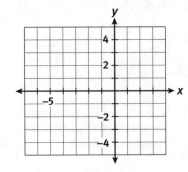

7. Use the coordinate grid at the right.
   **a.** Graph the parent function $f(x) = |x|$ and the function $g(x) = |2x|$.
   **b.** Describe the graph of $g(x)$ as a horizontal stretch or horizontal shrink of the graph of the parent function.

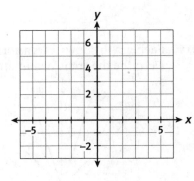

**MATH TIP**

A horizontal stretch or shrink by a factor of $k$ maps a point $(x, y)$ on the graph of the original function to the point $(kx, y)$ on the graph of the transformed function.

Similarly, a vertical stretch or shrink by a factor of $k$ maps a point $(x, y)$ on the graph of the original function to the point $(x, ky)$ on the graph of the transformed function.

8. **Express regularity in repeated reasoning.** Use the results from Item 7 to predict how the graph of $h(x) = \left| \frac{1}{2} x \right|$ is transformed from the graph of the parent function. Then graph $h(x)$ to confirm or revise your prediction.

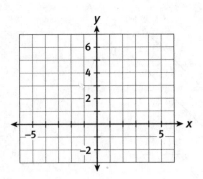

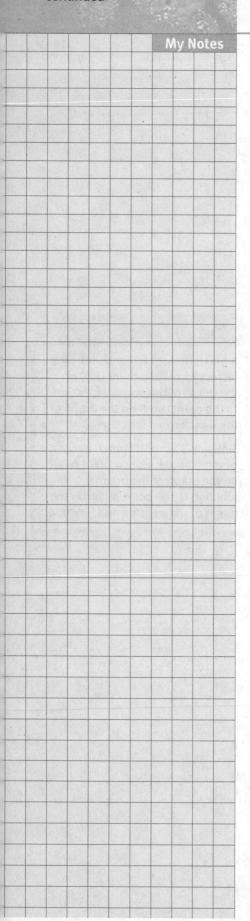

9. In the absolute value function $f(x) = |kx|$ with $k > 1$, describe how the graph of the function changes compared to the graph of the parent function. What if $k < -1$?

10. In the absolute value function $f(x) = |kx|$ with $0 < k < 1$, describe how the graph of the function changes compared to the graph of the parent function. What if $-1 < k < 0$?

11. Each graph shows a transformation $g(x)$ of the parent function $f(x) = |x|$. Describe the transformation and write the equation of $g(x)$.

a.

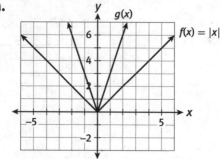

b.

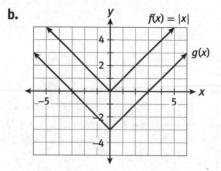

### Example A

Describe the transformations of $g(x) = 2|x + 3|$ from the parent absolute value function and use them to graph $g(x)$.

**Step 1:** Describe the transformations.

$g(x)$ is a horizontal translation of $f(x) = |x|$ by 3 units to the left, followed by a vertical stretch by a factor of 2.

Apply the horizontal translation first, and then apply the vertical stretch.

**Step 2:** Apply the horizontal translation.

Graph $f(x) = |x|$. Then shift each point on the graph of $f(x)$ by 3 units to the left. To do so, subtract 3 from the $x$-coordinates and keep the $y$-coordinates the same.

Name the new function $h(x)$. Its equation is $h(x) = |x + 3|$.

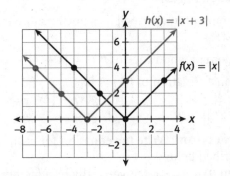

> **MATH TIP**
>
> To graph an absolute value function of the form $g(x) = a|b(x - c)| + d$, apply the transformations of $f(x) = |x|$ in this order:
> 1. horizontal translation
> 2. reflection in the $y$-axis and/or horizontal shrink or stretch
> 3. reflection in the $x$-axis and/or vertical shrink or stretch
> 4. vertical translation

**Step 3:** Apply the vertical stretch.

Now stretch each point on the graph of $h(x)$ vertically by a factor of 2. To do so, keep the $x$-coordinates the same and multiply the $y$-coordinates by 2.

**Solution:** The new function is $g(x) = 2|x + 3|$.

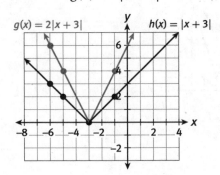

> **TECHNOLOGY TIP**
>
> You can check that you have graphed $g(x)$ correctly by graphing it on a graphing calculator.

### Try These A

For each absolute value function, describe the transformations represented in the rule and use them to graph the function.

**a.** $h(x) = -|x - 1| + 2$  **b.** $k(x) = 4|x + 1| - 3$

**My Notes**

### Check Your Understanding

12. Graph the function $g(x) = |-x|$. What is the relationship between $g(x)$ and $f(x) = |x|$? Why does this relationship make sense?

13. Compare and contrast a vertical stretch by a factor of 4 with a horizontal stretch by a factor of 4.

14. Without graphing the function, determine the coordinates of the vertex of $f(x) = |x + 2| - 5$. Explain how you determined your answer.

### LESSON 4-3 PRACTICE

15. The graph of $g(x)$ is the graph of $f(x) = |x|$ translated 6 units to the right. Write the equation of $g(x)$.

16. Describe the graph of $h(x) = -5|x|$ as one or more transformations of the graph of $f(x) = |x|$.

17. What are the domain and range of $f(x) = |x + 4| - 1$? Explain.

18. Graph each transformation of $f(x) = |x|$.
    a. $g(x) = |x - 4| + 2$   b. $g(x) = |2x| - 3$
    c. $g(x) = -|x + 4| + 3$   d. $g(x) = -3|x + 2| + 4$

19. **Attend to precision.** Write the equation for each transformation of $f(x) = |x|$ described below.
    a. Translate left 9 units, stretch vertically by a factor of 5, and translate down 23 units.
    b. Translate left 12 units, stretch horizontally by a factor of 4, and reflect over the $x$-axis.
    c.

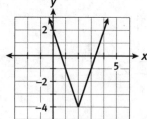

## ACTIVITY 4 PRACTICE
**Write your answers on notebook paper.**
**Show your work.**

### Lesson 4-1

1. Graph each of the following piecewise-defined functions. Then write its domain and range using inequalities, interval notation, and set notation.

   **a.**
   $$f(x) = \begin{cases} -3x - 4 & \text{if } x < -1 \\ x & \text{if } x \geq -1 \end{cases}$$

   **b.**
   $$f(x) = \begin{cases} x^2 & \text{if } x \leq 1 \\ -2x + 3 & \text{if } x > 1 \end{cases}$$

2. Explain why the graph shown below does not represent a function.

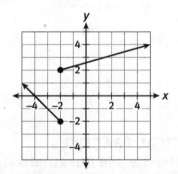

A welder earns $20 per hour for the first 40 hours she works in a week and $30 per hour for each hour over 40 hours. Use this information for Items 3–5.

3. Write a piecewise function $f(x)$ that can be used to determine the welder's earnings when she works $x$ hours in a week.

4. Graph the piecewise function.

5. How much does the welder earn when she works 48 hours in a week?
   **A.** $990  **B.** $1040
   **C.** $1200  **D.** $1440

6. The domain of a function is all real numbers greater than $-2$ and less than or equal to 8. Write the domain using an inequality, interval notation, and set notation.

7. The range of a function is $[4, \infty)$. Write the range using an inequality and set notation.

8. Evaluate $f(x)$ for $x = -4$, $x = 1$, and $x = 4$.
   $$f(x) = \begin{cases} -5x & \text{if } x < -3 \\ x^2 & \text{if } -3 \leq x < 4 \\ 2x + 4 & \text{if } x \geq 4 \end{cases}$$

9. Write the equation of the piecewise function $f(x)$ shown below.

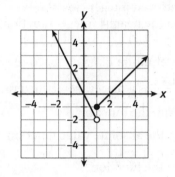

### Lesson 4-2

10. **a.** Graph the step function $f(x) = \begin{cases} 4 & \text{if } x < -2 \\ 1 & \text{if } -2 \leq x < 3. \\ -3 & \text{if } x \geq 3 \end{cases}$

    **b.** What are the domain and range of the step function?

11. It costs $30 per day or $90 per week to rent a wallpaper steamer. If the time in days is not a whole number, it is rounded up to the next-greatest day. Customers are given the weekly rate if it is cheaper than using the daily rate.
    **a.** Write the equation of a step function $f(x)$ that can be used to determine the cost in dollars of renting a wallpaper steamer for $x$ days. Use a domain of $0 < x \leq 7$.
    **b.** Graph the step function.

12. A step function called the *integer part function* gives the value $f(x)$ that is the integer part of $x$.
   a. Graph the integer part function.
   b. Find $f(-2.1)$, $f(0.5)$, and $f(3.6)$.

13. A step function called the *nearest integer function* gives the value $g(x)$ that is the integer closest to $x$. For half integers, such as 1.5, 2.5, and 3.5, the nearest integer function gives the value of $g(x)$ that is the even integer closest to $x$.
   a. Graph the nearest integer function.
   b. Find $g(-2.1)$, $g(0.5)$, and $g(3.6)$.

14. Use the definition of $f(x) = |x|$ to rewrite
$$f(x) = \frac{|x|}{x}$$ as a piecewise-defined function.
Then graph the function.

15. Consider the absolute value function $f(x) = |x + 2| - 1$.
   a. Graph the function.
   b. What are the domain and range of the function?
   c. What are the $x$-intercept(s) and $y$-intercept of the function?
   d. Describe the symmetry of the graph.

## Lesson 4-3

16. Write the equation of the function $g(x)$ shown in the graph, and describe the graph as a transformation of the graph of $f(x) = |x|$.

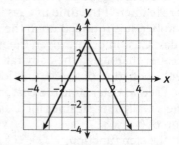

17. Graph the following transformations of $f(x) = |x|$. Then identify the transformations.
   a. $g(x) = |x + 3| - 1$
   b. $g(x) = \frac{1}{3}|x| + 2$
   c. $g(x) = -2|x - 1| - 1$
   d. $g(x) = 5|x - 1| - 4$

18. Write the equation for each transformation of $f(x) = |x|$ described below.
   a. translated right 7 units, shrunk vertically by a factor of 0.5, and translated up $\sqrt{5}$ units
   b. stretched horizontally by a factor of 5, reflected over the $x$-axis, and translated down 10 units
   c. translated right 9 units and translated down 6 units

19. Which function is shown in the graph?

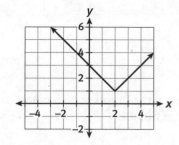

   A. $f(x) = |x - 2| + 1$
   B. $f(x) = |x - 1| + 2$
   C. $f(x) = |x + 2| + 1$
   D. $f(x) = |x + 1| + 2$

## MATHEMATICAL PRACTICES
### Reason Abstractly and Quantitatively

20. Before answering each part, review them carefully to ensure you understand all the terminology and what is being asked.
   a. Describe how the graph of $g(x) = |x| + k$ changes compared to the graph of $f(x) = |x|$ when $k > 0$ and when $k < 0$.
   b. Describe how the graph of $h(x) = k|x|$ changes compared to the graph of $f(x) = |x|$ when $k > 1$ and when $0 < k < 1$.
   c. Describe how the graph of $j(x) = |kx|$ changes compared to the graph of $f(x) = |x|$ when $k < 0$.

# Function Composition and Operations

New from Old

## Lesson 5-1 Operations with Functions

**Learning Targets:**
- Combine functions using arithmetic operations.
- Build functions that model real-world scenarios.

> **SUGGESTED LEARNING STRATEGIES:** Activating Prior Knowledge, Discussion Groups, Debriefing, Close Reading, Think-Pair-Share, Summarizing, Paraphrasing, Quickwrite

Jim Green has a lawn service called Green's Grass Guaranteed. Tori and Stephan are two of his employees. Tori earns $10 per hour, and Stephan earns $8 per hour. Jim sends Tori and Stephan on a job that takes them 4 hours.

1. **Model with mathematics.** Write a function $t(h)$ to represent Tori's earnings in dollars for working $h$ hours and a function $s(h)$ to represent Stephan's earnings in dollars for working $h$ hours.

2. Find $t(4)$ and $s(4)$ and tell what these values represent in this situation.

> **MATH TIP**
>
> Addition, subtraction, multiplication, and division are operations on real numbers. You can also perform these operations with functions.

3. Find $t(4) + s(4)$ and tell what it represents in this situation.

You can add two functions by adding their function rules.

4. **a.** Add the functions $t(h)$ and $s(h)$ to find $(t + s)(h)$. Then simplify the function rule.

> **WRITING MATH**
>
> The notation $(f + g)(x)$ represents the sum of the functions $f(x)$ and $g(x)$. In other words, $(f + g)(x) = f(x) + g(x)$.

   **b.** What does the function $(t + s)(h)$ represent in this situation?

5. Find $(t + s)(4)$. How does the answer compare to $t(4) + s(4)$?

6. How much will Jim spend on Tori and Stephan's earnings for the 4-hour job?

7. How much would Jim spend on Tori and Stephan's earnings for a job that takes 6 hours? Explain how you determined your answer.

For a basic tree-trimming job, Jim charges customers a fixed $25 fee plus $150 per tree. One of Jim's competitors, Vista Lawn & Garden, charges customers a fixed fee of $75 plus $175 per tree for the same service.

8. Write a function $j(t)$ to represent the total charge in dollars for trimming $t$ trees by Jim's company and a function $v(t)$ to represent the total charge in dollars for trimming $t$ trees by Vista.

9. **a.** Subtract $j(t)$ from $v(t)$ to find $(v - j)(t)$. Then simplify the function rule.

**MATH TIP**

When subtracting an algebraic expression, remember to subtract *each* term of the expression. For example, subtract $6x - 2$ from $10x$ as follows.
$10x - (6x + 2) = 10x - 6x - 2$
$\qquad\qquad\qquad = 4x - 2$

**b.** What does the function $(v - j)(t)$ represent in this situation?

10. Find $(v - j)(5)$. What does this value represent in this situation?

**WRITING MATH**

The notation $(f - g)(x)$ represents the difference of the functions $f(x)$ and $g(x)$. In other words, $(f - g)(x) = f(x) - g(x)$.

11. How much will a customer save by choosing Jim's company to trim 8 trees rather than choosing Vista? Explain how you determined your answer.

12. **Look for and make use of structure.** Given $f(x) = 3x + 2$, $g(x) = 2x - 1$, and $h(x) = x^2 - 2x + 8$, find each function and simplify the function rule.

   **a.** $(f + g)(x)$                **b.** $(g + h)(x)$

   **c.** $(h + f)(x)$                **d.** $(f - g)(x)$

   **e.** $(g - f)(x)$                **f.** $(h - g)(x)$

## Lesson 5-1
### Operations with Functions

Jim has been asked to make a bid for installing the shrubs around a new office building. In the bid, he needs to include the number of shrubs he can install in an 8-hour day, the cost per shrub including installation, and the total cost of his services for an 8-hour day.

**13. a.** Write a function $n(h)$ to represent the number of shrubs Jim can install in an 8-hour day when it takes him $h$ hours to install one shrub.

**b.** What are the restrictions on the domain of $n(h)$? Explain.

> **MATH TIP**
>
> When considering restrictions on the domain of a real-world function, consider both values of the domain for which the function would be undefined and values of the domain that would not make sense in the situation.

**14.** Jim will charge $16 for each shrub. He will also charge $65 per hour for installation services. Write a function $c(h)$ to represent the amount Jim will charge for a shrub that takes $h$ hours to install.

The total cost of Jim's services for an 8-hour day is equal to the number of shrubs he can install times the charge for each shrub.

**15. a.** Find the total cost of Jim's services using the functions $n(h)$ and $c(h)$ to find $(n \cdot c)(h)$. Then simplify the function rule.

> **WRITING MATH**
>
> The notation $(f \cdot g)(x)$ represents the product of the functions $f(x)$ and $g(x)$. In other words, $(f \cdot g)(x) = f(x) \cdot g(x)$.

**b. Attend to precision.** What are the restrictions on the domain of $(n \cdot c)(h)$?

**CONNECT** **TO** **BUSINESS**

When a company makes a bid on a job, the company states the price at which it is willing to do the job. The company must make its bid high enough to cover all of its expenses. If it bids too high, however, the job may be offered to one of its competitors.

**My Notes**

16. **Reason quantitatively.** Jim estimates that it will take 0.5 hour to install each shrub. Use the functions $n(h)$, $c(h)$, and $(n \cdot c)(h)$ to determine the following values for Jim's bid, and explain how you determined your answers.

   a. the number of shrubs Jim can install in an 8-hour day

   b. the cost per shrub, including installation

   c. the total cost of Jim's services for an 8-hour day

17. Explain how you could check your answer to Item 16c.

Jim offers two lawn improvement services, as described in the table.

**Lawn Improvement Services**

| Service | Hourly Charge ($) | Material Cost for Average Yard ($) |
|---------|-------------------|------------------------------------|
| Compost | 40 | 140 |
| Fertilizer | 30 | 30 |

18. a. Write a function $c(h)$ to represent the total charge for applying compost to a lawn, where $h$ is the number of hours the job takes.

   b. Write a function $f(h)$ to represent the total charge for applying fertilizer to a lawn, where $h$ is the number of hours the job takes.

19. **a.** Divide $c(h)$ by $f(h)$ to find $(c \div f)(h)$ given that $f(h) \neq 0$.

   **b.** What does the function $(c \div f)(h)$ represent in this situation?

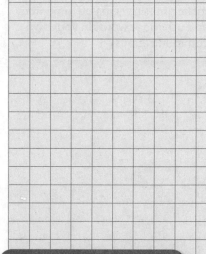

**WRITING MATH**

The notation $(f \div g)(x)$, $g(x) \neq 0$ represents the quotient of the functions $f(x)$ and $g(x)$ given that $g(x) \neq 0$. In other words, $(f \div g)(x) = f(x) \div g(x)$, $g(x) \neq 0$.

20. Find $(c \div f)(4)$. What does this value represent in this situation?

21. **Look for and make use of structure.** Given $f(x) = 2x$, $g(x) = x + 3$, and $h(x) = 2x + 6$, find each function and simplify the function rule. Note any values that must be excluded from the domain.
   **a.** $(f \cdot g)(x)$

   **b.** $(g \cdot h)(x)$

**MATH TIP**

You may be able to simplify the function rules in Items 21c, d, and e by factoring the expression's numerator and denominator and dividing out common factors.

   **c.** $(f \div h)(x)$, $h(x) \neq 0$

   **d.** $(h \div g)(x)$, $g(x) \neq 0$

   **e.** $(g \div f)(x)$

**My Notes**

**DISCUSSION GROUP TIP**

As you listen to your group members' discussions, you may hear math terms or other words that you do not know. Use your math notebook to record words that are frequently used. Ask for clarification of their meaning, and make notes to help you remember and use those words in your own communications.

**22.** Discuss and then answer this question with your group. How are operations on functions similar to and different from operations on real numbers?

**Check Your Understanding**

**23.** Given that $f(x) = 2x + 1$ and $g(x) = 3x - 2$, what value(s) of $x$ are excluded from the domain of $(f \div g)(x)$? Explain your answer.

**24.** Make a conjecture about whether addition of functions is commutative. Give an example that supports your conjecture.

**25.** Given that $h(x) = 4x + 5$ and $(h - j)(x) = x - 2$, find $j(x)$. Explain how you determined your answer.

## LESSON 5-1 PRACTICE

For Items 26–30, use the following functions.

$$f(x) = 5x + 1 \qquad g(x) = 3x - 4$$

Find each function and simplify the function rule. Note any values that must be excluded from the domain.

**26.** $(f + g)(x)$　　　　**27.** $(f - g)(x)$

**28.** $(f \cdot g)(x)$　　　　**29.** $(f \div g)(x), g(x) \neq 0$

**30.** A student incorrectly found $(g - f)(x)$ as follows. What mistake did the student make, and what is the correct answer?

$$(g - f)(x) = 3x - 4 - 5x + 1 = -2x - 3$$

**31. Make sense of problems and persevere in solving them.** Jim plans to make a radio ad for his lawn company. The function $a(t) = 800 + 84t$ gives the cost of making the ad and running it $t$ times on an AM station. The function $f(t) = 264t$ gives the cost of running the ad $t$ times on a more popular FM station.

**a.** Find $(a + f)(t)$ and tell what it represents in this situation.

**b.** Find $(a + f)(12)$ and tell what it represents in this situation.

## Learning Targets:

- Write functions that describe the relationship between two quantities.
- Explore the composition of two functions through a real-world scenario.

**SUGGESTED LEARNING STRATEGIES:** Create Representations, Identify a Subtask, Group Presentation, Graphic Organizer, Debriefing, Self Revision/Peer Revision

Recall that Jim has a lawn service called Green's Grass Guaranteed. On every mowing job, Jim charges a fixed $30 fee to cover equipment and travel expenses plus a $20 per hour labor charge. Work with your group on Items 1–14.

1. On a recent mowing job, Jim worked for 6 hours. What was the total charge for this job?

2. **Model with mathematics.** If Jim works for $t$ hours, what will he charge for a mowing job? Write your answer as a cost function where $c(t)$ is Jim's charge for $t$ hours of work.

It takes Jim 4 hours to mow 1 acre. Jim prepares a cost estimate for each customer based on the size (number of acres) of the property.

3. The APCON company is one of Jim's customers. APCON has 2 acres that need mowing. How many hours does that job take?

4. Another customer has $a$ acres of property. Write the equation of a function in terms of $a$ for the number of hours $t$ it will take Jim to mow the property.

5. How much will Jim charge APCON to mow its property? Justify your answer.

**DISCUSSION GROUP TIP**

With your group, reread the problem scenarios in this lesson as needed. Make notes on the information provided in the problems. Respond to questions about the meaning of key information. Summarize the information needed to create reasonable solutions, and describe the mathematical concepts your group uses to create its solutions.

**My Notes**

**MATH TIP**

In a linear function $f(x) = mx + b$, the $y$-intercept is $b$. The variable $m$ is the rate of change in the values of the function—the change of units of $f(x)$ per change of unit of $x$. When the function is graphed, the rate of change is interpreted as the slope. So $y = mx + b$ is called the slope-intercept form of a linear equation.

The functions in Items 2 and 4 relate three quantities that vary, based on the needs of Jim's customers:

- The size in acres $a$ of the property
- The time in hours $t$ needed to perform the work
- The cost in dollars $c$ of doing the work.

6. **Attend to precision.** Complete the table below by writing the rate of change with units and finding the slope of the graph of the function.

| Function | Rate of Change (with units) | Slope |
|---|---|---|
| $c(t) =$ | | |
| $t(a) =$ | | |

7. Complete the table below by naming the measurement units for the domain and range of each function.

| Function Notation | Description of Function | Domain (units) | Range (units) |
|---|---|---|---|
| $c(t)$ | cost for job | | |
| $t(a)$ | time to mow | | |

8. Calculating the cost to mow a lawn is a two-step process. Complete the graphic organizer below by describing the input and output, including units, for each part of the process.

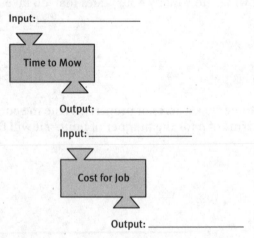

Input: _____

**Time to Mow**

Output: _____

Input: _____

**Cost for Job**

Output: _____

## Lesson 5-2
### Function Composition

The graphic organizer shows an operation on two functions, called a **composition**. The function that results from using the output of the first function as the input for the second function is a **composite function**.

In this context, the composite function is formed by the time-to-mow function and the cost-for-job function. Its domain is the input for the time function, and its range is the output from the cost function.

9. **Make sense of problems.** The cost to mow is a composite function. Describe its input and output as you did in Item 8.

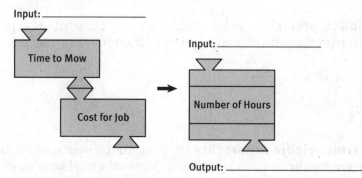

Input: _____

Input: _____

Output: _____

When a composite function is formed, the function is often named to show the functions used to create it. The cost-to-mow function, $c(t(a))$, is composed of the cost-for-job and the time-to-mow functions.

The $c(t(a))$ notation implies that $a$ was assigned a value $t(a)$ by the time-to-mow function. Then the resulting $t(a)$ value was assigned a value $c(t(a))$ by the cost-to-mow function.

10. Complete the table by writing a description for the composite function $c(t(a))$. Then name the measurement units of the domain and range.

| Function Notation | Description of Function | |
|---|---|---|
| $c(t(a))$ | | |
| | **Domain (units)** | **Range (units)** |
| | | |

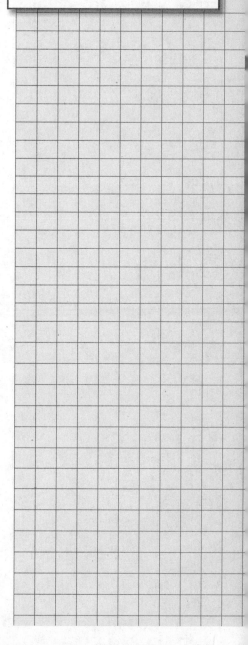

**My Notes**

### MATH TERMS

A **composition** is an operation on two functions that forms a new function. To form the new function, the rule for the first function is used as the input for the second function.

A **composite function** is the function that results from the composition of two functions. The range of the first function becomes the domain for the second function.

Jim wants to write one cost function for mowing $a$ acres of property. To write the cost $c$ as a function of $a$ acres of property, he substitutes $t(a)$ into the cost function and simplifies.

$$c(t) = c(t(a))$$  Substitute $t(a)$ for $t$ in the cost function.

$$c(t(a)) = c(4a)$$  $t(a) = 4a$, so write the function in terms of $a$.

$$= 30 + 20(4a)$$  Substitute $4a$ for $t$ in the original $c(t)$ function.

$$c(t(a)) = 30 + 80a$$

**11. Attend to precision.** Write a sentence to explain what the expression $c(t(2))$ represents. Include appropriate units in your explanation.

**12. Construct viable arguments.** Why might Jim want a single function to determine the cost of a job when he knows the total number of acres?

**13.** Explain what the expression $c(t(50))$ represents. Include appropriate units in your explanation.

**14.** Explain what information the equation $c(t(a)) = 50$ represents. Include appropriate units in your explanation.

### Check Your Understanding

15. Given the functions $a(b) = b + 8$ and $b(c) = 5c$, write the equation for the composite function $a(b(c))$ and evaluate it for $c = -2$.

16. The first function used to form a composite function has a domain of all real numbers and a range of all real numbers greater than 0. What is the domain of the second function in the composite function? Explain.

17. The notation $f(g(x))$ represents a composite function. Explain what this notation indicates about the composite function.

## LESSON 5-2 PRACTICE

**Model with mathematics.** Hannah's Housekeeping charges a $20 flat fee plus $12 an hour to clean a house.

18. Write a function $c(h)$ for the cost to clean a house for $h$ hours.

19. What are the units of the domain and range of this function?

20. What is the slope of this function? Interpret the slope as a rate of change.

Hannah's Housekeeping can clean one room every half hour.

21. Write a function $h(r)$ for the hours needed to clean $r$ rooms.

22. Write a function $c(h(r))$ to represent the cost of cleaning $r$ rooms.

23. What is the value and meaning of $c(h(12))$?

24. **Look for and make use of structure.** Explain how a composition of functions forms a new function from the old (original) functions.

**Learning Targets:**
- Write the composition of two functions.
- Evaluate the composition of two functions.

> **SUGGESTED LEARNING STRATEGIES:** Note Taking, Create Representations, Think-Pair-Share, Group Presentation, Debriefing

A *composition of functions* forms a new function by substituting the output of the inner function into the outer function. The function $y = f(g(x))$ is a composition of $f$ and $g$ where $g$ is the inner function and $f$ is the outer function.

1. The tables show information about Jim's mowing service. Use the tables to evaluate each expression. Then tell what the expression represents.

| Area of Property $a$ (acres) | Time to Mow $t(a)$ (hours) |
|:---:|:---:|
| 1 | 4 |
| 2 | 8 |
| 3 | 12 |
| 4 | 16 |

| Time to Mow $t$ (hours) | Cost to Mow $c(t)$ ($) |
|:---:|:---:|
| 4 | 110 |
| 8 | 190 |
| 12 | 270 |
| 16 | 350 |

a. $t(4)$

b. $c(4)$

c. $c(t(1))$

d. $c(t(4))$

2. **Reason quantitatively.** Use the tables of values below to evaluate each expression.

| $x$ | $f(x)$ |
|:---:|:---:|
| 1 | 3 |
| 2 | 2 |
| 3 | 1 |
| 4 | 4 |

| $x$ | $g(x)$ |
|:---:|:---:|
| 1 | 4 |
| 2 | 3 |
| 3 | 2 |
| 4 | 1 |

a. $f(3)$          b. $g(3)$

c. $g(f(3))$          d. $f(g(3))$

> **MATH TIP**
>
> The order matters when you compose two functions.
> $y = g(f(x))$ and $y = f(g(x))$ are two different functions.

3. Using *f* and *g* from Item 2, complete each table of values to represent the composite functions $(f \circ g)(x)$ and $(g \circ f)(x)$.

a.

| x | $(f \circ g)(x) =$ $f(g(x))$ |
|---|---|
| 1 | |
| 2 | |
| 3 | |
| 4 | |

b.

| x | $(g \circ f)(x) =$ $g(f(x))$ |
|---|---|
| 1 | |
| 2 | |
| 3 | |
| 4 | |

**My Notes**

**WRITING MATH**

The notation $(f \circ g)(x)$ represents a composition of two functions.

$(f \circ g)(x) = f(g)(x)$

Read the notation as "*f* of *g* of *x*."

### Check Your Understanding

4. What does the notation $(g \circ h)(t)$ represent? What is another way you can write $(g \circ h)(t)$?

5. **Reason abstractly.** Explain how $(f \circ g)(x)$ is different from $(f \cdot g)(x)$.

6. Given that $p(t) = t^2 + 4$ and $q(t) = t + 3$, write the equation for $(p \circ q)(t)$. Explain how you determined your answer.

For Items 7–11, use these three functions:

- $f(x) = x^2$
- $g(x) = 2x - 1$
- $h(x) = 4x - 3$

7. Evaluate each expression.
   **a.** $g(f(2))$      **b.** $f(g(2))$

8. Write each composite function in terms of *x*.
   **a.** $y = g(f(x))$      **b.** $y = f(g(x))$

9. Verify that you composed *g* and *f* correctly by evaluating $g(f(2))$ and $f(g(2))$ using the functions you wrote in Item 8. Compare your answers with those from Item 7.

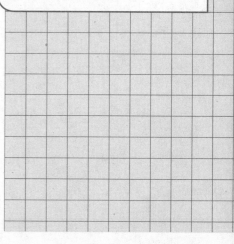

**CONNECT TO AP**

In AP Calculus, you will identify the "inner" function and the "outer" function that form a composite function.

For example, the function $h(x) = f(g(x)) = (2x + 3)^2$ could be the composition of the inner function $g(x) = 2x + 3$ and the outer function $f(x) = x^2$.

**My Notes**

**10. a.** Evaluate $h(g(3))$.

**b.** Write the composition $(h \circ g)(x)$ in terms of $x$.

**11. a.** Evaluate $g(g(2))$.

**b.** Write the composition $(g \circ g)(x)$ in terms of $x$.

> **MATH TIP**
>
> As shown in Item 11, the inner and outer functions that form a composite function can be the same function.

**Check Your Understanding**

**12.** Explain how you found the rule for the composition $(g \circ g)(x)$ in Item 11b.

**13.** Given that $p(n) = 4n$ and $q(n) = n + 2$, for what value of $n$ is $(p \circ q)(n) = 8$? Explain how you determined your answer.

## LESSON 5-3 PRACTICE

For Items 14 and 15, use the following functions:

- $f(x) = 5x + 1$
- $g(x) = 3x - 4$

**14.** Evaluate $f(2)$, $g(2)$, $(f \circ g)(2)$, and $(g \circ f)(2)$.

**15.** Write the composite functions $h(x) = g(f(x))$ and $k(x) = f(g(x))$.

The jeans at a store are on sale for 20% off, and the sales tax rate is 8%. Use this information for Items 16–18.

**16.** Write a function $s(p)$ that gives the sale price of a pair of jeans regularly priced at $p$ dollars.

**17.** Write a function $t(p)$ that gives the total cost including tax for a pair of jeans priced at $p$ dollars.

**18. Construct viable arguments.** A customer wants to buy a pair of jeans regularly priced at $25. Does it matter whether the sales clerk applies the sale discount first or adds on the sales tax first to find the total cost? Use compositions of the functions $s$ and $t$ to support your answer.

# ACTIVITY 5 PRACTICE
**Write your answers on notebook paper.**
**Show your work.**

## Lesson 5-1

Use $f(x) = 5x + 2$, $g(x) = 3 - x$, and $h(x) = x - 3$ to answer Items 1–8. Find each function and simplify the function rule. Note any values that must be excluded from the domain.

1. $(f + g)(x)$
2. $(h + g)(x)$
3. $(f - g)(x)$
4. $(h - f)(x)$
5. $(f \cdot g)(x)$
6. $(g \cdot h)(x)$
7. $(f \div g)(x), g(x) \neq 0$
8. $(g \div h)(x), h(x) \neq 0$

9. A rectangular skate park is 60 yards long and 50 yards wide. Plans call for increasing both the length and the width of the park by $x$ yards.

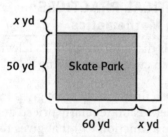

$x$ yd

50 yd  **Skate Park**

60 yd    $x$ yd

   a. Write a function $l(x)$ that gives the new length of the skate park in terms of $x$.
   b. Write a function $w(x)$ that gives the new width of the skate park in terms of $x$.
   c. What does $(l \cdot w)(x)$ represent in this situation? Write and simplify the equation for $(l \cdot w)(x)$.
   d. Find $(l \cdot w)(5)$, and tell what it represents in this situation.

10. Given that $p(n) = 4n^2 + 4n - 6$ and $q(n) = n^2 - 5n + 8$, find $(p - q)(3)$.
    **A.** 26          **B.** 38
    **C.** 40          **D.** 42

11. Make a conjecture about whether subtraction of functions is commutative. Give an example that supports your answer.

12. The cost in dollars of renting a car for $d$ days is given by $c(d) = 22d + 25$. The cost in dollars of renting a hotel room for $d$ days is given by $h(d) = 74d$.
    a. What does $(c + h)(d)$ represent in this situation? Write and simplify the equation for $(c + h)(d)$.
    b. For what value of $d$ is $(c + h)(d) = 600$? What does this value of $d$ represent in this situation?

## Lesson 5-2

Jim wants to calculate the cost of running his lawn mowers. The mowers consume 2.5 gallons of gasoline each hour. Gasoline costs $3.50 per gallon.

13. Write a function $g(h)$ that gives the number of gallons $g$ that the mowers will use in $h$ hours. Identify the units of the domain and range.

14. Write a function $c(g)$ for the cost $c$ in dollars for $g$ gallons of gasoline. Identify the units of the domain and range.

15. Use composition of functions to create a function for the cost $c$ in dollars of gasoline to mow $h$ hours. Identify the units of the domain and range. Then explain how the domain and range of the composite function are related to the domain and range of $g(h)$ and $c(g)$.

16. Use the composite function in Item 15 to determine the cost of gasoline to mow 12 hours. Show your work.

17. What is the slope of the composite function, and what does it represent in this situation?

An empty swimming pool is shaped like a rectangular prism with a length of 18 feet and a width of 9 feet. Once water begins to be pumped into the pool, the depth of the water increases at a rate of 0.5 foot per hour.

18. Write a function $d(t)$ that gives the depth in feet of the water in the pool after $t$ hours.

19. Write a function $v(d)$ that gives the volume in cubic feet of the water in the pool when the depth of the water is $d$ feet.

20. Write the equation of the composite function $v(d(t))$, and tell what this function represents in this situation.

21. What is $v(d(4))$, and what does it represent in this situation?

22. The range of the function $d(t)$ is $0 \leq d \leq 4$. Based on this information, what is the greatest volume of water the pool can hold?

## Lesson 5-3

Use $f(x) = x^2$, $g(x) = x + 5$, and $h(x) = 4x - 6$ to answer Items 23–28. Find each function and simplify the function rule.

23. $(f \circ g)(x)$          24. $(g \circ f)(x)$

25. $(f \circ h)(x)$          26. $(h \circ f)(x)$

27. $(g \circ h)(x)$          28. $(h \circ g)(x)$

The function $c(f) = \frac{5}{9}(f - 32)$ converts a temperature $f$ in degrees Fahrenheit to degrees Celsius. The function $k(c) = c + 273$ converts a temperature $c$ in degrees Celsius to units called kelvins.

29. Write a composite function that can be used to convert a temperature in degrees Fahrenheit to kelvins.

30. In Item 29, does it matter whether you wrote $(c \circ k)(f)$ or $(k \circ c)(f)$? Explain.

31. Given that $(r \circ s)(t) = 2t + 11$, which could be the functions $r$ and $s$?
    **A.** $r(t) = t + 1$, $s(t) = 2t + 5$
    **B.** $r(t) = t + 5$, $s(t) = 2t + 1$
    **C.** $r(t) = 2t + 1$, $s(t) = t + 5$
    **D.** $r(t) = 2t + 5$, $s(t) = t + 1$

32. What is the composition $f \circ g$ if $f(x) = 4 - 2x$ and $g(x) = 3x^2$?
    **A.** $f(g(x)) = 12x^2 - 6x^3$
    **B.** $f(g(x)) = 4 - 6x^2$
    **C.** $f(g(x)) = 3(4 - 2x)^2$
    **D.** $f(g(x)) = 12 - 12x^4$

Use $f(x) = 5x + 2$ and $g(x) = 3 - x$ to answer Items 33–35.

33. What is the value of $f(g(-1))$ and $g(f(-1))$?

34. What is the composite function $y = f(g(x))$?

35. What is the composite function $y = g(f(x))$?

## MATHEMATICAL PRACTICES
**Model with Mathematics**

36. A store is discounting all of its television sets by $50 for an after-Thanksgiving sale. The sales tax rate is 7.5%.
    **a.** Write a function $s(p)$ that gives the sale price of a television regularly priced at $p$ dollars.
    **b.** Write a function $t(p)$ that gives the total cost including tax for a television priced at $p$ dollars.
    **c.** A customer wants to buy a television regularly priced at $800. Does it matter whether the sales clerk applies the sale discount first or adds on the sales tax first to find the total cost? Use compositions of the functions $s$ and $t$ to support your answer.

# Inverse Functions

## Old from New
### Lesson 6-1 Finding Inverse Functions

**Learning Targets:**

- Find the inverse of a function.
- Write the inverse using the proper notation.

**SUGGESTED LEARNING STRATEGIES:** Questioning the Text, Think-Pair-Share, Work Backward, Debriefing, Quickwrite, Create Representations, Look for a Pattern, Group Presentation, Note Taking

Green's Grass Guaranteed charges businesses a flat fee of $30 plus $80 per acre for lawn mowing. For residential customers who may have a more limited budget, Jim Green needs to determine the size of the yard he could mow for a particular weekly fee.

Work on Items 1–10 with your group.

1. The cost function $F$ is $C = F(A)$. It can be written $C = 30 + 80A$, where $C$ is the cost to mow $A$ acres. Use the function to determine what part of an acre Jim could mow for each weekly fee.

   **a.** $60

   **b.** $80

   **c.** $110

To make a profit and still charge a fair price, Jim needs a function for calculating the maximum acreage that he can mow, based on the amount of money a customer is willing to spend.

2. **Attend to precision.** What are the units of the domain and range of the cost function in Item 1?

3. **Make use of structure.** Solve the function equation from Item 1 for $A$ in terms of $C$.

   $C = 30 + 80A$

4. Write the answer equation from Item 3 using function notation, where $G$ is the acreage function.

---

**My Notes**

**DISCUSSION GROUP TIP**

As you work in groups, review the problem scenario carefully and explore together the information provided and how to use it to create a potential solution. Discuss your understanding of the problem and ask peers or your teacher to clarify any areas that are not clear.

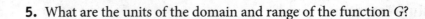

**My Notes**

**5.** What are the units of the domain and range of the function $G$?

**6. Reason abstractly.** Discuss the following question with your group and prepare to share your group's answer with the rest of the class. How are the domain and range of $F(A)$ related to those of $G(C)$? Use your response to Item 3 to explain why the relationship exists.

**7.** Use the appropriate functions to evaluate each expression.
**a.** $G(60)$

**b.** $F(G(60))$

**c.** $F(2)$

**d.** $G(F(2))$

**8. Attend to precision.** Interpret the meaning of each expression and its corresponding value in Item 7. Be sure to include units in your explanation.
**a.**

**b.**

**c.**

**d.**

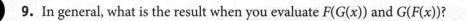

**9.** In general, what is the result when you evaluate $F(G(x))$ and $G(F(x))$?

**10.** What do the answers in Items 7–9 suggest about $F$ and $G$?

Two functions $f$ and $g$ are ***inverse functions*** if and only if:

$$f(g(x)) = x \text{ for all } x \text{ in the domain of } g,$$
$$\text{and}$$
$$g(f(x)) = x \text{ for all } x \text{ in the domain of } f.$$

The function notation $f^{-1}$ denotes the inverse of function $f$ and is read "$f$ inverse."

Item 6 showed that the domain of a function is the range of its inverse. Likewise, the range of a function is the domain of its inverse. To find the inverse of a function algebraically, interchange the $x$ and $y$ variables and then solve for $y$.

### Example A

Find the inverse of the function $f(x) = 2x - 4$.

| | | |
|---|---|---|
| **Step 1:** | Let $y = f(x)$. | $y = 2x - 4$ |
| **Step 2:** | Interchange the $x$ and $y$ variables. | $x = 2y - 4$ |
| **Step 3:** | Solve for $y$. | $x + 4 = 2y$ |
| | | $y = \dfrac{x + 4}{2}$ |
| **Step 4:** | Let $y = f^{-1}(x)$. | $f^{-1}(x) = \dfrac{x + 4}{2}$ |

**Solution:** $f^{-1}(x) = \dfrac{x + 4}{2}$

### Try These A

Find the inverse of each function.

**a.** $f(x) = -3x + 8$

**b.** $g(x) = \frac{1}{4}(x + 12)$

**c.** $h(x) = \frac{2}{3}x - 5$

**d.** $j(x) = \dfrac{3x - 2}{6}$

**MATH TERMS**

Functions $f$ and $g$ are **inverse functions** if and only if $f(g(x)) = x$ for all $x$ in the domain of $g$ and $g(f(x)) = x$ for all $x$ in the domain of $f$.

**WRITING MATH**

If $f$ and $g$ are inverse functions, you can also write two equivalent composite functions:

$$f \circ g = x$$
$$g \circ f = x$$

**MATH TIP**

The −1 superscript in the function notation $f^{-1}$ is not an exponent, and $f^{-1} \neq \dfrac{1}{f}$ when referring to functions.

However, for any number $n$, the expression $n^{-1}$ is the multiplicative inverse, or reciprocal, of $n$.

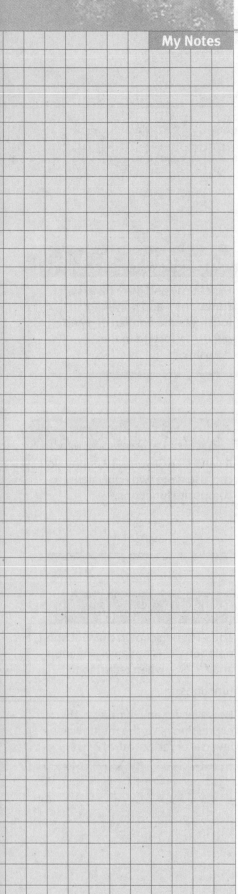

## Check Your Understanding

**11.** Given that $f$ and $g$ are inverse functions, explain how you can find $f(g(20))$ without knowing the equations for $f$ and $g$.

**12. Critique the reasoning of others.** A student claims that $h(x) = 3x$ and $j(x) = -3x$ are inverse functions. Is the student correct? Justify your answer.

**13.** The domain of a function is $x \geq 3$, and the range of the function is $y \leq -2$. What are the domain and range of the inverse function? Explain your answer.

**14.** Mariana's average running speed is 6 miles per hour.
  **a.** Write a function $D(T)$ that gives the distance in miles Mariana covers when running for $T$ minutes.

  **b.** What are the units of the domain and range of $D(T)$? Write the domain and range in both interval notation and set notation.

  **c.** What are the units of the domain and range of the inverse of $D(T)$? Write the domain and range of the inverse function in both interval notation and set notation.

  **d.** How many minutes will it take Mariana to run 2.5 miles? Explain how you can find the answer by using the inverse of $D(T)$.

## LESSON 6-1 PRACTICE

**Look for and make use of structure.** The function $T = F(H)$ estimates the temperature (degrees Celsius) on a mountain given the height (in meters) above sea level. Use the function $T = 50 - \dfrac{H}{20}$.

**15.** What is $F(500)$? What does $F(500)$ mean?

**16.** Find $H$ in terms of $T$. Label this function $G$.

**17.** What is $G(25)$? What does $G(25)$ mean?

**18.** Are the functions $F$ and $G$ inverses of each other? Explain.

Find the inverse of each function.

**19.** $f(x) = 3x + 6$

**20.** $g(x) = -\dfrac{1}{2}x$

**21.** $h(x) = \dfrac{x - 20}{4}$

**22.** $j(x) = 5(x - 1)$

## Lesson 6-2
### Graphs of Inverse Functions

**Learning Targets:**

- Use composition of functions to determine if functions are inverses of each other.
- Graph inverse functions and identify the symmetry.

**SUGGESTED LEARNING STRATEGIES:** Think-Pair-Share, Create Representations, Group Presentation, Quickwrite, Debriefing, Discussion Groups, Self Revision/Peer Revision

You can use the definition of inverse functions to show that two functions are inverses of each other.

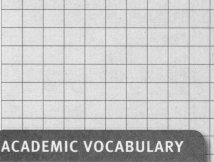

**ACADEMIC VOCABULARY**

When you ***prove*** a statement, you use logical reasoning to show that it is true.

### Example A

Use the definition of inverse functions to ***prove*** that $f(x) = 2x - 4$ and $f^{-1}(x) = \dfrac{x+4}{2}$ are inverse functions.

**Step 1:** Compose $f$ and $f^{-1}$. $\qquad\qquad f(f^{-1}(x)) = 2(f^{-1}(x)) - 4$

**Step 2:** Substitute $f^{-1}$ into $f$. $\qquad\qquad = 2(\dfrac{x+4}{2}) - 4$

**Step 3:** Simplify. $\qquad\qquad\qquad\qquad = x + 4 - 4$
$\qquad\qquad\qquad\qquad\qquad\qquad\quad = x$

**Step 4:** Compose $f^{-1}$ and $f$. $\qquad\quad f^{-1}(f(x)) = \dfrac{f(x)+4}{2}$

**Step 5:** Substitute $f$ into $f^{-1}$. $\qquad\qquad = \dfrac{2x-4+4}{2}$

**Step 6:** Simplify. $\qquad\qquad\qquad\qquad = \dfrac{2x}{2}$
$\qquad\qquad\qquad\qquad\qquad\qquad\quad = x$

**Solution:** $f(x) = 2x - 4$ and $f^{-1}(x) = \dfrac{x+4}{2}$ are inverse functions.

### Try These A

**Make use of structure.** Find the inverse of the function. Then use the definition to prove the functions are inverses. Show your work.

**a.** $f(x) = 4x - 14$ $\qquad\qquad\qquad$ **b.** $g(x) = \dfrac{1}{2}x + 3$

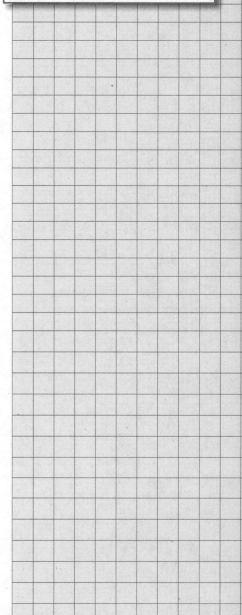

### Check Your Understanding

1. Suppose that the domain of $f(x) = 2x - 4$ in Example A was restricted to $\{x \mid x \in \mathbb{R}, x \geq 2\}$. What would be the domain and range in set notation of $f^{-1}(x)$? Explain your answer.

2. **Construct viable arguments.** Explain how to prove that two functions $h(x)$ and $j(x)$ are inverse functions.

3. The domain of $p(t)$ is $[0, \infty)$. The range of $q(t)$ is $(-\infty, 0]$. Based on this information, could $q(t)$ be the inverse of $p(t)$? Explain your answer.

You can use the relationship between the domain and range of a function and its inverse to graph the inverse of a function. If $(x, y)$ is a point on the graph of a given function, then $(y, x)$ is a point on the graph of its inverse.

4. Complete the table of values for $f(x) = 3x - 2$. Use the values to graph the function on the coordinate axes below.

| x | f(x) |
|----|------|
| −2 | |
| 0 | |
| 3 | |
| 4 | |

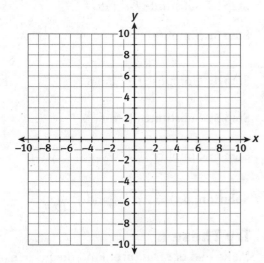

5. Use the table in Item 4 to make a table of values for the inverse of $f$. Then graph the inverse on the same coordinate axes.

| x | f⁻¹(x) |
|---|--------|
| | |
| | |
| | |
| | |

**6.** Show the graph of $y = x$ as a dotted line on the coordinate axes in Item 4. Describe any symmetry among the three graphs.

**7.** Find the inverse of $f(x) = x - 4$.

**8. a. Model with mathematics.** Graph $f(x) = x - 4$, its inverse $f^{-1}(x)$ from Item 7, and the dotted line $y = x$ on the coordinate axes.

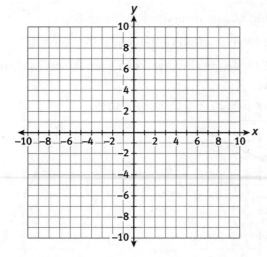

**b.** Describe any symmetry that you see on the graph in Item 8a.

**CONNECT TO GEOMETRY**

Geometric figures in the coordinate plane can have symmetry about a point, a line, or both.

---

**Check Your Understanding**

**9.** Graph the function $f(x) = 2$ and its inverse on the same coordinate plane. Is the inverse of $f(x) = 2$ a function? Explain your answer.

**10.** What is the relationship between the slope of a nonhorizontal linear function and the slope of its inverse function? Explain your reasoning.

**11.** What is the relationship between the $x$- and $y$-intercepts of a function and the $x$- and $y$-intercepts of its inverse? Explain your reasoning.

**MATH TIP**

Recall that the slope of a linear function is equal to $\dfrac{y_2 - y_1}{x_2 - x_1}$, where $(x_1, y_1)$ and $(x_2, y_2)$ are two points on the function's graph.

## LESSON 6-2 PRACTICE

In Items 12–14, find the inverse of each function. Use the definition of inverse functions to verify that the two functions are inverses.

**12.** $f(x) = 6 - 3x$

**13.** $g(x) = x + 2$

**14.** $h(x) = -x + 5$

**15. Express regularity in repeated reasoning.** Using your results in Items 12–14, state whether each statement is true or false. Explain your reasoning.

  **a.** A function and its inverse always intersect.

  **b.** The rule for a function cannot equal the rule for its inverse.

In Items 16 and 17, graph the inverse of each function shown on the coordinate plane.

**16.**

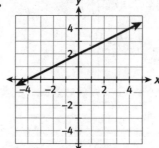

**17.**

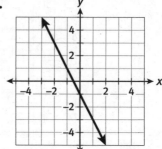

**18. Reason abstractly and quantitatively.** Summarize the relationship between a function and its inverse by listing at least three statements that must be true if two functions are inverses of each other.

## ACTIVITY 6 PRACTICE
Write your answers on notebook paper.
Show your work.

### Lesson 6-1
Mark's landscaping business Mowing Madness uses the function $c = F(a)$ to find the cost $c$ of mowing $a$ acres of land. He charges a \$50 fee plus \$60 per acre. Mark's cost-calculating function is $c = 60a + 50$. Use this function for Items 1–7.

1. What is $F(40)$? What does $F(40)$ mean?

2. Find $a$ in terms of $c$. Label this function $G$.

3. What is $G(170)$? What does $G(170)$ mean?

4. **a.** What are the units of the domain and range of $F(a)$?
   **b.** What are the units of the domain and range of $G(c)$?

5. **a.** What are the domain and range of $F(a)$ in interval notation?
   **b.** What are the domain and range of $G(c)$ in interval notation?

6. Are $F(a)$ and $G(c)$ inverse functions? Explain your answer.

7. A customer has \$200 to spend on mowing. How many acres will Mark mow for this amount? Explain how you determined your answer.

8. Find the inverse of each function.
   **a.** $f(x) = 2x - 10$
   **b.** $g(x) = \dfrac{x + 5}{4}$
   **c.** $h(x) = \dfrac{1}{6}(x - 8)$
   **d.** $j(x) = -5x + 2$

9. Given that $f(1) = 5$, which of the following statements must be true?
   **A.** $f^{-1}(1) = -5$    **B.** $f^{-1}(1) = 5$
   **C.** $f^{-1}(5) = -1$    **D.** $f^{-1}(5) = 1$

The function $m = F(a) = \dfrac{a}{8}$ gives the distance in inches on a map between two points that are actually $a$ miles apart. Use this function for Items 10–13.

10. What is $F(50)$? What does $F(50)$ represent?

11. **a.** What is the inverse of $F(a)$? Label this function $G$, and tell how you determined the rule for the inverse function.
    **b.** Tell what the inverse function represents.

12. What is $G(3)$? What does $G(3)$ represent?

13. Two towns on the map are $4\dfrac{1}{2}$ inches apart. What is the actual distance in miles between the two towns? Explain how you determined your answer.

14. What is the inverse of the function $p(t) = 6t + 8$?
    **A.** $p^{-1}(t) = -6t - 8$
    **B.** $p^{-1}(t) = \dfrac{-t + 8}{6}$
    **C.** $p^{-1}(t) = \dfrac{t - 8}{6}$
    **D.** $p^{-1}(t) = \dfrac{1}{6}t - 8$

### Lesson 6-2
15. Use the definition of *inverse* to determine whether or not each pair of functions are inverses.
    **a.** $f(x) = 5x - 3$, $g(x) = \dfrac{x}{5} + 3$
    **b.** $f(x) = \dfrac{x}{2} + 3$, $g(x) = 2x - 6$
    **c.** $f(x) = 2(x - 4)$, $g(x) = \dfrac{1}{2}x + 4$
    **d.** $f(x) = x + 3$, $g(x) = -x - 3$

16. Use a graph to determine which two of the three functions listed below are inverses.

    a. $f(x) = \frac{2}{3}x + 6$   b. $g(x) = \frac{3}{2}x - 6$

    c. $h(x) = \frac{3}{2}x - 9$

17. Write the inverse of the function defined by the table shown below.

| $x$ | $-2$ | 0 | 1 | 3 | 5 |
|-----|------|---|---|---|---|
| $f(x)$ | 4 | $-1$ | 2 | 0 | 5 |

18. Find the inverse of each function. Then use the definition of inverse functions to verify that the two functions are inverses.

    a. $f(x) = -3x + 3$
    b. $g(x) = 0.25x + 0.6$

19. a. Graph the absolute value function $f(x) = |x| + 2$.
    b. Graph the inverse of $f(x)$ on the same coordinate plane. Explain how you graphed the inverse.
    c. Give the domain and range of $f(x)$ and its inverse using set notation.
    d. Is the inverse of $f(x)$ a function? Explain your answer.

20. Graph the inverse of the function shown below.

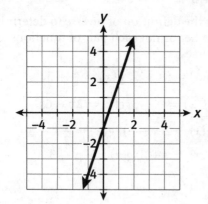

21. Graph each function and its inverse on the same coordinate plane.
    a. $f(x) = 2x + 4$
    b. $g(x) = -x - 2$

22. The graph of a function passes through the point $(-3, 4)$. Based on this information, which point *must* lie on the graph of the function's inverse?
    A. $(-4, 3)$      B. $(-3, 4)$
    C. $(3, -4)$      D. $(4, -3)$

23. Explain why the functions $f(x)$ and $g(x)$, graphed below, are not inverse functions.

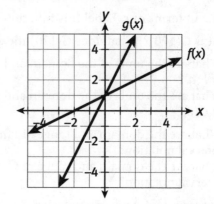

24. A function $h(x)$ has two different $x$-intercepts. Is the inverse of $h(x)$ a function? Explain your answer.

25. Describe a method for determining whether a function $f(x)$ is its own inverse.

### MATHEMATICAL PRACTICES
**Construct Viable Arguments and Critique the Reasoning of Others**

26. A student says that the functions $f(x) = 2x + 2$ and $g(x) = 2x - 2$ are inverse functions because their graphs are parallel. Is the student's reasoning correct? Justify your answer.

**CURRENCY CONVERSION**

Kathryn and Gaby are enrolled in a university program to study abroad in Spain and then in South Africa. They realize that they will have to convert US dollars (USD) to euros (EUR) in Spain, and then convert EUR into South African rand (ZAR) for their time in South Africa. They identified a currency exchange service in Spain that will convert $D$ dollars to euros with the function $E(D) = 0.64D - 5$ and a currency exchange service in South Africa that will convert $E$ euros to rand using $R(E) = 12.1E - 10$.

Use the information above to solve the following problems. Show your work.

1. For each function, give the units for the domain and range.

2. If Kathryn converts 450 USD in Spain to EUR, then converts that amount in EUR to ZAR, how much will she have in South African rand? Explain the process you used to arrive at your answer.

3. Explain how to compose the functions $E$ and $R$ to answer Item 2. Write the composite function and identify the domain and range.

4. After converting USD to EUR in Spain, Gaby had 139 EUR. Use an inverse function to find how much USD she converted.

5. Kathryn buys a wooden bowl as a souvenir while in South Africa. She wants to ship it back to the United States. The table below shows the costs for one shipping service.

**Shipping Costs to U.S.**

| Mass of Package (g) | Cost to Ship (ZAR) |
|---|---|
| No more than 100 | 14.00 |
| More than 100 and no more than 200 | 28.00 |
| More than 200 and no more than 1000 | 35.00 |

   a. Write a piecewise-defined function that gives the cost $C$ in South African rand for shipping a package with a mass of $M$ grams.
   b. Write the domain of the function using an inequality, interval notation, and set notation.
   c. Write the range of the function using set notation.
   d. Graph the function.
   e. The package containing Kathryn's bowl has a mass of 283 grams. If she needs to convert euros to rand to pay for the shipping, how many euros will she need? Explain how you determined your answer.

6. Kathryn and Gaby are shopping for plane tickets back to their home city of Chicago. The average cost of a plane ticket from Johannesburg, South Africa, to Chicago is $1300. The function $g(x) = |x - 1300|$ gives the variation of a ticket costing $x$ dollars from the average ticket price.
   a. Graph $g(x)$.
   b. Describe the graph of $g(x)$ as a transformation of the graph of $f(x) = |x|$.
   c. At one travel website, all of the ticket prices are within $200 of the average price. Explain how you can use the graph of $g(x)$ to find the least and greatest ticket prices offered at the website.

| Scoring Guide | Exemplary | Proficient | Emerging | Incomplete |
|---|---|---|---|---|
| | The solution demonstrates these characteristics: | | | |
| **Mathematics Knowledge and Thinking** (Items 1, 3, 4, 5b, 5c, 6b) | • Clear and accurate identification of and understanding of function concepts including domain, range, composition, inverse, and function transformations | • A functional understanding and accurate identification of function concepts including domain, range, composition, inverse, and function transformations | • Partial understanding and partially accurate identification of function concepts including domain, range, composition, inverse, and function transformations | • Little or no understanding and inaccurate identification of function concepts including domain, range, composition, inverse, and function transformations |
| **Problem Solving** (Items 2, 5e, 6c) | • An appropriate and efficient strategy that results in a correct answer | • A strategy that may include unnecessary steps but results in a correct answer | • A strategy that results in some incorrect answers | • No clear strategy when solving problems |
| **Mathematical Modeling / Representations** (Items 3, 4, 5a–d, 6a) | • Fluency in creating piecewise-defined, inverse, and composite functions to model real-world scenarios <br> • Clear and accurate understanding of how to graph piecewise-defined functions and represent intervals using inequalities, interval notation, and set notation | • Little difficulty in creating piecewise-defined, inverse, and composite functions to model real-world scenarios <br> • Mostly accurate understanding of how to graph piecewise-defined functions and represent intervals using inequalities, interval notation, and set notation | • Partial understanding of how to create piecewise-defined, inverse, and composite functions to model real-world scenarios <br> • Partial understanding of how to graph piecewise-defined functions and represent intervals using inequalities, interval notation, and set notation | • Little or no understanding of how to create piecewise-defined, inverse, and composite functions to model real-world scenarios <br> • Inaccurate or incomplete understanding of how to graph piecewise-defined functions and represent intervals using inequalities, interval notation, and set notation |
| **Reasoning and Communication** (Items 2, 3, 5e, 6b, 6c) | • Precise use of appropriate math terms and language to describe function transformation and function composition <br> • Clear and accurate explanation of the steps to solve a problem based on a real-world scenario | • Adequate description of function transformation and function composition <br> • Adequate explanation of the steps to solve a problem based on a real-world scenario | • Misleading or confusing description of function transformation and function composition <br> • Misleading or confusing explanation of the steps to solve a problem based on a real-world scenario | • Incomplete or inaccurate description of function transformation and function composition <br> • Incomplete or inadequate explanation of the steps to solve a problem based on a real-world scenario |

# Quadratic Functions

## Unit Overview

This unit focuses on quadratic functions and equations. You will write the equations of quadratic functions to model situations. You will also graph quadratic functions and other parabolas and interpret key features of the graphs. In addition, you will study methods of finding solutions of quadratic equations and interpreting the meaning of the solutions. You will also extend your knowledge of number systems to the complex numbers.

## Key Terms

As you study this unit, add these and other terms to your math notebook. Include in your notes your prior knowledge of each word, as well as your experiences in using the word in different mathematical examples. If needed, ask for help in pronouncing new words and add information on pronunciation to your math notebook. It is important that you learn new terms and use them correctly in your class discussions and in your problem solutions.

### Academic Vocabulary
- justify
- derive
- verify
- advantage
- disadvantage
- counterexample

### Math Terms
- quadratic equation
- standard form of a quadratic equation
- imaginary number
- complex number
- complex conjugate
- completing the square
- discriminant
- root
- zero
- parabola
- focus
- directrix
- axis of symmetry
- vertex
- quadratic regression
- vertex form

## ESSENTIAL QUESTIONS

? How can you determine key attributes of a quadratic function from an equation or graph?

? How do graphic, symbolic, and numeric methods of solving quadratic equations compare to one another?

## EMBEDDED ASSESSMENTS

This unit has three embedded assessments, following Activities 9, 11, and 13. By completing these embedded assessments, you will demonstrate your understanding of key features of quadratic functions and parabolas, solutions to quadratic equations, and systems that include nonlinear equations.

**Embedded Assessment 1:**

Applications of Quadratic Functions and Equations          p. 151

**Embedded Assessment 2:**

Writing and Transforming Quadratic Functions          p. 191

**Embedded Assessment 3:**

Graphing Quadratic Functions and Solving Systems          p. 223

# Getting Ready

**Write your answers on notebook paper.**
**Show your work.**

Factor the expressions in Items 1–4 completely.

1. $6x^3y + 12x^2y^2$

2. $x^2 + 3x - 40$

3. $x^2 - 49$

4. $x^2 - 6x + 9$

5. Graph $f(x) = \frac{3}{4}x - \frac{3}{2}$.

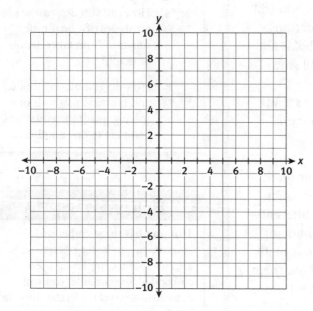

6. Graph a line that has an $x$-intercept of 5 and a $y$-intercept of $-2$.

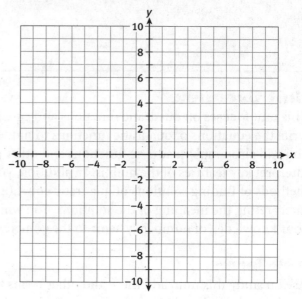

7. Graph $y = |x|$, $y = |x + 3|$, and $y = |x| + 3$ on the same grid.

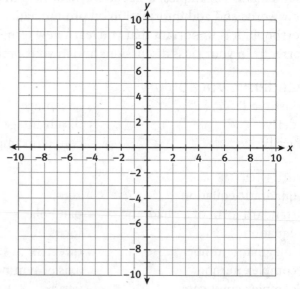

8. Solve $x^2 - 3x - 5 = 0$.

# Applications of Quadratic Functions

## Fences

### Lesson 7-1 Analyzing a Quadratic Function

**My Notes**

**Learning Targets:**
- Formulate quadratic functions in a problem-solving situation.
- Graph and interpret quadratic functions.

> **SUGGESTED LEARNING STRATEGIES:** Marking the Text, Guess and Check, Create Representations, Quickwrite, Self Revision/Peer Revision

Fence Me In is a business that specializes in building fenced enclosures. One client has purchased 100 ft of fencing to enclose the largest possible rectangular area in her yard.

Work with your group on Items 1–7. As you share ideas, be sure to explain your thoughts using precise language and specific details to help group members understand your ideas and your reasoning.

1. If the width of the rectangular enclosure is 20 ft, what must be the length? Find the area of this rectangular enclosure.

2. Choose several values for the width of a rectangle with a perimeter of 100 ft. Determine the corresponding length and area of each rectangle. Share your values with members of your class. Then record each set of values in the table below.

| Width (ft) | Length (ft) | Area (ft²) |
|---|---|---|
|  |  |  |
|  |  |  |
|  |  |  |
|  |  |  |
|  |  |  |
|  |  |  |
|  |  |  |
|  |  |  |

**DISCUSSION GROUP TIP**

Reread the problem scenario as needed. Make notes on the information provided in the problem. Respond to questions about the meaning of key information. Summarize or organize the information needed to create reasonable solutions, and describe the mathematical concepts your group will use to create its solutions.

3. **Make sense of problems.** What is the relationship between the length and width of a rectangle with perimeter of 100 ft?

4. Based on your observations, predict if it is possible for a rectangle with perimeter of 100 ft to have each area. Explain your reasoning.

   a. 400 ft²

   b. 500 ft²

**My Notes**

**c.** 700 ft$^2$

5. Let *l* represent the length of a rectangle with a perimeter of 100 ft. Write an expression for the width of the rectangle in terms of *l*.

6. Express the area $A(l)$ for a rectangle with a perimeter of 100 ft as a function of its length, *l*.

7. Graph the quadratic function $A(l)$ on the coordinate grid.

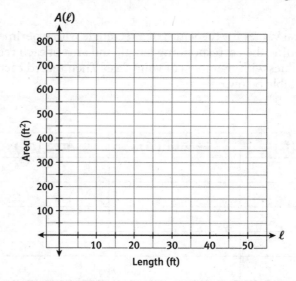

8. **Use appropriate tools strategically.** Now use a graphing calculator to graph the quadratic function $A(l)$. Set your window to correspond to the values on the axes on the graph in Item 7.

9. Use the function $A(l)$ and your graphs from Items 7 and 8 to complete the following.
   **a.** What is the reasonable domain of the function in this situation? Express the domain as an inequality, in interval notation, and in set notation.

**TECHNOLOGY TIP**

To graph the function on a graphing calculator, you will first need to substitute *y* for $A(\ell)$ and *x* for $\ell$ before you can enter the equation.

**b.** Over what interval of the domain is the value of the function increasing? Over what interval of the domain is the value of the function decreasing?

**10.** What is the maximum rectangular area that can be enclosed by 100 ft of fencing? *Justify* your answer.

**11. a.** What is the reasonable range of $A(\ell)$ in this situation? Express the range as an inequality, in interval notation, and in set notation.

**b.** Explain how your answer to Item 10 helped you determine the reasonable range.

**12. Reason quantitatively.** Revise or confirm your predictions from Item 4. If a rectangle is possible, estimate its dimensions and explain your reasoning. Review the draft of your revised or confirmed predictions. Be sure to check that you have included specific details, the correct mathematical terms to support your explanations, and that your sentences are complete and grammatically correct. You may want to pair-share with another student to critique each other's drafts and make improvements.
**a.** 400 ft$^2$

**b.** 500 ft$^2$

**c.** 700 ft$^2$

**ACADEMIC VOCABULARY**

When you *justify* an answer, you show that your answer is correct or reasonable.

**CONNECT TO AP**

The process of finding the maximum (or minimum) value of a function is called *optimization*, a topic addressed in calculus.

**13.** What are the length and width of the largest rectangular area that can be enclosed by 100 ft of fencing?

**14.** The length you gave in Item 13 is the solution of a quadratic equation in terms of $l$. Write this equation. Explain how you arrived at this equation.

### Check Your Understanding

**15.** Explain why the function $A(l)$ that you used in this lesson is a quadratic function.

**16.** How does the graph of a quadratic function differ from the graph of a linear function?

**17.** Can the range of a quadratic function be all real numbers? Explain.

**18.** Explain how you could solve the quadratic equation $x^2 + 2x = 3$ by graphing the function $f(x) = x^2 + 2x$.

### LESSON 7-1 PRACTICE

For Items 19–21, consider a rectangle that has a perimeter of 120 ft.

**19.** Write a function $B(l)$ that represents the area of the rectangle with length $l$.

**20.** Graph the function $B(l)$, using a graphing calculator. Then copy it on your paper, labeling axes and using an appropriate scale.

**21.** Use the graph of $B(l)$ to find the dimensions of the rectangle with a perimeter of 120 feet that has each area. Explain your answer.
   **a.** 500 ft²          **b.** 700 ft²

**22. Critique the reasoning of others.** An area of 1000 ft² is not possible. Explain why this is true.

**23.** How is the maximum value of a function shown on the graph of the function? How would a minimum value be shown?

## Learning Targets:
- Factor quadratic expressions of the form $x^2 + bx + c$.
- Factor quadratic expressions of the form $ax^2 + bx + c$.

SUGGESTED LEARNING STRATEGIES: Interactive Word Wall, Vocabulary Organizer, Marking the Text, Guess and Check, Work Backward, RAFT

In the previous lesson, you used the function $A(l) = -l^2 + 50l$ to model the area in square feet of a rectangle that can be enclosed with 100 ft of fencing.

1. **Reason quantitatively.** What are the dimensions of the rectangle if its area is 525 ft²? Explain how you determined your answer.

2. One way to find the dimensions of the rectangle is to solve a quadratic equation algebraically. What *quadratic equation* could you have solved to answer Item 1?

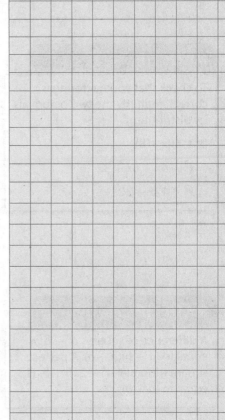

### MATH TERMS

A **quadratic equation** can be written in the form $ax^2 + bx + c = 0$, where $a \neq 0$. An expression in the form $ax^2 + bx + c$, $a \neq 0$, is a *quadratic expression*.

3. Write the quadratic equation from Item 2 in the form $al^2 + bl + c = 0$, where $a > 0$. Give the values of $a$, $b$, and $c$.

As you have seen, graphing is one way to solve a quadratic equation. However, you can also solve quadratic equations algebraically by factoring.

You can use the graphic organizer shown in Example A on the next page to recall factoring trinomials of the form $x^2 + bx + c = 0$. Later in this activity, you will solve the quadratic equation from Item 3 by factoring.

**My Notes**

## Example A

Factor $x^2 + 12x + 32$.

**Step 1:** Place $x^2$ in the upper left box and the constant term 32 in the lower right.

| $x^2$ | |
|---|---|
| | 32 |

**Step 2:** List factor pairs of 32, the constant term. Choose the pair that has a sum equal to 12, the coefficient $b$ of the $x$–term.

| Factors | | Sum |
|---|---|---|
| 32 | 1 | $32 + 1 = 33$ |
| 16 | 2 | $16 + 2 = 18$ |
| 8 | 4 | $8 + 4 = 12$ |

**Step 3:** Write each factor as coefficients of $x$ and place them in the two empty boxes. Write common factors from each row to the left and common factors for each column above.

|  | $x$ | 8 |
|---|---|---|
| $x$ | $x^2$ | $8x$ |
| 4 | $4x$ | 32 |

**Step 4:** Write the sum of the common factors as binomials. Then write the factors as a product.

$(x + 4)(x + 8)$

**Solution:** $x^2 + 12x + 32 = (x + 4)(x + 8)$

## Try These A

**a.** Factor $x^2 - 7x + 12$, using the graphic organizer. Then check by multiplying.

|  |  |
|---|---|
|  |  |

Factor, and then check by multiplying. Show your work.

**b.** $x^2 + 9x + 14$       **c.** $x^2 - 7x - 30$

**d.** $x^2 - 12x + 36$       **e.** $x^2 - 144$

**f.** $5x^2 + 40x + 75$       **g.** $-12x^2 + 108$

---

**MATH TIP**

To check that your factoring is correct, multiply the two binomials by distributing.

$(x + 4)(x + 8)$
$= x^2 + 4x + 8x + 32$
$= x^2 + 12x + 32$

---

**MATH TIP**

A difference of squares $a^2 - b^2$ is equal to $(a - b)(a + b)$. A perfect square trinomial $a^2 + 2ab + b^2$ is equal to $(a + b)^2$.

## Lesson 7-2
### Factoring Quadratic Expressions

Before factoring quadratic expressions $ax^2 + bx + c$, where the leading coefficient $a \neq 1$, consider how multiplying binomial factors results in that form of a quadratic expression.

4. **Make sense of problems.** Use a graphic organizer to multiply $(2x + 3)(4x + 5)$.

   a. Complete the graphic organizer by filling in the two empty boxes.

   b. $(2x + 3)(4x + 5)$

   $= 8x^2 + \rule{1.5cm}{0.4pt} + \rule{1.5cm}{0.4pt} + 15$

   $= 8x^2 + \rule{1.5cm}{0.4pt} + 15$

|      | 2x     | 3   |
|------|--------|-----|
| 4x   | $8x^2$ |     |
| 5    |        | 15  |

Using the Distributive Property, you can see the relationship between the numbers in the binomial factors and the terms of the trinomial.

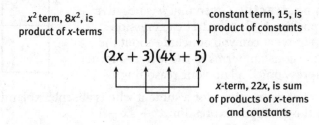

$x^2$ term, $8x^2$, is product of x-terms

constant term, 15, is product of constants

$(2x + 3)(4x + 5)$

x-term, 22x, is sum of products of x-terms and constants

To factor a quadratic expression $ax^2 + bx + c$, work backward from the coefficients of the terms.

### Example B

Factor $6x^2 + 13x - 5$. Use a table to organize your work.

**Step 1:** Identify the factors of 6, which is $a$, the coefficient of the $x^2$-term.

**Step 2:** Identify the factors of $-5$, which is $c$, the constant term.

**Step 3:** Find the numbers whose products add together to equal 13, which is $b$, the coefficient of the $x$-term.

**Step 4:** Then write the binomial factors.

| Factors of 6 | Factors of −5 | Sum = 13? |
|--------------|---------------|-----------|
| 1 and 6      | −1 and 5      | $1(5) + 6(-1) = -1$ |
| 1 and 6      | 5 and −1      | $1(-1) + 6(5) = 29$ |
| 2 and 3      | −1 and 5      | $2(5) + 3(-1) = 7$  |
| 2 and 3      | 5 and −1      | $2(-1) + 3(5) = 13$ ✔ |

**Solution:** $6x^2 + 13x - 5 = (2x + 5)(3x - 1)$

**MATH TIP**

Check your answer by multiplying the two binomials.

$(2x + 5)(3x - 1)$

$= 6x^2 - 2x + 15x - 5$

$= 6x^2 + 13x - 5$

**Try These B**
Factor, and then check by multiplying. Show your work.

a. $10x^2 + 11x + 3$

b. $4x^2 + 17x - 15$

c. $2x^2 - 13x + 21$

d. $6x^2 - 19x - 36$

## Check Your Understanding

5. Explain how the graphic organizer shows that $x^2 + 8x + 15$ is equal to $(x + 5)(x + 3)$.

6. **Reason abstractly.** Given that $b$ is negative and $c$ is positive in the quadratic expression $x^2 + bx + c$, what can you conclude about the signs of the constant terms in the factored form of the expression? Explain your reasoning.

|       | $x$     | 5    |
|-------|---------|------|
| $x$   | $x^2$   | $5x$ |
| 3     | $3x$    | 15   |

7. Write a set of instructions for a student who is absent, explaining how to factor the quadratic expression $x^2 + 4x - 12$.

## LESSON 7-2 PRACTICE

Factor each quadratic expression.

8. $2x^2 + 15x + 28$

9. $3x^2 + 25x - 18$

10. $x^2 + x - 30$

11. $x^2 + 15x + 56$

12. $6x^2 - 7x - 5$

13. $12x^2 - 43x + 10$

14. $2x^2 + 5x$

15. $9x^2 - 3x - 2$

16. A customer of Fence Me In wants to increase both the length and width of a rectangular fenced area in her backyard by $x$ feet. The new area in square feet enclosed by the fence is given by the expression $x^2 + 30x + 200$.
    a. Factor the quadratic expression.
    b. **Reason quantitatively.** What were the original length and width of the fenced area? Explain your answer.

**Learning Targets:**
- Solve quadratic equations by factoring.
- Interpret solutions of a quadratic equation.
- Create quadratic equations from solutions.

**SUGGESTED LEARNING STRATEGIES:** Marking the Text, Paraphrasing, Think-Pair-Share, Create Representations, Quickwrite

To solve a quadratic equation $ax^2 + bx + c = 0$ by factoring, the equation must be in factored form to use the Zero Product Property.

**My Notes**

**MATH TIP**

The *Zero Product Property* states that if $a \cdot b = 0$, then either $a = 0$ or $b = 0$.

### Example A

Solve $x^2 + 5x - 14 = 0$ by factoring.

| | |
|---|---|
| Original equation | $x^2 + 5x - 14 = 0$ |

**Step 1:** Factor the left side. $\qquad$ $(x + 7)(x - 2) = 0$

**Step 2:** Apply the Zero Product Property. $\quad x + 7 = 0$ or $x - 2 = 0$

**Step 3:** Solve each equation for $x$.

**Solution:** $x = -7$ or $x = 2$

### Try These A

**a.** Solve $3x^2 - 17x + 10 = 0$ and check by substitution.

| | |
|---|---|
| | Original equation |
| | Factor the left side. |
| | Apply the Zero Product Property. |
| | Solve each equation for $x$. |

Solve each equation by factoring. Show your work.

**b.** $12x^2 - 7x - 10 = 0$ $\qquad$ **c.** $x^2 + 8x - 9 = 0$ $\qquad$ **d.** $4x^2 + 12x + 9 = 0$

**MATH TIP**

You can check your solutions by substituting the values into the original equation.

**e.** $18x^2 - 98 = 0$ $\qquad$ **f.** $x^2 + 6x = -8$ $\qquad$ **g.** $5x^2 + 2x = 3$

**My Notes**

In the previous lesson, you were asked to determine the dimensions of a rectangle with an area of 525 ft$^2$ that can be enclosed by 100 ft of fencing. You wrote the quadratic equation $l^2 - 50l + 525 = 0$ to model this situation, where $l$ is the length of the rectangle in feet.

1. **a.** Solve the quadratic equation by factoring.

   **b.** What do the solutions of the equation represent in this situation?

   **c.** What are the dimensions of a rectangle with an area of 525 ft$^2$ that can be enclosed by 100 ft of fencing?

   **d. Reason quantitatively.** Explain why your answer to part c is reasonable.

2. A park has two rectangular tennis courts side by side. Combined, the courts have a perimeter of 160 yd and an area of 1600 yd$^2$.
   **a.** Write a quadratic equation that can be used to find $l$, the length of the court in yards.

   **b. Construct viable arguments.** Explain why you need to write the equation in the form $al^2 + bl + c = 0$ before you can solve it by factoring.

   **c.** Solve the quadratic equation by factoring, and interpret the solution.

   **d.** Explain why the quadratic equation has only one distinct solution.

**MATH TIP**

It is often easier to factor a quadratic equation if the coefficient of the $x^2$-term is positive. If necessary, you can multiply both sides of the equation by $-1$ to make the coefficient positive.

**3.** The equation $2x^2 + 9x - 3 = 0$ cannot be solved by factoring. Explain why this is true.

### Check Your Understanding

**4.** Explain how to use factoring to solve the equation $2x^2 + 5x = 3$.

**5.** **Critique the reasoning of others.** A student incorrectly states that the solution of the equation $x^2 + 2x - 35 = 0$ is $x = -5$ or $x = 7$. Describe the student's error, and solve the equation correctly.

**6.** Fence Me In has been asked to install a fence around a cabin. The cabin has a length of 10 yd and a width of 8 yd. There will be a space $x$ yd wide between the cabin and the fence on all sides, as shown in the diagram. The area to be enclosed by the fence is 224 yd$^2$.
   **a.** Write a quadratic equation that can be used to determine the value of $x$.
   **b.** Solve the equation by factoring.
   **c.** Interpret the solutions.

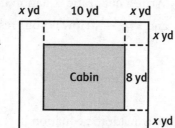

If you know the solutions to a quadratic equation, then you can write the equation.

### Example B

Write a quadratic equation in **standard form** with the solutions $x = 4$ and $x = -5$.

**Step 1:** Write linear equations that correspond to the solutions.
$$x - 4 = 0 \text{ or } x + 5 = 0$$

**Step 2:** Write the linear expressions as factors.
$$(x - 4) \text{ and } (x + 5)$$

**Step 3:** Multiply the factors to write the equation in factored form.
$$(x - 4)(x + 5) = 0$$

**Step 4:** Multiply the binomials and write the equation in standard form.
$$x^2 + x - 20 = 0$$

**Solution:** $x^2 + x - 20 = 0$ is a quadratic equation with solutions $x = 4$ and $x = -5$.

### MATH TERMS

The **standard form of a quadratic equation** is $ax^2 + bx + c = 0$, where $a \neq 0$.

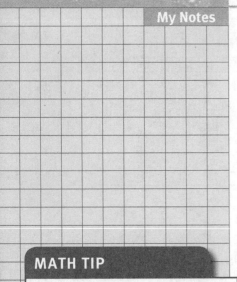

**My Notes**

### Try These B

**a.** Write a quadratic equation in standard form with the solutions $x = -1$ and $x = -7$.

| | |
|---|---|
| | Write linear equations that correspond to the solutions. |
| | Write the linear expressions as factors. |
| | Multiply the factors to write the equation in factored form. |
| | Multiply the binomials and write the equation in standard form. |

**b.** Write a quadratic equation in standard form whose solutions are $x = \dfrac{2}{5}$ and $x = -\dfrac{1}{2}$. How is your result different from those in Example B?

Write a quadratic equation in standard form with integer coefficients for each pair of solutions. Show your work.

**c.** $x = \dfrac{2}{3}, x = 2$

**d.** $x = -\dfrac{3}{2}, x = \dfrac{5}{2}$

### Check Your Understanding

**7.** Write the equation $3x^2 - 6x = 10x + 12$ in standard form.

**8.** Explain how you could write the equation $x^2 - \dfrac{7}{6}x + \dfrac{1}{3} = 0$ with integer values of the coefficients and constants.

**9. Reason quantitatively.** Is there more than one quadratic equation whose solutions are $x = -3$ and $x = -1$? Explain.

**10.** How could you write a quadratic equation in standard form whose only solution is $x = 4$?

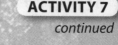
## LESSON 7-3 PRACTICE

Solve each quadratic equation by factoring.

**11.** $2x^2 - 11x + 5 = 0$

**12.** $x^2 + 2x = 15$

**13.** $3x^2 + x - 4 = 0$

**14.** $6x^2 - 13x - 5 = 0$

Write a quadratic equation in standard form with integer coefficients for which the given numbers are solutions.

**15.** $x = 2$ and $x = -5$

**16.** $x = -\frac{2}{3}$ and $x = -5$

**17.** $x = \frac{3}{5}$ and $x = 3$

**18.** $x = -\frac{1}{2}$ and $x = \frac{3}{4}$

**19. Model with mathematics.** The manager of Fence Me In is trying to determine the best selling price for a particular type of gate latch. The function $p(s) = -4s^2 + 400s - 8400$ models the yearly profit the company will make from the latches when the selling price is $s$ dollars.

    **a.** Write a quadratic equation that can be used to determine the selling price that would result in a yearly profit of $1600.

    **b.** Write the quadratic equation in standard form so that the coefficient of $s^2$ is 1.

    **c.** Solve the quadratic equation by factoring, and interpret the solution(s).

    **d.** Explain how you could check your answer to part c.

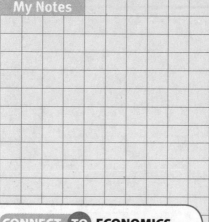

**CONNECT TO ECONOMICS**

The selling price of an item has an effect on how many of the items are sold. The number of items that are sold, in turn, has an effect on the amount of profit a company makes by selling the item.

**My Notes**

**Learning Targets:**
- Solve quadratic inequalities.
- Graph the solutions to quadratic inequalities.

**SUGGESTED LEARNING STRATEGIES:** Identify a Subtask, Guess and Check, Think Aloud, Create Representations, Quickwrite

Factoring is also used to solve quadratic inequalities.

### Example A

Solve $x^2 - x - 6 > 0$.

**Step 1:** Factor the quadratic expression on the left side. $(x + 2)(x - 3) > 0$

**Step 2:** Determine where each factor equals zero. $(x + 2) = 0$ at $x = -2$
$(x - 3) = 0$ at $x = 3$

**Step 3:** Use a number line to visualize the intervals for which each factor is positive and negative. (Test a value in each interval to determine the signs.)

$(x + 2)$
$(x - 3)$

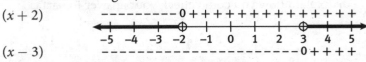

**MATH TIP**

For a product of two numbers to be positive, both factors must have the same sign. If the product is negative, then the factors must have opposite signs.

**Step 4:** Identify the sign of the product of the two factors on each interval. $(x + 2)(x - 3)$

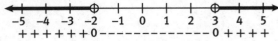

**Step 5:** Choose the appropriate interval.

Since $x^2 - x - 6$ is positive ($> 0$), the intervals that show $(x + 2)(x - 3)$ as positive represent the solutions.

**Solution:** $x < -2$ or $x > 3$

### Try These A

**a.** Use the number line provided to solve $2x^2 + x - 10 \leq 0$.

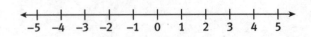

Solve each quadratic inequality.

**b.** $x^2 + 3x - 4 < 0$

**c.** $3x^2 + x - 10 \geq 0$

A farmer wants to enclose a rectangular pen next to his barn. A wall of the barn will form one side of the pen, and the other three sides will be fenced. He has purchased 100 ft of fencing and has hired Fence Me In to install it so that it encloses an area of at least 1200 ft².

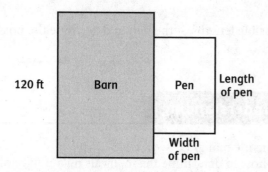

120 ft    Barn    Pen    Length of pen

Width of pen

Work with your group on Items 1–5. As you share ideas with your group, be sure to explain your thoughts using precise language and specific details to help group members understand your ideas and your reasoning.

1. **Attend to precision.** If Fence Me In makes the pen 50 ft in length, what will be the width of the pen? What will be its area? Explain your answers.

2. Let $l$ represent the length in feet of the pen. Write an expression for the width of the pen in terms of $l$.

3. Write an inequality in terms of $l$ that represents the possible area of the pen. Explain what each part of your inequality represents.

4. Write the inequality in standard form with integer coefficients.

5. Use factoring to solve the quadratic inequality.

**My Notes**

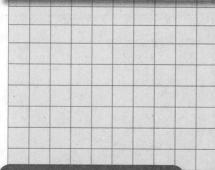

**DISCUSSION GROUP TIP**

Reread the problem scenario as needed. Make notes on the information provided in the problem. Respond to questions about the meaning of key information. Summarize or organize the information needed to create reasonable solutions, and describe the mathematical concepts your group will use to create solutions.

**MATH TIP**

If you multiply or divide both sides of an inequality by a negative number, you must reverse the inequality symbol.

6. Interpret the solutions of the inequality.

7. Use the possible lengths of the pen to determine the possible widths.

**Check Your Understanding**

8. Consider the inequality $(x + 4)(x - 5) \geq 0$.
   a. Explain how to determine the intervals on a number line for which each of the factors $(x + 4)$ and $(x - 5)$ is positive or negative.
   b. **Reason abstractly.** How do you determine the sign of the product $(x + 4)(x - 5)$ on each interval?
   c. Once you know the sign of the product $(x + 4)(x - 5)$ on each interval, how do you identify the solutions of the inequality?

9. Explain how the solutions of $x^2 + 5x - 24 = 0$ differ from the solutions of $x^2 + 5x - 24 \leq 0$.

10. Explain why the quadratic inequality $x^2 + 4 < 0$ has no real solutions.

## LESSON 7-4 PRACTICE

Solve each inequality.

11. $x^2 + 3x - 10 \geq 0$

12. $2x^2 + 3x - 9 < 0$

13. $x^2 + 9x + 18 \leq 0$

14. $3x^2 - 10x - 8 > 0$

15. $x^2 - 12x + 27 < 0$

16. $5x^2 + 12x + 4 > 0$

17. The function $p(s) = -500s^2 + 15,000s - 100,000$ models the yearly profit Fence Me In will make from installing wooden fences when the installation price is $s$ dollars per foot.
   a. Write a quadratic inequality that can be used to determine the installation prices that will result in a yearly profit of at least $8000.
   b. Write the quadratic inequality in standard form so that the coefficient of $s^2$ is 1.
   c. **Make sense of problems.** Solve the quadratic inequality by factoring, and interpret the solution(s).

## ACTIVITY 7 PRACTICE
**Write your answers on notebook paper.**
**Show your work.**

### Lesson 7-1

A rectangle has perimeter 40 cm. Use this information for Items 1–7.

1. Write the dimensions and areas of three rectangles that fit this description.

2. Let the length of one side be $x$. Then write a function $A(x)$ that represents that area of the rectangle.

3. Graph the function $A(x)$ on a graphing calculator. Then sketch the graph on grid paper, labeling the axes and using an appropriate scale.

4. An area of 96 cm$^2$ is possible. Use $A(x)$ to demonstrate this fact algebraically and graphically.

5. An area of 120 cm$^2$ is not possible. Use $A(x)$ to demonstrate this fact algebraically and graphically.

6. What are the reasonable domain and reasonable range of $A(x)$? Express your answers as inequalities, in interval notation, and in set notation.

7. What is the greatest area that the rectangle could have? Explain.

Use the quadratic function $f(x) = x^2 - 6x + 8$ for Items 8–11.

8. Graph the function.

9. Write the domain and range of the function as inequalities, in interval notation, and in set notation.

10. What is the function's $y$-intercept?
    **A.** 0      **B.** 2
    **C.** 4      **D.** 8

11. Explain how you could use the graph of the function to solve the equation $x^2 - 6x + 8 = 3$.

### Lesson 7-2

12. Factor $x^2 + 11x + 28$ by copying and completing the graphic organizer. Then check by multiplying.

| | ? | ? |
|---|---|---|
| ? | $x^2$ | ? |
| ? | ? | 28 |

13. Factor each quadratic expression.
    **a.** $2x^2 - 3x - 27$    **b.** $4x^2 - 121$
    **c.** $6x^2 + 11x - 10$    **d.** $3x^2 + 7x + 4$
    **e.** $5x^2 - 42x - 27$    **f.** $4x^2 - 4x - 35$
    **g.** $36x^2 - 100$      **h.** $12x^2 + 60x + 75$

14. Given that $b$ is positive and $c$ is negative in the quadratic expression $x^2 + bx + c$, what can you conclude about the signs of the constant terms in the factored form of the expression? Explain your reasoning.

15. The area in square inches of a framed photograph is given by the expression $4f^2 + 32f + 63$, where $f$ is the width in inches of the frame.

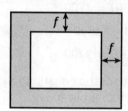

    **a.** Factor the quadratic expression.
    **b.** What are the dimensions of the opening in the frame? Explain your answer.
    **c.** If the frame is 2 inches wide, what are the overall dimensions of the framed photograph? Explain your answer.

## Lesson 7-3

**16.** Solve each quadratic equation by factoring.
   **a.** $2x^2 - 5x - 12 = 0$
   **b.** $3x^2 + 7x = -2$
   **c.** $4x^2 - 20x + 25 = 0$
   **d.** $27x^2 - 12 = 0$
   **e.** $6x^2 - 4 = 5x$

**17.** For each set of solutions, write a quadratic equation in standard form.
   **a.** $x = 5, x = -8$    **b.** $x = \frac{2}{3}, x = 4$
   **c.** $x = -\frac{7}{5}, x = \frac{1}{2}$    **d.** $x = 6$

**18.** A student claims that you can find the solutions of $(x - 2)(x - 3) = 2$ by solving the equations $x - 2 = 2$ and $x - 3 = 2$. Is the student's reasoning correct? Explain why or why not.

One face of a building is shaped like a right triangle with an area of 2700 ft². The height of the triangle is 30 ft greater than its base. Use this information for Items 19–21.

**19.** Which equation can be used to determine the base $b$ of the triangle in feet?
   **A.** $b(b + 30) = 2700$
   **B.** $\frac{1}{2}b(b + 30) = 2700$
   **C.** $b(b - 30) = 2700$
   **D.** $\frac{1}{2}b(b - 30) = 2700$

**20.** Write the quadratic equation in standard form so that the coefficient of $b^2$ is 1.

**21.** Solve the quadratic equation by factoring, and interpret the solutions. If any solutions need to be excluded, explain why.

## Lesson 7-4

**22.** For what values of $x$ is the product $(x + 4)(x - 6)$ positive? Explain.

**23.** Solve each quadratic inequality.
   **a.** $x^2 - 3x - 4 \leq 0$    **b.** $3x^2 - 7x - 6 > 0$
   **c.** $x^2 - 16x + 64 < 0$    **d.** $2x^2 + 8x + 6 \geq 0$
   **e.** $x^2 - 4x - 21 \leq 0$    **f.** $5x^2 - 13x - 6 < 0$

The function $h(t) = -16t^2 + 20t + 6$ models the height in feet of a football $t$ seconds after it is thrown. Use this information for Items 24–26.

**24.** Write a quadratic inequality that can be used to determine when the football will be at least 10 ft above the ground.

**25.** Write the quadratic inequality in standard form.

**26.** Solve the quadratic inequality by factoring, and interpret the solution(s).

## MATHEMATICAL PRACTICES
### Make Sense of Problems and Persevere in Solving Them

**27.** The graph of the function $y = -\frac{1}{8}x^2 + 2x$ models the shape of an arch that forms part of a bridge, where $x$ and $y$ are the horizontal and vertical distances in feet from the left end of the arch.

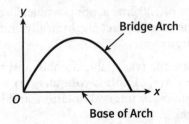

**a.** The greatest width of the arch occurs at its base. Use a graph to determine the greatest width of the arch. Explain how you used the graph to find the answer.

**b.** Now write a quadratic equation that can help you find the greatest width of the arch. Solve the equation by factoring, and explain how you used the solutions to find the greatest width.

**c.** Compare and contrast the methods of using a graph and factoring an equation to solve this problem.

# Introduction to Complex Numbers
**Cardano's Imaginary Numbers**
**Lesson 8-1  The Imaginary Unit, _i_**

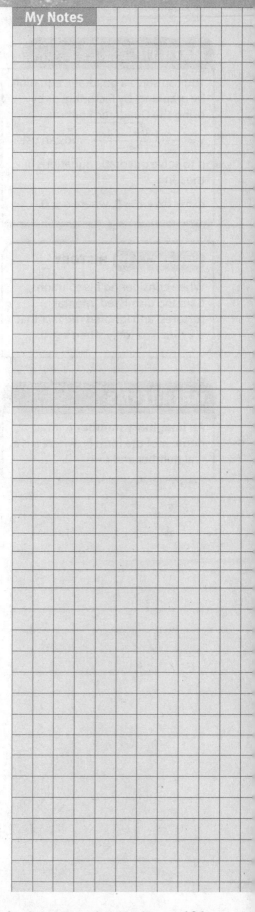
My Notes

● **Learning Targets:**
- Know the definition of the complex number _i_.
- Know that complex numbers can be written as $a + bi$, where $a$ and $b$ are real numbers.
- Graph complex numbers on the complex plane.

> **SUGGESTED LEARNING STRATEGIES:** Create Representations, Interactive Word Wall, Marking the Text, Think-Pair-Share, Quickwrite

The equation $x^2 + 1 = 0$ has special historical and mathematical significance. At the beginning of the sixteenth century, mathematicians believed that the equation had no solutions.

1. Why would mathematicians of the early sixteenth century think that $x^2 + 1 = 0$ had no solutions?

A breakthrough occurred in 1545 when the talented Italian mathematician Girolamo Cardano (1501–1576) published his book, _Ars Magna_ (_The Great Art_). In the process of solving one cubic (third-degree) equation, he encountered—and was required to make use of—the square roots of negative numbers. While skeptical of their existence, he demonstrated the situation with this famous problem: Find two numbers with the sum 10 and the product 40.

2. **Make sense of problems.** To better understand this problem, first find two numbers with the sum 10 and the product 21.

3. Letting $x$ represent one number, write an expression for the other number in terms of $x$. Use the expressions to write an equation that models the problem in Item 2: "find two numbers with the product 21."

**My Notes**

**MATH TIP**

You can solve a quadratic equation by graphing, by factoring, or by using the Quadratic Formula,

$x = \dfrac{-b \pm \sqrt{b^2 - 4ac}}{2a}$. You can use

it to solve quadratic equations in the form

$ax^2 + bx + c = 0$, where $a \neq 0$.

**CONNECT TO HISTORY**

When considering his solutions, Cardano dismissed "mental tortures" and ignored the fact that $\sqrt{x} \cdot \sqrt{x} = x$ only when $x \geq 0$.

**MATH TERMS**

An **imaginary number** is any number of the form $bi$, where $b$ is a real number and $i = \sqrt{-1}$.

4. Solve your equation in Item 3 in two different ways. Explain each method.

5. Write an equation that represents the problem that Cardano posed.

6. Cardano claimed that the solutions to the problem are $x = 5 + \sqrt{-15}$ and $x = 5 - \sqrt{-15}$. Verify his solutions by using the Quadratic Formula with the equation in Item 5.

Cardano avoided any more problems in *Ars Magna* involving the square root of a negative number. However, he did demonstrate an understanding about the properties of such numbers. Solving the equation $x^2 + 1 = 0$ yields the solutions $x = \sqrt{-1}$ and $x = -\sqrt{-1}$. The number $\sqrt{-1}$ is represented by the symbol $i$, the imaginary unit. You can say $i = \sqrt{-1}$. The imaginary unit $i$ is considered the solution to the equation $x^2 + 1 = 0$, or $x^2 = -1$.

To simplify an **imaginary number** $\sqrt{-s}$, where $s$ is a positive number, you can write $\sqrt{-s} = i\sqrt{s}$.

## Example A

Write the numbers $\sqrt{-17}$ and $\sqrt{-9}$ in terms of $i$.

|  | | $\sqrt{-17}$ | $\sqrt{-9}$ |
|---|---|---|---|
| **Step 1:** | Definition of $\sqrt{-s}$ | $= i \cdot \sqrt{17}$ | $= i \cdot \sqrt{9}$ |
| **Step 2:** | Take the square root of 9. | $= i\sqrt{17}$ | $= i \cdot 3$ |
|  | | | $= 3i$ |

**Solution:** $\sqrt{-17} = i\sqrt{17}$ and $\sqrt{-9} = 3i$

**WRITING MATH**

Write $i\sqrt{17}$ instead of $\sqrt{17}i$, which may be confused with $\sqrt{17i}$.

## Try These A

Write each number in terms of $i$.

**a.** $\sqrt{-25}$          **b.** $\sqrt{-7}$

**c.** $\sqrt{-12}$          **d.** $\sqrt{-150}$

**CONNECT TO HISTORY**

René Descartes (1596–1650) was the first to call these numbers *imaginary*. Although his reference was meant to be derogatory, the term *imaginary number* persists. Leonhard Euler (1707–1783) introduced the use of *i* for the imaginary unit.

### Check Your Understanding

7. **Make use of structure.** Rewrite the imaginary number $4i$ as the square root of a negative number. Explain how you determined your answer.

8. Simplify each of these expressions: $-\sqrt{20}$ and $\sqrt{-20}$. Are the expressions equivalent? Explain.

9. Write each number in terms of $i$.

   **a.** $\sqrt{-98}$          **b.** $-\sqrt{-27}$

   **c.** $\sqrt{(-8)(3)}$          **d.** $\sqrt{25 - 4(2)(6)}$

10. Why do you think imaginary numbers are useful for mathematicians?

11. Write the solutions to Cardano's problem, $x = 5 + \sqrt{-15}$ and $x = 5 - \sqrt{-15}$, using the imaginary unit $i$.

**My Notes**

The set of complex numbers consists of the real numbers and the imaginary numbers. A **complex number** has two parts: the real part $a$ and the imaginary part $bi$. For example, in $2 + 3i$, the real part is 2 and the imaginary part is $3i$.

## Check Your Understanding

**12.** Identify the real part and the imaginary part of each complex number.

   **a.** $5 + 8i$                  **b.** $8$

   **c.** $i\sqrt{10}$                **d.** $\dfrac{5 + 3i}{2}$

**13.** Using the definition of complex numbers, show that the set of real numbers is a subset of the complex numbers.

**14.** Using the definition of complex numbers, show that the set of imaginary numbers is a subset of the complex numbers.

Complex numbers in the form $a + bi$ can be represented geometrically as points in the *complex plane*. The complex plane is a rectangular grid, similar to the Cartesian plane, with the horizontal axis representing the real part $a$ of a complex number and the vertical axis representing the imaginary part $bi$ of a complex number. The point $(a, b)$ on the complex plane represents the complex number $a + bi$.

### Example B

Point $A$ represents $0 + 4i$.

Point $B$ represents $-3 + 2i$.

Point $C$ represents $1 - 4i$.

Point $D$ represents $3 + 0i$.

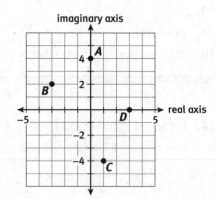

### Try These B

**a.** Graph $2 + 3i$ and $-3 - 4i$ on the complex plane above.

Graph each complex number on a complex plane grid.

   **b.** $2 + 5i$    **c.** $4 - 3i$    **d.** $-1 + 3i$    **e.** $-2i$    **f.** $-5$

**My Notes**

## Check Your Understanding

15. **Reason abstractly.** Compare and contrast the Cartesian plane with the complex plane.

16. What set of numbers do the points on the real axis of the complex plane represent? Explain.

17. Name the complex number represented by each labeled point on the complex plane below.

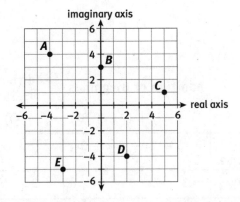

## LESSON 8-1 PRACTICE

18. Write each expression in terms of *i*.
    a. $\sqrt{-49}$
    b. $\sqrt{-13}$
    c. $3 + \sqrt{-8}$
    d. $5 - \sqrt{-36}$

19. Identify the real part and the imaginary part of the complex number $16 - i\sqrt{6}$.

20. **Reason quantitatively.** Is π a complex number? Explain.

21. Draw the complex plane. Then graph each complex number on the plane.
    a. $6i$
    b. $3 + 4i$
    c. $-2 - 5i$
    d. $4 - i$
    e. $-3 + 2i$

22. The sum of two numbers is 8, and their product is 80.
    a. Let *x* represent one of the numbers, and write an expression for the other number in terms of *x*. Use the expressions to write an equation that models the situation given above.
    b. Use the Quadratic Formula to solve the equation. Write the solutions in terms of *i*.

**MATH TIP**

π is the ratio of a circle's circumference to its diameter. π is an irrational number, and its decimal form neither terminates nor repeats.

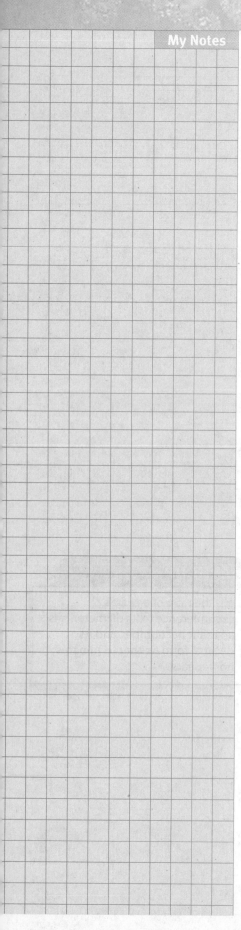

## Learning Targets:
- Add and subtract complex numbers.
- Multiply and divide complex numbers.

**SUGGESTED LEARNING STRATEGIES:** Group Presentation, Self Revision/Peer Revision, Look for a Pattern, Quickwrite

Perform addition of complex numbers as you would for addition of binomials of the form $a + bx$. To add such binomials, you collect like terms.

### Example A

|  |  | Addition of Binomials | Addition of Complex Numbers |
|---|---|---|---|
|  |  | $(5 + 4x) + (-2 + 3x)$ | $(5 + 4i) + (-2 + 3i)$ |
| **Step 1** | Collect like terms. | $= (5 - 2) + (4x + 3x)$ | $= (5 - 2) + (4i + 3i)$ |
| **Step 2** | Simplify. | $= 3 + 7x$ | $= 3 + 7i$ |

### Try These A
Add the complex numbers.

**a.** $(6 + 5i) + (4 - 7i)$

**b.** $(-5 + 3i) + (-3 - i)$

**c.** $(2 + 3i) + (-2 - 3i)$

1. **Express regularity in repeated reasoning.** Use Example A above and your knowledge of operations of real numbers to write general formulas for the sum and difference of two complex numbers.

   $(a + bi) + (c + di) =$

   $(a + bi) - (c + di) =$

2. Find each sum or difference of the complex numbers.
   **a.** $(12 - 13i) - (-5 + 4i)$

   **b.** $\left(\dfrac{1}{2} - i\right) + \left(\dfrac{5}{2} + 9i\right)$

   **c.** $(\sqrt{2} - 7i) + (2 + i\sqrt{3})$

   **d.** $(8 - 5i) - (3 + 5i) + (-5 + 10i)$

### Check Your Understanding

3. Recall that the sum of a number and its additive inverse is equal to 0. What is the additive inverse of the complex number $3 - 5i$? Explain how you determined your answer.

4. **Reason abstractly.** Is addition of complex numbers commutative? In other words, is $(a + bi) + (c + di)$ equal to $(c + di) + (a + bi)$? Explain your reasoning.

5. Give an example of a complex number you could subtract from $8 + 3i$ that would result in a real number. Show that the difference of the complex numbers is equal to a real number.

Perform multiplication of complex numbers as you would for multiplication of binomials of the form $a + bx$. The only change in procedure is to substitute $i^2$ with $-1$.

### Example B

**Multiply Binomials**

$(2 + 3x)(4 - 5x)$

$2(4) + 2(-5x) + 3x(4) + 3x(-5x)$

$8 - 10x + 12x - 15x^2$

$8 + 2x - 15x^2$

**Multiply Complex Numbers**

$(2 + 3i)(4 - 5i)$

$2(4) + 2(-5i) + 3i(4) + 3i(-5i)$

$8 - 10i + 12i - 15i^2$

$8 + 2i - 15i^2$

Now substitute $-1$ for $i^2$.

$8 + 2i - 15i^2 = 8 + 2i - 15(-1)$

$\qquad\qquad\qquad = 23 + 2i$

### Try These B

Multiply the complex numbers.
**a.** $(6 + 5i)(4 - 7i)$

**b.** $(2 - 3i)(3 - 2i)$

**c.** $(5 + i)(5 + i)$

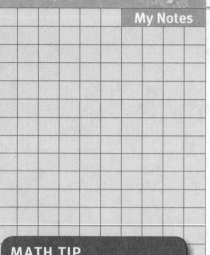

**My Notes**

6. **Express regularity in repeated reasoning.** Use Example B and your knowledge of operations of real numbers to write a general formula for the multiplication of two complex numbers.

   $(a + bi) \cdot (c + di) =$

7. Use operations of complex numbers to verify that the two solutions that Cardano found, $x = 5 + \sqrt{-15}$ and $x = 5 - \sqrt{-15}$, have a sum of 10 and a product of 40.

**MATH TIP**

Since $i = \sqrt{-1}$, the powers of $i$ can be evaluated as follows:

$i^1 = i$
$i^2 = -1$
$i^3 = i^2 \cdot i = -1i = -i$
$i^4 = i^2 \cdot i^2 = (-1)^2 = 1$

Since $i^4 = 1$, further powers repeat the pattern shown above.

$i^5 = i^4 \cdot i = i$
$i^6 = i^4 \cdot i^2 = i^2 = -1$
$i^7 = i^4 \cdot i^3 = i^3 = -i$
$i^8 = i^4 \cdot i^4 = i^4 = 1$

**Check Your Understanding**

8. Find each product.
   a. $(5 + 3i)(5 - 3i)$        b. $(-6 - 4i)(-6 + 4i)$
   c. $(8 + i)(8 - i)$

9. What patterns do you observe in the products in Item 8?

10. Explain how the product of two complex numbers can be a real number, even though both factors are not real numbers.

11. **Critique the reasoning of others.** A student claims that the product of any two imaginary numbers is a real number. Is the student correct? Explain your reasoning.

## Lesson 8-2
**Operations with Complex Numbers**

The ***complex conjugate*** of $a + bi$ is defined as $a - bi$. For example, the complex conjugate of $2 + 3i$ is $2 - 3i$.

**12.** A special property of multiplication of complex numbers occurs when a number is multiplied by its conjugate. Multiply each number by its conjugate and then describe the product when a number is multiplied by its conjugate.

**a.** $2 - 9i$

**b.** $-5 + 2i$

**13.** Write an expression to complete the general formula for the product of a complex number and its complex conjugate.

$$(a + bi)(a - bi) =$$

To divide two complex numbers, start by multiplying both the dividend and the divisor by the conjugate of the divisor. This step results in a divisor that is a real number.

### Example C

Divide $\dfrac{4 - 5i}{2 + 3i}$.

**Step 1:** Multiply the numerator and denominator by the complex conjugate of the divisor.
$$\frac{4 - 5i}{2 + 3i} = \frac{4 - 5i}{2 + 3i} \cdot \frac{(2 - 3i)}{(2 - 3i)}$$

**Step 2:** Simplify and substitute $-1$ for $i^2$.
$$= \frac{8 - 22i + 15i^2}{4 - 6i + 6i - 9i^2}$$
$$= \frac{8 - 22i - 15}{4 + 9}$$

**Step 3:** Simplify and write in the form $a + bi$.
$$= \frac{-7 - 22i}{13} = -\frac{7}{13} - \frac{22}{13}i$$

**Solution:** $\dfrac{4 - 5i}{2 + 3i} = -\dfrac{7}{13} - \dfrac{22}{13}i$

**MATH TERMS**

The **complex conjugate** of a complex number $a + bi$ is $a - bi$.

**My Notes**

## Try These C

**a.** In Example C, why is the quotient $-\dfrac{7}{13} - \dfrac{22}{13}i$ equivalent to the original expression $\dfrac{4 - 5i}{2 + 3i}$?

Divide the complex numbers. Write your answers on notebook paper. Show your work.

**b.** $\dfrac{5i}{2 + 3i}$

**c.** $\dfrac{5 + 2i}{3 - 4i}$

**d.** $\dfrac{1 - i}{\sqrt{3} + 4i}$

**14. Express regularity in repeated reasoning.** Use Example C and your knowledge of operations of real numbers to write a general formula for the division of two complex numbers.

$$\frac{(a + bi)}{(c + di)} =$$

## Check Your Understanding

**15.** Make a conjecture about the quotient of two imaginary numbers where the divisor is not equal to $0i$. Is the quotient real, imaginary, or neither? Give an example to support your conjecture.

**16.** Make a conjecture about the quotient of a real number divided by an imaginary number not equal to $0i$. Is the quotient real, imaginary, or neither? Give an example to support your conjecture.

**17.** Which of the following is equal to $i^{-1}$?

    **A.** 1      **B.** $-1$      **C.** $i$      **D.** $-i$

**18.** Explain your reasoning for choosing your answer to Item 17.

**MATH TIP**

For Item 17, $n^{-1} = \dfrac{1}{n}$ for $n \neq 0$.

So, $i^{-1} = \dfrac{1}{i}$.

My Notes

## LESSON 8-2 PRACTICE

19. Find each sum or difference.
    a. $(6 - 5i) + (-2 + 6i)$   b. $(4 + i) + (-4 + i)$

    c. $(5 - 3i) - (3 - 5i)$   d. $(-3 + 8i) - \left(\frac{3}{2} + \frac{1}{2}i\right)$

20. Multiply. Write each product in the form $a + bi$.
    a. $(2 + 9i)(3 - i)$        b. $(-5 + 8i)(2 - i)$

    c. $(8 + 15i)(8 - 15i)$     d. $(8 - 4i)(5i)$

21. Divide. Write each quotient in the form $a + bi$.

    a. $\dfrac{1 + 4i}{4 - i}$          b. $\dfrac{-2 + 5i}{3 - 4i}$          c. $\dfrac{7 - 3i}{i}$

22. Use substitution to show that the solutions of the equation $x^2 - 4x + 20 = 0$ are $x = 2 + 4i$ and $x = 2 - 4i$.

23. **Make use of structure.** What is the sum of any complex number $a + bi$ and its complex conjugate?

24. Explain how to use the Commutative, Associative, and Distributive Properties to add the complex numbers $5 + 8i$ and $6 + 2i$.

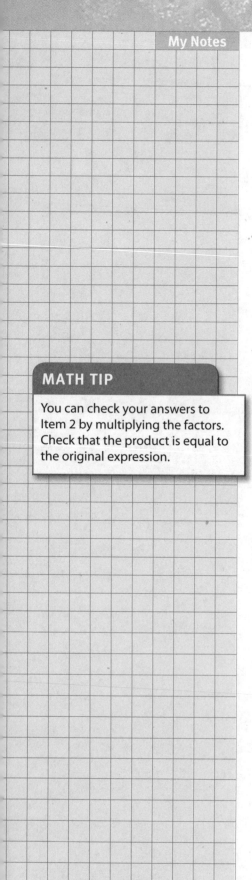

**Learning Targets:**
- Factor quadratic expressions using complex conjugates.
- Solve quadratic equations with complex roots by factoring.

**SUGGESTED LEARNING STRATEGIES:** Discussion Groups, Look for a Pattern, Quickwrite, Self Revision/Peer Revision, Paraphrasing

1. Look back at your answer to Item 13 in the previous lesson.
   **a.** Given your answer, what are the factors of the expression $a^2 + b^2$? Justify your answer.

   **b.** What is the relationship between the factors of $a^2 + b^2$?

You can use complex conjugates to factor quadratic expressions that can be written in the form $a^2 + b^2$. In other words, you can use complex conjugates to factor the sum of two squares.

2. **Express regularity in repeated reasoning.** Use complex conjugates to factor each expression.
   **a.** $16x^2 + 25$

   **b.** $36x^2 + 100y^2$

   **c.** $2x^2 + 8y^2$

   **d.** $3x^2 + 20y^2$

**MATH TIP**

You can check your answers to Item 2 by multiplying the factors. Check that the product is equal to the original expression.

### Check Your Understanding

3. Explain how to factor the expression $81x^2 + 64$.

4. Compare and contrast factoring an expression of the form $a^2 - b^2$ and an expression of the form $a^2 + b^2$.

5. **Critique the reasoning of others.** A student incorrectly claims that the factored form of the expression $4x^2 + 5$ is $(4x + 5i)(4x - 5i)$.
   a. Describe the error that the student made.
   b. How could the student have determined that his or her answer is incorrect?
   c. What is the correct factored form of the expression?

You can solve some quadratic equations with complex solutions by factoring.

### Example A
Solve $9x^2 + 16 = 0$ by factoring.

Original equation $\qquad\qquad 9x^2 + 16 = 0$

**Step 1:** Factor the left side. $\qquad (3x + 4i)(3x - 4i) = 0$

**Step 2:** Apply the Zero Product Property. $\quad 3x + 4i = 0$ or $3x - 4i = 0$

**Step 3:** Solve each equation for $x$.

**Solution:** $x = -\frac{4}{3}i$ or $x = \frac{4}{3}i$

### Try These A
a. Solve $x^2 + 81 = 0$ and check by substitution.

| | |
|---|---|
| | Original equation |
| | Factor the left side. |
| | Apply the Zero Product Property. |
| | Solve each equation for $x$. |

Solve each equation by factoring. Show your work.

b. $100x^2 + 49 = 0$ $\qquad$ c. $25x^2 = -4$

d. $2x^2 + 36 = 0$ $\qquad$ e. $4x^2 = -45$

### Check Your Understanding

**6.** Tell whether each equation has real solutions or imaginary solutions and explain your answer.
   **a.** $x^2 - 144 = 0$                  **b.** $x^2 + 144 = 0$

**7. a.** What are the solutions of a quadratic equation that can be written in the form $a^2x^2 + b^2 = 0$, where $a$ and $b$ are real numbers and $a \neq 0$? Show how you determined the solutions.
   **b.** What is the relationship between the solutions of a quadratic equation that can be written in the form $a^2x^2 + b^2 = 0$?

**8.** Explain how you could find the solutions of the quadratic function $f(x) = x^2 + 225$ when $f(x) = 0$.

### LESSON 8-3 PRACTICE

Use complex conjugates to factor each expression.

**9.** $3x^2 + 12$                        **10.** $5x^2 + 80y^2$

**11.** $9x^2 + 11$                        **12.** $2x^2 + 63y^2$

Solve each equation by factoring.

**13.** $2x^2 + 50 = 0$                    **14.** $3x^2 = -54$

**15.** $4x^2 + 75 = 0$                    **16.** $32x^2 = -98$

**17. Reason quantitatively.** Solve the equations $9x^2 - 64 = 0$ and $9x^2 + 64 = 0$ by factoring. Then describe the relationship between the solutions of $9x^2 - 64 = 0$ and the solutions of $9x^2 + 64 = 0$.

## ACTIVITY 8 PRACTICE
Write your answers on notebook paper. Show your work.

### Lesson 8-1

1. Write each expression in terms of $i$.
   a. $\sqrt{-64}$
   b. $\sqrt{-31}$
   c. $-7 + \sqrt{-12}$
   d. $5 - \sqrt{-50}$

2. Which expression is equivalent to $5i$?
   A. $\sqrt{-5}$        B. $-\sqrt{5}$
   C. $\sqrt{-25}$       D. $-\sqrt{25}$

3. Use the Quadratic Formula to solve each equation.
   a. $x^2 + 5x + 9 = 0$
   b. $2x^2 - 4x + 5 = 0$

4. The sum of two numbers is 12, and their product is 100.
   a. Let $x$ represent one of the numbers. Write an expression for the other number in terms of $x$. Use the expressions to write an equation that models the situation given above.
   b. Use the Quadratic Formula to solve the equation. Write the solutions in terms of $i$.

5. Explain why each of the following is a complex number, and identify its real part and its imaginary part.
   a. $5 + 3i$        b. $\sqrt{2} - i$
   c. $-14i$          d. $\dfrac{3}{4}$

6. Draw the complex plane on grid paper. Then graph each complex number on the plane.
   a. $-4i$           b. $6 + 2i$
   c. $-3 - 4i$       d. $3 - 5i$
   e. $-2 + 5i$

7. What complex number does the ordered pair $(5, -3)$ represent on the complex plane? Explain.

8. Name the complex number represented by each labeled point on the complex plane below.

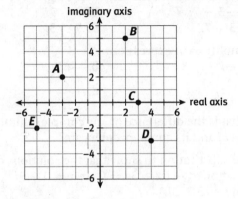

### Lesson 8-2

9. Find each sum or difference.
   a. $(5 - 6i) + (-3 + 9i)$
   b. $(2 + 5i) + (-5 + 3i)$
   c. $(9 - 2i) - (1 + 6i)$
   d. $(-5 + 4i) - \left(\dfrac{7}{3} + \dfrac{1}{6}i\right)$

10. Find each product, and write it in the form $a + bi$.
    a. $(1 + 4i)(5 - 2i)$
    b. $(-2 + 3i)(3 - 2i)$
    c. $(7 + 24i)(7 - 24i)$
    d. $(8 - 3i)(4 - 2i)$

11. Find each quotient, and write it in the form $a + bi$.
    a. $\dfrac{3 + 2i}{5 - 2i}$        b. $\dfrac{-1 + i}{5 - 2i}$
    c. $\dfrac{10 - 2i}{5i}$           d. $\dfrac{3 + i}{3 - i}$

12. Explain how to use the Commutative, Associative, and Distributive Properties to perform each operation.
    a. Subtract $(3 + 4i)$ from $(8 + 5i)$.
    b. Multiply $(-2 + 3i)$ and $(4 - 6i)$.

13. Give an example of a complex number you could add to $4 - 8i$ that would result in an imaginary number. Show that the sum of the complex numbers is equal to an imaginary number.

14. What is the complex conjugate of $-3 + 7i$?
    **A.** $-3 - 7i$      **B.** $3 - 7i$
    **C.** $3 + 7i$      **D.** $7 - 3i$

15. Simplify each expression.
    **a.** $-i^2$      **b.** $-6i^4$
    **c.** $(2i)^3$      **d.** $\left(\dfrac{3}{2i^3}\right)^2$

16. What is the difference of any complex number $a + bi$ and its complex conjugate?

17. Use substitution to show that the solutions of the equation $x^2 - 6x + 34 = 0$ are $x = 3 + 5i$ and $x = 3 - 5i$.

18. **a.** Graph the complex number $4 + 2i$ on a complex plane.
    **b.** Multiply $4 + 2i$ by $i$, and graph the result.
    **c.** Multiply the result from part b by $i$, and graph the result.
    **d.** Multiply the result from part c by $i$, and graph the result.
    **e.** Describe any patterns you see in the complex numbers you graphed.
    **f.** What happens when you multiply a complex number $a + bi$ by $i$?

**Lesson 8-3**

19. Use complex conjugates to factor each expression.
    **a.** $x^2 + 121$      **b.** $2x^2 + 128y^2$
    **c.** $4x^2 + 60y^2$      **d.** $9x^2 + 140y^2$

20. Explain how to solve the equation $2x^2 + 100 = 0$ by factoring.

21. Solve each equation by factoring.
    **a.** $x^2 + 64 = 0$      **b.** $x^2 = -120$
    **c.** $4x^2 + 169 = 0$      **d.** $25x^2 = -48$

22. Which equation has solutions of $x = -\dfrac{2}{3}i$ and $x = \dfrac{2}{3}i$?
    **A.** $3x^2 - 2 = 0$      **B.** $3x^2 + 2 = 0$
    **C.** $9x^2 - 4 = 0$      **D.** $9x^2 + 4 = 0$

23. What are the solutions of each quadratic function?
    **a.** $f(x) = x^2 + 1$
    **b.** $f(x) = 25x^2 + 36$

24. Without solving the equation, explain how you know that $x^2 + 48 = 0$ has imaginary solutions.

**MATHEMATICAL PRACTICES**
**Look for and Express Regularity in Repeated Reasoning**

25. Find the square of each complex number.
    **a.** $(4 + 5i)$
    **b.** $(2 + 3i)$
    **c.** $(4 - 2i)$
    **d.** Use parts a–c and your knowledge of operations of real numbers to write a general formula for the square of a complex number $(a + bi)$.

# Solving $ax^2 + bx + c = 0$
## Deriving the Quadratic Formula
## Lesson 9-1 Completing the Square and Taking Square Roots

**Learning Targets:**
- Solve quadratic equations by taking square roots.
- Solve quadratic equations $ax^2 + bx + c = 0$ by completing the square.

> **SUGGESTED LEARNING STRATEGIES:** Marking the Text, Group Presentation, Quickwrite, Create Representations

To solve equations of the form $ax^2 + c = 0$, isolate $x^2$ and take the square root of both sides of the equation.

**MATH TIP**

When taking the square root of both sides of an equation, include both positive and negative roots. For example,
$$x^2 = 4$$
$$x = \pm\sqrt{4}$$
$$x = \pm 2$$

### Example A

Solve $5x^2 - 23 = 0$ for $x$.

$$5x^2 - 23 = 0$$

**Step 1:** Add 23 to both sides.     $5x^2 = 23$

**Step 2:** Divide both sides by 5.     $\dfrac{5x^2}{5} = \dfrac{23}{5}$

**Step 3:** Simplify to isolate $x^2$.     $x^2 = \dfrac{23}{5}$

**Step 4:** Take the square root of both sides.     $x = \pm\dfrac{\sqrt{23}}{\sqrt{5}}$

**Step 5:** Rationalize the denominator.     $x = \pm\dfrac{\sqrt{23}}{\sqrt{5}} \cdot \dfrac{\sqrt{5}}{\sqrt{5}}$

**Step 6:** Simplify.     $x = \pm\dfrac{\sqrt{115}}{5}$

**Solution:** $x = \pm\dfrac{\sqrt{115}}{5}$

**MATH TIP**

To rewrite an expression so that there are no radicals in the denominator, you must *rationalize the denominator* by multiplying both the numerator and denominator by the radical.

Example:

$$\frac{7}{\sqrt{3}} = \frac{7}{\sqrt{3}} \cdot \frac{\sqrt{3}}{\sqrt{3}} = \frac{7\sqrt{3}}{3}$$

### Try These A

**Make use of structure.** Solve for $x$. Show your work.

**a.** $9x^2 - 49 = 0$     **b.** $25x^2 - 7 = 0$

**c.** $5x^2 - 16 = 0$     **d.** $4x^2 + 15 = 0$

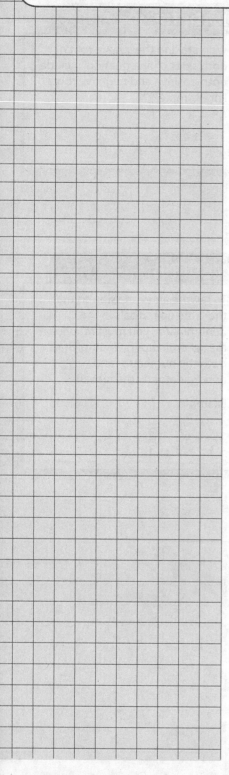

**My Notes**

**CONNECT TO AP**

In calculus, *rationalizing a numerator* is a skill used to evaluate certain types of limit expressions.

1. Compare and contrast the solutions to the equations in Try These A.

To solve the equation $2(x - 3)^2 - 5 = 0$, you can use a similar process.

**Example B**

Solve $2(x - 3)^2 - 5 = 0$ for $x$.

$$2(x - 3)^2 - 5 = 0$$

**Step 1:** Add 5 to both sides. $\qquad 2(x - 3)^2 = 5$

**Step 2:** Divide both sides by 2. $\qquad (x - 3)^2 = \dfrac{5}{2}$

**Step 3:** Take the square root of both sides. $\qquad x - 3 = \pm \dfrac{\sqrt{5}}{\sqrt{2}}$

**Step 4:** Rationalize the denominator and solve for $x$. $\qquad x - 3 = \pm \dfrac{\sqrt{10}}{2}$

**Solution:** $x = 3 \pm \dfrac{\sqrt{10}}{2}$

**Try These B**

Solve for $x$. Show your work.

**a.** $4(x + 5)^2 - 49 = 0$ $\qquad\qquad$ **b.** $3(x - 2)^2 - 16 = 0$

**c.** $5(x + 1)^2 - 8 = 0$ $\qquad\qquad$ **d.** $4(x + 7)^2 + 25 = 0$

2. **Reason quantitatively.** Describe the differences among the solutions to the equations in Try These B.

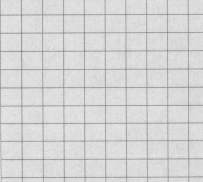

### Check Your Understanding

3. Use Example A to help you write a general formula for the solutions of the equation $ax^2 - c = 0$, where $a$ and $c$ are both positive.

4. Is the equation solved in Example B a quadratic equation? Explain.

5. Solve the equation $-2(x + 4)^2 + 3 = 0$, and explain each of your steps.

6. **a.** Solve the equation $3(x - 5)^2 = 0$.
   **b. Make use of structure.** Explain why the equation has only one solution and not two solutions.

The standard form of a quadratic equation is $ax^2 + bx + c = 0$. You can solve equations written in standard form by *completing the square*.

> **MATH TERMS**
>
> **Completing the square** is the process of adding a constant to a quadratic expression to transform it into a perfect square trinomial.

### Example C
Solve $2x^2 + 12x + 5 = 0$ by completing the square.

$$2x^2 + 12x + 5 = 0$$

**Step 1:** Divide both sides by the leading coefficient and simplify.

$$\frac{2x^2}{2} + \frac{12x}{2} + \frac{5}{2} = \frac{0}{2}$$

$$x^2 + 6x + \frac{5}{2} = 0$$

**Step 2:** Isolate the variable terms on the left side.

$$x^2 + 6x = -\frac{5}{2}$$

**Step 3:** Divide the coefficient of the linear term by 2 $[6 \div 2 = 3]$, square the result $[3^2 = 9]$, and add it $[9]$ to both sides. This completes the square.

$$x^2 + 6x + \boxed{\phantom{9}} = -\frac{5}{2} + \boxed{\phantom{9}}$$

$$x^2 + 6x + \boxed{9} = -\frac{5}{2} + \boxed{9}$$

> **MATH TIP**
>
> You can factor a perfect square trinomial $x^2 + 2xy + y^2$ as $(x + y)^2$.

**Step 4:** Factor the perfect square trinomial on the left side into two binomials.

$$(x + 3)^2 = \frac{13}{2}$$

**Step 5:** Take the square root of both sides of the equation.

$$x + 3 = \pm\sqrt{\frac{13}{2}}$$

**Step 6:** Rationalize the denominator and solve for $x$.

$$x + 3 = \pm\frac{\sqrt{13}}{\sqrt{2}} \cdot \frac{\sqrt{2}}{\sqrt{2}} = \pm\frac{\sqrt{26}}{2}$$

**Solution:** $x = -3 \pm \dfrac{\sqrt{26}}{2}$

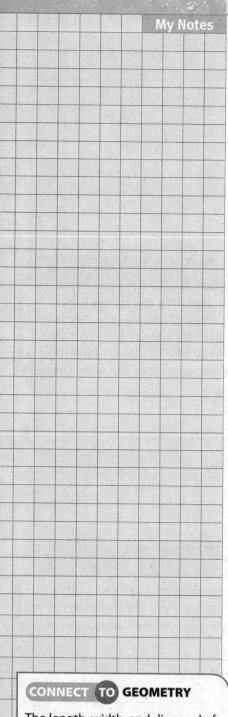

**My Notes**

### Try These C
Solve for $x$ by completing the square.

**a.** $4x^2 + 16x - 5 = 0$      **b.** $5x^2 - 30x - 3 = 0$

**c.** $2x^2 - 6x - 1 = 0$      **d.** $2x^2 - 4x + 7 = 0$

### Check Your Understanding

**7.** Explain how to complete the square for the quadratic expression $x^2 + 8x$.

**8.** How does completing the square help you solve a quadratic equation?

**9.** **Construct viable arguments.** Which method would you use to solve the quadratic equation $x^2 + x - 12 = 0$: factoring or completing the square? Justify your choice.

### LESSON 9-1 PRACTICE

**10.** Use the method for completing the square to make a perfect square trinomial. Then factor the perfect square trinomial.
     **a.** $x^2 + 10x$      **b.** $x^2 - 7x$

**11.** Solve each quadratic equation by taking the square root of both sides of the equation. Identify the solutions as rational, irrational, or complex conjugates.
     **a.** $9x^2 - 64 = 0$      **b.** $5x^2 - 12 = 0$
     **c.** $16(x - 2)^2 - 25 = 0$      **d.** $2(x - 3)^2 - 15 = 0$
     **e.** $4x^2 + 49 = 0$      **f.** $3(x - 1)^2 + 10 = 0$

**12.** Solve by completing the square.
     **a.** $x^2 - 4x - 12 = 0$      **b.** $2x^2 - 5x - 3 = 0$
     **c.** $x^2 + 6x - 2 = 0$      **d.** $3x^2 + 9x + 2 = 0$
     **e.** $x^2 - x + 5 = 0$      **f.** $5x^2 + 2x + 3 = 0$

**13.** The diagonal of a rectangular television screen measures 42 in. The ratio of the length to the width of the screen is $\frac{16}{9}$.

     **a.** **Model with mathematics.** Write an equation that can be used to determine the length $l$ in inches of the television screen.
     **b.** Solve the equation, and interpret the solutions.
     **c.** What are the length and width of the television screen, to the nearest half-inch?

**CONNECT TO GEOMETRY**

The length, width, and diagonal of the television screen form a right triangle.

## Learning Targets:

- Derive the Quadratic Formula.
- Solve quadratic equations using the Quadratic Formula.

> **SUGGESTED LEARNING STRATEGIES:** Create Representations, Discussion Groups, Self Revision/Peer Revision, Think-Pair-Share, Quickwrite

Previously you learned that solutions to the general quadratic equation $ax^2 + bx + c = 0$ can be found using the Quadratic Formula:

$$x = \frac{-b \pm \sqrt{b^2 - 4ac}}{2a}, \text{ where } a \neq 0$$

You can ***derive*** the quadratic formula by completing the square on the general quadratic equation.

1. **Reason abstractly and quantitatively.** Derive the quadratic formula by completing the square for the equation $ax^2 + bx + c = 0$. (Use Example C from Lesson 9-1 as a model.)

**ACADEMIC VOCABULARY**

When you ***derive*** a formula, you use logical reasoning to show that the formula is correct. In this case, you will derive the Quadratic Formula by solving the standard form of a quadratic equation, $ax^2 + bx + c = 0$, for $x$.

**My Notes**

My Notes

**ACADEMIC VOCABULARY**

When you *verify* a solution, you check that it is correct.

**2.** Solve $2x^2 - 5x + 3 = 0$ by completing the square. Then *verify* that the solution is correct by solving the same equation using the Quadratic Formula.

## Check Your Understanding

**3.** In Item 1, why do you need to add $\left(\dfrac{b}{2a}\right)^2$ to both sides?

**4.** Derive a formula for solving a quadratic equation of the form $ax^2 + bx = 0$, where $a \neq 0$.

**5.** **Construct viable arguments.** Which method did you prefer for solving the quadratic equation in Item 2: completing the square or using the Quadratic Formula? Justify your choice.

**6.** Consider the equation $x^2 - 6x + 7 = 0$.
   **a.** Solve the equation by using the Quadratic Formula.
   **b.** Could you have solved the equation by factoring? Explain.

**My Notes**

# LESSON 9-2 PRACTICE

7. Solve each equation by using the Quadratic Formula.
   a. $2x^2 + 4x - 5 = 0$
   b. $3x^2 + 7x + 10 = 0$
   c. $x^2 - 9x - 1 = 0$
   d. $-4x^2 + 5x + 8 = 0$
   e. $2x^2 - 3 = 7x$
   f. $4x^2 + 3x = -6$

8. Solve each quadratic equation by using any of the methods you have learned. For each equation, tell which method you used and why you chose that method.
   a. $x^2 + 6x + 9 = 0$
   b. $8x^2 + 5x - 6 = 0$
   c. $(x + 4)^2 - 36 = 0$
   d. $x^2 + 2x = 7$

9. a. **Reason abstractly.** Under what circumstances will the radicand in the Quadratic Formula, $x = \dfrac{-b \pm \sqrt{b^2 - 4ac}}{2a}$, be negative?

   b. If the radicand is negative, what does this tell you about the solutions of the quadratic equation? Explain.

10. A player shoots a basketball from a height of 7 ft with an initial vertical velocity of 18 ft/s. The equation $-16t^2 + 18t + 7 = 10$ can be used to determine the time $t$ in seconds at which the ball will have a height of 10 ft—the same height as the basket.
    a. Solve the equation by using the Quadratic Formula.
    b. **Attend to precision.** To the nearest tenth of a second, when will the ball have a height of 10 ft?
    c. Explain how you can check that your answers to part b are reasonable.

> **MATH TIP**
>
> A *radicand* is an expression under a radical symbol. For $\sqrt{b^2 - 4ac}$, the radicand is $b^2 - 4ac$.

> **CONNECT** TO **PHYSICS**
>
> The function $h(t) = -16t^2 + v_0t + h_0$ can be used to model the height $h$ in feet of a thrown object $t$ seconds after it is thrown, where $v_0$ is the initial vertical velocity of the object in ft/s and $h_0$ is the initial height of the object in feet.

**MATH TIP**

The complex numbers include the real numbers, so real solutions are also complex solutions. However, when asked to classify solutions as real or complex, you can assume that "complex" does not include the reals.

**Learning Targets:**

- Solve quadratic equations using the Quadratic Formula.
- Use the discriminant to determine the nature of the solutions of a quadratic equation.

**SUGGESTED LEARNING STRATEGIES:** Look for a Pattern, Group Presentation, Self Revision/Peer Revision, Think-Pair-Share, Quickwrite

1. Solve each equation by using the Quadratic Formula. For each equation, write the number of solutions. Tell whether the solutions are real or complex, and, if real, whether the solutions are rational or irrational.

   a. $4x^2 + 5x - 6 = 0$

   solutions:

   number of solutions:

   real or complex:

   rational or irrational:

   b. $4x^2 + 5x - 2 = 0$

   solutions:

   number of solutions:

   real or complex:

   rational or irrational:

   c. $4x^2 + 4x + 1 = 0$

   solutions:

   number of solutions:

   real or complex:

   rational or irrational:

   d. $4x^2 + 4x + 5 = 0$

   solutions:

   number of solutions:

   real or complex:

   rational or irrational:

2. **Express regularity in repeated reasoning.** What patterns can you identify from your responses to Item 1?

## Check Your Understanding

3. **a.** In Item 1, was the expression under the square root symbol of the Quadratic Formula positive, negative, or zero when there were two real solutions?
   **b.** What about when there was one real solution?
   **c.** What about when there were two complex solutions?

4. In Item 1, how did you determine whether the real solutions of a quadratic equation were rational or irrational?

5. **Reason quantitatively.** The quadratic function related to the equation in Item 1a is $f(x) = 4x^2 + 5x - 6$. Without graphing the function, determine how many $x$-intercepts it has and what their values are. Explain how you determined your answer.

6. Make a conjecture about the relationship between the solutions of a quadratic equation that has complex roots.

**MATH TERMS**

The **discriminant** is the expression $b^2 - 4ac$ under the radical sign in the Quadratic Formula.

**MATH TERMS**

A solution to an equation is also called a **root** of the equation.

The roots of a quadratic equation $ax^2 + bx + c = 0$ represent the **zeros** (or $x$-intercepts) of the quadratic function $y = ax^2 + bx + c$.

**MATH TIP**

If the values of $a$, $b$, and $c$ are integers and the discriminant $b^2 - 4ac$ is a perfect square, then the quadratic expression $ax^2 + bx + c$ is factorable over the integers.

The **discriminant** of a quadratic equation $ax^2 + bx + c = 0$ is defined as the expression $b^2 - 4ac$. The value of the discriminant determines the *nature of the solutions* of a quadratic equation in the following manner.

| Discriminant | Nature of Solutions |
|---|---|
| $b^2 - 4ac > 0$ and $b^2 - 4ac$ is a perfect square | Two real, rational solutions |
| $b^2 - 4ac > 0$ and $b^2 - 4ac$ is *not* a perfect square | Two real, irrational solutions |
| $b^2 - 4ac = 0$ | One real, rational solution (a double **root**) |
| $b^2 - 4ac < 0$ | Two complex conjugate solutions |

7. Compute the value of the discriminant for each equation in Item 1 to determine the number and nature of the solutions.
   **a.** $4x^2 + 5x - 6 = 0$

   **b.** $4x^2 + 5x - 2 = 0$

   **c.** $4x^2 + 4x + 1 = 0$

   **d.** $4x^2 + 4x + 5 = 0$

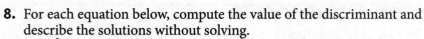

**My Notes**

8. For each equation below, compute the value of the discriminant and describe the solutions without solving.
   a. $2x^2 + 5x + 12 = 0$

   b. $3x^2 - 11x + 4 = 0$

   c. $5x^2 + 3x - 2 = 0$

   d. $4x^2 - 12x + 9 = 0$

**Check Your Understanding**

9. **Critique the reasoning of others.** A student solves a quadratic equation and gets solutions of $x = -\dfrac{7}{3}$ and $x = 8$. To check the reasonableness of his answer, the student calculates the discriminant of the equation and finds it to be $-188$. Explain how the value of the discriminant shows that the student made a mistake when solving the equation.

10. One of the solutions of a quadratic equation is $x = 6 + 4i$. What is the other solution of the quadratic equation? Explain your answer.

11. The discriminant of a quadratic equation is 225. Are the roots of the equation rational or irrational? Explain.

12. Consider the quadratic equation $2x^2 + 5x + c = 0$.
    a. For what value(s) of $c$ does the equation have two real solutions?
    b. For what value(s) of $c$ does the equation have one real solution?
    c. For what value(s) of $c$ does the equation have two complex conjugate solutions?

## LESSON 9-3 PRACTICE

13. For each equation, evaluate the discriminant and determine the nature of the solutions. Then solve each equation using the Quadratic Formula to verify the nature of the roots.

   a. $x^2 + 5x - 6 = 0$      b. $2x^2 - 7x - 15 = 0$
   c. $x^2 - 8x + 16 = 0$      d. $5x^2 - 4x + 2 = 0$
   e. $2x^2 + 9x + 20 = 0$    f. $3x^2 - 5x - 1 = 0$

14. **Reason abstractly.** What is the discriminant? How does the value of the discriminant affect the solutions of a quadratic equation?

15. The discriminant of a quadratic equation is 1. What can you conclude about the solutions of the equation? Explain your reasoning.

16. Give an example of a quadratic equation that has two irrational solutions. Use the discriminant to show that the solutions of the equation are irrational.

17. **Make sense of problems.** A baseball player throws a ball from a height of 6 ft with an initial vertical velocity of 32 ft/s. The equation $-16t^2 + 32t + 6 = 25$ can be used to determine the time $t$ in seconds at which the ball will reach a height of 25 ft.
   a. Evaluate the discriminant of the equation.
   b. What does the discriminant tell you about whether the ball will reach a height of 25 ft?

**MATH TIP**

In Item 17, remember to write the equation in standard form before you evaluate the discriminant.

## ACTIVITY 9 PRACTICE

Write your answers on notebook paper.
Show your work.

### Lesson 9-1

For Items 1–8, solve each equation by taking the square root of both sides.

1. $4x^2 - 49 = 0$
2. $5x^2 = 36$
3. $9x^2 - 32 = 0$
4. $(x + 4)^2 - 25 = 0$
5. $3(x + 2)^2 = 15$
6. $-2(x - 4)^2 = 16$
7. $4(x - 8)^2 - 10 = 14$
8. $6(x + 3)^2 + 20 = 12$

9. Which of the following represents a formula that can be used to solve quadratic equations of the form $a(x - h)^2 + k = 0$, where $a \neq 0$?

   **A.** $x = -h \pm \sqrt{-\dfrac{k}{a}}$
   **B.** $x = -h \pm \sqrt{\dfrac{k}{a}}$

   **C.** $x = h \pm \sqrt{-\dfrac{k}{a}}$
   **D.** $x = h \pm \sqrt{\dfrac{k}{a}}$

10. A plane begins flying due east from an airport at the same time as a helicopter begins flying due north from the airport. After half an hour, the plane and helicopter are 260 mi apart, and the plane is five times the distance from the airport as the helicopter.

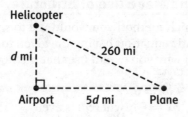

Helicopter

$d$ mi

260 mi

Airport    $5d$ mi    Plane

Not to scale

   **a.** Write an equation that can be used to determine $d$, the helicopter's distance in miles from the airport after half an hour.
   **b.** Solve the equation and interpret the solutions.
   **c.** What are the average speeds of the plane and the helicopter? Explain.

For Items 11–14, complete the square for each quadratic expression. Then factor the perfect square trinomial.

11. $x^2 + 10x$
12. $x^2 - 16x$
13. $x^2 + 9x$
14. $x^2 - x$

For Items 15–20, solve each equation by completing the square.

15. $x^2 + 2x + 5 = 0$
16. $x^2 - 10x = 26$
17. $x^2 + 5x - 9 = 0$
18. $2x^2 + 8x - 7 = 0$
19. $3x^2 - 15x = 20$
20. $6x^2 + 16x + 9 = 0$

### Lesson 9-2

For Items 21–28, solve each equation by using the Quadratic Formula.

21. $x^2 + 12x + 6 = 0$
22. $3x^2 - 5x + 3 = 0$
23. $2x^2 + 6x = 25$
24. $42x^2 + 11x - 20 = 0$
25. $x^2 + 6x + 8 = 4x - 3$
26. $10x^2 - 5x = 9x + 8$
27. $4x^2 + x - 12 = 3x^2 - 5x$
28. $x^2 - 20x = 6x^2 - 2x + 20$
29. Write a formula that represents the solutions of a quadratic equation of the form $mx^2 + nx + p = 0$. Explain how you arrived at your formula.
30. Derive a formula for solving a quadratic equation of the form $x^2 + bx + c = 0$.

For Items 31–36, solve each equation, using any method that you choose. For each equation, tell which method you used and why you chose that method.

**31.** $(x + 3)^2 - 25 = 0$

**32.** $2x^2 - 9x + 5 = 0$

**33.** $x^2 + 7x + 12 = 0$

**34.** $3x^2 + x - 14 = 0$

**35.** $x^2 + 8x = 7$

**36.** $4x^2 - 33 = 0$

**37.** The more concert tickets a customer buys, the less each individual ticket costs. The function $c(t) = -2t^2 + 82t + 5$ gives the total cost in dollars of buying $t$ tickets to the concert. Customers may buy no more than 15 tickets.
  **a.** Megan spent a total of $301 on concert tickets. Write a quadratic equation that can be used to determine the number of tickets Megan bought.
  **b.** Use the Quadratic Formula to solve the equation. Then interpret the solutions.
  **c.** What was the cost of each ticket Megan bought?

**Lesson 9-3**

For each equation, find the value of the discriminant and describe the nature of the solutions.

**38.** $2x^2 + 3x + 4 = 0$

**39.** $9x^2 + 30x + 25 = 0$

**40.** $6x^2 - 7x - 20 = 0$

**41.** $5x^2 + 12x - 7 = 0$

**42.** $x^2 - 8x = 18$

**43.** The discriminant of a quadratic equation is $-6$. What types of solutions does the equation have?
  **A.** 1 real solution
  **B.** 2 rational solutions
  **C.** 2 irrational solutions
  **D.** 2 complex conjugate solutions

**44.** Consider the quadratic equation $ax^2 - 6x + 3 = 0$, where $a \neq 0$.
  **a.** For what value(s) of $a$ does the equation have two real solutions?
  **b.** For what value(s) of $a$ does the equation have one real solution?
  **c.** For what value(s) of $a$ does the equation have two complex conjugate solutions?

**45.** The function $p(s) = -14s^2 + 440s - 2100$ models the monthly profit in dollars made by a small T-shirt company when the selling price of its shirts is $s$ dollars.
  **a.** Write an equation that can be used to determine the selling price that will result in a monthly profit of $1200.
  **b.** Evaluate the discriminant of the equation.
  **c.** What does the discriminant tell you about whether the company can have a monthly profit of $1200?

**MATHEMATICAL PRACTICES**
**Look for and Make Use of Structure**

**46.** Tell which method you would use to solve each quadratic equation having the given form. Then explain why you would use that method.
  **a.** $ax^2 + c = 0$
  **b.** $ax^2 + bx = 0$
  **c.** $x^2 + bx = -c$, where $b$ is even
  **d.** $x^2 + bx + c = 0$, where $c$ has a factor pair with a sum of $b$
  **e.** $ax^2 + bx + c = 0$, where $a$, $b$, and $c$ are each greater than 10

## NO HORSING AROUND

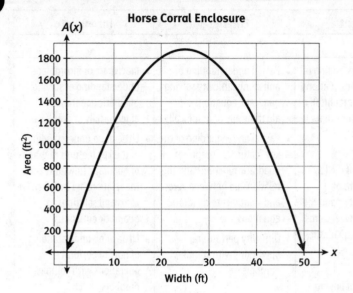

Horse Corral Enclosure

*A(x)* — Area (ft²) vs Width (ft)

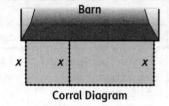

Barn

Corral Diagram

1. Kun-cha has 150 feet of fencing to make a corral for her horses. The barn will be one side of the partitioned rectangular enclosure, as shown in the diagram above. The graph illustrates the function that represents the area that could be enclosed.

   **a.** Write a function, $A(x)$, that represents the area that can be enclosed by the corral.

   **b.** What information does the graph provide about the function?

   **c.** Which ordered pair indicates the maximum area possible for the corral? Explain what each coordinate tells about the problem.

   **d.** What values of $x$ will give a total area of 1000 ft²? 2000 ft²?

2. **Critique the reasoning of others.** Tim is the punter for the Bitterroot Springs Mustangs football team. He wrote a function $h(t) = 16t^2 + 8t + 1$ that he thinks will give the height of a football in terms of $t$, the number of seconds after he kicks the ball. Use two different methods to determine the values of $t$ for which $h(t) = 0$. Show your work. Is Tim's function correct? Why or why not?

3. Tim has been studying complex numbers and quadratic equations. His teacher, Mrs. Pinto, gave the class a quiz. Demonstrate your understanding of the material by responding to each item below.

   **a.** Write a quadratic equation that has two solutions, $x = 2 + 5i$ and $x = 2 - 5i$.

   **b.** Solve $3x^2 + 2x - 8 = 0$, using an algebraic method.

   **c.** Rewrite $\dfrac{4 + i}{3 - 2i}$ in the form $a + bi$, where $a$ and $b$ are rational numbers.

| Scoring Guide | Exemplary | Proficient | Emerging | Incomplete |
|---|---|---|---|---|
| | The solution demonstrates these characteristics: | | | |
| **Mathematics Knowledge and Thinking** (Items 1c, 1d, 2, 3a-c) | • Effective understanding of and accuracy in solving quadratic equations algebraically or graphically<br>• Clear and accurate understanding of the key features of graphs of quadratic functions and the relationship between zeros and solutions to quadratic equations<br>• Clear and accurate understanding of how to perform operations with complex numbers | • Adequate understanding of solving quadratic equations algebraically or graphically, leading to solutions that are usually correct<br>• Largely correct understanding of the key features of graphs of quadratic functions and the relationship between zeros and solutions to quadratic equations<br>• Largely correct understanding of how to perform operations with complex numbers | • Partial understanding of and some difficulty solving quadratic equations algebraically or graphically<br>• Partial understanding of the key features of graphs of quadratic functions and the relationship between zeros and solutions to quadratic equations<br>• Difficulty performing operations with complex numbers | • Inaccurate or incomplete understanding of solving quadratic equations algebraically or graphically<br>• Little or no understanding of the key features of graphs of quadratic functions and the relationship between zeros and solutions to quadratic equations<br>• Little or no understanding of how to perform operations with complex numbers |
| **Problem Solving** (Items 1c, 1d, 2) | • An appropriate and efficient strategy that results in a correct answer | • A strategy that may include unnecessary steps but results in a correct answer | • A strategy that results in some incorrect answers | • No clear strategy when solving problems |
| **Mathematical Modeling / Representations** (Item 1) | • Effective understanding of how to write a quadratic equation or function from a verbal description, graph or diagram<br>• Clear and accurate understanding of how to interpret features of the graphs of quadratic functions and the solutions to quadratic equations | • Adequate understanding of how to write a quadratic equation or function from a verbal description, graph or diagram<br>• Largely correct understanding of how to interpret features of the graphs of quadratic functions and the solutions to quadratic equations | • Partial understanding of how to write a quadratic equation or function from a verbal description, graph or diagram<br>• Some difficulty with interpreting the features of graphs of quadratic functions and the solutions to quadratic equations | • Little or no understanding of how to write a quadratic equation or function from a verbal description, graph or diagram<br>• Inaccurate or incomplete interpretation of the features of graphs of quadratic functions and the solutions to quadratic equations |
| **Reasoning and Communication** (Items 1b, 1c, 2) | • Precise use of appropriate math terms and language to relate equations and graphs of quadratic functions and their key features to a real-world scenario<br>• Clear and accurate use of mathematical work to justify or refute a claim | • Adequate descriptions to relate equations and graphs of quadratic functions and their key features to a real-world scenario<br>• Correct use of mathematical work to justify or refute a claim | • Misleading or confusing descriptions to relate equations and graphs of quadratic functions and their key features to a real-world scenario<br>• Partially correct use of mathematical work to justify or refute a claim | • Incomplete or inaccurate descriptions to relate equations and graphs of quadratic functions and their key features to a real-world scenario<br>• Incorrect or incomplete use of mathematical work to justify or refute a claim |

# Writing Quadratic Equations

## What Goes Up Must Come Down

### Lesson 10-1 Parabolas and Quadratic Equations

**Learning Targets:**

- Derive a general equation for a parabola based on the definition of a parabola.
- Write the equation of a parabola given a graph and key features.

**SUGGESTED LEARNING STRATEGIES:** Predict and Confirm, Discussion Groups, Interactive Word Wall, Create Representations, Close Reading

Take a look at the graphs shown below.

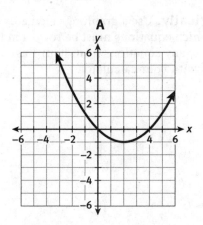

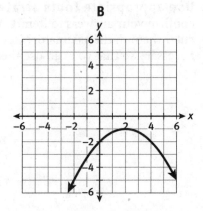

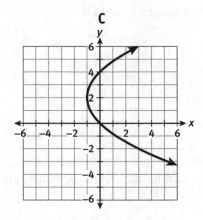

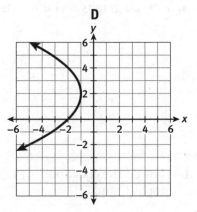

1. **Make use of structure.** Match each equation with one of the graphs above.

$$x = \frac{1}{4}(y - 2)^2 - 1 \qquad y = \frac{1}{4}(x - 2)^2 - 1$$

$$y = -\frac{1}{4}(x - 2)^2 - 1 \qquad x = -\frac{1}{4}(y - 2)^2 - 1$$

**My Notes**

**2.** Explain how you matched each equation with one of the graphs.

**TECHNOLOGY TIP**

If an equation includes the $\pm$ symbol, you will need to enter it in a graphing calculator as two separate equations. For example, enter the equation $y = 2 \pm \sqrt{x}$ as $y = 2 + \sqrt{x}$ and $y = 2 - \sqrt{x}$.

**3. Use appropriate tools strategically.** Use a graphing calculator to confirm your answers to Item 1. Which equations must be rewritten to enter them in the calculator? Rewrite any equations from Item 1 as necessary so that you can use them with your calculator.

**4. a.** How do graphs A and B differ from graphs C and D?

**b.** How do the equations of graphs A and B differ from the equations of graphs C and D?

**5.** Work with your group. Consider graphs A and B and their equations.
   **a.** Describe the relationship between the graphs.

   **b.** What part of the equation determines whether the graph opens up or down? How do you know?

   **c. Attend to precision.** What are the coordinates of the lowest point on graph A? What are the coordinates of the highest point on graph B? How do the coordinates of these points relate to the equations of the graphs?

**6.** Continue to work with your group. Consider graphs C and D and their equations.
   **a.** Describe the relationship between the graphs.

   **b.** What part of the equation determines whether the graph opens to the right or left? How do you know?

   **c.** What are the coordinates of the leftmost point on graph C? What are the coordinates of the rightmost point on graph D? How do the coordinates of these points relate to the equations of the graphs?

**My Notes**

**DISCUSSION GROUP TIP**

As you share ideas for Items 5 and 6 in your group, ask your group members or your teacher for clarification of any language, terms, or concepts that you do not understand.

**MATH TIP**

A graph is said to open upward when both ends of the graph point up. A graph is said to open downward when both ends of the graph point down.

The vertex of a graph that opens upward is the *minimum* of the graph, and is its lowest point. The vertex of a graph that opens downward is the *maximum* of the graph, and is its highest point.

**Check Your Understanding**

7. Which equation does the graph at right represent? Explain your answer.

    A. $y = -\frac{1}{2}(x + 2)^2 - 4$

    B. $y = -\frac{1}{2}(x + 2)^2 + 4$

    C. $y = -\frac{1}{2}(x - 2)^2 + 4$

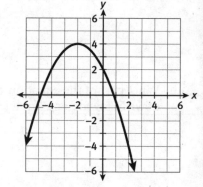

8. **Construct viable arguments.** Which of the equations in Item 1 represent functions? Explain your reasoning.

9. Consider the equation $x = -2(y + 4)^2 - 1$. Without graphing the equation, tell which direction its graph opens. Explain your reasoning.

The graphs shown at the beginning of this lesson are all parabolas. A **parabola** can be defined as the set of points that are the same distance from a point called the **focus** and a line called the **directrix**.

10. The focus of graph A, shown below, is (2, 0), and the directrix is the horizontal line $y = -2$:

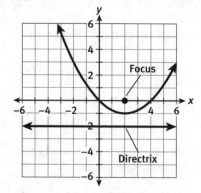

a. The point $(-2, 3)$ is on the parabola. Find the distance between this point and the focus.

**MATH TERMS**

A **parabola** is the set of points in a plane that are equidistant from a fixed point and a fixed line.

The fixed point is called the **focus**.

The fixed line is called the **directrix**.

**MATH TIP**

The distance between two points $(x_1, y_1)$ and $(x_2, y_2)$ is given by $\sqrt{(x_2 - x_1)^2 + (y_2 - y_1)^2}$.

**MATH TIP**

The distance between a point and a horizontal line is the length of the vertical segment with one endpoint at the point and one endpoint on the line.

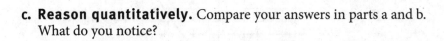

**b.** Find the distance between the point (−2, 3) and the directrix.

**c. Reason quantitatively.** Compare your answers in parts a and b. What do you notice?

**11.** The focus of graph D, shown below, is (−2, 2), and the directrix is the vertical line $x = 0$.

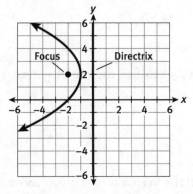

**a.** The point (−2, 4) is on the parabola. Show that this point is the same distance from the focus as from the directrix.

**MATH TIP**

The distance between a point and a vertical line is the length of the horizontal segment with one endpoint at the point and one endpoint on the line.

**b.** The point (−5, −2) is also on the parabola. Show that this point is the same distance from the focus as from the directrix.

**My Notes**

The focus of the parabola shown below is $(-2, -1)$, and the directrix is the line $y = -5$.

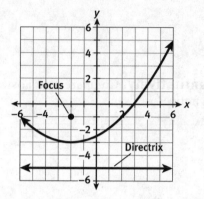

**12. a.** Draw and label the *axis of symmetry* on the graph above. What is the equation of the axis of symmetry?

**b.** Explain how you identified the axis of symmetry of the parabola.

**13. a.** Draw and label the *vertex* on the graph above. What are the coordinates of the vertex?

**b.** Explain how you identified the vertex of the parabola.

**c.** What is another way you could have identified the vertex?

**My Notes**

You can use what you have learned about parabolas to derive a general equation for a parabola whose vertex is located at the origin. Start with a parabola that has a vertical axis of symmetry, a focus of $(0, p)$, and a directrix of $y = -p$. Let $P(x, y)$ represent any point on the parabola.

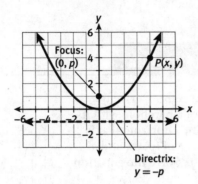

14. Write, but do not simplify, an expression for the distance from point $P$ to the focus.

15. Write, but do not simplify, an expression for the distance from point $P$ to the directrix.

16. **Make use of structure.** Based on the definition of a parabola, the distance from point $P$ to the focus is the same as the distance from point $P$ to the directrix. Set your expressions from Items 14 and 15 equal to each other, and then solve for $y$.

**MATH TIP**

In Item 16, start by squaring each side of the equation to eliminate the square root symbols. Next, simplify each side and expand the squared terms.

**My Notes**

17. What is the general equation for a parabola with its vertex at the origin, a focus of $(0, p)$, and a directrix of $y = -p$?

## Check Your Understanding

18. See the diagram at right. Derive the general equation of a parabola with its vertex at the origin, a horizontal axis of symmetry, a focus of $(p, 0)$, and a directrix of $x = -p$. Solve the equation for $x$.

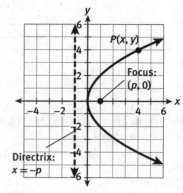

19. **Model with mathematics.** The vertex of a parabola is at the origin and its focus is $(0, -3)$. What is the equation of the parabola? Explain your reasoning.

20. A parabola has a focus of $(3, 4)$ and a directrix of $x = -1$. Answer each question about the parabola, and explain your reasoning.

    a. What is the axis of symmetry?

    b. What is the vertex?

    c. In which direction does the parabola open?

### MATH TIP

A parabola always opens toward the focus and away from the directrix.

You can also write general equations for parabolas that do not have their vertex at the origin. You will derive these equations later in this activity.

|  | Vertical Axis of Symmetry | Horizontal Axis of Symmetry |
|---|---|---|
| **Vertex** | $(h, k)$ | $(h, k)$ |
| **Focus** | $(h, k + p)$ | $(h + p, k)$ |
| **Directrix** | horizontal line $y = k - p$ | vertical line $x = h - p$ |
| **Equation** | $y = \frac{1}{4p}(x - h)^2 + k$ | $x = \frac{1}{4p}(y - k)^2 + h$ |

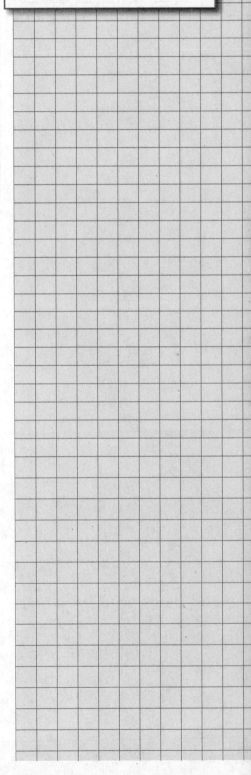

21. **Reason quantitatively.** Use the given information to write the equation of each parabola.

   **a.** axis of symmetry: $y = 0$; vertex: $(0, 0)$; directrix: $x = \frac{1}{2}$

**MATH TIP**

You may find it helpful to make a quick sketch of the information you are given.

   **b.** vertex: $(3, 4)$; focus: $(3, 6)$

   **c.** vertex: $(-2, 1)$; directrix: $y = 4$

   **d.** focus: $(-4, 0)$; directrix: $x = 4$

   **e.** opens up; focus: $(5, 7)$; directrix: $y = 3$

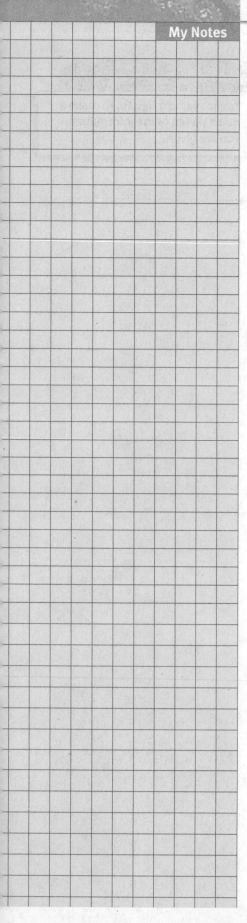

**My Notes**

## Check Your Understanding

**22.** See the diagram at right. Derive the general equation of a parabola with its vertex at $(h, k)$, a vertical axis of symmetry, a focus of $(h, k + p)$, and a directrix of $y = k - p$. Solve the equation for $y$.

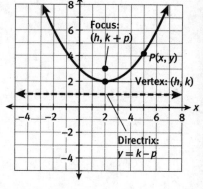

**23. Construct viable arguments.**
Can you determine the equation of a parabola if you know only its axis of symmetry and its vertex? Explain.

**24.** The equation of a parabola is
$x = \frac{1}{8}(y - 2)^2 + 1$. Identify the vertex, axis of symmetry, focus, and directrix of the parabola.

## LESSON 10-1 PRACTICE

**25.** Which equation does the graph at right represent?
**A.** $x = -2(y + 3)^2 - 2$
**B.** $x = 2(y + 3)^2 - 2$
**C.** $y = -2(x + 3)^2 - 2$
**D.** $y = 2(x + 3)^2 - 2$

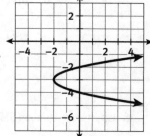

**26.** Graph the parabola given by the equation
$y = \frac{1}{4}(x + 3)^2 - 4$.

**27. Make sense of problems.** The focus of a parabola is $(0, 2)$, and its directrix is the vertical line $x = -6$. Identify the axis of symmetry, the vertex, and the direction the parabola opens.

Use the given information to write the equation of each parabola.

**28.** vertex: $(0, 0)$; focus: $\left(0, -\frac{1}{2}\right)$

**29.** focus: $(4, 0)$; directrix: $x = -4$

**30.** opens to the left; vertex: $(0, 5)$; focus: $(-5, 5)$

**31.** axis of symmetry: $x = 3$; focus: $(3, -1)$; directrix: $y = -7$

**32.** vertex: $(-2, 4)$; directrix: $x = -3$

**My Notes**

● **Learning Targets:**
- Explain why three points are needed to determine a parabola.
- Determine the quadratic function that passes through three given points on a plane.

> **SUGGESTED LEARNING STRATEGIES:** Create Representations, Quickwrite, Questioning the Text, Create Representations, Identify a Subtask

Recall that if you are given any two points on the coordinate plane, you can write the equation of the line that passes through those points. The two points are said to determine the line because there is only one line that can be drawn through them.

Do two points on the coordinate plane determine a parabola? To answer this question, work through the following items.

1. Follow these steps to write the equation of a quadratic function whose graph passes through the points $(2, 0)$ and $(5, 0)$.

   a. Write a quadratic equation in standard form with the solutions $x = 2$ and $x = 5$.

   b. Replace 0 in your equation from part a with $y$ to write the corresponding quadratic function.

   c. Use substitution to check that the points $(2, 0)$ and $(5, 0)$ lie on the function's graph.

2. a. **Use appropriate tools strategically.** Graph your quadratic function from Item 1 on a graphing calculator.

   b. On the same screen, graph the quadratic functions $y = 2x^2 - 14x + 20$ and $y = -x^2 + 7x - 10$.

**MATH TIP**

To review writing a quadratic equation when given its solutions, see Lesson 7-3.

**My Notes**

**MATH TIP**

Three or more points are *collinear* if they lie on the same straight line.

**c.** Describe the graphs. Do all three parabolas pass through the points $(2, 0)$ and $(5, 0)$?

**3. Reason abstractly.** Do two points on the coordinate plane determine a parabola? Explain.

Three points in the coordinate plane that are not on the same line determine a parabola given by a quadratic function. If you are given three noncollinear points on the coordinate plane, you can write the equation of the quadratic function whose graph passes through them.

Consider the quadratic function whose graph passes through the points $(1, 2)$, $(3, 0)$, and $(5, 6)$.

**4.** Write an equation by substituting the coordinates of the point $(1, 2)$ into the standard form of a quadratic function, $y = ax^2 + bx + c$.

**5.** Write a second equation by substituting the coordinates of the point $(3, 0)$ into the standard form of a quadratic function.

**6.** Write a third equation by substituting the coordinates of the point $(5, 6)$ into the standard form of a quadratic function.

**7.** Use your equations from Items 4–6 to write a system of three equations in the three variables $a$, $b$, and $c$.

**8.** Use substitution or Gaussian elimination to solve your system of equations for $a$, $b$, and $c$.

**9.** Now substitute the values of $a$, $b$, and $c$ into the standard form of a quadratic function.

**10. Model with mathematics.** Graph the quadratic function to confirm that it passes through the points $(1, 2)$, $(3, 0)$, and $(5, 6)$.

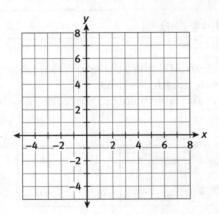

**My Notes**

**MATH TIP**

To review solving a system of three equations in three variables, see Lesson 3-2.

## Check Your Understanding

**11.** Describe how to write the equation of a quadratic function whose graph passes through three given points.

**12. a.** What happens when you try to write the equation of the quadratic function that passes through the points $(0, 4)$, $(2, 2)$, and $(4, 0)$?
   **b.** What does this result indicate about the three points?

**13. a. Reason quantitatively.** The graph of a quadratic function passes through the point $(2, 0)$. The vertex of the graph is $(-2, -16)$. Use symmetry to identify another point on the function's graph. Explain how you determined your answer.
   **b.** Write the equation of the quadratic function.

## LESSON 10-2 PRACTICE

Write the equation of the quadratic function whose graph passes through each set of points.

**14.** $(-3, 2), (-1, 0), (1, 6)$        **15.** $(-2, -5), (0, -3), (1, 4)$

**16.** $(-1, -5), (1, -9), (4, 0)$       **17.** $(-3, 7), (0, 4), (1, 15)$

**18.** $(1, 0), (2, -7), (5, -16)$       **19.** $(-2, -11), (-1, -12), (1, 16)$

**20.** The table below shows the first few terms of a sequence. This sequence can be described by a quadratic function, where $f(n)$ represents the $n$th term of the sequence. Write the quadratic function that describes the sequence.

| Term Number, $n$ | 1 | 2 | 3 | 4 | 5 |
|---|---|---|---|---|---|
| Term of Sequence, $f(n)$ | 2 | 6 | 12 | 20 | 30 |

**21.** A quadratic function $A(s)$ gives the area in square units of a regular hexagon with a side length of $s$ units.
   **a.** Use the data in the table below to write the equation of the quadratic function.

| Side Length, $s$ | 2 | 4 | 6 |
|---|---|---|---|
| Area, $A(s)$ | $6\sqrt{3}$ | $24\sqrt{3}$ | $54\sqrt{3}$ |

   **b. Attend to precision.** To the nearest square centimeter, what is the area of a regular hexagon with a side length of 8 cm?

---

**MATH TIP**

A sequence is an ordered list of numbers or other items. Each number or item in a sequence is called a term.

**CONNECT TO GEOMETRY**

A regular hexagon is a six-sided polygon with all sides having the same length and all angles having the same measure.

### Learning Targets:
- Find a quadratic model for a given table of data.
- Use a quadratic model to make predictions.

**SUGGESTED LEARNING STRATEGIES:** Think Aloud, Discussion Groups, Create Representations, Interactive Word Wall, Quickwrite, Close Reading, Predict and Confirm, Look for a Pattern, Group Presentation

A model rocketry club placed an altimeter on one of its rockets. An altimeter measures the altitude, or height, of an object above the ground. The table shows the data the club members collected from the altimeter before it stopped transmitting a little over 9 seconds after launch.

**Model Rocket Test**

| Time Since Launch (s) | 0 | 1 | 2 | 3 | 4 | 5 | 6 | 7 | 8 | 9 |
|---|---|---|---|---|---|---|---|---|---|---|
| Height (m) | 0 | 54 | 179 | 255 | 288 | 337 | 354 | 368 | 378 | 363 |

1. Predict the height of the rocket 12 seconds after launch. Explain how you made your prediction.

2. **Model with mathematics.** Make a scatter plot of the data on the coordinate grid below.

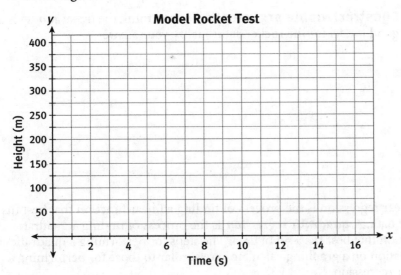

Model Rocket Test

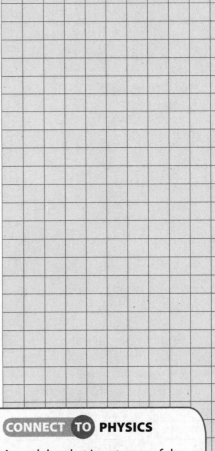

**CONNECT TO PHYSICS**

A model rocket is not powerful enough to escape Earth's gravity. The maximum height that a model rocket will reach depends in part on the weight and shape of the rocket, the amount of force generated by the rocket motor, and the amount of fuel the motor contains.

My Notes

3. Enter the rocket data into a graphing calculator. Enter the time data as List 1 (L1) and the height data as List 2 (L2). Then use the calculator to perform a linear regression on the data. Write the equation of the linear model that results from the regression. Round coefficients and constants to the nearest tenth.

4. Use a dashed line to graph the linear model from Item 3 on the coordinate grid showing the rocket data.

5. a. **Attend to precision.** To the nearest meter, what height does the linear model predict for the rocket 12 seconds after it is launched?

   b. How does this prediction compare with the prediction you made in Item 1?

6. **Construct viable arguments.** Do you think the linear model is a good model for the rocket data? Justify your answer.

**MATH TIP**

A calculator may be able to generate a linear model for a data set, but that does not necessarily mean that the model is a good fit or makes sense in a particular situation.

**MATH TERMS**

**Quadratic regression** is the process of determining the equation of a quadratic function that best fits the given data.

A linear regression is the process of finding a linear function that best fits a set of data. A *quadratic regression* is the process of finding a quadratic function that best fits a set of data. The steps for performing a quadratic regression on a graphing calculator are similar to those for performing a linear regression.

**My Notes**

7. Use these steps to perform a quadratic regression for the rocket data.
   - Check that the data set is still entered as List 1 and List 2.
   - Press [STAT] to select the Statistics menu. Then move the cursor to highlight the Calculate (CALC) submenu.
   - Select 5:QuadReg to perform a quadratic regression on the data in Lists 1 and 2. Press [ENTER].
   - The calculator displays the values of *a*, *b*, and *c* for the standard form of the quadratic function that best fits the data.

   Write the equation of the quadratic model that results from the regression. Round coefficients and constants to the nearest tenth.

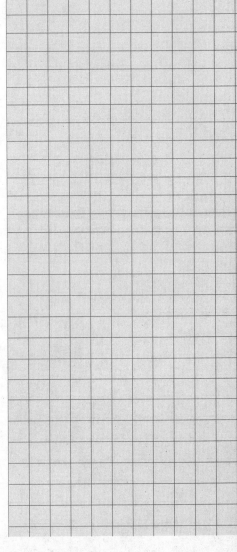

**TECHNOLOGY TIP**

You can graph the equation from a quadratic regression by using these steps: After selecting **5:QuadReg** as described at the left, do not press [ENTER]. Instead, press [VARS] to select the VARS menu. Then move the cursor to highlight the Y-VARS submenu. Select **1:Function**. Then select **1:Y1**. Press [ENTER]. The equation from the quadratic regression is now assigned to Y1. You can press [GRAPH] to view the graph of the equation.

8. Graph the quadratic model from Item 7 on the coordinate grid showing the rocket data.

9. **Construct viable arguments.** Contrast the graph of the linear model with the graph of the quadratic model. Which model is a better fit for the data?

10. **a.** To the nearest meter, what height does the quadratic model predict for the rocket 12 seconds after it is launched?

    **b.** How does this prediction compare with the prediction you made in Item 1?

11. **Reason quantitatively.** Use the quadratic model to predict when the rocket will hit the ground. Explain how you determined your answer.

### Check Your Understanding

12. **Make sense of problems.** Most model rockets have a parachute or a similar device that releases shortly after the rocket reaches its maximum height. The parachute helps to slow the rocket so that it does not hit the ground with as much force. Based on this information, do you think your prediction from Item 11 is an underestimate or an overestimate if the rocket has a parachute? Explain.

13. **a.** Could you use a graphing calculator to perform a quadratic regression on three data points? Explain.
   **b.** How closely would the quadratic model fit the data set in this situation? Explain.
   **c.** How would your answers to parts a and b change if you knew that the three points lie on the same line?

## LESSON 10-3 PRACTICE

Tell whether a linear model or a quadratic model is a better fit for each data set. Justify your answer, and give the equation of the better model.

14.

| x | 10 | 12 | 14 | 16 | 18 | 20 | 22 | 24 |
|---|----|----|----|----|----|----|----|----|
| y | 19 | 15 | 13 | 11 | 9 | 9 | 10 | 11 |

15.

| x | 2 | 4 | 6 | 8 | 10 | 12 | 14 | 16 |
|---|---|---|---|---|----|----|----|----|
| y | 10 | 22 | 26 | 35 | 45 | 50 | 64 | 66 |

The tables show time and height data for two other model rockets.

| Rocket A | Time (s) | 0 | 1 | 2 | 3 | 4 | 5 | 6 | 7 |
|----------|----------|---|---|---|---|---|---|---|---|
|          | Height (m) | 0 | 54 | 179 | 255 | 288 | 337 | 354 | 368 |

| Rocket B | Time (s) | 0 | 1 | 2 | 3 | 4 | 5 | 6 | 7 |
|----------|----------|---|---|---|---|---|---|---|---|
|          | Height (m) | 0 | 37 | 92 | 136 | 186 | 210 | 221 | 229 |

16. **Use appropriate tools strategically.** Use a graphing calculator to perform a quadratic regression for each data set. Write the equations of the quadratic models. Round coefficients and constants to the nearest tenth.

17. Use your models to predict which rocket had a greater maximum height. Explain how you made your prediction.

18. Use your models to predict which rocket hit the ground first and how much sooner. Explain how you made your prediction.

## ACTIVITY 10 PRACTICE

Write your answers on notebook paper.
Show your work.

### Lesson 10-1

Use the parabola shown in the graph for Items 1 and 2.

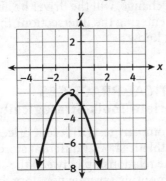

1. What is the equation of the parabola?
   **A.** $y = -(x - 1)^2 - 2$    **B.** $y = -(x + 1)^2 - 2$
   **C.** $y = (x - 1)^2 - 2$    **D.** $y = (x + 1)^2 + 2$

2. The focus of the parabola is $\left(-1, -\dfrac{9}{4}\right)$, and the directrix is the line $y = -\dfrac{7}{4}$. Show that the point $(-2, -3)$ on the parabola is the same distance from the focus as from the directrix.

3. Graph the parabola given by the equation $x = \dfrac{1}{2}(y - 3)^2 + 3$.

4. Identify the following features of the parabola given by the equation $y = \dfrac{1}{8}(x - 4)^2 + 3$.
   **a.** vertex      **b.** focus
   **c.** directrix      **d.** axis of symmetry
   **e.** direction of opening

5. Describe the relationships among the vertex, focus, directrix, and axis of symmetry of a parabola.

6. The focus of a parabola is $(3, -2)$, and its directrix is the line $x = -5$. What are the vertex and the axis of symmetry of the parabola?

For Items 7–11, use the given information to write the equation of each parabola.

7. vertex: $(0, 0)$; focus: $(0, 5)$

8. vertex: $(0, 0)$; directrix: $x = -3$

9. vertex: $(2, 2)$; axis of symmetry: $y = 2$; focus: $(1, 2)$

10. opens downward; vertex: $(-1, -2)$; directrix: $y = -1$

11. focus: $(-1, 3)$; directrix: $x = -5$

12. Use the diagram below to help you derive the general equation of a parabola with its vertex at $(h, k)$, a horizontal axis of symmetry, a focus of $(h + p, k)$, and a directrix of $x = h - p$. Solve the equation for $x$.

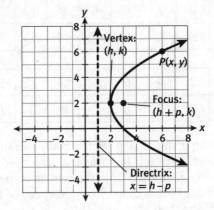

### Lesson 10-2

Write the equation of the quadratic function whose graph passes through each set of points.

13. $(-3, 0), (-2, -3), (2, 5)$

14. $(-2, -6), (1, 0), (2, 10)$

15. $(-5, -3), (-4, 0), (0, -8)$

16. $(-3, 10), (-2, 0), (0, -2)$

17. $(1, 0), (4, 6), (7, -6)$

18. $(-2, -9), (-1, 0), (1, -12)$

19. Demonstrate that the points $(-8, 0)$ and $(6, 0)$ do not determine a unique parabola by writing the equations of two different parabolas that pass through these two points.

20. **a.** The graph of a quadratic function passes through the point $(7, 5)$. The vertex of the graph is $(3, 1)$. Use symmetry to identify another point on the function's graph. Explain your answer.

    **b.** Write the equation of the quadratic function.

### Lesson 10-3

Tell whether a linear model or a quadratic model is a better fit for each data set. Justify your answer and give the equation of the better model.

21.

| x | 0 | 2 | 4 | 6 | 8 | 10 | 12 | 14 |
|---|---|---|---|---|---|---|----|----|----|
| y | 17 | 29 | 40 | 45 | 59 | 63 | 76 | 88 |

22.

| x | 2 | 4 | 6 | 8 | 10 | 12 | 14 | 16 |
|---|---|---|---|---|----|----|----|----|
| y | 15 | 9 | 5 | 2 | 6 | 7 | 16 | 22 |

The stopping distance of a vehicle is the distance the vehicle travels between the time the driver recognizes the need to stop and the time the vehicle comes to a stop. The table below shows how the speed of two vehicles affects their stopping distances.

| Speed (mi/h) | Stopping distance (ft) | |
|---|---|---|
| | Car | Truck |
| 10 | 27 | 28 |
| 15 | 44 | 47 |
| 20 | 63 | 69 |
| 25 | 85 | 95 |
| 30 | 109 | 123 |
| 35 | 135 | 155 |
| 40 | 164 | 190 |

23. Use a graphing calculator to perform a quadratic regression on the data for each vehicle. Write the equations of the quadratic models. Round coefficients and constants to the nearest thousandth.

24. Use your models to predict how much farther it would take the truck to stop from a speed of 50 mi/h than it would the car.

25. Suppose the truck is 300 ft from an intersection when the light at the intersection turns yellow. If the truck's speed is 60 mi/h when the driver sees the light change, will the driver be able to stop without entering the intersection? Explain how you know.

## MATHEMATICAL PRACTICES
### Use Appropriate Tools Strategically

26. A shoe company tests different prices of a new type of athletic shoe at different stores. The table shows the relationship between the selling price and the monthly revenue per store the company made from selling the shoes.

| Selling Price ($) | Monthly Revenue per Store ($) |
|---|---|
| 80 | 9680 |
| 90 | 10,520 |
| 100 | 11,010 |
| 110 | 10,660 |
| 120 | 10,400 |
| 130 | 9380 |

**a.** Use a graphing calculator to determine the equation of a quadratic model that can be used to predict $y$, the monthly revenue per store in dollars when the selling price is $x$ dollars. Round values to the nearest tenth.

**b.** Is a quadratic model a good model for the data set? Explain.

**c.** Use your model to determine the price at which the company should sell the shoes to generate the greatest revenue.

# Transformations of $y = x^2$

**Parent Parabola**

**Lesson 11-1 Translations of Parabolas**

### Learning Targets:

- Describe translations of the parent function $f(x) = x^2$.
- Given a translation of the function $f(x) = x^2$, write the equation of the function.

> **SUGGESTED LEARNING STRATEGIES:** Create Representations, Quickwrite, Group Presentation, Look for a Pattern, Discussion Groups

1. Graph the parent quadratic function, $f(x) = x^2$, on the coordinate grid below. Include the points that have $x$-values $-2, -1, 0, 1,$ and $2$.

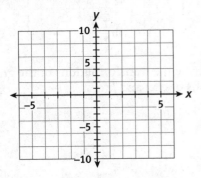

The points on the parent function graph that have $x$-values $-2, -1, 0, 1,$ and $2$ are *key points* that can be used when graphing any quadratic function as a transformation of the parent quadratic function.

2. Graph $f(x) = x^2$ on the coordinate grid below. Then graph and label $g(x) = x^2 - 3$ and $h(x) = x^2 + 2$.

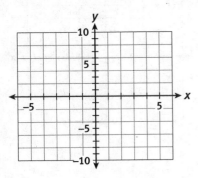

3. **Make use of structure.** Identify and describe the transformations of the graph of $f(x) = x^2$ that result in the graphs of $g(x)$ and $h(x)$.

**My Notes**

**MATH TIP**

A *parent function* is the simplest function of a particular type. For example, the parent linear function is $f(x) = x$. The parent absolute value function is $f(x) = |x|$.

**MATH TIP**

A *transformation* of a graph of a parent function is a change in the position, size, or shape of the graph.

**MATH TIP**

*Translations* are transformations that change the location of a graph but maintain the original shape of a graph. For this reason, they are known as *rigid transformations*.

4. **Model with mathematics.** Graph $f(x) = x^2$ on the coordinate grid below. Then graph and label $g(x) = (x - 2)^2$ and $h(x) = (x + 3)^2$.

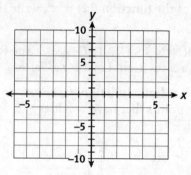

5. Identify and describe the transformations of the graph of $f(x) = x^2$ that result in the graphs of $g(x)$ and $h(x)$.

6. Describe each function as a transformation of $f(x) = x^2$. Then use that information to graph each function on the coordinate grid.
   **a.** $a(x) = (x - 1)^2$

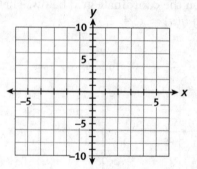

   **b.** $w(x) = x^2 + 4$

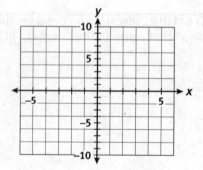

**My Notes**

**c.** $d(x) = (x + 3)^2 - 5$

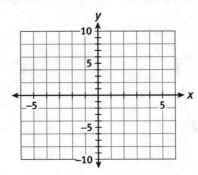

**d.** $j(x) = (x - 1)^2 + 2$

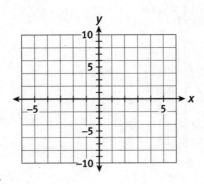

### Check Your Understanding

7. **Express regularity in repeated reasoning.** The graph of each function below is a translation of the graph of $f(x) = x^2$ by $k$ units, where $k > 0$. For each function, tell which direction the graph of $f(x)$ is translated.
   **a.** $g(x) = x^2 + k$
   **b.** $h(x) = (x + k)^2$
   **c.** $j(x) = x^2 - k$
   **d.** $m(x) = (x - k)^2$

8. What is the vertex of the function $p(x) = x^2 - 5$? Justify your answer in terms of a translation of $f(x) = x^2$.

9. What is the axis of symmetry of the function $q(x) = (x + 1)^2$? Justify your answer in terms of a translation of $f(x) = x^2$.

10. **Reason abstractly.** The function $r(x)$ is a translation of the function $f(x) = x^2$. What can you conclude about the direction in which the parabola given by $r(x)$ opens? Justify your answer.

> **MATH TIP**
>
> If you need help with Item 7, try substituting a positive number for $k$ and then graphing each function.

**My Notes**

11. Each function graphed below is a translation of $f(x) = x^2$. Describe the transformation. Then write the equation of the transformed function.

a.

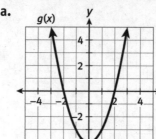

b.

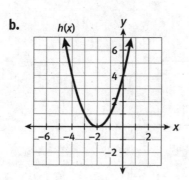

c.

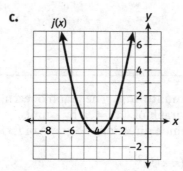

d.

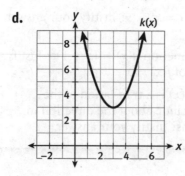

12. Use a graphing calculator to graph each of the equations you wrote in Item 11. Check that the graphs on the calculator match those shown in Item 11. Revise your answers to Item 11 as needed.

**TECHNOLOGY TIP**

When you graph a function on a graphing calculator, the distance between tick marks on the *x*-axis is not always the same as the distance between tick marks on the *y*-axis. To make these distances the same, press ZOOM, and select **5 : ZSquare**. This step will make it easier to compare your calculator graphs to the graphs in Item 11.

### Check Your Understanding

13. Explain how you determined the equation of $k(x)$ in Item 11d.

14. **Critique the reasoning of others.**
The graph shows a translation of $f(x) = x^2$. A student says that the equation of the transformed function is $g(x) = (x - 4)^2$. Is the student correct? Explain.

15. The graph of $h(x)$ is a translation of the graph of $f(x) = x^2$. If the vertex of the graph of $h(x)$ is $(-1, -2)$, what is the equation of $h(x)$? Explain your answer.

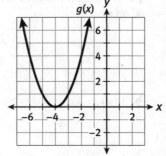

### LESSON 11-1 PRACTICE

**Make sense of problems.** Describe each function as a transformation of $f(x) = x^2$.

16. $g(x) = x^2 - 6$

17. $h(x) = (x + 5)^2$

18. $j(x) = (x - 2)^2 + 8$

19. $k(x) = (x + 6)^2 - 4$

Each function graphed below is a translation of $f(x) = x^2$. Describe the transformation. Then write the equation of the transformed function.

20.

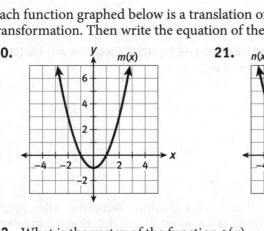

21.

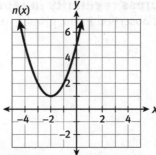

22. What is the vertex of the function $p(x) = (x - 5)^2 + 4$? Justify your answer in terms of a translation of $f(x) = x^2$.

23. What is the axis of symmetry of the function $q(x) = (x + 8)^2 - 10$? Justify your answer in terms of a translation of $f(x) = x^2$.

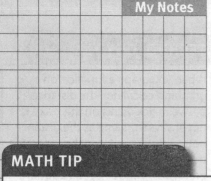

**My Notes**

**Learning Targets:**

- Describe transformations of the parent function $f(x) = x^2$.
- Given a transformation of the function $f(x) = x^2$, write the equation of the function.

> **SUGGESTED LEARNING STRATEGIES:** Create Representations, Look for a Pattern, Group Presentation, Quickwrite, Identify a Subtask

1. Graph the function $f(x) = x^2$ as Y1 on a graphing calculator. Then graph each of the following functions as Y2. Describe the graph of each function as a transformation of the graph of $f(x) = x^2$.
   a. $g(x) = 2x^2$

   b. $h(x) = 4x^2$

   c. $j(x) = \frac{1}{2}x^2$

   d. $k(x) = \frac{1}{4}x^2$

2. **Express regularity in repeated reasoning.** Describe any patterns you observed in the graphs from Item 1.

3. Graph the function $f(x) = x^2$ as Y1 on a graphing calculator. Then graph each of the following functions as Y2. Identify and describe the graph of each function as a transformation of the graph of $f(x) = x^2$.
   a. $g(x) = -x^2$

> **MATH TIP**
>
> Unlike a rigid transformation, a *vertical stretch* or *vertical shrink* will change the shape of the graph.
>
> A vertical stretch stretches a graph away from the *x*-axis by a factor and a vertical shrink shrinks the graph toward the *x*-axis by a factor.

> **MATH TIP**
>
> *Reflections* over axes do not change the shape of the graph, so they are also rigid transformations.

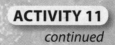
**My Notes**

**b.** $h(x) = -4x^2$

**c.** $j(x) = -\dfrac{1}{4}x^2$

**4.** Describe any patterns you observed in the graphs from Item 3.

**5.** Make a conjecture about how the sign of $k$ affects the graph of $g(x) = kx^2$ compared to the graph of $f(x) = x^2$. Assume that $k \neq 0$.

**6.** Make a conjecture about whether the absolute value of $k$ affects the graph of $g(x) = kx^2$ when compared to the graph of $f(x) = x^2$. Assume that $k \neq 0$ and write your answer using absolute value notation.

**MATH TIP**

In Item 6, consider the situation in which $|k| > 1$ and the situation in which $|k| < 1$.

**7. Make use of structure.** Without graphing, describe each function as a transformation of $f(x) = x^2$.
**a.** $h(x) = 6x^2$

**b.** $j(x) = -\dfrac{1}{10}x^2$

**My Notes**

c. $p(x) = -9x^2$

d. $q(x) = \frac{1}{5}x^2$

### Check Your Understanding

8. The graph of $g(x)$ is a vertical shrink of the graph of $f(x) = x^2$ by a factor of $\frac{1}{6}$. What is the equation of $g(x)$?

9. **Reason quantitatively.** The graph of $h(x)$ is a vertical stretch of the graph of $f(x) = x^2$. If the graph of $h(x)$ passes through the point $(1, 7)$, what is the equation of $h(x)$? Explain your answer.

10. The graph of $j(x) = kx^2$ opens downward. Based on this information, what can you conclude about the value of $k$? Justify your conclusion.

11. Graph the function $f(x) = x^2$ as Y1 on a graphing calculator. Then graph each of the following functions as Y2. Identify and describe the graph of each function as a horizontal stretch or shrink of the graph of $f(x) = x^2$.
   a. $g(x) = (2x)^2$

   b. $h(x) = (4x)^2$

   c. $j(x) = \left(\frac{1}{2}x\right)^2$

   d. $k(x) = \left(\frac{1}{4}x\right)^2$

**MATH TIP**

A horizontal stretch stretches a graph away from the *y*-axis by a factor and a vertical shrink shrinks the graph toward the *y*-axis by a factor.

## Lesson 11-2
### Shrinking, Stretching, and Reflecting Parabolas

**ACTIVITY 11**
*continued*

Work with your group on Items 12–16.

**12.** Describe any patterns you observed in the graphs from Item 11.

**13. a. Use appropriate tools strategically.** Graph the function $f(x) = x^2$ as Y1 on a graphing calculator. Then graph $h(x) = (-x)^2$ as Y2. Describe the result.

**b. Reason abstractly.** Explain why this result makes sense.

**14.** Make a conjecture about how the sign of $k$ affects the graph of $g(x) = (kx)^2$ compared to the graph of $f(x) = x^2$. Assume that $k \neq 0$.

**15.** Make a conjecture about whether the absolute value of $k$ affects the graph of $g(x) = (kx)^2$ when compared to the graph of $f(x) = x^2$. Assume that $k \neq 0$.

**16.** Describe each function as a transformation of $f(x) = x^2$.
 **a.** $p(x) = (6x)^2$

 **b.** $q(x) = \left(\dfrac{1}{10}x\right)^2$

**My Notes**

### Check Your Understanding

**17.** Describe how the graph of $g(x) = 4x^2$ differs from the graph of $h(x) = (4x)^2$.

**18.** The graph of $g(x)$ is a horizontal stretch of the graph of $f(x) = x^2$ by a factor of 5. What is the equation of $g(x)$?

**19. Reason quantitatively.** The graph of $h(x)$ is a horizontal shrink of the graph of $f(x) = x^2$. If the graph of $h(x)$ passes through the point $(1, 25)$, what is the equation of $h(x)$? Explain your answer.

**20.** Each function graphed below is a transformation of $f(x) = x^2$. Describe the transformation. Then write the equation of the transformed function.

**a.**

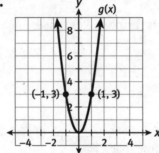

**b.**

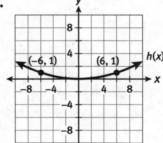

**c.**

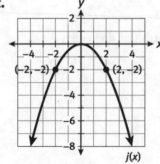

**d.**

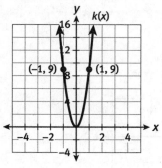

21. **Model with mathematics.** Multiple transformations can be represented in the same function. Describe the transformations from the parent function. Then graph the function, using your knowledge of transformations only.

**a.** $f(x) = -4(x + 3)^2 + 2$

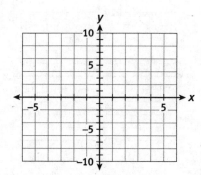

**MATH TIP**

When graphing multiple transformations of quadratic functions, follow this order:

1. horizontal translation

2. horizontal shrink or stretch

3. reflection over the x-axis and/or vertical shrink or stretch

4. vertical translation

**b.** $f(x) = 2(x - 4)^2 - 3$

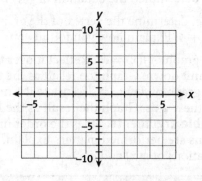

**c.** $f(x) = 2(x + 1)^2 - 4$

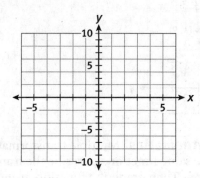

**d.** $f(x) = -(x - 3)^2 + 5$

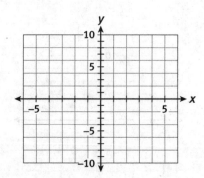

## Check Your Understanding

**22.** Explain how you determined the equation of $g(x)$ in Item 20a.

**23.** Without graphing, determine the vertex of the graph of $h(x) = 2(x - 3)^2 + 4$. Explain how you found your answer.

**24. a.** Start with the graph of $f(x) = x^2$. Reflect it over the $x$-axis and then translate it 1 unit down. Graph the result as the function $p(x)$.
   **b.** Start with the graph of $f(x) = x^2$. Translate it 1 unit down and then reflect it over the $x$-axis. Graph the result as the function $q(x)$.
   **c.** **Construct viable arguments.** Does the order in which the two transformations are performed matter? Explain.
   **d.** Write the equations of $p(x)$ and $q(x)$.

## LESSON 11-2 PRACTICE

Describe each function as a transformation of $f(x) = x^2$.

**25.** $g(x) = -5x^2$

**26.** $h(x) = (8x)^2$

**27. Make sense of problems.** The graph of $j(x)$ is a horizontal stretch of the graph of $f(x) = x^2$ by a factor of 7. What is the equation of $j(x)$?

Each function graphed below is a transformation of $f(x) = x^2$. Describe the transformation. Then write the equation of the transformed function.

**28.**

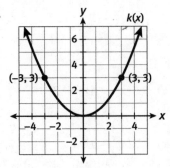

**29.**

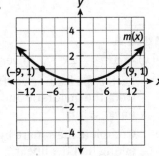

Describe the transformations from the parent function. Then graph the function, using your knowledge of transformations only.

**30.** $n(x) = -3(x - 4)^2$

**31.** $p(x) = \frac{1}{2}(x + 3) - 5$

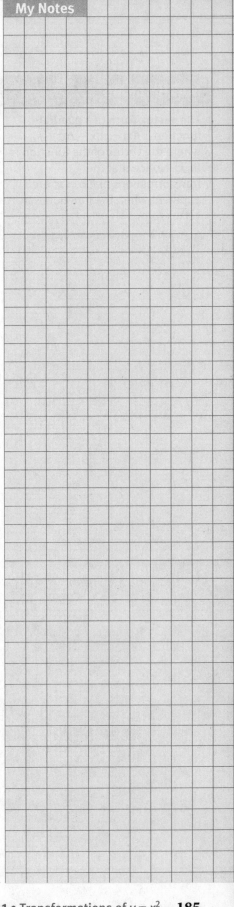

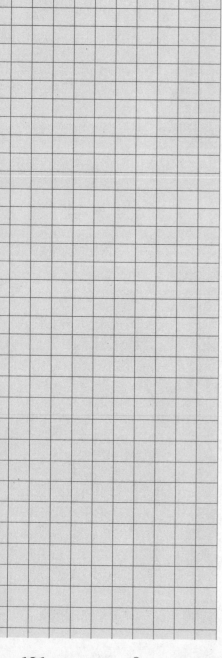

## MATH TERMS

The **vertex form** of a quadratic function is $f(x) = a(x - h)^2 + k$, where the vertex of the function is $(h, k)$. Notice that the transformations of $f(x) = x^2$ are apparent when the function is in vertex form.

### Learning Targets:
- Write a quadratic function in vertex form.
- Use transformations to graph a quadratic function in vertex form.

**SUGGESTED LEARNING STRATEGIES:** Interactive Word Wall, Marking the Text, Create Representations, Group Presentation, RAFT

A quadratic function in standard form, $f(x) = ax^2 + bx + c$, can be changed into **vertex form** by completing the square.

### Example A
Write $f(x) = 3x^2 - 12x + 7$ in vertex form.

**Step 1:** Factor the leading coefficient from the quadratic and linear terms.
$$f(x) = 3(x^2 - 4x) + 7$$

**Step 2:** Complete the square by taking half the linear coefficient $[0.5(-4) = -2]$, squaring it $[(-2)^2 = 4]$, and then adding it inside the parentheses.
$$f(x) = 3(x^2 - 4x + \quad) + 7$$
$$\uparrow$$
$$+ 4$$

**Step 3:** To maintain the value of the expression, multiply the leading coefficient [3] by the number added inside the parentheses [4]. Then subtract that product [12].
$$f(x) = 3(x^2 - 4x + 4) - 3(4) + 7$$
$$f(x) = 3(x^2 - 4x + 4) - 12 + 7$$

**Step 4:** Write the trinomial inside the parentheses as a perfect square. The function is in vertex form.
$$f(x) = 3(x - 2)^2 - 5$$

**Solution:** The vertex form of $f(x) = 3x^2 - 12x + 7$ is $f(x) = 3(x - 2)^2 - 5$.

### Try These A
**Make use of structure.** Write each quadratic function in vertex form. Show your work.

**a.** $f(x) = 5x^2 + 40x - 3$

**b.** $g(x) = -4x^2 - 12x + 1$

1. **Make sense of problems.** Write each function in vertex form. Then describe the transformation(s) from the parent function and graph without the use of a graphing calculator.

   **a.** $f(x) = -2x^2 + 4x + 3$

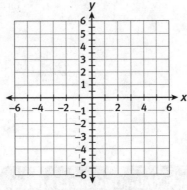

   **b.** $g(x) = \frac{1}{2}x^2 + 3x + \frac{3}{2}$

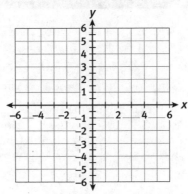

2. Consider the function $f(x) = 2x^2 - 16x + 34$.
   **a.** Write the function in vertex form.

   **b.** What is the vertex of the graph of the function? Explain your answer.

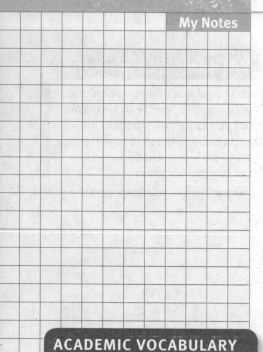

c. What is the axis of symmetry of the function's graph? How do you know?

d. Does the graph of the function open upward or downward? How do you know?

### Check Your Understanding

3. Write a set of instructions for a student who is absent explaining how to write the function $f(x) = x^2 + 6x + 11$ in vertex form.

4. What are some *advantages* of the vertex form of a quadratic function compared to the standard form?

5. A student is writing $f(x) = 4x^2 - 8x + 8$ in vertex form. What number should she write in the first box to complete the square inside the parentheses? What number should she write in the second box to keep the expression on the right side of the equation balanced? Explain.

$$f(x) = 4(x^2 - 2x + \Box) - \Box + 8$$

### ACADEMIC VOCABULARY

An *advantage* is a benefit or a desirable feature.

A *disadvantage* is an undesirable feature.

## LESSON 11-3 PRACTICE

Write each function in vertex form. Then describe the transformation(s) from the parent function and use the transformations to graph the function.

6. $g(x) = x^2 + 6x + 5$

7. $h(x) = x^2 - 8x + 17$

8. $j(x) = 2x^2 + 4x + 5$

9. $k(x) = -3x^2 + 12x - 7$

Write each function in vertex form. Then identify the vertex and axis of symmetry of the function's graph, and tell which direction the graph opens.

10. $f(x) = x^2 - 20x + 107$

11. $f(x) = -x^2 - 16x - 67$

12. $f(x) = 5x^2 - 20x + 31$

13. $f(x) = -2x^2 - 12x + 5$

14. **Critique the reasoning of others.** Rebecca says that the function $f(x) = x^2 - 5$ is written in standard form. Lane says that the function is written in vertex form. Who is correct? Explain.

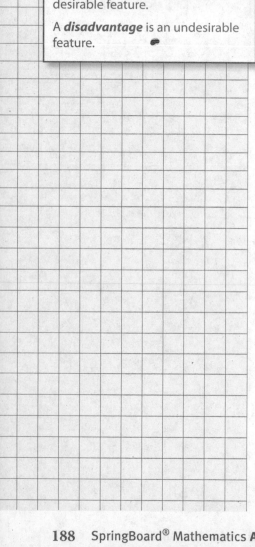

## ACTIVITY 11 PRACTICE
**Write your answers on notebook paper.**
**Show your work.**

### Lesson 11-1

For each function, identify all transformations of the function $f(x) = x^2$. Then graph the function.

**1.** $g(x) = x^2 + 1$

**2.** $g(x) = (x - 4)^2$

**3.** $g(x) = (x + 2)^2 + 3$

**4.** $g(x) = (x - 3)^2 - 4$

Each function graphed below is a translation of $f(x) = x^2$. Describe the transformation. Then write the equation of the transformed function.

**5.**

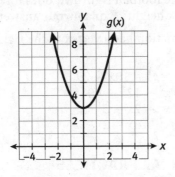

**6.**

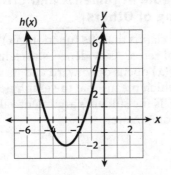

Use transformations of the parent quadratic function to determine the vertex and axis of symmetry of the graph of each function.

**7.** $g(x) = (x - 8)^2$

**8.** $g(x) = (x + 6)^2 - 4$

Write a quadratic function $g(x)$ that represents each transformation of the function $f(x) = x^2$.

**9.** translate 6 units right

**10.** translate 10 units down

**11.** translate 9 units right and 6 units up

**12.** translate 4 units left and 8 units down

**13.** The function $g(x)$ is a translation of $f(x) = x^2$. The vertex of the graph of $g(x)$ is $(-4, 7)$. What is the equation of $g(x)$? Explain your answer.

### Lesson 11-2

For each function, identify all transformations of the function $f(x) = x^2$. Then graph the function.

**14.** $g(x) = -\frac{1}{3}x^2$

**15.** $g(x) = \frac{1}{5}x^2$

**16.** $g(x) = \frac{1}{2}(x - 3)^2$

**17.** $g(x) = -2(x + 3)^2 + 1$

**18.** $g(x) = -3(x + 2)^2 - 5$

Write a quadratic function $g(x)$ that represents each transformation of the function $f(x) = x^2$.

**19.** shrink horizontally by a factor of $\frac{1}{4}$

**20.** stretch vertically by a factor of 8

**21.** shrink vertically by a factor of $\frac{1}{3}$, translate 6 units up

**22.** translate 1 unit right, stretch vertically by a factor of $\frac{3}{2}$, reflect over the $x$-axis, translate 7 units up

Each function graphed below is a transformation of $f(x) = x^2$. Describe the transformation. Then write the equation of the transformed function.

**23.**

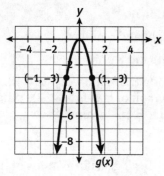

**24.**

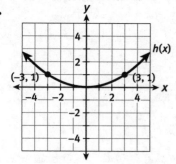

**25.** Which of these functions has the widest graph when they are graphed on the same coordinate plane?

**A.** $f(x) = -2x^2$
**B.** $f(x) = 5x^2$
**C.** $f(x) = \frac{1}{2}x^2$
**D.** $f(x) = -\frac{1}{5}x^2$

### Lesson 11-3

Write each function in vertex form. Then describe the transformation(s) from the parent function and use the transformations to graph the function.

**26.** $g(x) = x^2 - 4x - 1$

**27.** $g(x) = -2x^2 + 12x - 17$

**28.** $g(x) = 3x^2 + 6x + 1$

Write each function in vertex form. Then identify the vertex and axis of symmetry of the function's graph, and tell which direction the graph opens.

**29.** $f(x) = x^2 - 16x + 71$

**30.** $f(x) = 2x^2 + 36x + 142$

**31.** $f(x) = -3x^2 + 6x + 9$

**32.** $f(x) = x^2 - 2x + 5$

**33.** The function $h(t) = -16t^2 + 22t + 4$ models the height $h$ in feet of a football $t$ seconds after it is thrown.
   **a.** Write the function in vertex form.
   **b.** To the nearest foot, what is the greatest height that the football reaches? Explain your answer.
   **c.** To the nearest tenth of a second, how long after the football is thrown does it reach its greatest height? Explain your answer.

**34.** Which function has a vertex to the right of the $y$-axis?

   **A.** $f(x) = -x^2 - 10x - 29$
   **B.** $f(x) = x^2 - 12x + 40$
   **C.** $f(x) = x^2 + 2x - 5$
   **D.** $f(x) = x^2 + 6x + 2$

### MATHEMATICAL PRACTICES
**Construct Viable Arguments and Critique the Reasoning of Others**

**35.** A student claims that the function $g(x) = -x^2 - 5$ has no real zeros. As evidence, she claims that the graph of $g(x)$ opens downward and its vertex is $(0, -5)$, which means that the graph never crosses the $x$-axis. Is the student's argument valid? Support your answer.

## THE SAFARI EXPERIENCE

A zoo is constructing a new exhibit of African animals called the Safari Experience. A path called the Lion Loop will run through the exhibit. The Lion Loop will have the shape of a parabola and will pass through these points shown on the map: (3, 8) near the lions, (7, 12) near the hyenas, and (10, 4.5) near the elephants.

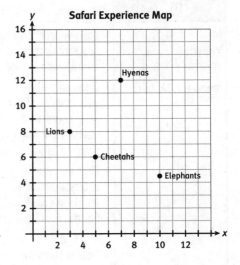

Safari Experience Map

1. Write the standard form of the quadratic function that passes through the points (3, 8), (7, 12), and (10, 4.5). This function models the Lion Loop on the map.

2. A lemonade stand will be positioned at the vertex of the parabola formed by the Lion Loop.
   a. Write the equation that models the Lion Loop in vertex form, $y = a(x - h)^2 + k$.
   b. What are the map coordinates of the lemonade stand? Explain how you know.

3. A graphic artist needs to draw the Lion Loop on the map.
   a. Provide instructions for the artist that describe the shape of the Lion Loop as a set of transformations of the graph of $f(x) = x^2$.
   b. Use the transformations of $f(x)$ to draw the Lion Loop on the map.

4. The Safari Experience will also have a second path called the Cheetah Curve. This path will also be in the shape of a parabola. It will open to the right and have its focus at the cheetah exhibit at map coordinates (5, 6).
   a. Choose a vertex for the Cheetah Curve. Explain why the coordinates you chose for the vertex are appropriate.
   b. Use the focus and the vertex to write the equation that models the Cheetah Curve.
   c. What are the directrix and the axis of symmetry of the parabola that models the Cheetah Curve?
   d. Draw and label the Cheetah Curve on the map.

| Scoring Guide | Exemplary | Proficient | Emerging | Incomplete |
|---|---|---|---|---|
| | The solution demonstrates these characteristics: | | | |
| **Mathematics Knowledge and Thinking** (Items 1, 2, 3a, 4a-c) | • Effective understanding of quadratic functions as transformations of $f(x) = x^2$<br>• Clear and accurate understanding of how to write a quadratic function in standard form given three points on its graph<br>• Clear and accurate understanding of how to transform a quadratic function from standard to vertex form<br>• Clear and accurate understanding of how to identify key features of a graph of a parabola and how they relate to the equation for a parabola | • Adequate understanding of quadratic functions as transformations of $f(x) = x^2$<br>• Largely correct understanding of how to write a quadratic function in standard form given three points on its graph<br>• Largely correct understanding of how to transform a quadratic function from standard to vertex form<br>• Largely correct understanding of how to identify key features of a graph of a parabola and how they relate to the equation for a parabola | • Partial understanding of quadratic functions as transformations of $f(x) = x^2$<br>• Partial understanding of how to write a quadratic function in standard form given three points on its graph<br>• Difficulty with transforming a quadratic function from standard to vertex form<br>• Partial understanding of how to identify key features of a graph of a parabola and how they relate to the equation for a parabola | • Inaccurate or incomplete understanding of quadratic functions as transformations of $f(x) = x^2$<br>• Little or no understanding of how to write a quadratic function in standard form given three points on its graph<br>• Little or no understanding of how to transform a quadratic function from standard to vertex form<br>• Little or no understanding of how to identify key features of a graph of a parabola and how they relate to the equation for a parabola |
| **Problem Solving** (Items 1, 2b, 4b) | • An appropriate and efficient strategy that results in a correct answer | • A strategy that may include unnecessary steps but results in a correct answer | • A strategy that results in some incorrect answers | • No clear strategy when solving problems |
| **Mathematical Modeling / Representations** (Items 1, 2b, 3b, 4b, 4d) | • Effective understanding of how to model real-world scenarios with quadratic functions and parabolas and interpret their key features<br>• Clear and accurate understanding of how to graph quadratic functions using transformations, and how to graph parabolas | • Adequate understanding of how to model real-world scenarios with quadratic functions and parabolas and interpret their key features<br>• Largely correct understanding of how to graph quadratic functions using transformations, and how to graph parabolas | • Partial understanding of how to model real-world scenarios with quadratic functions and parabolas and interpret their key features<br>• Some difficulty with understanding how to graph quadratic functions using transformations and with graphing parabolas | • Little or no understanding of how to model real-world scenarios with quadratic functions and parabolas and interpret their key features<br>• Inaccurate or incomplete understanding of how to graph quadratic functions using transformations, and how to graph parabolas |
| **Reasoning and Communication** (Items 2b, 3a, 4a) | • Precise use of appropriate math terms and language to describe how to graph a quadratic function as a transformation of $f(x) = x^2$<br>• Precise use of appropriate math terms and language to explain how features of a graph relate to a real-world scenario | • Adequate descriptions of how to graph a quadratic function as a transformation of $f(x) = x^2$<br>• Adequate explanation of how features of a graph relate to a real-world scenario | • Misleading or confusing descriptions of how to graph a quadratic function as a transformation of $f(x) = x^2$<br>• Partially correct explanation of how features of a graph relate to a real-world scenario | • Incomplete or inaccurate descriptions of how to graph a quadratic function as a transformation of $f(x) = x^2$<br>• Incorrect or incomplete explanation of how features of a graph relate to a real-world scenario |

Calendar Art

## Lesson 12-1 Key Features of Quadratic Functions

**Learning Targets:**

- Write a quadratic function from a verbal description.
- Identify and interpret key features of the graph of a quadratic function.

> **SUGGESTED LEARNING STRATEGIES:** Marking the Text, Paraphrasing, Create Representations, Quickwrite, Self Revision/Peer Revision

Ms. Picasso, sponsor for her school's art club, sells calendars featuring student artwork to raise money for art supplies. A local print shop sponsors the calendar sale and donates the printing and supplies. From past experience, Ms. Picasso knows that she can sell 150 calendars for $3.00 each. She considers raising the price to try to increase the profit that the club can earn from the sale. However, she realizes that by raising the price, the club will sell fewer than 150 calendars.

1. If Ms. Picasso raises the price of the calendar by $x$ dollars, write an expression for the price of one calendar.

2. In previous years, Ms. Picasso found that for each $0.40 increase in price, the number of calendars sold decreased by 10. Complete the table below to show that relationship between the price increase and the number of calendars sold.

| Increase in price ($), $x$ | Number of calendars sold |
|---|---|
| 0.00 | 150 |
| 0.40 | |
| 0.80 | |
| 1.20 | |

3. **Model with mathematics.** Use the data in the table to write an expression that models the number of calendars sold in terms of $x$, the price increase.

4. Write a function that models $A(x)$, the amount of money raised selling calendars when the price is increased $x$ dollars.

**My Notes**

**MATH TIP**

A quadratic function in *standard form* is written as $f(x) = ax^2 + bx + c$.

**5.** Write your function $A(x)$ in standard form. Identify the constants $a$, $b$, and $c$.

**6.** Graph $A(x)$ on the coordinate grid.

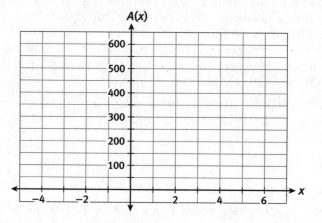

**7. a.** For what values of $x$ does the value of $A(x)$ increase as you move from left to right on the graph?

**b.** For what values of $x$ does the value of $A(x)$ decrease as you move from left to right on the graph?

**8. Reason quantitatively.** Based on the model, what is the maximum amount of money that can be earned? What is the increase in price of a calendar that will yield that maximum amount of money?

My Notes

**9. a.** What feature of the graph gives the information that you used to answer Item 8?

**b.** How does this feature relate to the intervals of $x$ for which $A(x)$ is increasing and decreasing?

The point that represents the maximum value of $A(x)$ is the *vertex* of this parabola. The $x$-coordinate of the vertex of the graph of $f(x) = ax^2 + bx + c$ can be found using the formula $x = -\dfrac{b}{2a}$.

**10.** Use this formula to find the $x$-coordinate of the vertex of $A(x)$.

**MATH TIP**

Substitute the $x$-coordinate of the vertex into the quadratic equation to find the $y$-coordinate of the vertex.

**Check Your Understanding**

**11.** Look back at the expression you wrote for $A(x)$ in Item 4. Explain what each part of the expression equal to $A(x)$ represents.

**12.** Is the vertex of the graph of a quadratic function always the highest point? Explain.

**13.** The graph of a quadratic function $f(x)$ opens upward, and its vertex is $(-2, 5)$. For what values of $x$ is the value of $f(x)$ increasing? For what values of $x$ is the value of $f(x)$ decreasing? Explain your answers.

**14. Construct viable arguments.** Suppose you are asked to find the vertex of the graph of $f(x) = -3(x - 4)^2 + 1$. Which method would you use? Explain why you would choose that method.

**My Notes**

## LESSON 12-1 PRACTICE

Mr. Picasso would like to create a small rectangular vegetable garden adjacent to his house. He has 24 ft of fencing to put around three sides of the garden.

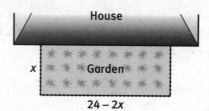

15. **Construct viable arguments.** Explain why $24 - 2x$ is an appropriate expression for the length of the garden in feet given that the width of the garden is $x$ ft.

16. Write the standard form of a quadratic function $G(x)$ that gives the area of the garden in square feet in terms of $x$. Then graph $G(x)$.

17. What is the vertex of the graph of $G(x)$? What do the coordinates of the vertex represent in this situation?

18. **Reason quantitatively.** What are the dimensions of the garden that yield that maximum area? Explain your answer.

Write each quadratic function in standard form and identify the vertex.

19. $f(x) = (3x - 6)(x + 4)$       20. $f(x) = 2(x - 6)(20 - 3x)$

**Learning Targets:**
- Write a quadratic function from a verbal description.
- Identify and interpret key features of the graph of a quadratic function.

**SUGGESTED LEARNING STRATEGIES:** Interactive Word Wall, Quickwrite, Think Aloud, Discussion Groups, Self Revision/Peer Revision

An intercept occurs at the point of intersection of a graph and one of the axes. For a function $f$, an $x$-intercept is a value $n$ for which $f(n) = 0$. The $y$-intercept is the value of $f(0)$. Use the graph that you made in Item 6 in the previous lesson for Items 1 and 2 below.

1. What is the $y$-intercept of the graph of $A(x)$? What is the significance of the $y$-intercept in terms the calendar problem?

2. **Make sense of problems.** What are the $x$-intercepts of the graph of $A(x)$? What is the significance of each $x$-intercept in terms of the calendar problem?

3. The $x$-intercepts of the graph of $f(x) = ax^2 + bx + c$ can be found by solving the equation $ax^2 + bx + c = 0$. Solve the equation $A(x) = 0$ to verify the $x$-intercepts of the graph.

4. **a.** Recall that $x$ represents the increase in the price of the calendars. Explain what negative values of $x$ represent in this situation.

   **b.** Recall that $A(x)$ represents the amount of money raised from selling the calendars. Explain what negative values of $A(x)$ represent in this situation.

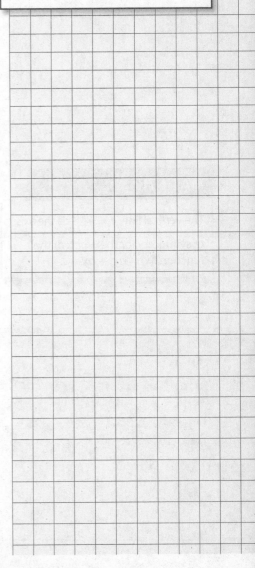

**MATH TIP**

As with graphs of linear functions, graphs of quadratic functions have intercepts where the graph intersects one of the axes.

An **x-intercept** is the $x$-coordinate of a point where a graph intersects the $x$-axis. Quadratic functions can have 0, 1, or 2 $x$-intercepts.

A **y-intercept** is the $y$-coordinate of a point where a graph intersects the $y$-axis. A quadratic function will only have one $y$-intercept.

**MATH TIP**

The reasonable domain and range of a function are the values in the domain and range of the function that make sense in a given real-world situation.

**WRITING MATH**

You can write a domain of $4 < x \le 2$ in interval notation as $(4, 2]$ and in set notation as $\{x \mid x \in \mathbb{R}, 4 < x \le 2\}$.

**MATH TIP**

The vertical line $x = -\dfrac{b}{2a}$ is the axis of symmetry for the graph of the function $f(x) = ax^2 + bx + c$.

5. **a. Reason quantitatively.** What is a reasonable domain of $A(x)$, assuming that the club makes a profit from the calendar sales? Write the domain as an inequality, in interval notation, and in set notation.

   **b.** Explain how you determined the reasonable domain.

6. **a.** What is a reasonable range of $A(x)$, assuming that the club makes a profit from the calendar sales? Write the range as an inequality, in interval notation, and in set notation.

   **b.** Explain how you determined the reasonable range.

7. What is the average of the $x$-intercepts in Item 2? How does this relate to the symmetry of a parabola?

### Check Your Understanding

8. **Construct viable arguments.** Explain why a quadratic function is an appropriate model for the amount the club will make from selling calendars.

9. Can a function have more than one $y$-intercept? Explain.

10. Do all quadratic functions have two $x$-intercepts? Explain.

11. **Reason abstractly.** Explain how the reasonable domain of a quadratic function helps to determine its reasonable range.

## LESSON 12-2 PRACTICE

Ms. Picasso is also considering having the students in the art club make and sell candles to raise money for supplies. The function $P(x) = -20x^2 + 320x - 780$ models the profit the club would make by selling the candles for $x$ dollars each.

12. What is the $y$-intercept of the graph of $P(x)$, and what is its significance in this situation?

13. What are the $x$-intercepts of the graph of $P(x)$, and what is their significance in this situation?

14. Give the reasonable domain and range of $P(x)$, assuming that the club does not want to lose money by selling the candles. Explain how you determined the reasonable domain and range.

15. **Make sense of problems.** What selling price for the candles would maximize the club's profit? Explain your answer.

Identify the $x$- and $y$-intercepts of each function.

16. $f(x) = x^2 + 11x + 30$          17. $f(x) = 4x^2 + 14x - 8$

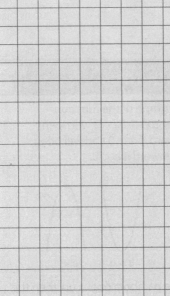

**CONNECT TO TECHNOLOGY**

When answering Items 12–15, it may help you to view a graph of the function on a graphing calculator.

**My Notes**

### Learning Targets:
- Identify key features of a quadratic function from an equation written in standard form.
- Use key features to graph a quadratic function.

**SUGGESTED LEARNING STRATEGIES:** Note Taking, Create Representations, Group Presentation, Identify a Subtask, Quickwrite

### Example A
For the quadratic function $f(x) = 2x^2 - 9x + 4$, identify the vertex, the $y$-intercept, $x$-intercept(s), and the axis of symmetry. Graph the function.

Identify $a$, $b$, and $c$.      $a = 2, b = -9, c = 4$

**Vertex**

Use $-\dfrac{b}{2a}$ to find the $x$-coordinate of the vertex.      $-\dfrac{(-9)}{2(2)} = \dfrac{9}{4}; f\left(\dfrac{9}{4}\right) = -\dfrac{49}{8}$

Then use $f\left(-\dfrac{b}{2a}\right)$ to find the $y$-coordinate.      vertex: $\left(\dfrac{9}{4}, -\dfrac{49}{8}\right)$

**$y$-intercept**

Evaluate $f(x)$ at $x = 0$.      $f(0) = 4$, so $y$-intercept is 4.

**$x$-intercepts**

Let $f(x) = 0$.      $2x^2 - 9x + 4 = 0$

Then solve for $x$ by factoring or by using the Quadratic Formula.      $x = \dfrac{1}{2}$ and $x = 4$ are solutions, so $x$-intercepts are $\dfrac{1}{2}$ and 4.

**Axis of Symmetry**

Find the vertical line through the vertex, $x = -\dfrac{b}{2a}$.      $x = \dfrac{9}{4}$

**Graph**

Graph the points identified above: vertex, point on $y$-axis, points on $x$-axis.

Then draw the smooth curve of a parabola through the points.

The $y$-coordinate of the vertex represents the minimum value of the function. The minimum value is $-\dfrac{49}{8}$.

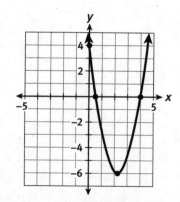

### MATH TIP
The graph of the function $f(x) = ax^2 + bx + c$ will open upward if $a > 0$ and will open downward if $a < 0$.

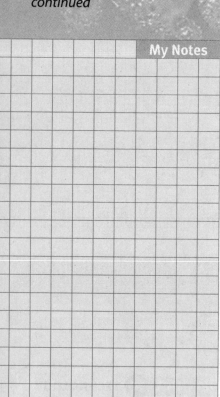

$a > 0$      $a < 0$

If the parabola opens up, then the $y$-coordinate of the vertex is the *minimum* value of the function. If it opens down, the $y$-coordinate of the vertex is the *maximum* value of the function.

**Try These A**

For each quadratic function, identify the vertex, the $y$-intercept, the $x$-intercept(s), and the axis of symmetry. Then graph the function and classify the vertex as a maximum or minimum.

**a.** $f(x) = x^2 - 4x - 5$

**b.** $f(x) = -3x^2 + 8x + 16$

**c.** $f(x) = 2x^2 + 8x + 3$

**d.** $f(x) = -x^2 + 4x - 7$

Consider the calendar fund-raising function from Lesson 12-1, Item 5, $A(x) = -25x^2 + 75x + 450$, whose graph is below.

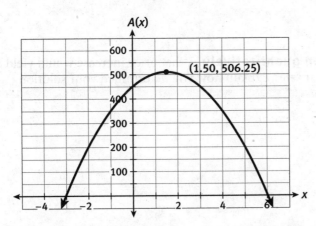

1. **Make sense of problems.** Suppose that Ms. Picasso raises $450 in the calendar sale. By how much did she increase the price? Explain your answer graphically and algebraically.

> **MATH TIP**
>
> Quadratic equations may be solved by algebraic methods such as factoring or the Quadratic Formula.
>
> An equation can be solved on a graphing calculator by entering each side of the equation as a function, graphing both functions, and finding the points of intersection. The $x$-coordinates of the intersection points are the solutions.

2. Suppose Ms. Picasso wants to raise $600. Describe why this is not possible, both graphically and algebraically.

3. In Lesson 12-1, Item 8, you found that the maximum amount of money that could be raised was $506.25. Explain both graphically and algebraically why this is true for only one possible price increase.

4. **Reason quantitatively.** What price increase would yield $500 in the calendar sale? Explain how you determined your solution.

### Check Your Understanding

5. **Make use of structure.** If you are given the equation of a quadratic function in standard form, how can you determine whether the function has a minimum or maximum?

6. Explain how to find the $x$-intercepts of the quadratic function $f(x) = x^2 + 17x + 72$ without graphing the function.

7. Explain the relationships among these features of the graph of a quadratic function: the vertex, the axis of symmetry, and the minimum or maximum value.

## LESSON 12-3 PRACTICE

Recall that the function $P(x) = -20x^2 + 320x - 780$ models the profit the art club would make by selling candles for $x$ dollars each. The graph of the function is below.

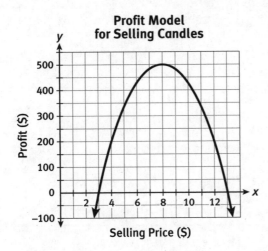

**Profit Model for Selling Candles**

8. Based on the model, what selling price(s) would result in a profit of $320? Explain how you determined your answer.

9. **Construct viable arguments.** Could the club make $600 in profit by selling candles? Justify your answer both graphically and algebraically.

10. If the club sells the candles for $6 each, how much profit can it expect to make? Explain how you determined your answer.

For each function, identify the vertex, $y$-intercept, $x$-intercept(s), and axis of symmetry. Graph the function. Identify whether the function has a maximum or minimum and give its value.

11. $f(x) = -x^2 + x + 12$

12. $g(x) = 2x^2 - 11x + 15$

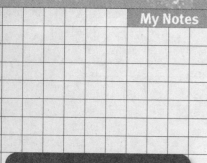

**MATH TIP**

The *x-intercepts* of a quadratic function $y = ax^2 + bx + c$ are the **zeros** of the function. The solutions of a quadratic equation $ax^2 + bx + c = 0$ are the **roots** of the equation.

**Learning Targets:**

- Use the discriminant to determine the nature of the solutions of a quadratic equation.
- Use the discriminant to help graph a quadratic function.

**SUGGESTED LEARNING STRATEGIES:** Summarizing, Note Taking, Create Representations, Quickwrite, Self Revision/Peer Revision

The discriminant of a quadratic equation $ax^2 + bx + c = 0$ can determine not only the nature of the solutions of the equation, but also the number of *x*-intercepts of its related function $f(x) = ax^2 + bx + c$.

| Discriminant of $ax^2 + bx + c = 0$ | Solutions and *x*-intercepts | Sample Graph of $f(x) = ax^2 + bx + c$ |
|---|---|---|
| $b^2 - 4ac > 0$<br><br>If $b^2 - 4ac$ is:<br>• a perfect square<br>• not a perfect square | • Two real solutions<br>• Two *x*-intercepts<br><br>• roots are rational<br>• roots are irrational | 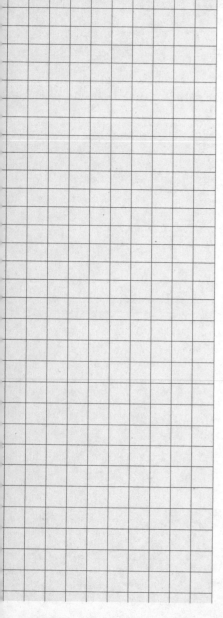 |
| $b^2 - 4ac = 0$ | • One real, rational solution (a double root)<br>• One *x*-intercept | |
| $b^2 - 4ac < 0$ | • Two complex conjugate solutions<br>• No *x*-intercepts | |

### Check Your Understanding

For each equation, find the value of the discriminant and describe the nature of the solutions. Then graph the related function and find the *x*-intercepts.

**1.** $4x^2 + 12x + 9 = 0$
**2.** $2x^2 + x + 5 = 0$
**3.** $2x^2 + x - 10 = 0$
**4.** $x^2 + 3x + 1 = 0$

**5. Reason abstractly.** How can calculating the discriminant help you decide whether to use factoring to solve a quadratic equation?

**6.** The graph of a quadratic function $f(x)$ is shown at right. Based on the graph, what can you conclude about the value of the discriminant and the nature of the solutions of the related quadratic equation? Explain.

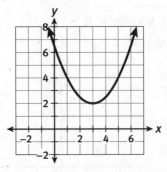

## LESSON 12-4 PRACTICE

**7.** A quadratic equation has two rational solutions. How many *x*-intercepts does the graph of the related quadratic function have? Explain your answer.

**8. Make sense of problems.** The graph of a quadratic function has one *x*-intercept. What can you conclude about the value of the discriminant of the related quadratic equation? Explain your reasoning.

**9.** A quadratic equation has two irrational roots. What can you conclude about the value of the discriminant of the equation?

For each equation, find the value of the discriminant and describe the nature of the solutions. Then graph the related function and find the *x*-intercepts.

**10.** $x^2 - 4x + 1 = 0$
**11.** $x^2 - 6x + 15 = 0$
**12.** $4x^2 + 4x + 1 = 0$
**13.** $x^2 - 2x - 15 = 0$

**My Notes**

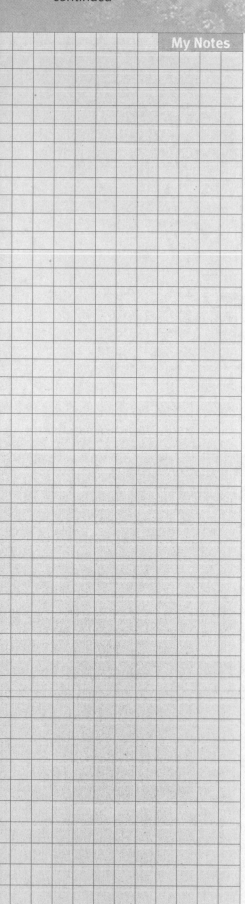

### Learning Targets:
- Graph a quadratic inequality in two variables.
- Determine the solutions to a quadratic inequality by graphing.

> **SUGGESTED LEARNING STRATEGIES:** Marking the Text, Create Representations, Guess and Check, Think-Pair-Share, Quickwrite

The solutions to quadratic inequalities of the form $y > ax^2 + bx + c$ or $y < ax^2 + bx + c$ can be most easily described using a graph. An important part of solving these inequalities is graphing the related quadratic functions.

### Example A
Solve $y > -x^2 - x + 6$.

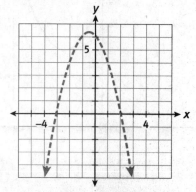

Graph the related quadratic function $y = -x^2 - x + 6$.

If the inequality symbol is $>$ or $<$, use a *dotted curve.*

If the symbol is $\geq$ or $\leq$, then use a *solid curve.*

This curve divides the plane into two regions.

Test $(0, 0)$ in $y > -x^2 - x + 6$.

$0 > -0^2 - 0 + 6$

$0 > 6$ is a false statement.

Choose a point on the plane, but not on the curve, to test.

$(0, 0)$ is an easy point to use, if possible.

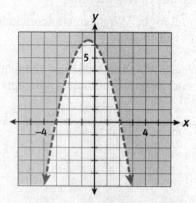

If the statement is true, shade the region that contains the point. If it is false, shade the other region.

The shaded region represents all solutions to the quadratic inequality.

**My Notes**

### Try These A

Solve each inequality by graphing.

**a.** $y \geq x^2 + 4x - 5$

**b.** $y > 2x^2 - 5x - 12$

**c.** $y < -3x^2 + 8x + 3$

---

### Check Your Understanding

1. The solutions of which inequality are shown in the graph?

   **A.** $y \leq -2x^2 + 8x - 7$
   **B.** $y \geq -2x^2 + 8x - 7$
   **C.** $y \leq 2x^2 - 8x - 7$
   **D.** $y \geq 2x^2 - 8x - 7$

   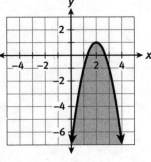

2. **Reason abstractly.** How does graphing a quadratic inequality in two variables differ from graphing the related quadratic function?

3. Graph the quadratic inequality $y \geq -x^2 - 6x - 13$. Then state whether each ordered pair is a solution of the inequality.

   **a.** $(-1, -6)$     **b.** $(-4, -8)$     **c.** $(-6, -10)$     **d.** $(-2, -5)$

My Notes

## LESSON 12-5 PRACTICE

Graph each inequality.

**4.** $y \leq x^2 + 4x + 7$

**5.** $y < x^2 - 6x + 10$

**6.** $y > \frac{1}{2}x^2 + 2x + 1$

**7.** $y \geq -2x^2 + 4x + 1$

**8. Construct viable arguments.** Give the coordinates of two points that are solutions of the inequality $y \leq x^2 - 6x + 4$ and the coordinates of two points that are not solutions of the inequality. Explain how you found your answers.

**9. Model with mathematics.** The students in Ms. Picasso's art club decide to sell candles in the shape of square prisms. The height of each candle will be no more than 10 cm. Write an inequality to model the possible volumes in cubic centimeters of a candle with a base side length of $x$ cm.

**10. Make sense of problems.** Brendan has 400 cm$^3$ of wax. Can he make a candle with a base side length of 6 cm that will use all of the wax if the height is limited to 10 cm? Explain your answer using your inequality from Item 9.

---

**CONNECT TO GEOMETRY**

A square prism has two square bases. The volume of a square prism is equal to the area of one of its bases times its height.

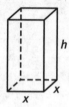

## ACTIVITY 12 PRACTICE
Write your answers on notebook paper.
Show your work.

### Lesson 12-1

The cost of tickets to a whale-watching tour depends on the number of people in the group. For each additional person, the cost per ticket decreases by $1. For a group with only two people, the cost per ticket is $44. Use this information for Items 1–7.

1. Complete the table below to show the relationship between the number of people in a group and the cost per ticket.

| Number of People | Cost per Ticket ($) |
|:---:|:---:|
| 2 | |
| 3 | |
| 4 | |
| 5 | |

2. Use the data in the table to write an expression that models the cost per ticket in terms of $x$, the number of people in a group.

3. Write a quadratic function in standard form that models $T(x)$, the total cost of the tickets for a group with $x$ people.

4. Graph $T(x)$ on a coordinate grid.

5. **a.** For what values of $x$ does the value of $T(x)$ increase as you move from left to right on the graph?
   **b.** For what values of $x$ does the value of $T(x)$ decrease as you move from left to right on the graph?

6. What is the vertex of the graph of $T(x)$? What do the coordinates of the vertex represent in this situation?

7. Groups on the tour are limited to a maximum size of 20 people. What is the total cost of the tickets for a group of 20 people? Explain how you found your answer.

Write each quadratic function in standard form and identify the vertex.

8. $f(x) = (4x - 4)(x + 5)$

9. $f(x) = 4(x + 8)(10 - x)$

### Lesson 12-2

Mr. Gonzales would like to create a playground in his backyard. He has 20 ft of fencing to enclose the play area. Use this information for Items 10–13.

10. Write a quadratic function in standard form that models $f(x)$, the total area of the playground in square feet in terms of its width $x$ in feet. Then graph $f(x)$.

11. Write the $x$- and $y$-intercepts of $f(x)$ and interpret them in terms of the problem.

12. Give the reasonable domain and range of $f(x)$ as inequalities, in interval notation, and in set notation. Explain how you determined the reasonable domain and range.

13. What is the maximum area for the playground? What are the dimensions of the playground with the maximum area?

Identify the $x$- and $y$-intercepts of each function.

14. $f(x) = x^2 + 3x - 28$

15. $f(x) = 2x^2 + 13x + 15$

### Lesson 12-3

For each function, identify the vertex, $y$-intercept, $x$-intercept(s), and axis of symmetry. Identify whether the function has a maximum or minimum and give its value.

16. $f(x) = -x^2 + 4x + 5$

17. $f(x) = 2x^2 - 12x + 13$

18. $f(x) = -3x^2 + 12x - 9$

19. Explain how to find the $y$-intercept of the quadratic function $f(x) = x^2 - 3x - 18$ without graphing the function.

The function $h(t) = -5t^2 + 15t + 1$ models the height in meters of an arrow $t$ seconds after it is shot. Use this information for Items 20 and 21.

20. Based on the model, when will the arrow have a height of 10 m? Round times to the nearest tenth of a second. Explain how you determined your answer.

21. Does the arrow reach a height of 12 m? Justify your answer both graphically and algebraically.

## Lesson 12-4

For each equation, find the value of the discriminant and describe the nature of the solutions. Then find the $x$-intercepts.

22. $2x^2 - 5x - 3 = 0$

23. $3x^2 + x + 2 = 0$

24. $4x^2 + 4x + 1 = 0$

25. $2x^2 + 6x + 3 = 0$

26. A quadratic equation has two distinct rational roots. Which one of the following could be the discriminant of the equation?

   **A.** −6      **B.** 0
   **C.** 20      **D.** 64

27. A quadratic equation has one distinct rational solution. How many $x$-intercepts does the graph of the related quadratic function have? Explain your answer.

28. The graph of a quadratic function has no $x$-intercepts. What can you conclude about the value of the discriminant of the related quadratic equation? Explain your reasoning.

## Lesson 12-5

Graph each quadratic inequality.

29. $y < x^2 + 7x + 10$

30. $y \geq 2x^2 + 4x - 1$

31. $y > x^2 - 6x + 9$

32. $y \leq -x^2 + 3x + 4$

33. Which of the following is a solution of the inequality $y > -x^2 - 8x - 12$?

   **A.** $(-6, 0)$      **B.** $(-4, -2)$
   **C.** $(-3, 1)$      **D.** $(-2, \ 4)$

The time in minutes a factory needs to make $x$ cell phone parts in a single day is modeled by the inequality $y \leq -0.0005x^2 + x + 20$, for the domain $0 \leq x \leq 1000$. Use this information for Items 34–36.

34. **a.** Is the ordered pair (200, 100) a solution of the inequality? How do you know?
   **b.** What does the ordered pair (200, 100) represent in this situation?

35. What is the longest it will take the factory to make 600 cell phone parts? Explain how you determined your answer.

36. Can the factory complete an order for 300 parts in 4 hours? Explain.

37. Give the coordinates of two points that are solutions of the inequality $y \leq x^2 - 3x - 10$ and the coordinates of two points that are not solutions of the inequality. Explain how you found your answers.

## MATHEMATICAL PRACTICES
### Look for and Make Use of Structure

38. Describe the relationship between solving a quadratic equation and graphing the related quadratic function.

# Systems of Linear and Nonlinear Equations

## Supply and Demand
### Lesson 13-1 Solving a System Graphically

**Learning Targets:**

- Use graphing to solve a system consisting of a linear and a nonlinear equation.
- Interpret the solutions of a system of equations.

> **SUGGESTED LEARNING STRATEGIES:** Close Reading, Think Aloud, Discussion Groups, Create Representations, Look for a Pattern

The owner of Salon Ultra Blue is working with a pricing consultant to determine the best price to charge for a basic haircut. The consultant knows that, in general, as the price of a haircut at a salon goes down, demand for haircuts at the salon goes up. In other words, if Salon Ultra Blue decreases its prices, more customers will want to get their hair cut there.

Based on the consultant's research, customers will demand 250 haircuts per week if the price per haircut is $20. For each $5 increase in price, the demand will decrease by 25 haircuts per week.

1. Let the function $f(x)$ model the quantity of haircuts demanded by customers when the price of haircuts is $x$ dollars.

   a. **Reason quantitatively.** What type of function is $f(x)$? How do you know?

   b. Write the equation of $f(x)$.

The price of a haircut not only affects demand, but also affects supply. As the price charged for a haircut increases, cutting hair becomes more profitable. More stylists will want to work at the salon, and they will be willing to work longer hours to provide more haircuts.

© 2015 College Board. All rights reserved.

**CONNECT TO ECONOMICS**

In economics, *demand* is the quantity of an item that customers are willing to buy at a particular price. The *law of demand* states that as the price of an item decreases, the demand for the item tends to increase.

**CONNECT TO ECONOMICS**

*Supply* is the quantity of an item that businesses are willing to sell at a particular price. The *law of supply* states that as the price of an item increases, the supply of the item tends to increase.

**My Notes**

The consultant gathered the following data on how the price of haircuts affects the number of haircuts the stylists are willing to supply each week.

**Supply of Haircuts**

| Price per Haircut ($) | Number of Haircuts Available per Week |
|---|---|
| 20 | 15 |
| 30 | 55 |
| 40 | 115 |
| 50 | 195 |

2. The relationship shown in the table is quadratic. Write the equation of a quadratic function $g(x)$ that models the quantity of haircuts the stylists are willing to supply when the price of haircuts is $x$ dollars.

**CONNECT TO TECHNOLOGY**

One way to write the equation of the quadratic function is to perform a quadratic regression on the data in the table. See Activity 10 for more information.

3. **Model with mathematics.** Write a system of two equations in two variables for the demand and supply functions. In each equation, let $y$ represent the quantity of haircuts and $x$ represent the price in dollars per haircut.

4. Graph the system on the coordinate plane.

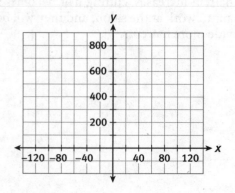

**5.** Explain how you determine the location of the solutions on the graph in Item 4.

**6.** Explain the relationship of the solution to the demand function $f(x)$ and the supply function $g(x)$.

**7.** Use the graph to approximate the solutions of the system of equations.

Now use a graphing calculator to make better approximations of the solutions of the system of equations. First, enter the equations from the system as Y1 and Y2.

**8. Use appropriate tools strategically.** Now view a table showing values of X, Y1, and Y2.
   **a.** How can you approximate solutions of a system of two equations in two variables by using a table of values on a graphing calculator?

   **b.** Use the table to approximate the solutions of the system. Find the coordinates of the solutions to the nearest integer.

> **TECHNOLOGY TIP**
>
> You can change the table settings on a graphing calculator by pressing 2nd and then the key with TblSet printed above it. The table start setting (TblStart) lets you change the first value of X displayed in the table. The table step setting ($\triangle$Tbl) lets you adjust the change in X between rows of the table.

My Notes

**TECHNOLOGY TIP**

To use the intersect feature on a graphing calculator, access the calculate menu by pressing [2nd] and then the key with Calc printed above it. Next, select **5: Intersect**, and then follow the instructions.

9. Next, view a graph of the system of equations on the graphing calculator. Adjust the viewing window as needed so that the intersection points of the graphs of the equations are visible. Then use the intersect feature to approximate the solutions of the system of equations.

10. Explain why one of the solutions you found in Item 9 does not make sense in the context of the supply and demand functions for haircuts at the salon.

11. **Make sense of problems.** Interpret the remaining solution in the context of the situation.

12. Explain why the solution you described in Item 11 is reasonable.

13. The pricing consultant recommends that Salon Ultra Blue price its haircuts so that the weekly demand is equal to the weekly supply. Based on this recommendation, how much should the salon charge for a basic haircut?

My Notes

14. **Model with mathematics.** Graph each system of one linear equation and one quadratic equation. For each system, list the number of real solutions.

a. $\begin{cases} y = x \\ y = x^2 - 2 \end{cases}$

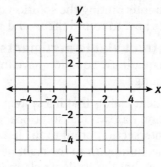

b. $\begin{cases} y = 2x - 3 \\ y = x^2 - 2 \end{cases}$

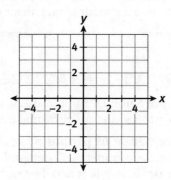

c. $\begin{cases} y = 3x - 9 \\ y = x^2 - 2 \end{cases}$

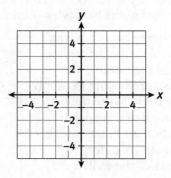

15. Make a conjecture about the possible number of real solutions of a system of two equations that includes one linear equation and one quadratic equation.

My Notes

ACADEMIC VOCABULARY

A **counterexample** is an example that demonstrates that a statement is not true.

## Check Your Understanding

16. When interpreting the solution of the system in Item 11, how did you decide how to round the $x$- and $y$-coordinates of the solution?

17. **Construct viable arguments.** Can a system of a linear equation and a quadratic equation have infinitely many solutions? Explain your reasoning.

18. A student claims that if a system of a linear equation and a quadratic equation has two real solutions, then a graph of the system will have one intersection point to the left of the vertex of the parabola and one intersection point to the right of the vertex. Provide a **counterexample** to show that the student's claim is not correct.

19. Compare and contrast using a graph and a table to approximate the solution of a system of one linear equation and one quadratic equation.

## LESSON 13-1 PRACTICE

The owner of Salon Ultra Blue also wants to set the price for styling hair for weddings, proms, and other formal events.

20. **Make sense of problems.** Based on the pricing consultant's research, customers will demand 34 formal hairstyles per week if the price per hairstyle is $40. For each $10 increase in price, the demand will decrease by 4 hairstyles per week. Write a linear function $f(x)$ that models the quantity of formal hairstyles demanded by customers when the price of the hairstyles is $x$ dollars.

21. The table shows how the price of formal hairstyles affects the number the stylists are willing to supply each week. Write the equation of a quadratic function $g(x)$ that models the quantity of formal hairstyles the stylists are willing to supply when the price of hairstyles is $x$ dollars.

### Supply of Formal Hairstyles

| Price per Hairstyle ($) | Number Available per Week |
|---|---|
| 40 | 3 |
| 50 | 9 |
| 60 | 17 |

22. **Model with mathematics.** Write a system of two equations in two variables for the demand and supply functions. In each equation, let $y$ represent the quantity of formal hairstyles and $x$ represent the price in dollars per hairstyle.

23. Approximate the solutions of the system by using a graph or table.

24. How much should the salon charge for a formal hairstyle so that the weekly demand is equal to the weekly supply? Explain how you determined your answer.

25. Explain why your answer to Item 24 is reasonable.

**Learning Targets:**

- Use substitution to solve a system consisting of a linear and nonlinear equation.
- Determine when a system consisting of a linear and nonlinear equation has no solution.

**SUGGESTED LEARNING STRATEGIES:** Summarizing, Identify a Subtask, Think-Pair-Share, Drafting, Self Revision/Peer Revision

In the last lesson, you approximated the solutions to systems of one linear equation and one quadratic equation by using tables and graphs. You can also solve such systems algebraically, just as you did when solving systems of two linear equations.

### Example A

The following system represents the supply and demand functions for basic haircuts at Salon Ultra Blue, where $y$ is the quantity of haircuts demanded or supplied when the price of haircuts is $x$ dollars. Solve this system algebraically to find the price at which the supply of haircuts equals the demand.

$$\begin{cases} y = -5x + 350 \\ y = \dfrac{1}{10}x^2 - x - 5 \end{cases}$$

**Step 1:** Use substitution to solve for $x$.

$y = -5x + 350$     The first equation is solved for $y$.

$-5x + 350 = \dfrac{1}{10}x^2 - x - 5$     Substitute for $y$ in the second equation.

$0 = \dfrac{1}{10}x^2 + 4x - 355$     Write the equation in standard form.

$0 = x^2 + 40x - 3550$     Multiply both sides by 10 to eliminate the fraction.

$x = \dfrac{-40 \pm \sqrt{40^2 - 4(1)(-3550)}}{2(1)}$     Use the Quadratic Formula.

$x = -20 \pm 5\sqrt{158}$

$x \approx -82.85$ or $x \approx 42.85$

**Step 2:** Substitute each value of $x$ into one of the original equations to find the corresponding value of $y$.

$y = -5x + 350$        $y = -5x + 350$

$y \approx -5(-82.85) + 350$        $y \approx -5(42.85) + 350$

$y \approx 764$                  $y \approx 136$

**My Notes**

**MATH TIP**

In this example, the exact values of $x$ are irrational. Because $x$ represents a price in dollars, use a calculator to find rational approximations of $x$ to two decimal places.

**Step 3:** Write the solutions as ordered pairs.

The solutions are approximately $(-82.85, 764)$ and $(42.85, 136)$. Ignore the first solution because a negative value of $x$ does not make sense in this situation.

**Solution:** The price at which the supply of haircuts equals the demand is $42.85. At this price, customers will demand 136 haircuts, and the stylists will supply them.

## Try These A

Solve each system algebraically. Check your answers by substituting each solution into one of the original equations. Show your work.

a. $\begin{cases} y = -2x - 7 \\ y = -2x^2 + 4x + 1 \end{cases}$ 

b. $\begin{cases} y = x^2 + 6x + 5 \\ y = 2x + 1 \end{cases}$

c. $\begin{cases} y = \dfrac{1}{2}(x + 4)^2 + 5 \\ y = \dfrac{17}{2} - x \end{cases}$ 

d. $\begin{cases} y = -4x^2 + 5x - 8 \\ y = -3x - 24 \end{cases}$

1. Use substitution to solve the following system of equations. Show your work.

$$\begin{cases} y = 4x + 24 \\ y = -x^2 + 18x - 29 \end{cases}$$

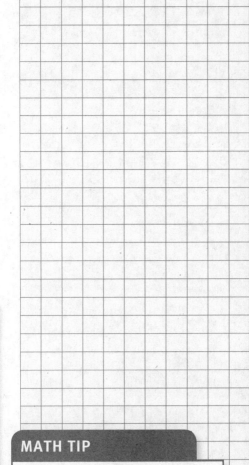

**2.** Describe the solutions of the system of equations from Item 1.

**3. Use appropriate tools strategically.** Confirm that the system of equations from Item 1 has no real solutions by graphing the system on a graphing calculator. How does the graph show that the system has no real solutions?

## Check Your Understanding

**4.** How does solving a system of one linear equation and one quadratic equation by substitution differ from solving a system of two linear equations by substitution?

**5. Reason abstractly.** What is an advantage of solving a system of one linear equation and one quadratic equation algebraically rather than by graphing or using a table of values?

**6.** Write a journal entry in which you explain step by step how to solve the following system by using substitution.

$$\begin{cases} y = 2x^2 - 3x + 6 \\ y = -2x + 9 \end{cases}$$

**7.** Could you solve the system in Item 6 by using elimination rather than substitution? Explain.

**8.** Explain how you could use the discriminant of a quadratic equation to determine how many real solutions the following system has.

$$\begin{cases} y = 4x - 21 \\ y = x^2 - 4x - 5 \end{cases}$$

**MATH TIP**

To review solving a system of equations by elimination, see Activity 3.

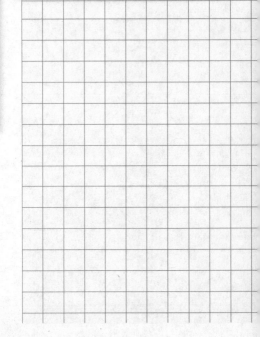

**My Notes**

## LESSON 13-2 PRACTICE

Find the real solutions of each system algebraically. Show your work.

9. $\begin{cases} y = -3x - 8 \\ y = x^2 + 4x + 2 \end{cases}$

10. $\begin{cases} y = -2x^2 + 16x - 26 \\ y = 72 - 12x \end{cases}$

11. $\begin{cases} y = \dfrac{1}{4}x^2 - 6x + 1 \\ y = \dfrac{3}{4}x - \dfrac{23}{2} \end{cases}$

12. $\begin{cases} y = (x - 5)^2 - 3 \\ y = -2x - 3 \end{cases}$

The owner of Salon Ultra Blue is setting the price for hair highlights. The following system represents the demand and supply functions for hair highlights, where $y$ is the quantity demanded or supplied per week for a given price $x$ in dollars.

$$\begin{cases} y = -0.8x + 128 \\ y = 0.03x^2 - 1.5x + 18 \end{cases}$$

13. Use substitution to solve the system of equations.

14. **Attend to precision.** How much should the salon charge for hair highlights so that the weekly demand is equal to the weekly supply? Explain how you determined your answer.

15. Explain why your answer to Item 14 is reasonable.

## ACTIVITY 13 PRACTICE
Write your answers on notebook paper.
Show your work.

### Lesson 13-1

Lori was partway up an escalator when her friend Evie realized that she had Lori's keys. Evie, who was still on the ground floor, tossed the keys up to Lori. The function $f(x) = -16x^2 + 25x + 5$ models the height in feet of the keys $x$ seconds after they were thrown. Use this information for Items 1–5.

1. When the keys are thrown, Lori's hands are 9 ft above ground level and moving upward at a rate of 0.75 ft/s. Write the equation of a function $g(x)$ that gives the height of Lori's hands compared to ground level $x$ seconds after the keys are thrown.

2. Write the functions $f(x)$ and $g(x)$ as a system of two equations in two variables. In each equation, let $y$ represent height in feet and $x$ represent time in seconds.

3. Graph the system of equations, and use the graph to approximate the solutions of the system.

4. How long after the keys are thrown will Lori be able to catch them? Assume that Lori can catch the keys when they are at the same height as her hands. Explain how you determined your answer.

5. Explain why your answer to Item 4 is reasonable.

Solve each system by using a graph or table (answers will be approximate).

6. $\begin{cases} y = 10 - 2x \\ y = x^2 - 12x + 31 \end{cases}$

7. $\begin{cases} y = 5x + 39 \\ y = x^2 + 14x + 52 \end{cases}$

8. $\begin{cases} y = -2(x-3)^2 + 9 \\ y = -4x + 3 \end{cases}$

Use a graph to determine the number of real solutions of each system.

9. $\begin{cases} y = 3x^2 + 6x + 4 \\ y = 0.5x + 8 \end{cases}$

10. $\begin{cases} y = -2x^2 + 8x - 10 \\ y = -2x + 4 \end{cases}$

11. $\begin{cases} y = 24 - 4x \\ y = x^2 - 12x + 40 \end{cases}$

12. Which ordered pair is a solution of the system of equations graphed below?

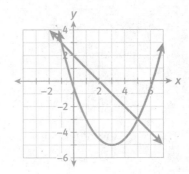

**A.** $(-3, 5)$  **B.** $(-1, 3)$
**C.** $(2, 0)$  **D.** $(3, -5)$

A parallelogram has a height of $x$ cm. The length of its base is 4 cm greater than its height. A triangle has the same height as the parallelogram. The length of the triangle's base is 20 cm.

13. Write a system of two equations in two variables that can be used to determine the values of $x$ for which the parallelogram and the triangle have the same area.

14. Solve the system by using a graph or table.

15. Interpret the solutions of the system in the context of the situation.

### Lesson 13-2

Solve each system algebraically. Check your answers by substituting each solution into one of the original equations. Show your work.

16. $\begin{cases} y = x - 7 \\ y = -x^2 - 2x - 7 \end{cases}$

17. $\begin{cases} y = 2x^2 - 12x + 26 \\ y = 8x - 24 \end{cases}$

18. $\begin{cases} y = -3(x - 4)^2 + 2 \\ y = 6x - 31 \end{cases}$

19. $\begin{cases} y = -0.5x - 1 \\ y = 0.5x^2 + 3x - 5 \end{cases}$

A map of a harbor is laid out on a coordinate grid, with the origin marking a buoy at the center of the harbor. A fishing boat is following a path that can be represented on the map by the equation $y = x^2 - 2x - 4$. A ferry is following a linear path that passes through the points $(-3, 7)$ and $(0, -5)$ when represented on the map. Use this information for Items 20–22.

20. Write a system of equations that can be used to determine whether the paths of the boats will cross.

21. Use substitution to solve the system.

22. Interpret the solution(s) of the system in the context of the situation.

23. How many real solutions does the following system have?

$$\begin{cases} y = -x^2 + 4x \\ y = 3x + 5 \end{cases}$$

   A. none      B. one
   C. two      D. infinitely many

24. Explain how you can support your answer to Item 23 algebraically.

A picture-framing company sells two types of glass: regular and nonglare. For a piece of nonglare glass, the charge is equal to the length of the longest side in inches multiplied by the rate $0.75 per inch. The table shows the charge for several sizes of regular glass.

**Charge for Regular Glass**

| Length of Longest Side (in.) | Charge ($) |
|---|---|
| 12 | 3.96 |
| 18 | 7.56 |
| 24 | 12.24 |

25. Write a linear function $f(x)$ that gives the charge in dollars for a piece of nonglare glass whose longest side measures $x$ inches.

26. Write a quadratic function $g(x)$ that gives the charge in dollars for a piece of regular glass whose longest side measures $x$ inches.

27. Write the functions $f(x)$ and $g(x)$ as a system of equations in terms of $y$, the charge in dollars for a piece of glass, and $x$, the length of the longest side in inches.

28. Solve the system by using substitution.

29. For what length will the charge for nonglare glass be the same as the charge for regular glass? What will the charge be? Explain your answers.

### MATHEMATICAL PRACTICES
#### Reason Abstractly and Quantitatively

30. Austin sells sets of magnets online. His cost in dollars of making the magnets is given by $f(x) = 200 + 8x - 0.01x^2$, where $x$ is the number of magnet sets he makes. His income in dollars from selling the magnets is given by $g(x) = 18x$, where $x$ is the number of magnet sets he sells. Write and solve the system, and then explain what the solution(s) mean in the context of the situation.

## THE GREEN MONSTER

During a Boston Red Sox baseball game at Fenway Park, the opposing team hit a home run over the left field wall. An unhappy Red Sox fan caught the ball and threw it back onto the field. The height of the ball, $h(t)$, in feet, $t$ seconds after the fan threw the baseball, is given by the function $h(t) = -16t^2 + 32t + 48$.

**1.** Graph the equation on the coordinate grid below.

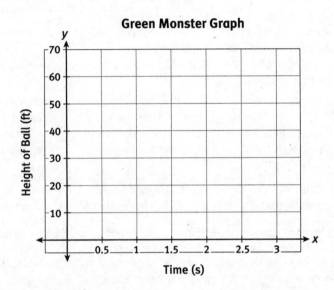

**Green Monster Graph**

*Height of Ball (ft)* / *Time (s)*

**CONNECT TO HISTORY**

The left field wall in Fenway Park is called the Green Monster, a reference to its unusual height.

**2.** Find each measurement value described below. Then tell how each value relates to the graph.
   **a.** At what height was the fan when he threw the ball?
   **b.** What was the maximum height of the ball after the fan threw it?
   **c.** When did the ball hit the field?

**3.** What are the reasonable domain and reasonable range of $h(t)$? Explain how you determined your answers.

**4.** Does the baseball reach a height of 65 ft? Explain your answer both graphically and algebraically.

**5.** Each baseball team in a minor league plays each other team three times during the regular season.
   **a.** The table shows the relationship between the number of teams in a baseball league and the total number of games required for each team to play each of the other teams three times. Write a quadratic equation that models the data in the table.

| Number of Teams, $x$ | Number of Games, $y$ |
|---|---|
| 2 | 3 |
| 3 | 9 |
| 4 | 18 |
| 5 | 30 |

   **b.** Last season, the total number of games played in the regular season was 35 more than 10 times the number of teams. Use this information to write a linear equation that gives the number of regular games $y$ in terms of the number of teams $x$.
   **c.** Write a system of equations using the quadratic equation from part a and the linear equation from part b. Then solve the system and interpret the solutions.

| Scoring Guide | Exemplary | Proficient | Emerging | Incomplete |
|---|---|---|---|---|
| | The solution demonstrates these characteristics: | | | |
| **Mathematics Knowledge and Thinking** (Items 2, 4, 5) | • Effective understanding of how to solve quadratic equations and systems of equations | • Adequate understanding of how to solve quadratic equations and systems of equations | • Partial understanding of how to solve quadratic equations and systems of equations | • Inaccurate or incomplete understanding of how to solve quadratic equations and systems of equations |
| | • Clear and accurate understanding of how to write linear and quadratic models from verbal descriptions or tables of data | • Largely correct understanding of how to write linear and quadratic models from verbal descriptions or tables of data | • Partial understanding of how to write linear and quadratic models from verbal descriptions or tables of data | • Little or no understanding of how to write linear and quadratic models from verbal descriptions or tables of data |
| | • Clear and accurate understanding of how to use an equation or graph to identify key features of a quadratic function | • Largely correct understanding of how to use an equation or graph to identify key features of a quadratic function | • Difficulty with using an equation or graph to identify key features of a quadratic function | • Little or no understanding of how to use an equation or graph to identify key features of a quadratic function |
| **Problem Solving** (Items 2, 4, 5c) | • An appropriate and efficient strategy that results in a correct answer | • A strategy that may include unnecessary steps but results in a correct answer | • A strategy that results in some incorrect answers | • No clear strategy when solving problems |
| **Mathematical Modeling / Representations** (Items 1, 2, 3, 4, 5) | • Effective understanding of how to interpret solutions to a system of equations that represents a real-world scenario | • Adequate understanding of how to interpret solutions to a system of equations that represents a real-world scenario | • Partial understanding of how to interpret solutions to a system of equations that represents a real-world scenario | • Little or no understanding of how to interpret solutions to a system of equations that represents a real-world scenario |
| | • Clear and accurate understanding of how to model real-world scenarios with quadratic and linear functions, including reasonable domain and range | • Largely correct understanding of how to model real-world scenarios with quadratic and linear functions, including reasonable domain and range | • Some difficulty with modeling real-world scenarios with quadratic and linear functions, including reasonable domain and range | • Inaccurate or incomplete understanding of how to model real-world scenarios with quadratic and linear functions, including reasonable domain and range |
| | • Clear and accurate understanding of how to graph and interpret key features of a quadratic function that represents a real-world scenario | • Largely correct understanding of how to graph and interpret key features of a quadratic function that represents a real-world scenario | • Some difficulty with graphing and interpreting key features of a quadratic function that represents a real-world scenario | • Inaccurate or incomplete understanding of how to graph and interpret key features of a quadratic function that represents a real-world scenario |
| **Reasoning and Communication** (Items 2, 3, 4) | • Precise use of appropriate math terms and language to relate the features of a quadratic model, including reasonable domain and range, to a real-world scenario | • Adequate explanations to relate the features of a quadratic model, including reasonable domain and range, to a real-world scenario | • Misleading or confusing explanations to relate the features of a quadratic model, including reasonable domain and range, to a real-world scenario | • Incomplete or inaccurate explanations to relate the features of a quadratic model, including reasonable domain and range, to a real-world scenario |
| | • Clear and accurate use of mathematical work to explain whether or not the height could reach 65 feet | • Correct use of mathematical work to explain whether or not the height could reach 65 feet | • Partially correct explanation of whether or not the height could reach 65 feet | • Incorrect or incomplete explanation of whether or not the height could reach 65 feet |

# Polynomials

## Unit Overview

In this unit you will study polynomials, beginning with real-world applications and polynomial operations. You will also investigate intercepts, end behavior, and relative extrema. You will learn to apply the Binomial Theorem to expand binomials, and you will be introduced to several theorems that will assist you in factoring, graphing, and understanding polynomial functions.

## Key Terms

As you study this unit, add these and other terms to your math notebook. Include in your notes your prior knowledge of each word, as well as your experiences in using the word in different mathematical examples. If needed, ask for help in pronouncing new words and add information on pronunciation to your math notebook. It is important that you learn new terms and use them correctly in your class discussions and in your problem solutions.

### Academic Vocabulary
- alternative

### Math Terms
- polynomial function
- degree
- standard form of a polynomial
- relative maximum
- relative minimum
- end behavior
- even function
- odd function
- synthetic division
- combination
- factorial
- summation notation
- Fundamental Theorem of Algebra
- extrema
- relative extrema
- global extrema

### ESSENTIAL QUESTIONS

? How do polynomial functions help to model real-world behavior?

? How do you determine the graph of a polynomial function?

### EMBEDDED ASSESSMENTS

This unit has two embedded assessments, following Activities 16 and 18. The first will give you the opportunity to demonstrate what you have learned about polynomial functions, including operations on polynomials. You will also be asked to apply the Binomial Theorem. The second assessment focuses on factoring and graphing polynomial functions.

**Embedded Assessment 1:**

Polynomial Operations                    p. 265

**Embedded Assessment 2:**

Factoring and Graphing Polynomials                    p. 291

# Getting Ready

**Write your answers on notebook paper.**
**Show your work.**

1. Find the surface area and volume of a rectangular prism formed by the net below. The length is 10 units, the width is 4 units, and the height is 5 units.

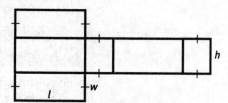

2. Simplify $(2x^2 + 3x + 7) - (4x - 2x^2 + 9)$.

3. Factor $9x^4 - 49x^2y^2$.

4. Factor $2x^2 - 9x - 5$.

5. Simplify $(x + 4)^4$.

6. Given a function $f(x) = 3x^4 - 5x^2 + 2x - 3$, evaluate $f(-1)$.

7. Find the $x$- and $y$-intercepts of the graph whose equation is $y = 3x - 12$.

8. Determine whether the graph below is symmetric. If it is, describe the symmetry.

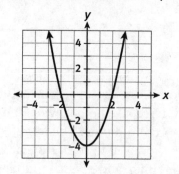

9. The graph below represents $f(x)$. Find $f(28)$.

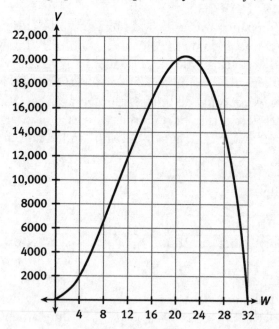

# Introduction to Polynomials
## Postal Service
### Lesson 14-1 Polynomials

**Learning Targets:**

- Write a third-degree equation that represents a real-world situation.
- Graph a portion of this equation and evaluate the meaning of a relative maximum.

> **SUGGESTED LEARNING STRATEGIES:** Create Representations, Note Taking, Think-Pair-Share

The United States Postal Service will not accept rectangular packages if the perimeter of one end of the package plus the length of the package is greater than 130 in. Consider a rectangular package with square ends as shown in the figure.

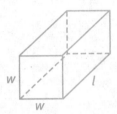

1. Work with your group on this item and on Items 2–5. Assume that the perimeter of one end of the package plus the length of the package equals the maximum 130 in. Complete the table with some possible measurements for the length and width of the package. Then find the corresponding volume of each package.

| Width (in.) | Length (in.) | Volume (in.³) |
|---|---|---|
|  |  |  |
|  |  |  |
|  |  |  |
|  |  |  |
|  |  |  |

2. Give an estimate for the largest possible volume of an acceptable United States Postal Service rectangular package with square ends.

---

**DISCUSSION GROUP TIP**

Reread the problem scenario as needed. Make notes on the information provided in the problem. Respond to questions about the meaning of key information. Summarize or organize the information needed to create reasonable solutions, and describe the mathematical concepts your group will use to create its solutions.

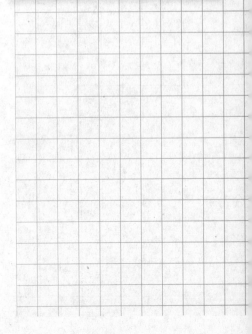

CONNECT TO AP

In calculus, you must be able to model a written description of a physical situation with a function.

3. **Model with mathematics.** Use the package described in Item 1.

   a. Write an expression for $\ell$, the length of the package, in terms of $w$, the width of the square ends of the package.

   b. Write the volume of the package $V$ as a function of $w$, the width of the square ends of the package.

   c. Justify your answer by explaining what each part of your equation represents. As you justify your answer, speak clearly and use precise mathematical language to describe your reasoning and your conclusions. Remember to use complete sentences, including transitions and words such as *and, or, since, for example, therefore, because of* to make connections between your thoughts.

4. Consider the smallest and largest possible values for $w$ that make sense for the function you wrote in Item 3b. Give the domain of the function as a model of the volume of the postal package. Express the domain as an inequality, in interval notation, and in set notation.

5. Sketch a graph of the function in Item 3b over the domain that you found in Item 4. Include the scale on each axis.

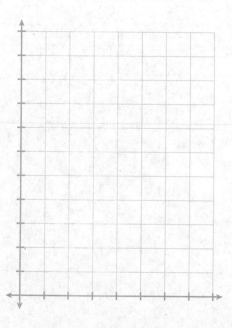

6. **Use appropriate tools strategically.** Use a graphing calculator to find the coordinates of the maximum point of the function that you graphed in Item 5.

7. What information do the coordinates of the maximum point of the function found in Item 6 provide with respect to an acceptable United States Postal Service package with square ends?

**CONNECT TO TECHNOLOGY**

Graphing calculators will allow you to find the maximum and minimum of functions in the graphing window.

**CONNECT TO AP**

In calculus, you will learn about the derivative of a function, which can be used to find the maximum and minimum values of a function.

### Check Your Understanding

8. Explain why the function $V(w)$ that you used in this lesson is a third-degree equation.

9. Explain why the value of $w$ cannot equal 0 in this situation.

10. Explain why the value of $w$ must be strictly less than 32.5 in this situation.

11. In this situation, is it possible for the range of the function to be all real numbers? Why or why not?

12. **Critique the reasoning of others.** Another method of shipping at the Post Office allows for the perimeter of one end of a box plus the length of that box to be no greater than 165 inches. Sarena wants to ship a box whose height is twice the width using this method. She says the formula for the volume of such a box is $V(w) = (165 - 6w)2w^2$. Her sister, Monique, says the formula is $V(w) = (165 - w)w^2$. Who is right? Justify your response.

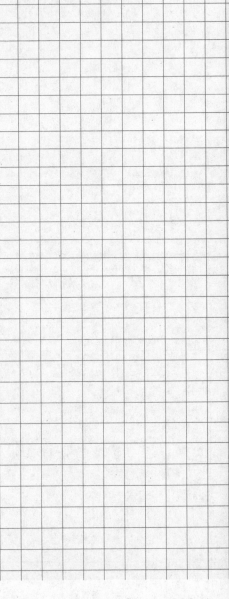

## LESSON 14-1 PRACTICE

13. The volume of a rectangular box is given by the function $V(w) = (60 - 4w)w^2$. What is a reasonable domain for the function in this situation? Express the domain as an inequality, in interval notation, and in set notation.

14. Sketch a graph of the function in Item 13 over the domain that you found. Include the scale on each axis.

15. Use a graphing calculator to find the coordinates of the maximum point of the function given in Item 13.

16. What is the width of the box, in inches, that produces the maximum volume?

17. **Reason abstractly.** An architect uses a cylindrical tube to ship blueprints to a client. The height of the tube plus twice its radius must be less than 60 cm.
    a. Write an expression for $h$, the height of the tube, in terms of $r$, the radius of the tube.
    b. Write an expression for $V$, the volume of the tube, in terms of $r$, the radius of the tube.
    c. Find the radius that produces the maximum volume.
    d. Find the maximum volume of the tube.

## Learning Targets:

- Sketch the graphs of cubic functions.
- Identify the end behavior of polynomial functions.

> **SUGGESTED LEARNING STRATEGIES:** Vocabulary Organizer, Marking the Text, Create Representations, Predict and Confirm

When using a function to model a given situation, such as the acceptable United States Postal Service package, the reasonable domain may be only a portion of the domain of real numbers. Moving beyond the specific situation, you can examine the *polynomial function* across the domain of the real numbers.

A *polynomial function* in one variable is a function that can be written in the form $f(x) = a_n x^n + a_{n-1} x^{n-1} + \ldots + a_1 x + a_0$, where $n$ is a nonnegative integer, the coefficients $a_0, a_1, \ldots a_n$ are real numbers, and $a_n \neq 0$. The highest power, $n$, is the *degree* of the polynomial function.

A polynomial is in *standard form* when all like terms have been combined, and the terms are written in descending order by exponent.

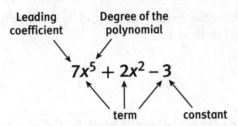

Leading coefficient    Degree of the polynomial

$$7x^5 + 2x^2 - 3$$

term    constant

Various attributes of the graph of a polynomial can be predicted by its equation. Here are some examples:

- the constant term is the $y$-intercept of the graph;
- the degree tells the maximum number of $x$-intercepts the graph of a polynomial can have; and
- the degree of the polynomial gives you information about the shape of the graph at its ends.

---

**MATH TERMS**

Some common types of **polynomial functions** are listed in the table. You are already familiar with some of these.

Polynomial functions are named by the **degree** of the function.

| Degree | Name |
|--------|------|
| 0 | Constant |
| 1 | Linear |
| 2 | Quadratic |
| 3 | Cubic |
| 4 | Quartic |

**My Notes**

1. Write a polynomial function $f(x)$ defined over the set of real numbers in standard form such that it has the same function rule as $V(w)$, the rule you found in Item 3b of the previous lesson for the volume of the rectangular box. Sketch a graph of the function.

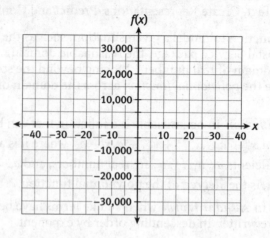

2. Name any **relative maximum** values and **relative minimum** values of the function $f(x)$ in Item 1.

### MATH TERMS

A function value $f(a)$ is called a **relative maximum** of $f$ if there is an interval around $a$ where, for any $x$ in the interval, $f(a) \geq f(x)$.

A function value $f(a)$ is called a **relative minimum** of $f$ if there is an interval around a where, for any $x$ in the interval, $f(a) \leq f(x)$.

3. Name any $x$- or $y$-intercepts of the function $f(x) = -4x^3 + 130x^2$.

### MATH TIP

Think of a *relative minimum* of a graph as being the bottom of a hill and the *relative maximum* as the top of a hill.

4. **Model with mathematics.** Use a graphing calculator to sketch a graph of the cubic function $f(x) = 2x^3 - 5x^2 - 4x + 12$.

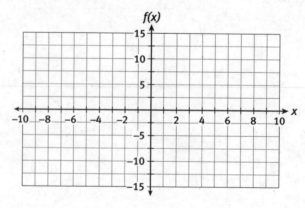

### TECHNOLOGY TIP

When the coefficients of an equation are relatively small, begin with a standard 10-by-10 viewing window, and then adjust the window if necessary.

**5.** Name any relative maximum values and relative minimum values of the function $f(x)$ in Item 4.

**6.** Name any $x$- or $y$-intercepts of the function in Item 4.

## Check Your Understanding

**7.** Decide if the function $f(x) = 7x - 2 + x^2 - 4x^3$ is a polynomial. If it is, write the function in standard form and then state the degree and leading coefficient.

**8. Construct viable arguments.** Explain why $f(x) = 2x + 5 - \dfrac{1}{x}$ is not a polynomial.

**9.** Use a graphing calculator to sketch a graph of the cubic function $f(x) = x^3 + x^2 - 4x - 2$.

**10.** Use a graphing calculator to determine how many $x$-intercepts the graph of $f(x) = x^3 + x^2 - 4x + 5$ has.

**11. Use appropriate tools strategically.** Use the graphs you have sketched in this lesson to speculate about the minimum number of times a cubic function must cross the $x$-axis and the maximum number of times it can cross the $x$-axis.

The **end behavior** of a graph is the appearance of the graph on the extreme right and left ends of the $x$-axis. That is, you look to see what happens to $y$ as $x$ approaches $-\infty$ and $\infty$.

Examine your graph from Item 1. To describe the end behavior of the graph, you would say: The left side of the graph increases (points upward) continuously and the right side of the graph decreases (points downward) continuously. You can also use mathematical notation, called *arrow notation*, to describe end behavior. For this graph you would write:
As $x \to -\infty$, $y \to \infty$, and as $x \to \infty$, $y \to -\infty$.

**12.** Examine your graph from Item 4. Describe the end behavior of the graph in words and by using arrow notation.

### MATH TERMS

**End behavior** describes what happens to a graph at the extreme ends of the $x$-axis, as $x$ approaches $-\infty$ and $\infty$.

### MATH TIP

Recall that the phrase *approaches positive infinity* or *approaches $\infty$* means "increases continuously," and that approaches *negative infinity* or *approaches $-\infty$* means "decreases continuously."

Values that increase or decrease continuously, or without stopping, are said to increase or decrease *without bound*.

My Notes

13. Examine the end behavior of $f(x) = 3x^2 - 6$.
   a. As $x$ goes to $\infty$, what behavior does the function have?

   b. How is the function behaving as $x$ approaches $-\infty$?

It is possible to determine the end behavior of a polynomial's graph simply by looking at the degree of the polynomial and the sign of the leading coefficient.

14. **Use appropriate tools strategically.** Use a graphing calculator to examine the *end behavior* of polynomial functions in general. Sketch each given function on the axes below.

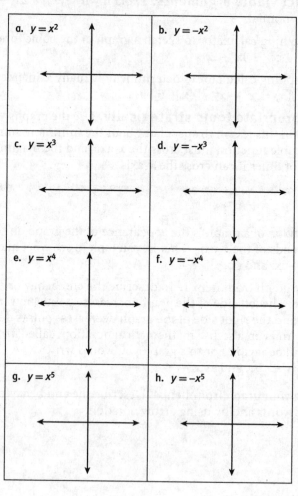

**MATH TIP**

The leading term of a polynomial (which has the greatest power when the polynomial is written in standard form) determines the end behavior. Learning these basic polynomial shapes will help you describe the end behavior of any polynomial.

**My Notes**

15. Which of the functions in Item 14 have the same end behavior on the right side of the graph as on the left side?

16. **Reason quantitatively.** What is true about the degree of each of the functions you identified in Item 15?

17. Make a conjecture about how the degree affects the end behavior of polynomial functions.

18. For which of the functions that you identified in Item 15 does the end behavior decrease without bound on both sides of the graph?

19. What is true about the leading coefficient of each of the functions you identified in Item 18?

20. **Express regularity in repeated reasoning.** Work with your group. Make a conjecture about how the sign of the leading coefficient affects the end behavior of polynomial functions.

**DISCUSSION GROUP TIPS**

Read the text carefully to clarify meaning. Reread definitions of terms as needed, or ask your teacher to clarify vocabulary terms.

If you need help in describing your ideas during group discussions, make notes about what you want to say. Listen carefully to other group members and ask for clarification of meaning for any words routinely used by group members.

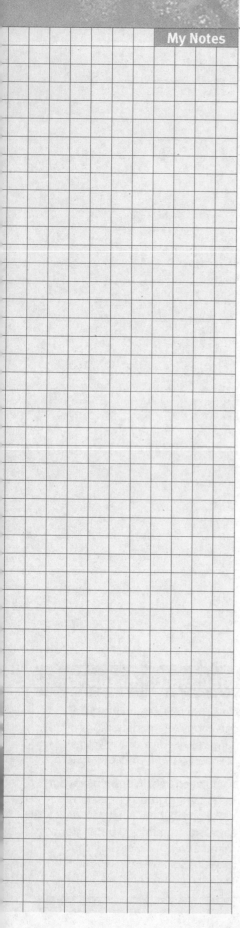

**My Notes**

---

### Check Your Understanding

**21.** Use arrow notation to describe the left-end behavior of a graph that decreases without bound.

**22.** Describe in words the end behavior of a graph that is described by the following arrow notation: As $x \to \pm\infty$, $y \to -\infty$.

**23.** **Reason abstractly.** If the end behavior of a graph meets the description in Item 22, is it possible that the graph represents a third-degree polynomial? Explain your answer.

**24.** Give two examples of a polynomial whose graph increases without bound as $x$ approaches both positive and negative infinity.

---

## LESSON 14-2 PRACTICE

**25.** Sketch the graph of the polynomial function $f(x) = x^3 - 6x^2 + 9x$.

**26.** Name any $x$-intercepts, $y$-intercepts, relative maximums, and relative minimums for the function in Item 25.

**27.** **Make sense of problems.** Sketch a graph of any third-degree polynomial function that has three distinct $x$-intercepts, a relative minimum at $(-6, -4)$, and a relative maximum at $(3, 5)$.

**28.** Decide if each function is a polynomial. If it is, write the function in standard form, and then state the degree and leading coefficient.
 **a.** $f(x) = 5x - x^3 + 3x^5 - 2$
 **b.** $f(x) = -\dfrac{2}{3}x^3 - 8x^4 - 2x + 7$
 **c.** $f(x) = 4^x + 2x^2 + x + 5$

**29.** Describe the end behavior of each function.
 **a.** $f(x) = x^6 - 2x^3 + 3x^2 + 2$
 **b.** $f(x) = -\dfrac{2}{3}x^3 - 8x^2 - 2x + 7$

**Learning Targets:**

- Recognize even and odd functions given an equation or graph.
- Distinguish between even and odd functions and even-degree and odd-degree functions.

**SUGGESTED LEARNING STRATEGIES:** Paraphrasing, Marking the Text, Create Representations

The graphs of some polynomial functions have special attributes that are determined by the value of the exponents in the polynomial.

1. Graph the functions $f(x) = 3x^2 + 1$ and $f(x) = 2x^3 + 3x$ on the axes.

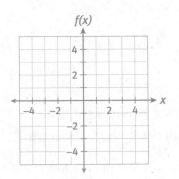
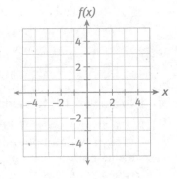

> **My Notes**

> **MATH TIP**
>
> The graph of a function can be symmetric across an axis or other line when the graph forms a mirror image across the line. The graph can be symmetric around a point when rotation of the graph can superimpose the image on the original graph.

2. Describe the symmetry of the graph of $f(x) = 3x^2 + 1$.

3. Describe the symmetry of the graph of $f(x) = 2x^3 + 3x$.

The function $f(x) = 3x^2 + 1$ is called an **even function**. Notice that *every* power of $x$ is an even number—there is no $x^1$ term. This is true for the constant term as well, since you can write a constant term as the coefficient of $x^0$. Symmetry over the $y$-axis is an attribute of all even functions.

The function $f(x) = 2x^3 + 3x$ is an **odd function**. Notice that every power of $x$ is an odd number—there is no $x^2$ or constant ($x^0$) term. Symmetry around the origin is an attribute of all odd functions.

> **MATH TERMS**
>
> Algebraically, an **even function** is one in which $f(-x) = f(x)$.
>
> An **odd function** is one in which $f(-x) = -f(x)$.

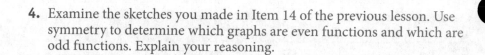

4. Examine the sketches you made in Item 14 of the previous lesson. Use symmetry to determine which graphs are even functions and which are odd functions. Explain your reasoning.

5. **Make use of structure.** Explain how an examination of the equations in Item 14 of the previous lesson supports your answer to Item 4.

### Check Your Understanding

6. Explain why the function $f(x) = 4x^2 + 8x$ is neither even nor odd.

7. For a given polynomial function, as $x$ approaches $-\infty$ the graph increases without bound, and as $x$ approaches $\infty$ the graph decreases without bound. Is it possible that this function is an even function? Explain your reasoning.

### LESSON 14-3 PRACTICE

8. Determine whether the function $f(x) = 2x^5 + 3x^3 + 7$ is even, odd, or neither. Explain your reasoning.

9. Determine whether the function below is even, odd, or neither. Justify your answer.

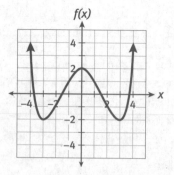

10. **Attend to precision.** Give an example of a polynomial function that has an odd degree, but is not an odd function.

## ACTIVITY 14 PRACTICE
Write your answers on notebook paper.
Show your work.

### Lesson 14-1

1. The volume of a rectangular box is given by the expression $V = (120 - 6w)w^2$, where $w$ is measured in inches.
   a. What is a reasonable domain for the function in this situation? Express the domain as an inequality, in interval notation, and in set notation.
   b. Sketch a graph of the function over the domain that you found. Include the scale on each axis.
   c. Use a graphing calculator to find the coordinates of the maximum point of the function.
   d. What is the width of the box, in inches, that produces the maximum volume?

2. A cylindrical can is being designed for a new product. The height of the can plus twice its radius must be 45 cm.
   a. Find an equation that represents the volume of the can, given the radius.
   b. Find the radius that yields the maximum volume.
   c. Find the maximum volume of the can.

### Lesson 14-2

3. Sketch the graph of the polynomial function $f(x) = -x^3 + 4x^2 - 4x$.

4. Name any $x$- or $y$-intercepts of the function $f(x)$ in Item 3.

5. Name any relative maximum values and relative minimum values of the function $f(x)$ in Item 3.

For Items 6–10, decide if each function is a polynomial. If it is, write the function in standard form, and then state the degree and leading coefficient.

6. $f(x) = 7x^2 - 9x^3 + 3x^7 - 2$
7. $f(x) = 2x^3 + x - 5^x + 9$
8. $f(x) = x^4 + x + 5 - \frac{1}{4}x^3$
9. $f(x) = -0.32x^3 + 0.08x^4 + 5^{x-1} - 3$
10. $f(x) = 3x + 5 + \sqrt{x}$

11. Examine the graph below.

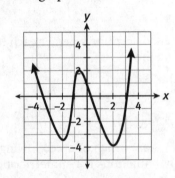

Which of the following statements is NOT true regarding the polynomial whose graph is shown?

A. The degree of the polynomial is even.
B. The leading coefficient is positive.
C. The function is a second-degree polynomial.
D. As $x \to \pm\infty, y \to \infty$.

For Items 12 and 13, describe the end behavior of each function using arrow notation.

**12.** $f(x) = x^6 - 2x^3 + 3x^2 + 2$

**13.** $f(x) = -x^3 + 7x^2 - 11$

**14.** Use the concept of end behavior to explain why a third-degree polynomial function must have at least one $x$-intercept.

**15.** Sketch a graph of any third-degree polynomial function that has exactly one $x$-intercept, a relative minimum at $(-2, 1)$, and a relative maximum at $(4, 3)$.

## Lesson 14-3

For Items 16–28, determine whether each function is even, odd, or neither.

**16.** $f(x) = 10 + 3x^2$

**17.** $f(x) = -x^3 + 2x + 5$

**18.** $f(x) = 6x^5 - 4x$

**19.** When graphed, which of the following polynomial functions is symmetric about the origin?
**A.** $f(x) = -x^3 + 2x + 5$
**B.** $f(x) = x^3 + 8x$
**C.** $f(x) = -7x^2 + 5$
**D.** $f(x) = 5x^3 + 3x^2 - 7x + 1$

**20.** Sketch a graph of an even function whose degree is greater than 2.

**21.** If $f(x)$ is an even function and passes through the point $(5, 3)$, what other point must lie on the graph of the function? Explain your reasoning.

## MATHEMATICAL PRACTICES
### Construct Viable Arguments and Critique the Reasoning of Others

**22.** Sharon described the function graphed below as follows:
- It is a polynomial function.
- It is an even function.
- It has a positive leading coefficient.
- The degree $n$ could be any even number greater than or equal to 2.

Critique Sharon's description. If you disagree with any of her statements, provide specific reasons as to why.

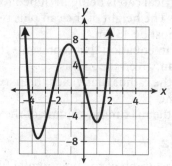

**Learning Targets:**

- Use a real-world scenario to introduce polynomial addition and subtraction.
- Add and subtract polynomials.

> SUGGESTED LEARNING STRATEGIES: Create Representations, Think-Pair-Share, Discussion Groups, Self Revision/Peer Revision

Polly's Pasta and Pizza Supply sells wholesale goods to local restaurants. They keep track of revenue earned from selling kitchen supplies and food products. The function $K$ models revenue from kitchen supplies and the function $F$ models revenue from food product sales for one year in dollars, where $t$ represents the number of the month (1–12) on the last day of the month.

$$K(t) = 15t^3 - 312t^2 + 1600t + 1100$$
$$F(t) = 36t^3 - 720t^2 + 3800t - 1600$$

**MATH TIP**

Some companies run their business on a fiscal year from July to June. Others, like Polly's Pasta, start the business year in January, so $t = 1$ represents January.

1. What kind of functions are these revenue functions?

2. How much did Polly make from kitchen supplies in March? How much did she make from selling food products in August?

3. In which month was her revenue from kitchen supplies the greatest? The least?

4. In which month was her revenue from food products the greatest? The least?

5. **Reason quantitatively.** What was her total revenue from both kitchen supplies and food products in January? Explain how you arrived at your answer.

**TECHNOLOGY TIP**

You can use "Table" on your graphing calculator to quickly find the value of a function at any given $x$. Enter $K(t)$ as $y_1$ and $F(t)$ as $y_2$ and you can see the values for each month side by side in the table.

6. The function $S(t)$ represents Polly's total revenue from both kitchen supplies and food products. Use Polly's revenue functions to complete the table for each given value of $t$.

| $t$ | $K(t)$ | $F(t)$ | $S(t) = K(t) + F(t)$ |
|---|---|---|---|
| 1 | | | |
| 2 | | | |
| 3 | | | |
| 4 | | | |
| 5 | | | |

7. **Model with mathematics.** The graph below shows $K(t)$ and $F(t)$. Graph $S(t) = K(t) + F(t)$, and explain how you used the graph to find the values of $S(t)$.

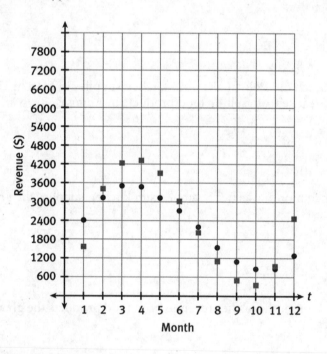

Month

**Check Your Understanding**

8. Use the graph from Item 7 to approximate $S(4)$.

9. How does your answer compare to $S(4)$ from the table in Item 6?

10. **Use appropriate tools strategically.** Approximate $S(7)$ and $S(10)$ using the graph.

11. Why is the value of $S(t)$ greater than $K(t)$ and $F(t)$ for every $t$?

Polly's monthly operating costs are represented by the function $C(t)$, where $t$ represents the number of the month (1–12) on the last day of the month.

$$C(t) = 5t^3 - 110t^2 + 600t + 1000$$

12. In a standard business model, profit equals total revenue minus total costs. How much profit did Patty earn in December? Explain how you found your solution.

13. Complete the table for each value of $t$.

| $t$ | $S(t)$ | $C(t)$ | $P(t) = S(t) - C(t)$ |
|---|---|---|---|
| 7 | | | |
| 8 | | | |
| 9 | | | |
| 10 | | | |
| 11 | | | |
| 12 | | | |

### Check Your Understanding

14. What time frame do the values of $t$ in the table in Item 13 represent?

15. In which month during the second half of the year did Polly's Pasta and Pizza Supply earn the least profits?

16. **Reason abstractly.** In any given month, would you expect the value of $P(t)$ to be greater than, less than, or equal to the value of $S(t)$ for that same month? Explain your reasoning.

17. Can you make a general statement about whether the value of $C(t)$ will be greater than, less than, or equal to the value of $P(t)$ for any given month? Use specific examples from the table in Item 13 to support your answer.

18. **Reason quantitatively.** Is it possible for the value of $P(t)$ to be a negative number? If so, under what circumstances?

Most businesses study profit patterns throughout the year. This helps them make important decisions about such things as when to hire additional personnel or when to advertise more (or less).

**19.** Find Polly's total profit for the first quarter of the year, January–March.

**20.** Find Polly's total profit for the second quarter of the year, April–June.

**21.** Use the table in Item 13 and your answers to Items 19 and 20 to determine in which quarter Polly's Pasta and Pizza Supply earned the most profits.

## LESSON 15-1 PRACTICE

**22.** Polly's Pasta and Pizza Supply hired a business consultant to try to reduce their operating costs. The consultant claims that if Polly implements all of his suggestions, her cost function for next year will be $C(t) = 6t^3 - 100t^2 + 400t + 900$.

   **a.** If the consultant is correct, how much should Polly's costs be in January of next year?

   **b.** How much savings is this compared to last January?

**23.** **Use appropriate tools strategically.** Use a graphing calculator to graph Polly's original and new cost functions simultaneously. Are there any months in which the consultant's plan would NOT save Polly money? If so, which months?

**24.** Kevin owns Kevin's Cars, and his wife Angela owns Angie's Autos. The function $K(t)$ represents the number of cars Kevin's dealership sold each month last year, and the function $A(t)$ represents the number of cars Angie's dealership sold each month. The variable $t$ represents the number of the month (1–12) on the last day of the month.

$$K(t) = t^2 - 11t + 39$$
$$A(t) = t^2 - 7t + 28$$

   **a.** In January, how many cars did the two dealerships sell together?

   **b.** Which dealership sold more cars in June? How many more?

### Learning Targets:

- Add, subtract, and multiply polynomials.
- Understand that polynomials are closed under the operations of addition, subtraction, and multiplication.

**SUGGESTED LEARNING STRATEGIES:** Note Taking, Marking the Text, Graphic Organizer

To add and subtract polynomials, add or subtract the coefficients of like terms.

### Example A

a. Add $(3x^3 + 2x^2 - 5x + 7) + (4x^2 + 2x - 3)$.

**Step 1:** Group like terms.

$$(3x^3) + (2x^2 + 4x^2) + (-5x + 2x) + (7 - 3)$$

**Step 2:** Combine like terms. $3x^3 + 6x^2 - 3x + 4$

**Solution:** $3x^3 + 6x^2 - 3x + 4$

b. Subtract $(2x^3 + 8x^2 + x + 10) - (5x^2 - 4x + 6)$.

**Step 1:** Distribute the negative.

$$2x^3 + 8x^2 + x + 10 - 5x^2 + 4x - 6$$

**Step 2:** Group like terms.

$$2x^3 + (8x^2 - 5x^2) + (x + 4x) + (10 - 6)$$

**Step 3:** Combine like terms.    $2x^3 + 3x^2 + 5x + 4$

**Solution:** $2x^3 + 3x^2 + 5x + 4$

### Try These A

Find each sum or difference. Show your work.

a. $(2x^4 - 3x + 8) + (3x^3 + 5x^2 - 2x + 7)$

b. $(4x - 2x^3 + 7 - 9x^2) + (8x^2 - 6x - 7)$

c. $(3x^2 + 8x^3 - 9x) - (2x^3 + 3x - 4x^2 - 1)$

**MATH TIP**

Another way to group like terms is to align them vertically. For example, $(2x^2 + 6) + (4x^2 - 5x + 3)$ could be arranged like this:

$$
\begin{array}{r}
2x^2 \qquad +6 \\
+\ 4x^2 - 5x + 3 \\
\hline
6x^2 - 5x + 9
\end{array}
$$

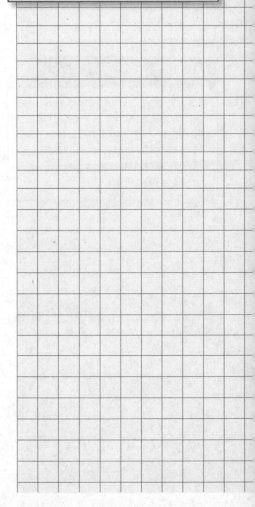

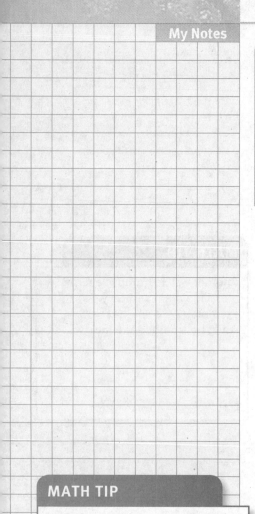

### Check Your Understanding

Find each sum or difference.

1. $(x^3 - 6x + 12) + (4x^2 + 7x - 11)$
2. $(5x^2 + 2x) - (3x^2 - 4x + 6)$
3. $(10x^3 + 2x - 5 + x^2) + (8 - 3x + x^3)$
4. What type of expression is each sum or difference above?

The *standard form of a polynomial* is $f(x) = a_n x^n + a_{n-1} x^{n-1} + \ldots + a_1 x + a_0$, where $a$ is a real number and $a_n \neq 0$, with all like terms combined and written in descending order.

5. **Reason abstractly and quantitatively.** Use what you learned about how to add and subtract polynomials to write $S(t)$ from Item 6 and $P(t)$ from Item 12 in standard form.

**MATH TIP**

Multiplying polynomials looks more complicated than it is. You simply distribute each term in the first expression to each term in the second expression and then combine like terms.

6. The steps to multiply $(x + 3)(4x^2 + 6x + 7)$ are shown below. Use precise and appropriate math terminology to describe what occurs in each step.

| | |
|---|---|
| $x(4x^2 + 6x + 7) + 3(4x^2 + 6x + 7)$ | |
| $(4x^3 + 6x^2 + 7x) + (12x^2 + 18x + 21)$ | |
| $4x^3 + 6x^2 + 12x^2 + 18x + 7x + 21$ | |
| $4x^3 + 18x^2 + 25x + 21$ | |

**My Notes**

### Check Your Understanding

7. Find each product. Show your work.
   a. $(x + 5)(x^2 + 4x - 5)$      b. $(2x^2 + 3x - 8)(2x - 3)$
   c. $(x^2 - x + 2)(x^2 + 3x - 1)$    d. $(x^2 - 1)(x^3 + 4x)$

8. What type of expression is each of the products in Item 7?

9. **Attend to precision.** When multiplying polynomials, how is the degree of the product related to the degrees of the factors?

### LESSON 15-2 PRACTICE

For Items 10–14, perform the indicated operation. Write your answers in standard form.

10. $(x^2 + 6x - 10) - (4x^3 + 7x - 8)$

11. $(3x^2 - 2x) + (x^2 - 7x + 11)$

12. $(5x^3 + 2x - 1 + 4x^2) + (6 - 5x + x^3) - (2x^2 + 5)$

13. $(6x - 2)(x^2 + 7x - 8)$

14. $(3x^2 - 2x + 1)(x^2 + x - 4)$

15. **Critique the reasoning of others.** Marcellus made the statement that the sum of two polynomials is always a polynomial with degree equal to the highest power of $x$ found in either of the original polynomials. He gave the following example to support his statement:

$$(3x^2 + 5x + 4) + (6x + 1) = 3x^2 + 11x + 5$$

Do you agree with Marcellus? If not, give a counterexample to support your answer.

My Notes

## Learning Targets:

● Determine the quotient of two polynomials.
● Prove a polynomial identity and use it to describe numerical relationships.

SUGGESTED LEARNING STRATEGIES: Note Taking, Marking the Text, Create Representations, Discussion Groups

Polynomial long division has a similar algorithm to numerical long division.

1. Use long division to find the quotient $\frac{592}{46}$.

### Example A

Divide $x^3 - 7x^2 + 14$ by $x - 5$, using long division.

**Step 1:** Set up the division problem with the divisor and dividend written in descending order of degree. Include zero coefficients for any missing terms.

$$x - 5 \overline{)\, x^3 - 7x^2 + 0x + 14}$$

**Step 2:** Divide the first term of the dividend $[x^3]$ by the first term of the divisor $[x]$.

$$\begin{array}{r} x^2 \phantom{aaaaaaaaaaaa} \\ x - 5 \overline{)\, x^3 - 7x^2 + 0x + 14} \end{array}$$

**Step 3:** Multiply the result $[x^2]$ by the divisor $[x^2(x - 5) = x^3 - 5x^2]$.

$$\begin{array}{r} x^2 \phantom{aaaaaaaaaaaa} \\ x - 5 \overline{)\, x^3 - 7x^2 + 0x + 14} \\ x^3 - 5x^2 \phantom{aaaaaa} \end{array}$$

**Step 4:** Subtract to get a new result $[-2x^2 + 0x + 14]$.

$$\begin{array}{r} x^2 \phantom{aaaaaaaaaaaa} \\ x - 5 \overline{)\, x^3 - 7x^2 + 0x + 14} \\ -\left(x^3 - 5x^2\right) \phantom{aaaa} \\ \hline -2x^2 + 0x + 14 \end{array}$$

**Step 5:** Repeat the steps.

$$\begin{array}{r} x^2 - 2x - 10 \phantom{aa} \\ x - 5 \overline{)\, x^3 - 7x^2 + 0x + 14} \\ -\left(x^3 - 5x^2\right) \phantom{aaaa} \\ \hline -2x^2 + 0x + 14 \\ -(-2x^2 + 10x) \\ \hline -10x + 14 \\ -(-10x + 50) \\ \hline -36 \end{array}$$

**Solution:** $\dfrac{x^3 - 7x^2 + 14}{x - 5} = x^3 - 2x - 10 - \dfrac{36}{x - 5}$

**MATH TIP**

When the division process is complete, the degree of the remainder will be less than the degree of the divisor.

# Lesson 15-3
## Dividing Polynomials

**ACTIVITY 15**
*continued*

### Try These A
Use long division to find each quotient.

**a.** $(x^3 - x^2 - 6x + 18) \div (x + 3)$     **b.** $\dfrac{x^4 - 2x^3 - 15x^2 + 31x - 12}{x - 4}$

When a polynomial function $f(x)$ is divided by another polynomial function $d(x)$, the outcome is a new quotient function consisting of a polynomial $p(x)$ plus a remainder function $r(x)$.

$$\frac{f(x)}{d(x)} = p(x) + \frac{r(x)}{d(x)}$$

**2.** Follow the steps from Example A to find the quotient of $\dfrac{x^3 - x^2 + 4x + 6}{x + 2}$.

$$x + 2 \overline{)x^3 - x^2 + 4x + 6}$$

**3.** Find the quotient of $\dfrac{-4x^3 - 8x^2 + 32x}{x^2 + 2x - 8}$.

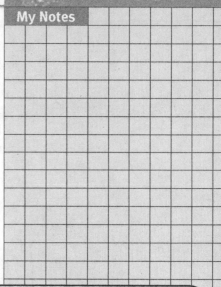

**CONNECT TO TECHNOLOGY**

You can use a CAS (computer algebra system) to perform division on more complicated quotients.

### Check Your Understanding

Use long division to find each quotient. Show your work.

**4.** $(x^2 + 5x - 3) \div (x - 5)$

**5.** $\dfrac{4x^4 + 12x^3 + 7x^2 + x + 6}{-2x + 3}$

**6.** $(x^3 - 9) \div (x + 3)$

**7.** $\dfrac{6x^4 + 3x^3 + 13x^2 - x - 5}{3x^2 - 1}$

**Synthetic division** is another method of polynomial division that is useful when the divisor has the form $x - k$.

### Example B

Divide $x^4 - 13x^2 + 32$ by $x - 3$ using synthetic division.

**Step 1:** Set up the division problem using only coefficients for the dividend and only the constant for the divisor. Include zero coefficients for any missing terms [$x^3$ and $x$].

$$3\,\big|\,1 \quad 0 \quad -13 \quad 0 \quad 32$$

**Step 2:** Bring down the leading coefficient [1].

$$
\begin{array}{r|rrrrr}
3 & 1 & 0 & -13 & 0 & 32 \\
  & \downarrow & & & & \\
\hline
  & 1 & & & &
\end{array}
$$

**Step 3:** Multiply the coefficient [1] by the divisor [3]. Write the product [$1 \cdot 3 = 3$] under the second coefficient [0] and add [$0 + 3 = 3$].

$$
\begin{array}{r|rrrrr}
3 & 1 & 0 & -13 & 0 & 32 \\
  &   & 3 & & & \\
\hline
  & 1 & 3 & & &
\end{array}
$$

**Step 4:** Repeat this process until there are no more coefficients.

$$
\begin{array}{r|rrrrr}
3 & 1 & 0 & -13 & 0 & 32 \\
  &   & 3 & 9 & -12 & -36 \\
\hline
  & 1 & 3 & -4 & -12 & -4
\end{array}
$$

**Step 5:** The numbers in the bottom row become the coefficients of the quotient. The number in the last column is the remainder. Write it over the divisor.

**Solution:** $x^3 + 3x^2 - 4x - 12 - \dfrac{4}{x - 3}$

## Try These B

Use synthetic division to find each quotient.

a. $\dfrac{x^3 + 3x^2 - 10x - 24}{x + 4}$    b. $\dfrac{-5x^5 - 2x^4 + 32x^2 - 48x + 32}{x - 2}$

**My Notes**

**MATH TIP**

Remember, when using synthetic division, the divisor must be in the form $x - k$. When the divisor is in the form $x + k$, write it as $x - (-k)$ before you begin the process.

### Check Your Understanding

8. Use synthetic division to divide $\dfrac{x^3 - x^2 + 4x + 6}{x + 2}$.

9. In synthetic division, how does the degree of the quotient compare to the degree of the dividend?

10. **Construct viable arguments.** Justify the following statement: The set of polynomials is closed under addition, subtraction, and multiplication, but not under division.

There are a number of polynomial identities that can be used to describe important numerical relationships in math. For example, the polynomial identity $(x^2 + y^2)^2 = (x^2 - y^2)^2 + (2xy)^2$ can be used to generate a famous numerical relationship that is used in geometry.

First, let's verify the identity using what we have learned in this lesson about polynomial operations.

$$
\begin{aligned}
(x^2 + y^2)^2 &= (x^2 - y^2)^2 + (2xy)^2 \\
&= (x^2 - y^2)(x^2 - y^2) + (2xy)(2xy) \\
&= x^4 - 2x^2y^2 + y^4 + 4x^2y^2 \\
&= x^4 + 2x^2y^2 + y^4 \\
&= (x^2 + y^2)^2
\end{aligned}
$$

**MATH TIP**

When verifying an identity, choose one side of the equation to work with and try to make that side look like the other side.

Now that we have verified the identity, let's see how it relates to a famous numerical relationship. If we evaluate it for $x = 2$ and $y = 1$, we get:

$$(2^2 - 1^2)^2 + (2 \cdot 2 \cdot 1)^2 = (2^2 + 1^2)^2$$
$$3^2 \quad + \quad 4^2 \quad = \quad 5^2$$
$$9 \quad + \quad 16 \quad = \quad 25$$

The numbers 3, 4, and 5 are known as *Pythagorean triples* because they fit the condition $a^2 + b^2 = c^2$, which describes the lengths of the legs and hypotenuse of a right triangle.

Thus, the polynomial identity $(x^2 + y^2)^2 = (x^2 - y^2)^2 + (2xy)^2$ can be used to generate Pythagorean triples.

### Check Your Understanding

**11.** Use the polynomial identity above to generate a Pythagorean triple given $x = 5$ and $y = 2$.

**12.** Use the polynomial identity to see what happens when the values of $x$ and $y$ are the same. Does the identity generate a Pythagorean triple in this case? Use an example to support your answer.

**13. Reason abstractly.** Are there any other specific values for $x$ and $y$ that would not generate Pythagorean triples? If so, what value(s)?

### LESSON 15-3 PRACTICE

**14.** Find each quotient using long division.
  **a.** $(6x^3 + x - 1) \div (x + 2)$

  **b.** $\dfrac{-2x^3 + 3x^2 - 1}{x - 1}$

**15. Make sense of problems.** Find each quotient using synthetic division.
  **a.** $(x^3 - 8) \div (x - 2)$

  **b.** $\dfrac{-2x^4 + 6x^3 + 3x - 1}{x - 2}$

## ACTIVITY 15 PRACTICE
Write your answers on notebook paper.
Show your work.

### Lesson 15-1

1. The graph below shows the number of visitors at a public library one day between the hours of 9:00 a.m. and 7:00 p.m. The round dots represent $A(t)$, the number of adult visitors, and the diamonds represent $C(t)$, the number of children and teenage visitors. Graph $V(t)$, the total number of visitors, and explain how you used the graph to find the values of $V(t)$.

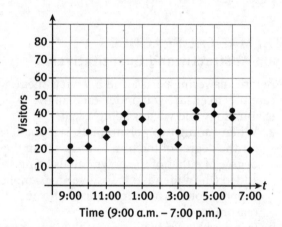

2. Examine the functions graphed in Item 1. Which of the statements is true over the given domain of the functions?
   A. $A(t) > C(t)$
   B. $C(t) > A(t)$
   C. $A(t) - C(t) > 0$
   D. $V(t) > C(t)$

3. The polynomial expressions $5x + 7$, $3x^2 + 9$, and $3x^2 - 2x$ represent the lengths of the sides of a triangle for all whole-number values of $x > 1$. Write an expression for the perimeter of the triangle.

4. In Item 3, what kind of expression is the perimeter expression?

### Lesson 15-2

5. An open box will be made by cutting four squares of equal size from the corners of a 10-inch-by-12-inch rectangular piece of cardboard and then folding up the sides. The expression $V(x) = x(10 - 2x)(12 - 2x)$ can be used to represent the volume of the box. Write this expression as a polynomial in standard form.

6. Write an expression for the volume of a box that is constructed in the same way as in Item 5, but from a rectangular piece of cardboard that measures 8 inches by 14 inches. Write your expression in factored form, and then as a polynomial in standard form.

7. Write an expression to represent the combined volume of the two boxes described in Items 5 and 6.

For Items 8–13, find each sum or difference.

8. $(3x - 4) + (5x + 1)$

9. $(x^2 - 6x + 5) - (2x^2 + x + 1)$

10. $(4x^2 - 12x + 9) + (3x - 11)$

11. $(6x^2 - 13x + 4) - (8x^2 - 7x + 25)$

12. $(4x^3 + 14) + (5x^2 + x)$

13. $(2x^2 - x + 1) - (x^2 + 5x + 9)$

For Items 14–18, find each product. Write your answer as a polynomial in standard form.

**14.** $5x^2(4x^2 + 3x - 9)$

**15.** $(2x - 5)^2$

**16.** $(x^3 + y^3)^2$

**17.** $(x + 2)(3x^3 - 8x^2 + 2x - 7)$

**18.** $(x - 3)(2x^3 - 9x^2 + x - 6)$

## Lesson 15-3

**19.** Which of the following quotients CANNOT be found using synthetic division?

A. $\dfrac{x^3 + 4x^2 + 5}{x^2 + 1}$

B. $\dfrac{-x^2 - x^2 + 1}{x - 1}$

C. $\dfrac{x^5 + 10}{x + 50}$

D. $\dfrac{2x^3}{x + 1}$

For Items 20–22, find each quotient using long division.

**20.** $\dfrac{x^2 - 6x + 4}{x + 1}$

**21.** $(5x^4 + 14x^3 + 9x) \div (x^2 + 3x + 1)$

**22.** $(2x^3 - 3x^2 + 4x - 7) \div (x - 2)$

For Items 23–25, find each quotient using synthetic division.

**23.** $(x^2 + 4) \div (x + 4)$

**24.** $\dfrac{3x^3 - 10x^2 + 12x - 22}{x - 4}$

**25.** $(2x^3 - 4x^2 - 15x + 4) \div (x + 3)$

## MATHEMATICAL PRACTICES
**Reason Abstractly and Quantitatively**

**26.** Before answering parts a and b, review them carefully to ensure you understand all the terminology and what is being asked.

a. When adding two polynomials, is it possible for the degree of the sum to be less than the degree of either of the polynomials being added (the addends)? If so, give an example to support your answer. If not, explain your reasoning.

b. Is it possible for the degree of the sum to be greater than the degree of either of the addends? If so, give an example to support your answer. If not, explain your reasoning.

# Binomial Theorem

## Pascal's Triangle
### Lesson 16-1 Introduction to Pascal's Triangle

**Learning Targets:**
- Find the number of combinations of an event.
- Create Pascal's triangle.

> **SUGGESTED LEARNING STRATEGIES:** Marking the Text, Vocabulary Organizer, Note Taking, Create Representations, Look for a Pattern

Many corporations, social clubs, and school classes that elect officers begin the election process by selecting a nominating committee. The responsibility of the nominating committee is to present the best-qualified nominees for the office. Mr. Darnel's class of 10 students is electing class officers. He plans to start the process by selecting a nominating committee of 4 students from the class.

Recall that in mathematics, collections of items, or in this case students, chosen without regard to order are called **combinations**. The number of combinations of $n$ distinct things taken $r$ at a time is denoted by $_nC_r$.

1. Use the notation above to write an expression for the number of different combinations of four-student nominating committees that Mr. Darnel could choose out of 10 students.

The formula for the number of combinations of $n$ distinct things taken $r$ at a time, written with **factorial** notation, is $_nC_r = \dfrac{n!}{r!(n-r)!}$.

2. Use the formula to find the number of different nominating committees that Mr. Darnel could choose.

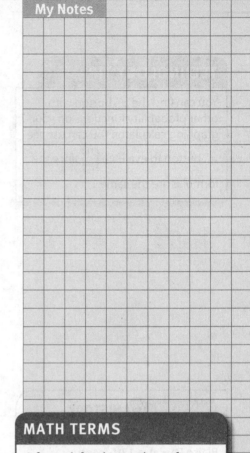

**MATH TERMS**

A **factorial** is the product of a natural number, $n$, and all natural numbers less than $n$, written as $n!$.

$$n! = n(n-1)(n-2) \cdot \ldots \cdot 2 \cdot 1$$

Zero factorial is defined as 1, or $0! = 1$.

An **alternative** notation for the number of combinations of $n$ distinct things taken $r$ at a time is $\begin{pmatrix} n \\ r \end{pmatrix}$.

3. Write an expression for the number of nominating committees using this notation.

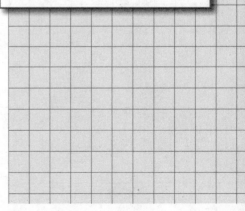

**ACADEMIC VOCABULARY**

An **alternative** is another available possibility.

**TECHNOLOGY TIP**

You can find the $_nC_r$ button with other probability functions on your graphing calculator. You can use the $_nC_r$ button to evaluate $\binom{n}{r}$ since the formulas are the same.

**CONNECT TO HISTORY**

Pascal's triangle is named after Blaise Pascal, a 17th-century French philosopher who made important contributions to the fields of mathematics and physics.

4. Find the values of each $_nC_r$ shown, and place them in a triangular pattern similar to the one given.

$$\binom{0}{0}$$

$$\binom{1}{0} \binom{1}{1}$$

$$\binom{2}{0} \binom{2}{1} \binom{2}{2}$$

$$\binom{3}{0} \binom{3}{1} \binom{3}{2} \binom{3}{3}$$

$$\binom{4}{0} \binom{4}{1} \binom{4}{2} \binom{4}{3} \binom{4}{4}$$

The triangular pattern that you created in Item 4 is called Pascal's triangle. Pascal's triangle has many interesting patterns.

5. What do you notice about the numbers at the end of every row in Pascal's triangle?

6. Make a conjecture about the value of $_nC_r$ when $r = 0$.

7. Make a conjecture about the value of $_nC_r$ when $r = n$.

8. **Reason quantitatively.** Starting with the second row, examine the second number in each row. Then make a conjecture about the value of $_nC_r$ when $r = 1$.

**My Notes**

9. Write the numbers that will fill in the next row of Pascal's triangle. How did you determine what the numbers would be?

Pascal's triangle also has a number of useful applications, particularly in algebra. The best-known application is related to binomial expansion.

10. Expand each binomial using algebraic techniques.

$(a + b)^0 =$ _____

$(a + b)^1 =$ _____

$(a + b)^2 =$ _____

$(a + b)^3 =$ _____

$(a + b)^4 =$ _____

> **MATH TIP**
>
> Recall that to expand $(a + b)^2$, you must write it as a product, $(a + b)(a + b)$, and then multiply.

11. **Make use of structure.** How do the coefficients of the expanded binomials relate to the numbers in Pascal's triangle?

12. **Express regularity in repeated reasoning.** What patterns do you notice in the exponents of $a$ and $b$ in the expanded binomials in Item 10?

13. How does the number of terms in the expansion of $(a + b)^n$ relate to the degree $n$?

### Check Your Understanding

14. Explain why the order in which a teacher selects nominating committee members is *not* important.

15. In Pascal's triangle, in which row do you find the coefficients for the expansion of $(a + b)^3$? In which row do you find the coefficients for $(a + b)^4$?

16. When expanding $(a + b)^n$, which row of Pascal's triangle gives you the coefficients of the resulting polynomial?

17. Use the numbers you found in Item 9, the patterns you have observed throughout the lesson, and the conjectures you have made to expand $(a + b)^5$.

18. **Attend to precision.** What do you notice about the sum of the exponents of each term in Item 17 in comparison to the degree ($n$) of the binomial you expanded?

### LESSON 16-1 PRACTICE

19. Evaluate $_8C_3$ and $_8C_5$.

20. Use a graphing calculator to determine how many different combinations of five-person dance committees can be selected from a class of 24 students.

21. Evaluate $_7C_2$ and $_7C_5$ without a calculator.

22. **Construct viable arguments.** Use the results of Items 19 and 21 to explain why you would expect $\begin{pmatrix} 10 \\ 3 \end{pmatrix}$ to equal $\begin{pmatrix} 10 \\ 7 \end{pmatrix}$. Then write a general statement of equality using $n$ and $r$.

23. Write the numbers that will fill in the seventh row of Pascal's triangle.

24. Expand $(a + b)^6$.

**My Notes**

## Learning Targets:
- Know the Binomial Theorem.
- Apply the Binomial Theorem to identify the coefficients or terms of any binomial expansion.

> **SUGGESTED LEARNING STRATEGIES:** Vocabulary Organizer, Think-Pair-Share, Note Taking, Create Representations, Simplify the Problem

The **Binomial Theorem** states what we have observed about binomial expansion in the previous lesson:

> For any positive $n$, the binomial expansion is:
> $$(a+b)^n = \binom{n}{0}a^n b^0 + \binom{n}{1}a^{n-1}b^1 + \binom{n}{2}a^{n-2}b^2 + \ldots + \binom{n}{n}a^0 b^n.$$

*Summation notation* is a shorthand notation that can be used to represent the sum of a finite or an infinite number of terms. Here, it can be used to represent the sum of the terms in an expanded binomial.

For example, in summation notation, $(a+b)^3 = \sum_{k=0}^{3} \binom{3}{k} a^{3-k} b^k$.

**MATH TERMS**

**Summation notation** is also known as *sigma notation* because of the use of the Greek letter $\Sigma$.

1. Use the example above to write the Binomial Theorem using summation notation and $\binom{n}{k}$ to represent each coefficient.

$$(a+b)^n =$$

To find the $r$th term of any binomial expansion $(a+b)^n$, use the expression $\binom{n}{r-1} a^{n-(r-1)} b^{r-1}$.

2. Evaluate the expression $\binom{n}{r-1} a^{n-(r-1)} b^{r-1}$ for $n=10$, $r=4$, $a=x$, and $b=3$. Simplify your answer.

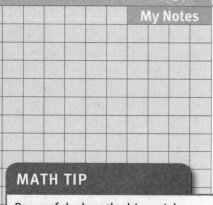

**My Notes**

3. Find the coefficient of the sixth term in the expansion of $(x + 2)^{11}$.

**MATH TIP**

Be careful when the binomial includes a negative number. If $b$ is negative, for example, be sure to apply the exponent in $b^{r-1}$ to the negative.

4. Find the coefficient of the fourth term in the expansion of $(x - 3)^8$.

5. **Reason quantitatively.** Find the seventh term in the expansion of $(x + 4)^9$.

**MATH TIP**

When the binomial contains a leading coefficient other than 1, apply the exponent to the coefficient as well as the variable.

6. Find the third term in the expansion of $(2x + 3)^7$.

**Check Your Understanding**

7. Find the coefficient of the fourth term in the expansion of $(x + 3)^8$.

8. Find the second term in the expansion of $(x + 5)^7$.

9. Why is the coefficient of the $r$th term in a binomial expansion $\binom{n}{r-1}$, and not $\binom{n}{r}$?

10. **Critique the reasoning of others.** Keisha found the third term in the expansion of the binomial $(2x + 1)^4$ using the following steps: $\binom{4}{2} 2x^{4-(3-1)} 1^{3-1} = 6 \cdot 2x^2 \cdot 1^2 = 12x^2$. Do you agree or disagree with Keisha's answer? Explain your reasoning.

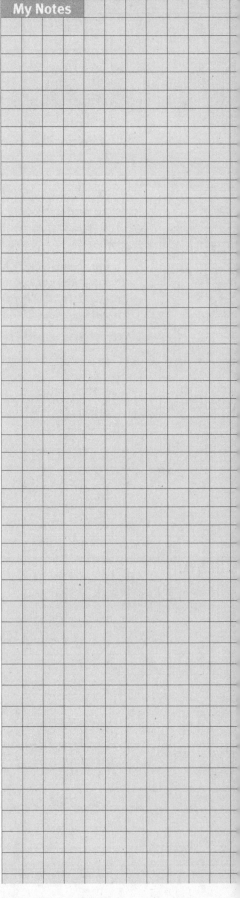

**11.** Use the Binomial Theorem to expand each of the following binomials.

   **a.** $(x + 4)^7$

   **b.** $(x - 4)^7$

   **c.** $(3x + 1)^6$

### Check Your Understanding

**12.** How many terms does the expansion of $(a + b)^{10}$ have?

**13.** What is the degree of $(a + b)^{10}$?

**14.** Use the Binomial Theorem to write the binomial expansion of:
   **a.** $(x + 3)^5$.
   **b.** $(x - 1)^8$.
   **c.** $(2x + 3)^4$.

**15. Construct viable arguments.** When is the Binomial Theorem useful?

## LESSON 16-2 PRACTICE

16. Write and evaluate the expression $\binom{n}{r-1} a^{n-(r-1)} b^{r-1}$ for $n = 6$, $r = 5$, $a = 2x$, and $b = 7$.

17. Find the coefficient of the third term in the expansion of $(x + 4)^5$.

18. Find the fourth term in the expansion of $(x + 3)^6$.

19. Find the second term in the expansion of $(3x - 2)^6$.

20. Use the Binomial Theorem to write the binomial expansion of $(x + 3)^4$.

21. Use the Binomial Theorem to write the binomial expansion of $(2a + 3b)^5$.

22. **Reason abstractly.** An *alternating series* is the sum of a finite or an infinite number of terms in which the signs of the terms alternate between positive and negative values. Daniel made the conjecture that when you expand $(a - b)^n$, the result will be an alternating series that always follows the pattern $+, -, +, \ldots$. Is Daniel's conjecture correct? Explain your reasoning.

## ACTIVITY 16 PRACTICE
Write your answers on notebook paper.
Show your work.

### Lesson 16-1

1. Which of the following would you use to find the number of different combinations of six-person nominating committees that could be chosen from a class of 25 students?

   **A.** $_6C_{25} = \dfrac{6!}{25!(25-6)!}$

   **B.** $_{25}C_6 = \dfrac{25!}{25!(25-6)!}$

   **C.** $_{25}C_6 = \dfrac{25!}{6!(25-6)!}$

   **D.** $_6C_{25} = \dfrac{6!}{6!(25-6)!}$

2. Simplify: $\dfrac{9 \times 8 \times 7 \times 6 \times 5 \times 4 \times 3 \times 2 \times 1}{(6 \times 5 \times 4 \times 3 \times 2 \times 1)(3 \times 2 \times 1)}$

3. Write the expression in Item 2 in $_nC_r$ notation.

4. Find the number of different combinations of four-person nominating committees that could be chosen from a class of 25 students.

5. Write the numbers that will fill in the eighth row of Pascal's triangle.

6. In which row of Pascal's triangle would you find the coefficients for the terms in the expansion of $(a + b)^{14}$?

7. Which of the following has the same value as $\begin{pmatrix} 12 \\ 7 \end{pmatrix}$?

   **A.** $_{12}C_7$

   **B.** $_{12}C_5$

   **C.** $\begin{pmatrix} 12 \\ 5 \end{pmatrix}$

   **D.** all of the above

8. Use what you have learned about the patterns in Pascal's triangle to expand $(a + b)^8$.

9. Manuela started expanding $(x + y)^9$. So far, she has written:

   $x^9 + 9x^8y + 36x^7y^2 + 84x^6y^3 + 126x^5y^4 + 126x^4y^5$

   Manuela explained to Karen that since both coefficients in the binomial are 1, the coefficients of the terms will start repeating, only backwards. Use Manuela's strategy to complete the expansion.

**Lesson 16-2**

10. Write $(a + b)^9$ using summation notation.

11. Write $(2x - 3)^7$ using summation notation.

12. Find the coefficient of the fourth term in the expansion of $(x + 4)^5$.

13. Which of the following is the coefficient of the third term in the expansion of $(x - 2)^7$?
    A. $-84$
    B. $-21$
    C. $21$
    D. $84$

14. Find the second term in the expansion of $(x + 4)^6$.

15. Find the fourth term in the expansion of $(3x - 2)^6$.

16. Use the Binomial Theorem to write the binomial expansion of $(x + 5)^4$.

17. Use the Binomial Theorem to write the binomial expansion of $(4a + b)^5$.

18. Use the Binomial Theorem to write the binomial expansion of $(x - 3)^5$.

19. Use the Binomial Theorem to write the binomial expansion of $(2x + y)^3$.

## MATHEMATICAL PRACTICES
**Make Sense of Problems and Persevere in Solving Them**

20. Consider the statement below.

    *In the expansion of every binomial, the powers of x decrease by 1 from left to right when written as a polynomial in standard form.*

    a. Expand the binomial $(x^2 + 1)^5$ and state whether the expansion supports or disproves the statement above and why.
    b. If the expansion disproves the statement, modify it so that it becomes a true statement.

Congruent squares of length $x$ are cut from the corners of a 10-inch-by-15-inch piece of cardboard to create a box without a lid.

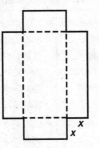

1. Write an expression in terms of $x$ for each.
   a. the height of the box
   b. the length of the box
   c. the width of the box

2. Write a function $V(x)$ for the volume of the box in terms of $x$. Leave your answer in factored form.

3. Express the domain of $V(x)$ as an inequality, in interval notation, and in set notation.

4. Sketch a graph of $V(x)$ over the domain that you found in Item 3. Include the scale on each axis.

5. Use a graphing calculator to find the coordinates of the maximum point of $V(x)$ over the domain for which you graphed it. Then interpret the meaning of the maximum point.

6. Use polynomial multiplication to rewrite $V(x)$, the volume function from Item 2, as a polynomial in standard form.

7. Consider the graph of $V(x)$ over the set of real numbers. Describe the end behavior of the function using arrow notation.

8. Use long division or synthetic division to find the quotient
$$\frac{x^5 + 3x^3 - 4x^2 + 2x + 6}{x - 1}.$$

9. Draw the first six rows of Pascal's triangle. Then use the triangle to expand $(a + b)^5$.

10. Use the Binomial Theorem to expand $(2x + 1)^6$.

| Scoring Guide | Exemplary | Proficient | Emerging | Incomplete |
|---|---|---|---|---|
| | The solution demonstrates these characteristics: | | | |
| **Mathematics Knowledge and Thinking** (Items 5-10) | • Effective understanding and identification of key features of polynomial functions including extreme values and end behavior <br><br> • Clear and accurate understanding of operations with polynomials (multiplication, division, binomial expansion) | • A functional understanding and accurate identification of key features of polynomial functions including extreme values and end behavior <br><br> • Largely correct understanding of operations with polynomials (multiplication, division, binomial expansion) | • Partial understanding and partially accurate identification of key features of polynomial functions including extreme values and end behavior <br><br> • Partially correct operations with polynomials (multiplication, division, binomial expansion) | • Little or no understanding and inaccurate identification of key features of polynomial functions including extreme values and end behavior <br><br> • Incomplete or mostly inaccurate operations with polynomials (multiplication, division, binomial expansion) |
| **Problem Solving** (Item 5) | • An appropriate and efficient strategy that results in a correct answer | • A strategy that may include unnecessary steps but results in a correct answer | • A strategy that results in some incorrect answers | • No clear strategy when solving problems |
| **Mathematical Modeling / Representations** (Items 1-5) | • Fluency in creating polynomial expressions and functions to model real-world scenarios, including reasonable domain <br><br> • Clear and accurate understanding of how to graph and identify features of polynomial functions by hand and using technology and represent intervals using inequalities, interval notation, and set notation | • Little difficulty in creating polynomial expressions and functions to model real-world scenarios, including reasonable domain <br><br> • Mostly accurate understanding of how to graph and identify features of polynomial functions by hand and using technology and represent intervals using inequalities, interval notation, and set notation | • Partial understanding of creating polynomial expressions and functions to model real-world scenarios, including reasonable domain <br><br> • Partial understanding of how to graph and identify features of polynomial functions by hand and using technology and represent intervals using inequalities, interval notation, and set notation | • Little or no understanding of creating polynomial expressions and functions to model real-world scenarios, including reasonable domain <br><br> • Inaccurate or incomplete understanding of how to graph and identify features of polynomial functions by hand and using technology and represent intervals using inequalities, interval notation, and set notation |
| **Reasoning and Communication** (Items 5, 7) | • Precise use of appropriate math terms and language to explain the maximum point in terms of a real-world scenario <br><br> • Clear and accurate explanation of the end behavior of a polynomial function | • Adequate explanation of the maximum point in terms of a real-world scenario <br><br> • Adequate explanation of the end behavior of a polynomial function | • Misleading or confusing explanation of the maximum point in terms of a real-world scenario <br><br> • Misleading or confusing explanation of the end behavior of a polynomial function | • Incomplete or inadequate explanation of the maximum point in terms of a real-world scenario <br><br> • Incomplete or inaccurate explanation of the end behavior of a polynomial function |

# Factors of Polynomials

## How Many Roots?
### Lesson 17-1 Algebraic Methods

**Learning Targets:**

- Determine the linear factors of polynomial functions using algebraic methods.
- Determine the linear or quadratic factors of polynomials by factoring the sum or difference of two cubes and factoring by grouping.

**SUGGESTED LEARNING STRATEGIES:** Marking the Text, Note Taking, Look for a Pattern, Simplify a Problem, Identify a Subtask

When you factor a polynomial, you rewrite the original polynomial as a product of two or more polynomial factors.

1. State the common factor of the terms in the polynomial $4x^3 + 2x^2 - 6x$. Then factor the polynomial.

2. **Make use of structure.** Consider the expression $x^2(x - 3) + 2x(x - 3) + 3(x - 3)$.

   **a.** How many terms does it have?

   **b.** What factor do all the terms have in common?

3. Factor $x^2(x - 3) + 2x(x - 3) - 3(x - 3)$.

Some quadratic trinomials, $ax^2 + bx + c$, can be factored into two binomial factors.

## Example A

Factor $2x^2 + 7x - 4$.

| | | |
|---|---|---|
| **Step 1:** | Find the product of $a$ and $c$. | $2(-4) = -8$ |
| **Step 2:** | Find the factors of $ac$ that have a sum of $b$, 7. | $8 + (-1) = 7$ |
| **Step 3:** | Rewrite the polynomial, separating the linear term. | $2x^2 + 8x - 1x - 4$ |
| **Step 4:** | Group the first two terms and the last two terms. | $(2x^2 + 8x) + (-x - 4)$ |
| **Step 5:** | Factor each group separately. | $2x(x + 4) - 1(x + 4)$ |
| **Step 6:** | Factor out the binomial. | $(x + 4)(2x - 1)$ |

**Solution:** $2x^2 + 7x - 4 = (x + 4)(2x - 1)$

**MATH TIP**

Check your answer to a factoring problem by multiplying the factors together to get the original polynomial.

## Try These A

**a.** Use Example A as a guide to factor $6x^2 + 19x + 10$. Show your work.

Factor each trinomial. Show your work.

**b.** $3x^2 - 8x - 3$                 **c.** $2x^2 + 7x + 6$

Some higher-degree polynomials can also be *factored by grouping*.

## Example B

**a.** Factor $3x^3 + 9x^2 + 4x + 12$ by grouping.

| | | |
|---|---|---|
| **Step 1:** | Group the terms. | $(3x^3 + 9x^2) + (4x + 12)$ |
| **Step 2:** | Factor each group separately. | $3x^2(x + 3) + 4(x + 3)$ |
| **Step 3:** | Factor out the binomial. | $(x + 3)(3x^2 + 4)$ |

**Solution:** $3x^3 + 9x^2 + 4x + 12 = (x + 3)(3x^2 + 4)$

**b.** Factor $3x^4 + 9x^3 + 4x + 12$ by grouping.

| | | |
|---|---|---|
| **Step 1:** | Group the terms. | $(3x^4 + 9x^3) + (4x + 12)$ |
| **Step 2:** | Factor each group separately. | $3x^3(x + 3) + 4(x + 3)$ |
| **Step 3:** | Factor out the binomial. | $(x + 3)(3x^3 + 4)$ |

**Solution:** $3x^4 + 9x^3 + 4x + 12 = (x + 3)(3x^3 + 4)$

## Try These B

Factor by grouping. Show your work.

**a.** $2x^3 + 10x^2 - 3x - 15$          **b.** $4x^4 + 7x^3 + 4x + 7$

### Check Your Understanding

4. Factor $7x^4 + 21x^3 - 14x^2$.
5. Factor $6x^2 + 11x + 4$.
6. Factor by grouping.
   **a.** $8x^3 - 64x^2 + x - 8$
   **b.** $12x^4 + 2x^3 - 30x - 5$
7. **Reason abstractly.** What is the purpose of separating the linear term in a quadratic trinomial when factoring?

A difference of two squares can be factored by using a specific pattern, $a^2 - b^2 = (a + b)(a - b)$. A *difference of two cubes* and a *sum of two cubes* also have a factoring pattern.

|  **Difference of Cubes**  |  **Sum of Cubes**  |
|---|---|
| $a^3 - b^3 = (a - b)(a^2 + ab + b^2)$ | $a^3 + b^3 = (a + b)(a^2 - ab + b^2)$ |

8. What patterns do you notice in the formulas that appear above?

9. **Express regularity in repeated reasoning.** Factor each difference or sum of cubes.
   **a.** $x^3 - 8$              **b.** $x^3 + 27$

   **c.** $8x^3 - 64$           **d.** $27 + 125x^3$

**MATH TIP**

It is a good strategy to first identify and label $a$ and $b$. This makes it easier to substitute into the formula.

Some higher-degree polynomials can be factored by using the same patterns or formulas that you used when factoring quadratic binomials or trinomials.

10. Use the difference of squares formula $a^2 - b^2 = (a + b)(a - b)$ to factor $16x^4 - 25$. (It may help to write each term as a square.)

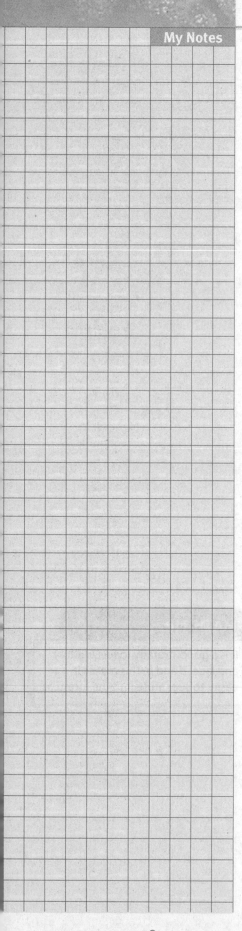

11. **Reason quantitatively.** Explain the steps used to factor $2x^5 + 6x^3 - 8x$.

| $2x^5 + 6x^3 - 8x$ | Original expression |
|---|---|
| $= 2x(x^4 + 3x^2 - 4)$ | |
| $= 2x(x^2 + 4)(x^2 - 1)$ | |
| $= 2x(x^2 + 4)(x + 1)(x - 1)$ | |

12. Use the formulas for quadratic binomials and trinomials to factor each expression.

   **a.** $x^4 + x^2 - 20$          **b.** $16x^4 - 81$

   **c.** $(x - 2)^4 + 10(x - 2)^2 + 9$

### Check Your Understanding

13. Factor each difference or sum of cubes.
    **a.** $125x^3 + 216$
    **b.** $x^6 - 27$

14. Use the formulas for factoring quadratic binomials and trinomials to factor each expression.
    **a.** $x^4 - 14x^2 + 33$
    **b.** $81x^4 - 625$

15. **Attend to precision.** A *linear factor* is a factor that has degree 1. A *quadratic factor* has degree 2. The factored expression in Item 11 has 3 linear factors and 1 quadratic factor. What is true about the degree of the factors in relation to the degree of the original expression?

### LESSON 17-1 PRACTICE

Factor each expression.

16. $3x^2 - 14x - 5$          17. $8x^3 + 27$

18. $x^4 - 5x^2 - 36$          19. $2x^4 - x^3 - 18x^2 + 9x$

20. **Model with mathematics.** The trinomial $4x^2 + 12x + 9$ represents the area of a square. Write an expression that represents the length of one side of the square. Explain your answer.

**Learning Targets:**

- Know and apply the Fundamental Theorem of Algebra.
- Write polynomial functions, given their degree and roots.

> **SUGGESTED LEARNING STRATEGIES:** Vocabulary Organizer, Note Taking, Graphic Organizer, Work Backward

As a consequence of the *Fundamental Theorem of Algebra*, a polynomial $p(x)$ of degree $n \geq 0$ has exactly $n$ linear factors, counting factors used more than once.

**My Notes**

## Example A

Find the zeros of $f(x) = 3x^3 + 2x^2 + 6x + 4$. Show that the Fundamental Theorem of Algebra is true for this function by counting the number of zeros.

**Step 1:** Set the function equal to 0.
$$3x^3 + 2x^2 + 6x + 4 = 0$$

**Step 2:** Look for a factor common to all terms, use the quadratic trinomial formulas, or factor by grouping, as was done here.
$$(3x^3 + 6x) + (2x^2 + 4) = 0$$

**Step 3:** Factor each group separately.
$$3x(x^2 + 2) + 2(x^2 + 2) = 0$$

**Step 4:** Factor out the binomial to write the factors.
$$(x^2 + 2)(3x + 2) = 0$$

**Step 5:** Use the Zero Product Property to solve for $x$.
$$x^2 + 2 = 0 \qquad 3x + 2 = 0$$
$$x = \pm i\sqrt{2} \qquad x = -\frac{2}{3}$$

**Solution:** $x = \pm i\sqrt{2}$; $x = -\frac{2}{3}$.

All three zeros are in the complex number system.

### MATH TERMS

Let $p(x)$ be a polynomial function of degree $n$, where $n > 0$. The **Fundamental Theorem of Algebra** states that $p(x) = 0$ has at least one zero in the complex number system.

### MATH TIP

When counting the number of zeros, remember that when solutions have the $\pm$ symbol, such as $\pm a$, this represents two different zeros, $a$ and $-a$.

## Try These A

Find the zeros of the functions by factoring and using the Zero Product Property. Show that the Fundamental Theorem of Algebra is true for each function by counting the number of complex zeros.

**a.** $f(x) = x^3 + 9x$

**b.** $g(x) = x^4 - 16$

**c.** $h(x) = (x - 2)^2 + 4(x - 2) + 4$

**d.** $p(x) = x^3 - 64$

**e.** $k(x) = x^3 + 5x^2 + 9x + 45$

**f.** $w(x) = x^3 + 216$

### MATH TIP

All real numbers are complex numbers with an imaginary part of zero.

### MATH TIP

When you factor the sum or difference of cubes, the result is a linear factor and a quadratic factor. To find the zeros of the quadratic factor, use the quadratic formula.

**My Notes**

### Check Your Understanding

For Items 1–4, find the zeros of the functions. Show that the Fundamental Theorem of Algebra is true for each function by counting the number of complex zeros.

1. $g(x) = x^4 - 81$
2. $h(x) = x^3 + 8$
3. $f(x) = x^4 + 25x^2$
4. $k(x) = x^3 - 7x^2 + 4x - 28$
5. **Make use of structure.** As a consequence of the Fundamental Theorem of Algebra, how many linear factors, including multiple factors, does the function
   $f(x) = ax^5 + bx^4 + cx^3 + dx^2 + ex + f$ have?
6. What is the minimum number of real zeros for the function in Item 4? Explain your reasoning.

7. Create a flowchart, other organizational scheme, or set of directions for finding the zeros of polynomials.

It is possible to find a polynomial function, given its zeros.

### Example B

Find a polynomial function of 3rd degree that has zeros 0, 2, and $-3$.

**Step 1:** Write the factors. $\qquad\qquad f(x) = (x)(x - 2)(x + 3)$

**Step 2:** Multiply the binomials. $\qquad f(x) = (x)(x^2 + x - 6)$

**Step 3:** Distribute the $x$. $\qquad\qquad f(x) = x^3 + x^2 - 6x$

**Solution:** $f(x) = x^3 + x^2 - 6x$

### Try These B

Find a polynomial function with the indicated degree and zeros.

a. $n = 3$; zeros 0, 5, $-7$
b. $n = 4$; zeros $\pm 1$, $\pm 5$

> **MATH TIP**
>
> If $a$ is a zero of a polynomial function, then $(x - a)$ is a factor of the polynomial.

The *Complex Conjugate Root Theorem* states that if $a + bi$, $b \neq 0$, is a zero of a polynomial function with real coefficients, the conjugate $a - bi$ is also a zero of the function.

### Example C
**a.** Find a polynomial function of 3rd degree that has zeros 3 and $4i$.

**Step 1:** Use the Complex Conjugate Root Theorem to find all zeros. $\quad x = 3, x = 4i, x = -4i$

**Step 2:** Write the factors. $\quad f(x) = (x - 3)(x - 4i)(x + 4i)$

**Step 3:** Multiply the factors that contain $i$. $\quad f(x) = (x - 3)(x^2 + 16)$

**Step 4:** Multiply out the factors to get the polynomial function. $\quad f(x) = x^3 - 3x^2 + 16x - 48$

**Solution:** $f(x) = x^3 - 3x^2 + 16x - 48$

**b.** Find a polynomial function of 4th degree that has zeros 1, −1, and $1 + 2i$.

**Step 1:** Use the Complex Conjugate Root Theorem to find all zeros. $\quad x = 1, x = -1, x = 1 + 2i, x = 1 - 2i$

**Step 2:** Write the factors. $\quad f(x) = (x - 1)(x + 1)$
$(x - (1 + 2i))(x - (1 - 2i))$

**Step 3:** Multiply using the fact that $(a - b)(a + b) = a^2 - b^2$. $\quad f(x) = (x^2 - 1)(x^2 - 2x + 5)$

**Step 4:** Multiply out the factors to get the polynomial function. $\quad f(x) = x^4 - 2x^3 + 4x^2 + 2x - 5$

**Solution:** $f(x) = x^4 - 2x^3 + 4x^2 + 2x - 5$

### Try These C
**Reason quantitatively.** Write a polynomial function of $n$th degree that has the given real or complex roots.

**a.** $n = 3$; $x = -2$, $x = 3i$

**b.** $n = 4$; $x = 3$, $x = -3$, $x = 1 + 2i$

**c.** $n = 4$; $x = 2$, $x = -5$, and $x = -4$ is a double root

**My Notes**

### Check Your Understanding

8. **Reason abstractly.** If $3 + 2i$ is a zero of $p(x)$, what is another zero of $p(x)$?

For Items 9–12, write a polynomial function of $n$th degree that has the given real or complex roots.

9. $n = 3; x = -2, x = 0, x = 5$

10. $n = 3; x = 3, x = 2i$

11. $n = 4; x = 5, x = -5, x = i$

12. $n = 4; x = 3, x = -4$, and $x = 2$ is a double root

## LESSON 17-2 PRACTICE

For Items 13–15, find the zeros of the functions. Show that the Fundamental Theorem of Algebra is true for each function by counting the number of complex zeros.

13. $f(x) = x^3 + 1000$

14. $f(x) = x^3 - 4x^2 + 25x - 100$

15. $f(x) = x^4 - 3x^3 + x^2 - 3x$

For Items 16–19, write a polynomial function of $n$th degree that has the given real or complex zeros.

16. $n = 3; x = 9, x = 2i$

17. $n = 3; x = -1, x = 4 + i$

18. $n = 4; x = -6$ is a double zero and $x = 2$ is a double zero

19. **Construct viable arguments.** Use the theorems you have learned in this lesson to determine the degree of a polynomial that has zeros $x = 3$, $x = 2i$, and $x = 4 + i$. Justify your answer.

## ACTIVITY 17 PRACTICE
Write your answers on notebook paper. Show your work.

### Lesson 17-1

1. State the common factor of the terms in the polynomial $5x^3 + 30x^2 - 10x$. Then factor the polynomial.

2. Which of the following is one of the factors of the polynomial $15x^2 - x - 2$?
   A. $x - 2$
   B. $5x - 2$
   C. $5x + 1$
   D. $3x - 1$

3. Factor each polynomial.
   a. $6x^2 + 7x - 5$
   b. $14x^2 + 25x + 6$

4. Factor by grouping.
   a. $8x^3 - 64x^2 + x - 8$
   b. $12x^4 + 2x^3 - 30x - 5$

5. Factor each difference or sum of cubes.
   a. $125x^3 + 216$
   b. $x^6 - 27$

6. Use the formulas for factoring quadratic binomials and trinomials to factor each expression.
   a. $x^4 - 14x^2 + 33$
   b. $81x^4 - 625$
   c. $x^4 + 17x^2 + 60$
   d. $x^6 - 100$

### Lesson 17-2

7. Which theorem states that a polynomial of degree $n$ has exactly $n$ linear factors, counting multiple factors?
   A. Binomial Theorem
   B. Quadratic Formula
   C. Fundamental Theorem of Algebra
   D. Complex Conjugate Root Theorem

8. Find the zeros of the functions by factoring and using the Zero Product Property. Identify any multiple zeros.
   a. $f(x) = 2x^4 + 18x^2$
   b. $g(x) = 3x^3 - 3$
   c. $h(x) = 5x^3 - 6x^2 - 45x + 54$
   d. $h(x) = 3x^4 - 36x^3 + 108x^2$

9. The table of values shows coordinate pairs on the graph of $f(x)$. Which of the following could be $f(x)$?
   A. $x(x + 1)(x - 1)$
   B. $(x - 1)(x + 1)(x - 3)$
   C. $(x + 1)^2(x + 3)$
   D. $(x + 1)(x - 2)^2$

   | $x$ | $f(x)$ |
   |-----|--------|
   | $-1$ | 0 |
   | 0 | 3 |
   | 1 | 0 |
   | 2 | $-3$ |

10. Write a polynomial function of $n$th degree that has the given zeros.
    a. $n = 3; x = 1, x = 6, x = -6$
    b. $n = 4; x = -3, x = 3, x = 0, x = 4$

**11.** Which of the following polynomial functions has multiple roots at $x = 0$?
  **A.** $f(x) = x^2 - x$
  **B.** $f(x) = x^3 - x^2$
  **C.** $f(x) = x^3 - x$
  **D.** all of the above

**12.** Write a polynomial function of $n$th degree that has the given real or complex roots.
  **a.** $n = 3; x = -2, x = 5, x = -5$
  **b.** $n = 4; x = -3, x = 3, x = 5i$
  **c.** $n = 3; x = -2, x = 1 + 2i$

**13.** Give the degree of the polynomial function with the given real or complex roots.
  **a.** $x = -7, x = 1, x = 4i$
  **b.** $x = -2, x = 2, x = 0, x = 4 + i$
  **c.** $x = 2i, x = 1 - 3i$

**14.** Which of the following could be the factored form of the polynomial function $f(x) = x^4 + \ldots + 48$?
  **I.** $f(x) = (x + 1)(x + 3)(x + 4i)(x - 4i)$
  **II.** $f(x) = (x + 2)^2(x - 1)(x + 4)(x - 6)$
  **III.** $f(x) = (x + 3)(x - 8)(x + 2i)(x - 2i)$
  **A.** I only
  **B.** I and II only
  **C.** II only
  **D.** I, II, and III

**15.** Explain your reason(s) for eliminating each of the polynomials you did not choose in Item 14.

## MATHEMATICAL PRACTICES
### Use Appropriate Tools Strategically

**16.** Use the information below to write a polynomial function, first in factored form and then in standard form.

*Fact:* The graph only touches the $x$-axis at a double zero; it does not cross through the axis.

*Clue:* One of the factors of the polynomial is $(x + i)$.

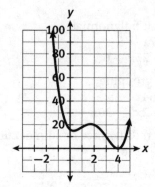

# Graphs of Polynomials
### Getting to the End Behavior
### Lesson 18-1 Graphing Polynomial Functions

**Learning Targets:**

- Graph polynomial functions by hand or using technology, identifying zeros when suitable factorizations are available, and showing end behavior.
- Recognize even and odd functions from their algebraic expressions.

> **SUGGESTED LEARNING STRATEGIES:** Look for a Pattern, Create Representations, Think-Pair-Share, Vocabulary Organizer, Marking the Text

1. **Make sense of problems.** Each graph below shows a polynomial of the form $f(x) = a_n x^n + a_{n-1} x^{n-1} + \ldots + a_1 x + a_0$, where $a_n \neq 0$. Apply what you know about graphs of polynomials to match each graph to one of the equations below. Write the equation under the graph. Justify your answers.

$$y = -2x^3 - 4x^2 + 1$$

$$y = 2x^3 - 4x^2 + 1$$

$$y = -3x^4 + 8x^2 + 1$$

$$y = 3x^4 - 8x^2 + 1$$

$$y = -2x^5 - 4x^4 + 5x^3 + 8x^2 - 5x$$

$$y = 2x^5 + 4x^4 - 5x^3 - 8x^2 + 5x$$

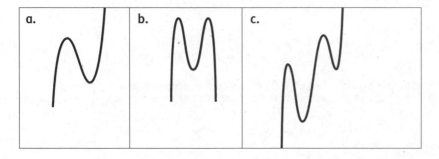

a.    b.    c.

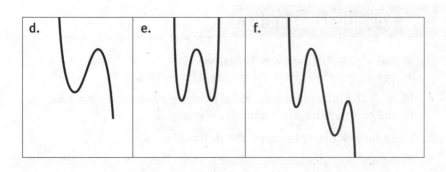

d.    e.    f.

Polynomials can be written in factored form or in standard form. Each form provides useful clues about how the graph will behave. Work on Item 2 with your group. As needed, refer to the Glossary to review translations of key terms. Incorporate your understanding into group discussions to confirm your knowledge and use of key mathematical language.

2. **Model with mathematics.** Sketch a graph of each function. For graphs **b** through **e**, identify the information revealed by the unfactored polynomial compared to the factored polynomial.
   a. $f(x) = x + 3$
   b. $g(x) = x^2 - 9 = (x + 3)(x - 3)$

   c. $h(x) = x^3 + x^2 - 9x - 9 = (x + 3)(x - 3)(x + 1)$

   d. $k(x) = x^4 - 10x^2 + 9 = (x + 3)(x - 3)(x + 1)(x - 1)$

   e. $p(x) = x^5 + 10x^4 + 37x^3 + 60x^2 + 36x = x(x + 2)^2(x + 3)^2$

### Check Your Understanding

3. Sketch a graph of the cubic function:
   $p(x) = x^3 - 2x^2 - 19x + 20 = (x + 4)(x - 1)(x - 5)$

4. Identify the information revealed by the unfactored polynomial in Item 3 compared to the factored polynomial.

5. Use your calculator to graph the function in Item 3.

6. Compare the calculator image with your sketch. What information is not revealed by either the standard form or factored form of a polynomial?

Polynomial functions are *continuous functions*, meaning that their graphs have no gaps or breaks. Their graphs are smooth, unbroken curves with no sharp turns. Graphs of polynomial functions with degree $n$ have $n$ zeros (real number zeros are $x$-intercepts), as you saw in the Fundamental Theorem of Algebra. They also have at most $n - 1$ **relative extrema**.

7. Find the $x$-intercepts of $f(x) = x^4 + 3x^3 - x^2 - 3x$.

8. Find the $y$-intercept of $f(x)$.

9. **Reason quantitatively.** How can the zeros of a polynomial function help you identify where the relative extrema will occur?

10. The relative extrema of the function $f(x) = x^4 + 3x^3 - x^2 - 3x$ occur at approximately $x = 0.6$, $x = -0.5$, and $x = -2.3$. Use these $x$-values to find the approximate values of the extrema and graph the function.

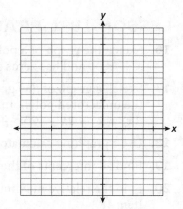

11. Sketch a graph of $f(x) = -x^3 - x^2 - 6x$.

12. Sketch a graph of $f(x) = x^4 - 10x^2 + 9$.

---

**MATH TERMS**

*Maxima* and *minima* are known as **extrema**. They are the greatest value (the maximum) or the least value (the minimum) of a function over an interval or the entire domain.

When referring to extrema that occur within a specific interval of the domain, they are called **relative extrema**.

When referring to values that are extrema for the entire domain of the function, they are called **global extrema**.

---

**CONNECT** **TO** **AP**

In calculus, you will use the first derivative of a polynomial function to algebraically determine the coordinates of the extrema.

### Check Your Understanding

13. **Use appropriate tools strategically.** Use a graphing calculator to graph the polynomial functions. Verify that their $x$- and $y$-intercepts are correct, and determine the coordinates of the relative extrema.
    a. $f(x) = x^3 + 7x^2 - x - 7$
    b. $h(x) = x^4 - 13x^2 + 36$

14. What is the maximum number of relative extrema a fifth-degree polynomial function can have?

15. **Construct viable arguments.** Explain why relative extrema occur between the zeros of a polynomial function.

### LESSON 18-1 PRACTICE

16. Sketch the graph of a polynomial function that decreases as $x \to \pm\infty$ and has zeros at $x = -10, -3, 1$, and 4.

17. Sketch a graph of $f(x)$ given below. Identify the information revealed by the unfactored polynomial compared to the factored polynomial.
    $f(x) = x^5 - 2x^4 - 25x^3 + 26x^2 + 120x = x(x-5)(x-3)(x+2)(x+4)$

18. Use a graphing calculator to graph $f(x) = x^3 - x^2 - 49x + 49$.

19. Find all intercepts of the function in Item 18.

20. Find the relative maximum and minimum values of the function in Item 18.

21. **Make sense of problems.** A fourth-degree even polynomial function has a relative maximum at $(0, 5)$ and relative minimums at $(-4, 1)$ and $(4, 1)$. How many real zeros does this function have? Explain your reasoning.

### Learning Targets:
- Know and apply the Rational Root Theorem and Descartes' Rule of Signs.
- Know and apply the Remainder Theorem and the Factor Theorem.

**SUGGESTED LEARNING STRATEGIES:** Shared Reading, Vocabulary Organizer, Marking the Text, Note Taking

Some polynomial functions, such as $f(x) = x^3 - 2x^2 - 5x + 6$, are not factorable using the tools that you have. However, it is still possible to graph these functions without a calculator. The following tools will be helpful.

| Rational Root Theorem | Finds possible rational roots |
|---|---|
| Descartes' Rule of Signs | Finds the possible number of real roots |
| Remainder Theorem | Determines if a value is a zero |
| Factor Theorem | Another way to determine if a value is a zero |

---

**Rational Root Theorem**

If a polynomial function $f(x) = a_n x^n + a_{n-1} x^{n-1} + \ldots + a_1 x + a_0$, $a_n \neq 0$, has integer coefficients, then every rational root of $f(x) = 0$ has the form $\frac{p}{q}$, where $p$ is a factor of $a_0$, and $q$ is a factor of $a_n$.

---

The Rational Root Theorem determines the possible rational roots of a polynomial.

1. Consider the quadratic equation $2x^2 + 9x - 3 = 0$.
   a. Make a list of the only possible rational roots to this equation.

   b. **Reason abstractly.** Explain why you think these are the only possible rational roots.

   c. Does your list of rational roots satisfy the equation?

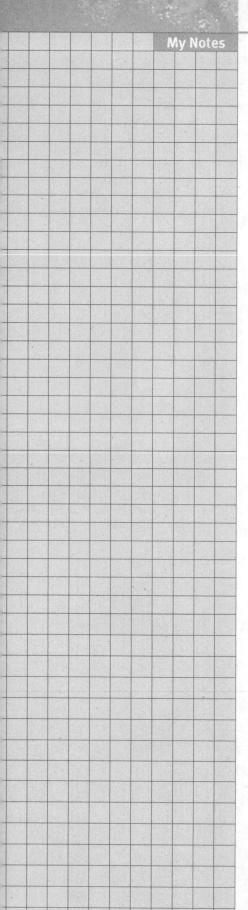

**2.** What can you conclude from Item 1 part c?

**3. Reason quantitatively.** Verify your conclusion in Item 1 part c by finding the roots of the equation in Item 1 using the Quadratic Formula. Show your work.

### Example A

Find all the possible rational roots of $f(x) = x^3 - 2x^2 - 5x + 6$.

**Step 1:** Find the factors $q$ of the leading coefficient 1 and the factors $p$ of the constant term 6.

$q$ could equal $\pm 1$
$p$ could equal $\pm 1, \pm 2, \pm 3, \pm 6$

**Step 2:** Write all combinations of $\frac{p}{q}$. Then simplify.

$\dfrac{\pm 1, \pm 2, \pm 3, \pm 6}{\pm 1}$

**Solution:** $\pm 1, \pm 2, \pm 3, \pm 6$

### Try These A

Find all the possible rational roots of $f(x) = 2x^3 + 7x^2 + 2x - 3$.

The Rational Root Theorem can yield a large number of possible roots. To help eliminate some possibilities, you can use Descartes' Rule of Signs. While Descartes' rule does not tell you the value of the roots, it does tell you the maximum number of positive and negative real roots.

**Descartes' Rule of Signs**

If $f(x)$ is a polynomial function with real coefficients and a nonzero constant term arranged in descending powers of the variable, then

- the number of positive real roots of $f(x) = 0$ equals the number of variations in sign of the terms of $f(x)$, or is less than this number by an even integer.

- the number of negative real roots of $f(x) = 0$ equals the number of variations in sign of the terms of $f(-x)$, or is less than this number by an even integer.

## Example B

Find the number of positive and negative roots of $f(x) = x^3 - 2x^2 - 5x + 6$.

**Step 1:** Determine the sign changes in $f(x)$: $f(x) = x^3 - 2x^2 - 5x + 6$
There are two sign changes:
- one between the first and second terms when the sign goes from positive to negative
- one between the third and fourth terms when the sign goes from negative to positive

So, there are either two or zero positive real roots.

**Step 2:** Determine the sign changes in $f(-x)$: $f(-x) = -x^3 - 2x^2 + 5x + 6$
There is one sign change:
- between the second and third terms when the sign goes from negative to positive

So, there is one negative real root.

**Solution:** There are either two or zero positive real roots and one negative real root.

## Try These B

Find the number of positive and negative roots of $f(x) = 2x^3 + 7x^2 + 2x - 3$.

### Check Your Understanding

4. Determine all the possible rational roots of $f(x) = 2x^3 - 2x^2 - 4x + 5$.

5. Determine the possible number of positive and negative real zeros for $h(x) = x^3 - 4x^2 + x + 5$.

6. The function $f(x) = x^3 + x^2 + x + 1$ has only one possible rational root. What is it? Explain your reasoning.

7. **Construct viable arguments.** Explain the circumstances under which the only possible rational roots of a polynomial are integers.

You have found all the possible rational roots and the number of positive and negative real roots for the function $f(x) = x^3 - 2x^2 - 5x + 6$. The next two theorems will help you find the zeros of the function. The Remainder Theorem tells if a possible root is actually a zero or just another point on the graph of the polynomial. The Factor Theorem gives another way to test if a possible root is a zero.

**My Notes**

> **Remainder Theorem**
>
> If a polynomial $P(x)$ is divided by $(x - k)$, where $k$ is a constant, then the remainder $r$ is $P(k)$.

> **Factor Theorem**
>
> A polynomial $P(x)$ has a factor $(x - k)$ if and only if $P(k) = 0$.

## Example C

Use synthetic division to find the zeros and factor $f(x) = x^3 - 2x^2 - 5x + 6$.

From Examples A and B, you know the possible rational zeros are $\pm 1$, $\pm 2$, $\pm 3$, $\pm 6$. You also know that the polynomial has either two or zero positive real roots and one negative real root. Now it is time to check each of the possible rational roots to determine if they are zeros of the function.

**Step 1:** Divide $(x^3 - 2x^2 - 5x + 6)$ by $(x + 1)$.

$$
\begin{array}{r|rrrr}
-1 & 1 & -2 & -5 & 6 \\
   &   & -1 &  3 & 2 \\
\hline
   & 1 & -3 & -2 & 8
\end{array}
$$
So, you have found a point, $(-1, 8)$.

**Step 2:** Continue this process, finding either points on the polynomial and/or zeros for each of the possible roots.

Divide $(x^3 - 2x^2 - 5x + 6)$ by $(x - 1)$.

$$
\begin{array}{r|rrrr}
1 & 1 & -2 & -5 &  6 \\
  &   &  1 & -1 & -6 \\
\hline
  & 1 & -1 & -6 &  0
\end{array}
$$
So, you have found a zero, $(1, 0)$, and a factor, $f(x) = (x - 1)(x^2 - x - 6)$.

**Step 3:** As soon as you have a quadratic factor remaining after the division process, you can factor the quadratic factor by inspection, if possible, or use the Quadratic Formula.

**Solution:** $f(x) = (x - 1)(x + 2)(x - 3)$; The real zeros are 1, $-2$, and 3.

## Try These C

Use synthetic division and what you know from Try These A and B to find the zeros and factor $f(x) = 2x^3 + 7x^2 + 2x - 3$.

### Check Your Understanding

8. One of the possible rational roots of $f(x) = x^3 - 2x^2 - 4x + 5$ is 5. If you divide $x^3 - 2x^2 - 4x + 5$ by $x - 5$, the remainder is 60. What information does this give you about the graph of $f(x)$?

9. If a polynomial $P(x)$ is divided by $(x - k)$ and the remainder is 0, what does this tell you about the value $k$?

● Using the Factor Theorem, follow a similar process to find the real zeros.

### Example D

Use the Factor Theorem to find the real zeros of $f(x) = x^3 - 2x^2 - 5x + 6$. Again, you know the possible rational roots are $\pm 1, \pm 2, \pm 3, \pm 6$.

**Step 1:** Test $(x + 1): f(-1) = (-1)^3 - 2(-1)^2 - 5(-1) + 6 = 8$
So, you have a point, $(-1, 8)$.

**Step 2:** Test $(x - 1): f(1) = (1)^3 - 2(1)^2 - 5(1) + 6 = 0$
So, you have a zero at $x = 1$.

**Step 3:** Test $(x - 2): f(2) = (2)^3 - 2(2)^2 - 5(2) + 6 = -4$
So, you have a point, $(2, -4)$.

**Step 4:** Continue to test rational zeros or use division to simplify the polynomial and factor or use the Quadratic Formula to find the real zeros.

**Solution:** The real zeros are 1, −2, and 3.

### Try These D

Use the Factor Theorem and what you know from Try These A and B to find the real zeros of $f(x) = 2x^3 + 7x^2 + 2x - 3$.

●

### Example E

Graph $f(x) = x^3 - 2x^2 - 5x + 6$ using the information you found in Examples A–D. Also include the $y$-intercept and what you know about the end behavior of the function.

| x | f(x) |
|----|------|
| −1 | 8 |
| 1 | 0 |
| −2 | 0 |
| 0 | 6 |
| 3 | 0 |
| 2 | −4 |

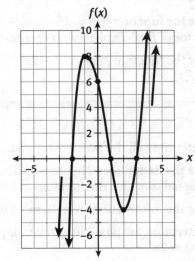

**My Notes**

**Try These E**

Graph $f(x) = 2x^3 + 7x^2 + 2x - 3$ using the information from Try These A–D. **Include a scale on both axes.**

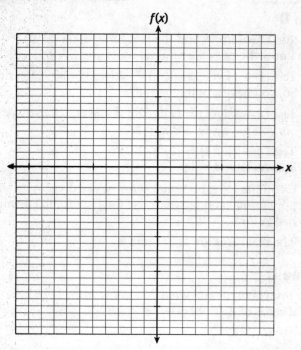

**Check Your Understanding**

10. The possible rational roots of $g(x) = 2x^4 + 5x^3 - x^2 + 5x - 1$ are $\pm\frac{1}{2}$ and $\pm 1$. List the possible factors of $g(x)$.

11. For the function $f(x) = x^3 - 2x^2 - 4x + 5$, $f(-1) = 6$. Is $(x + 1)$ a factor of $f(x)$? Explain your reasoning.

12. For the function $p(x) = x^3 - 2x^2 - 4x + 8$, $p(2) = 0$. Name one factor of $f(x)$.

**LESSON 18-2 PRACTICE**

13. Determine all the possible rational roots of $f(x) = x^3 - 5x^2 - 17x + 21$.

14. Use the Remainder Theorem to determine which of the possible rational roots for the function in Item 13 are zeros of the function.

15. Use the information from Item 14 to graph the function in Item 13.

16. Determine the possible number of positive and negative real roots for $h(x) = 2x^3 + x^2 - 5x + 2$.

17. **Model with mathematics.** Graph $h(x) = 2x^3 + x^2 - 5x + 2$.

18. **Reason quantitatively.** Use the Rational Root Theorem to write a fourth-degree polynomial function that has possible rational roots of $\pm\frac{1}{4}, \pm\frac{7}{4}, \pm 1, \pm 7$. Then use Descartes' Rule of Signs to modify your answer to ensure that none of the actual zeros are positive rational numbers.

**My Notes**

## Learning Targets:
- Compare properties of two functions each represented in a different way.
- Solve polynomial inequalities by graphing.

> **SUGGESTED LEARNING STRATEGIES:** Create Representations, Note Taking, Marking the Text, Identify a Subtask

Polynomial functions can be represented in a number of ways: algebraically, graphically, numerically in tables, or by verbal descriptions. Properties, theorems, and technological tools allow you to analyze and compare polynomial functions regardless of the way in which they are represented.

Each of the representations below is a representation of a fourth-degree polynomial.

**A.** $f(x) = -2x^4 + 10x^2 + 72$    **B.**

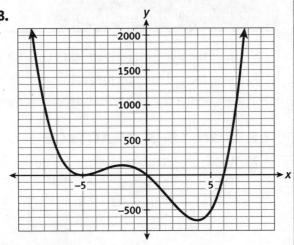

1. Work with your group. Use any method you like to answer the following questions. Justify each answer. As you justify your answers, speak clearly and use precise mathematical language to describe your reasoning and your conclusions. Remember to use complete sentences, including transitions and words such as *and, or, since, for example, therefore, because of* to make connections between your thoughts.

   **a.** Which polynomial has the larger maximum value?

   **b.** Which polynomial has more real roots?

### Check Your Understanding

2. **Construct viable arguments.** Which of the polynomials above has the larger *y*-intercept? Justify your answer.

3. For which of the polynomials above is $f(1000)$ smaller? Justify your answer.

**My Notes**

**MATH TIP**

The portions of a graph that are below the *x*-axis satisfy the inequality $f(x) < 0$, while the portions of the graph that are above the *x*-axis satisfy the inequality $f(x) > 0$.

To solve a **polynomial inequality** by graphing, use the fact that a polynomial can only change signs at its zeros.

**Step 1:** Write the polynomial inequality with one side equal to zero.

**Step 2:** Graph the inequality and determine the zeros.

**Step 3:** Find the intervals where the conditions of the inequality are met.

4. **Use appropriate tools strategically.** Solve the polynomial inequality $x^4 - 13x^2 + 6 < -30$ by graphing on a graphing calculator or by hand.

**Check Your Understanding**

5. Solve the polynomial inequality $(x + 9)(x + 2)(x - 4) > 0$ by graphing.

6. Solve the polynomial inequality $x^3 - 2x < 0$ by graphing.

## LESSON 18-3 PRACTICE

7. Which representation below is a quadratic function that has zeros at $x = -4$ and $x = 2$? Justify your answer.

   **A.** $h(x) = x^2 + 2x - 8$

   **B.**

   | x | 0 | 5 | 4 | 0 | −2 |
   |---|---|---|---|---|----|
   | y | −4 | −1 | 0 | 2 | 0 |

8. **Make sense of problems.** The function $f(x)$ is a polynomial that decreases without bound as $x \to \pm\infty$, has a double root at $x = 0$, and has no other real roots. The function $g(x)$ is given by the equation $g(x) = -x^4 + 16$. Which function has the greater range? Explain your reasoning.

9. The graph of $q(x)$ is shown below. Use the graph to solve $q(x) \geq 0$.

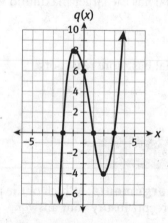

10. Solve the polynomial inequality $x^4 - 26x^2 < -25$.

11. **Reason abstractly.** Give an example of a quadratic function for which $f(x) > 0$ is true for all real numbers. Explain your reasoning.

## ACTIVITY 18 PRACTICE
**Write your answers on notebook paper.**
**Show your work.**

### Lesson 18-1

For Items 1–8, match each equation or description to one of the graphs below.

_____ 1. an even function with no real roots and a positive leading coefficient

_____ 2. an even function with three real roots and a negative leading coefficient.

_____ 3. an odd function with one real root and a negative leading coefficient.

_____ 4. $f(x) = -ax^3 + b$

_____ 5. $g(x) = ax^3 + \dots + d$

_____ 6. $h(x) = ax^4 + \dots - e$

_____ 7. $p(x) = ax^5 + \dots - f$

_____ 8. $p(x) = -ax^5 + \dots - f$

**A.** 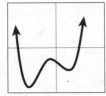  **B.**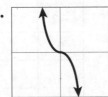

**C.** 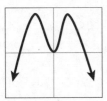  **D.**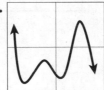

**E.** 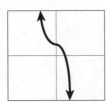  **F.**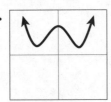

**G.**   **H.**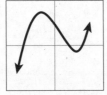

For Items 9–11, use what you know about end behavior and zeros to graph each function.

9. $f(x) = x^4 + 2x^3 - 43x^2 - 44x + 84$
   $= (x - 1)(x - 6)(x + 2)(x + 7)$

10. $y = x^5 - 14x^4 + 37x^3 + 260x^2 - 1552x + 2240$
    $= (x - 7)(x + 5)(x - 4)^3$

11. $f(x) = -x^4 + 11x^3 - 21x^2 - 59x + 70$
    $= -(x - 1)(x - 5)(x + 2)(x - 7)$

12. Make a general statement about what information is revealed by an unfactored polynomial compared to a factored polynomial.

13. Miguel identified the graph below as a polynomial function of the form $f(x) = ax^4 - bx^2 + c$, where $a$, $b$, and $c$ are positive real numbers.

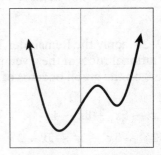

Which reason best describes why Miguel is incorrect?
   **A.** The graph is not a fourth-degree polynomial.
   **B.** The leading coefficient of Miguel's polynomial should be negative.
   **C.** The graph is of an even function, but Miguel's polynomial is not even.
   **D.** The $y$-intercept is below the $x$-axis, so Miguel's polynomial should end with $- c$, not $+ c$.

### Lesson 18-2

14. Determine all the possible rational roots of:
    a. $f(x) = -4x^3 - 13x^2 - 6x - 3$
    b. $g(x) = 2x^4 + 6x^3 - 3x^2 - 11x + 8$

15. Graph $f(x) = -4x^3 - 13x^2 - 6x - 3$.

16. Determine the possible number of positive and negative real roots for:
    a. $h(x) = 2x^3 + x^2 - 5x + 2$
    b. $p(x) = 2x^4 + 6x^3 - 3x^2 - 11x + 8$

17. Graph $h(x) = 2x^3 + x^2 - 5x + 2$.

18. Descartes' Rule of Signs states that the number of positive real roots of $f(x) = 0$ equals the number of variations in sign of the terms of $f(x)$, or is less than this number by an even integer. What theorem offers a reason as to why the number could be "less than this number by an <u>even</u> integer"?

For Items 19–20, apply the Remainder Theorem to all the possible rational roots of the given polynomial to identify points on the graph or zeros of the polynomial.

19. $p(x) = x^3 - 5x^2 + 8x - 4$

20. $h(x) = 2x^4 + 5x^3 - x^2 + 5x - 3$

21. The graph of $f(x)$ has an $x$-intercept at $(4, 0)$. Which of the following MUST be true?

    I. $f(4) = 0$
    II. $x - 4$ is a factor of $f(x)$.
    III. $f(x)$ also has an $x$-intercept at $(-4, 0)$.

    A. II only
    B. I and II only
    C. II and III only
    D. I, II, and III

### Lesson 18-3

For Items 22–24, solve the polynomial inequality.

22. $(x + 4)(x - 2)(x - 10) > 0$

23. $x^3 - x^2 - 36x + 36 < 0$

24. $-x^4 + 20x^2 - 32 \geq 32$

## MATHEMATICAL PRACTICES
### Look For and Express Regularity in Repeated Reasoning

25. Some polynomial functions are represented in a variety of forms below. For each representation, describe whether you think it is more efficient to graph the polynomial using a graphing calculator or by hand. Justify your choices.

    a. $f(x) = (x + 15)(x + 7)(x - 5)^2(x - 12)$
    b. $g(x) = 2x^4 + 6x^3 - 3x^2 - 11x + 7$

    c.

| x | f(x) |
|----|------|
| −3 | −8 |
| −1 | 1 |
| 0 | 2 |
| 1 | 1 |
| 3 | −6 |
| 4 | −2 |

1. Factor $f(x) = x^3 + 3x^2 - x - 3$. Then find the zeros and **y-intercept**. Sketch a graph of the function.

2. Find two different ways to show that $g(x) = -x^3 + 27$ has only one $x$-intercept. Use a sketch of the graph as one method, if **necessary**.

3. List all the characteristics of the graph for this polynomial function that you would expect to see, based on what you have learned thus far.

$$f(x) = (x + 3)(x - 3)(x + 2)(x - 1)(x + 2i)(x - 2i)$$

4. Find a polynomial function of fourth degree that has the zeros 2, −2, and $1 - 3i$. Then write it in standard form.

5. The graph below represents a fourth-degree polynomial **function with** no imaginary roots.

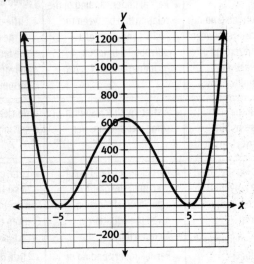

a. Is the function even, odd, or neither? Explain your **reasoning**.
b. State the domain and range of the function.
c. Given that $f(-5) = 0$ and $f(5) = 0$, use the graph to **find the equation** of the function, in factored form and in standard form.
d. Explain how you can use the $y$-intercept shown on **the graph to** check that your equation is correct.

| Scoring Guide | Exemplary | Proficient | Emerging | Incomplete |
|---|---|---|---|---|
| | The solution demonstrates these characteristics: | | | |
| **Mathematics Knowledge and Thinking** (Items 1-5) | • Clear and accurate understanding of how to rewrite polynomials in equivalent forms<br>• Effective understanding and identification of the features of a polynomial function and its graph, including even and odd functions<br>• Effective understanding of the relationship between the factors and zeros of a polynomial function, including complex zeros | • Largely correct understanding of how to rewrite polynomials in equivalent forms<br>• A functional understanding and accurate identification of the features of a polynomial function and its graph, including even and odd functions<br>• A functional understanding of the relationship between the factors and zeros of a polynomial function, including complex zeros | • Difficulty when rewriting polynomials in equivalent forms<br>• Partial understanding and partially accurate identification of the features of a polynomial function and its graph, including even and odd functions<br>• Partial understanding of the relationship between the factors and zeros of a polynomial function, including complex zeros | • Inaccurate or incomplete understanding of how to rewrite polynomials in equivalent forms<br>• Little or no understanding and inaccurate identification of the features of a polynomial function and its graph, including even and odd functions<br>• Little or no understanding of the relationship between the factors and zeros of a polynomial function, including complex zeros |
| **Problem Solving** (Items 2, 5d) | • An appropriate and efficient strategy that results in a correct answer | • A strategy that may include unnecessary steps but results in a correct answer | • A strategy that results in some incorrect answers | • No clear strategy when solving problems |
| **Mathematical Modeling / Representations** (Items 1, 4, 5c) | • Fluency in sketching the graph of a polynomial function, given the equation in factored form<br>• Fluency in finding the equation for a polynomial function, given the roots or a graph | • Little difficulty in sketching the graph of a polynomial function, given the equation in factored form<br>• Little difficulty in finding the equation for a polynomial function, given the roots or a graph | • Partial understanding of sketching the graph of a polynomial function, given the equation in factored form<br>• Partial understanding of finding the equation for a polynomial function, given the roots or a graph | • Little or no understanding of sketching the graph of a polynomial function, given the equation in factored form<br>• Little or no understanding of finding the equation for a polynomial function, given the roots or a graph |
| **Reasoning and Communication** (Items 2, 3, 5a, 5d) | • Precise use of appropriate math terms and language to describe the features of the graph of a polynomial function<br>• Clear and accurate explanations of why a function has one intercept and whether a function is even, odd, or neither<br>• Clear and accurate explanation of how to use the *y*-intercept to check an equation for a graph | • Adequate description of the features of the graph of a polynomial function<br>• Adequate explanation of why a function has one intercept and whether a function is even, odd, or neither<br>• Adequate explanation of how to use the *y*-intercept to check an equation for a graph | • Misleading or confusing description of the features of the graph of a polynomial function<br>• Misleading or confusing explanation of why a function has one intercept and whether a function is even, odd, or neither<br>• Misleading or confusing explanation of how to use the *y*-intercept to check an equation for a graph | • Incomplete or inaccurate description of the features of the graph of a polynomial function<br>• Incomplete or inadequate explanation of why a function has one intercept and whether a function is even, odd, or neither<br>• Incomplete or inadequate explanation of how to use the *y*-intercept to check an equation for a graph |

# Series, Exponential and Logarithmic Functions

**4**

## Unit Overview

In this unit, you will study arithmetic and geometric sequences and series and their applications. You will also study exponential functions and investigate logarithmic functions and equations.

## Key Terms

As you study this unit, add these and other terms to your math notebook. Include in your notes your prior knowledge of each word, as well as your experiences in using the word in different mathematical examples. If needed, ask for help in pronouncing new words and add information on pronunciation to your math notebook. It is important that you learn new terms and use them correctly in your class discussions and in your problem solutions.

## Math Terms

- sequence
- arithmetic sequence
- common difference
- recursive formula
- explicit formula
- series
- partial sum
- sigma notation
- geometric sequence
- common ratio
- geometric series
- finite series
- infinite series
- sum of the infinite geometric series
- exponential function
- exponential decay factor
- exponential growth factor
- asymptote
- logarithm
- common logarithm
- logarithmic function
- natural logarithm
- Change of Base Formula
- exponential equation
- compound interest
- logarithmic equation
- extraneous solution

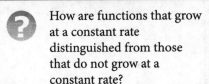

**ESSENTIAL QUESTIONS**

**?** How are functions that grow at a constant rate distinguished from those that do not grow at a constant rate?

**?** How are logarithmic and exponential equations used to model real-world problems?

**EMBEDDED ASSESSMENTS**

This unit has three embedded assessments, following Activities 20, 22, and 24. By completing these embedded assessments, you will demonstrate your understanding of arithmetic and geometric sequences and series, as well as exponential and logarithmic functions and equations.

**Embedded Assessment 1:**

Sequences and Series

**Embedded Assessment 2:**

Exponential Functions and Common Logarithms

**Embedded Assessment 3:**

Exponential and Logarithmic Equations

Write your answers on notebook paper.
Show your work.

1. Describe the pattern displayed by
   1, 2, 5, 10, 17, . . . .

2. Give the next three terms of the sequence
   0, −2, 1, −3, . . . .

3. Draw Figure 4, using the pattern below. Then
   explain how you would create any figure in
   the pattern.

   Figure 1      Figure 2      Figure 3

4. Simplify each expression.

   a. $\left(\dfrac{6x^2}{y^3}\right)^2$

   b. $(2a^2b)(3b^3)$

   c. $\dfrac{10a^{12}b^6}{5a^3b^{-2}}$

5. Evaluate the expression.
   $$\dfrac{3^{327}}{3^{323}}$$

6. Express the product in scientific notation.
   $$(2.9 \times 10^3)(3 \times 10^2)$$

7. Solve the equation for $x$.
   $$19 = -8x + 35$$

8. Write a function $C(t)$ to represent the cost of a
   taxicab ride, where the charge includes a fee of
   $2.50 plus $0.50 for each tenth of a mile $t$.
   Then give the slope and $y$-intercept of the
   graph of the function.

# Arithmetic Sequences and Series

## Arithmetic Alkanes
### Lesson 19-1 Arithmetic Sequences

**Learning Targets:**
- Determine whether a given sequence is arithmetic.
- Find the common difference of an arithmetic sequence.
- Write an expression for an arithmetic sequence, and calculate the $n$th term.

> **SUGGESTED LEARNING STRATEGIES:** Activating Prior Knowledge, Create Representations, Look for a Pattern, Summarizing, Paraphrasing, Vocabulary Organizer

Hydrocarbons are the simplest organic compounds, containing only carbon and hydrogen atoms. Hydrocarbons that contain only one pair of electrons between two atoms are called alkanes. Alkanes are valuable as clean fuels because they burn to form water and carbon dioxide. The number of carbon and hydrogen atoms in a molecule of the first six alkanes is shown in the table below.

| Alkane | Carbon Atoms | Hydrogen Atoms |
|--------|:---:|:---:|
| methane | 1 | 4 |
| ethane | 2 | 6 |
| propane | 3 | 8 |
| butane | 4 | 10 |
| pentane | 5 | 12 |
| hexane | 6 | 14 |

1. **Model with mathematics.** Graph the data in the table. Write a function $f$, where $f(n)$ is the number of hydrogen atoms in an alkane with $n$ carbon atoms. Describe the domain of the function.

Any function where the domain is a set of positive consecutive integers forms a *sequence*. The values in the range of the function are the *terms* of the sequence. When naming a term in a sequence, subscripts are used rather than traditional function notation. For example, the first term in a sequence would be called $a_1$ rather than $f(1)$.

Consider the sequence {4, 6, 8, 10, 12, 14} formed by the number of hydrogen atoms in the first six alkanes.

2. What is $a_1$? What is $a_3$?

3. Find the differences $a_2 - a_1$, $a_3 - a_2$, $a_4 - a_3$, $a_5 - a_4$, and $a_6 - a_5$.

Sequences like the one above are called *arithmetic sequences*. An **arithmetic sequence** is a sequence in which the difference of consecutive terms is a constant. The constant difference is called the ***common difference*** and is usually represented by $d$.

---

**My Notes**

**MATH TERMS**

A **sequence** is an ordered list of items.

**WRITING MATH**

If the fourth term in a sequence is 10, then $a_4 = 10$.

Sequences may have a finite or an infinite number of terms and are sometimes written in braces { }.

4. Use $a_n$ and $a_{n+1}$ to write a general expression for the common difference $d$.

5. Determine whether the numbers of carbon atoms in the first six alkanes {1, 2, 3, 4, 5, 6} form an arithmetic sequence. Explain why or why not.

### Check Your Understanding

Determine whether each sequence is arithmetic. If the sequence is arithmetic, state the common difference.

6. 3, 8, 13, 18, 23, . . .

7. 1, 2, 4, 8, 16, . . .

8. Find the missing terms in the arithmetic sequence 19, 28, _____, _____, 55, _____.

9. Write a formula for $a_{n+1}$ in Item 4.

10. What information is needed to find $a_{n+1}$ using this formula?

**MATH TIP**

In a sequence, $a_{n+1}$ is the term that follows $a_n$.

Finding the value of $a_{n+1}$ in the formula you wrote in Item 9 requires knowing the value of the previous term. Such a formula is called a **recursive formula**, which is used to determine a term of a sequence using one or more of the preceding terms.

The terms in an arithmetic sequence can also be written as the sum of the first term and a multiple of the common difference. Such a formula is called an **explicit formula** because it can be used to calculate any term in the sequence as long as the first term is known.

11. Complete the blanks for the sequence {4, 6, 8, 10, 12, 14, . . .} formed by the number of hydrogen atoms.

$a_1 = $ _____   $d = $ _____

$a_2 = 4 + $ _____ $\cdot 2 = 6$

$a_3 = 4 + $ _____ $\cdot 2 = 8$

$a_4 = 4 + $ _____ $\cdot 2 =$

$a_5 = 4 + $ _____ $\cdot 2 =$

$a_6 = 4 + $ _____ $\cdot 2 =$

$a_{10} = 4 + $ _____ $\cdot 2 =$

My Notes

**12.** Write a general expression $a_n$ in terms of $n$ for finding the number of hydrogen atoms in an alkane molecule with $n$ carbon atoms.

**13.** Use the expression you wrote in Item 12 to find the number of hydrogen atoms in decane, the alkane with 10 carbon atoms. Show your work.

**14.** Find the number of carbon atoms in a molecule of an alkane with 38 hydrogen atoms.

**15. Model with mathematics.** Use $a_1$, $d$, and $n$ to write an explicit formula for $a_n$, the $n$th term of any arithmetic sequence.

**16.** Use the formula from Item 15 to find the specified term in each arithmetic sequence.
   **a.** Find the 40th term when $a_1 = 6$ and $d = 3$.

   **b.** Find the 30th term of the arithmetic sequence 37, 33, 29, 25, . . . .

### Example A
Hope is sending invitations for a party. The cost of the invitations is $5.00, and postage for each is $0.45. Write an expression for the cost of mailing the invitations in terms of the number of invitations mailed. Then calculate the cost of mailing 16 invitations.

**Step 1:** Identify $a_1$ and $d$.
   The cost to mail the first invitation is equal to the cost of the invitations and the postage for that one invitation.
   $a_1 = 5.00 + 0.45 = 5.45$.
   The postage per invitation is the common difference, $d = 0.45$.

**Step 2:** Use the information from Step 1 to write a general expression for $a_n$. If $n$ equals the number of invitations mailed, then the expression for the cost of mailing $n$ invitations is:
   $a_n = a_1 + (n-1)d$
   $a_n = 5.45 + (n-1)(0.45)$
   $a_n = 5.45 + 0.45n - 0.45$
   $a_n = 5.00 + 0.45n$

**Step 3:** Use the general expression to evaluate $a_{16}$.
   The cost of mailing 16 invitations is found by solving for $n = 16$.
   $a_{16} = 5.00 + 0.45(16) = 5.00 + 7.20 = 12.20$.

### Try These A
Write an expression for the $n$th term of the arithmetic sequence, and then find the term.
   **a.** Find the 50th term when $a_1 = 7$ and $d = -2$.

   **b.** Find the 28th term of the arithmetic sequence 3, 7, 11, 15, 19, . . . .

   **c.** Which term in the arithmetic sequence 15, 18, 21, 24, . . . is equal to 72?

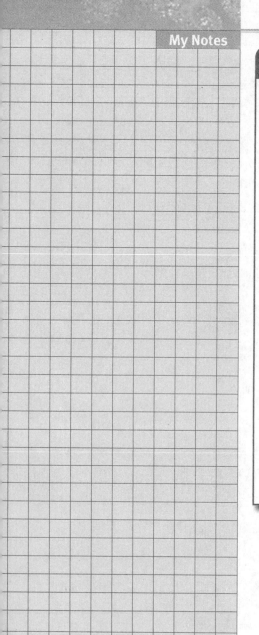

**My Notes**

## Check Your Understanding

**17.** Show that the expressions for $a_n$ in Item 12 and $f(n)$ in Item 1 are equivalent.

**18.** Find the 14th term for the sequence defined below.

| term | 1 | 2 | 3 | 4 |
|------|-----|-----|-----|-----|
| value | 1.7 | 1.3 | 0.9 | 0.5 |

**19.** Determine which term in the sequence in Item 18 has the value $-1.1$.

**20. Express regularity in repeated reasoning.** Shontelle used both the explicit and recursive formulas to calculate the fourth term in a sequence where $a_1 = 7$ and $d = 5$. She wrote the following:

Explicit:
$$a_n = a_1 + (n-1)d$$
$$a_4 = 7 + (4-1)5$$
$$a_4 = 7 + 3 \times 5$$

Recursive:
$$a_n = a_{n-1} + d$$
$$a_4 = a_3 + 5$$
$$a_4 = (a_2 + 5) + 5$$
$$a_4 = ((a_1 + 5) + 5) + 5$$
$$a_4 = ((7 + 5) + 5) + 5$$

Explain why Shontelle can substitute $(a_2 + 5)$ for $a_3$ and $(a_1 + 5)$ for $a_2$. Compare the result that Shontelle found when using the recursive formula with the result of the explicit formula. What does this tell you about the formulas?

## LESSON 19-1 PRACTICE

For Items 21–23, determine whether each sequence is arithmetic. If the sequence is arithmetic, then
   **a.** state the common difference.
   **b.** use the explicit formula to write a general expression for $a_n$ in terms of $n$.
   **c.** use the recursive formula to write a general expression for $a_n$ in terms of $a_{n-1}$.

**21.** $1, 1, 2, 3, 5, 8, \ldots$

**22.** $20, 17, 14, 11, 8, \ldots$

**23.** $3, 7, 11, \ldots$

**24.** A sequence is defined by $a_1 = 13$, $a_n = 5 + a_{n-1}$. Write the first five terms in the sequence.

**25. Make sense of problems.** Find the first term.

| $n$ | 3 | 4 | 5 | 6 |
|-----|-----|-----|-----|-----|
| $a_n$ | $\frac{7}{8}$ | $\frac{3}{4}$ | $\frac{5}{8}$ | $\frac{1}{2}$ |

**CONNECT TO HISTORY**

Item 21 is a famous sequence known as the Fibonacci sequence. Find out more about this interesting sequence. You can find its pattern in beehives, pinecones, and flowers.

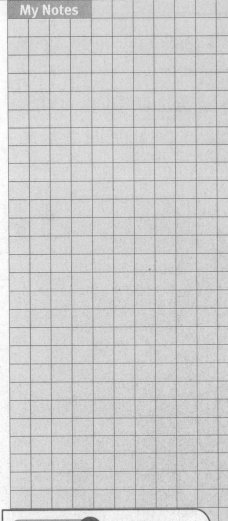

My Notes

## Learning Targets:
- Write a formula for the $n$th partial sum of an arithmetic series.
- Calculate partial sums of an arithmetic series.

**SUGGESTED LEARNING STRATEGIES:** Look for a Pattern, Think-Pair-Share, Create Representations

A **series** is the sum of the terms in a sequence. The sum of the first $n$ terms of a series is the $n$th **partial sum** of the series and is denoted by $S_n$.

1. Consider the arithmetic sequence $\{4, 6, 8, 10, 12, 14, 16, 18\}$.
   a. Find $S_4$.

   b. Find $S_5$.

   c. Find $S_8$.

   d. How does $a_1 + a_8$ compare to $a_2 + a_7$, $a_3 + a_6$, and $a_4 + a_5$?

   e. **Make use of structure.** Explain how to find $S_8$ using the value of $a_1 + a_8$.

2. Consider the arithmetic series $1 + 2 + 3 + \ldots + 98 + 99 + 100$.
   a. How many terms are in this series?

   b. If all the terms in this series are paired as shown below, how many pairs will there be?

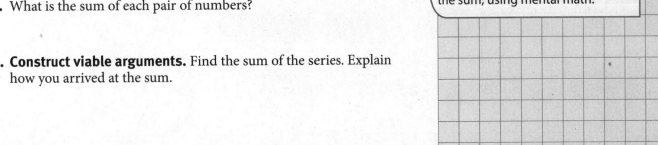

$$1 + 2 + 3 + 4 + \ldots + 97 + 98 + 99 + 100$$

   c. What is the sum of each pair of numbers?

   d. **Construct viable arguments.** Find the sum of the series. Explain how you arrived at the sum.

**CONNECT TO HISTORY**

A story is often told that in the 1780s, a German schoolmaster decided to keep his students quiet by having them find the sum of the first 100 integers. One young pupil was able to name the sum immediately. This young man, Carl Friedrich Gauss, would become one of the world's most famous mathematicians. He reportedly used the method in Item 2 to find the sum, using mental math.

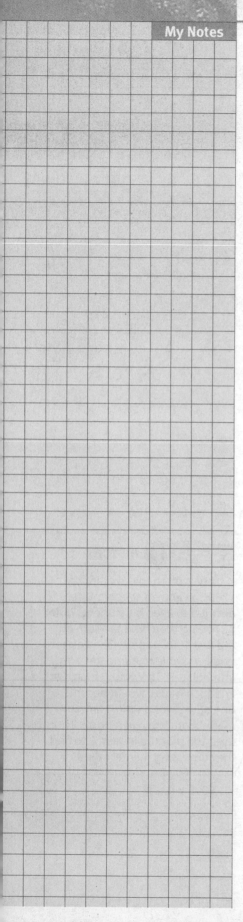

**3.** Consider the arithmetic series $a_1 + a_2 + a_3 + \ldots + a_{n-2} + a_{n-1} + a_n$.

$$a_1 + a_2 + a_3 + \ldots + a_{n-2} + a_{n-1} + a_n$$

**a.** Write an expression for the number of pairs of terms in this series.

**b.** Write a formula for $S_n$, the partial sum of the arithmetic series.

**4.** Use the formula from Item 3b to find each partial sum of the arithmetic sequence {4, 6, 8, 10, 12, 14, 16, 18}. Compare your results to your answers in Item 1.

**a.** $S_4$

**b.** $S_5$

**c.** $S_8$

5. A second form of the formula for finding the partial sum of an arithmetic series is $S_n = \frac{n}{2}[2a_1 + (n-1)d]$. Derive this formula, starting with the formula from Item 3b of this lesson and the $n$th term formula, $a_n = a_1 + (n-1)d$, from Item 15 of the previous lesson.

6. Use the formula $S_n = \frac{n}{2}[2a_1 + (n-1)d]$ to find the indicated partial sum of each arithmetic series. Show your work.

   **a.** $3 + 8 + 13 + 18 + \ldots;\ S_{20}$

   **b.** $-2 - 4 - 6 - 8 - \ldots;\ S_{18}$

### Example A

Find the partial sum $S_{10}$ of the arithmetic series with $a_1 = -3, d = 4$.

**Step 1:** Find $a_{10}$.

The terms are $-3, 1, 5, 9, \ldots$.

$a_1 = -3$

$a_{10} = a_1 + (n-1)d = -3 + (10-1)(4) = -3 + (9)(4) = -3 + 36 = 33$

**Step 2:** Substitute for $n$, $a_1$, and $a_{10}$ in the formula. Simplify.

$S_{10} = \frac{n}{2}(a_1 + a_n) = \frac{10}{2}(-3 + 33) = 5(30) = 150$

Or use the formula $S_n = \frac{n}{2}[2a_1 + (n-1)d]$:

$S_{10} = \frac{10}{2}[2(-3) + (10-1)\,4] = 5[-6 + 36] = 150$

### Try These A

Find the indicated sum of each arithmetic series. Show your work.

**a.** Find $S_8$ for the arithmetic series with $a_1 = 5$ and $a_8 = 40$.

**b.** $12 + 18 + 24 + 30 + \ldots;\ S_{10}$

**c.** $30 + 20 + 10 + 0 + \ldots;\ S_{25}$

**My Notes**

### Check Your Understanding

7. Explain what each term of the equation $S_6 = 3(12 + 37) = 147$ means in terms of $n$ and $a_n$.

8. Find each term of the arithmetic series in Item 7, and then verify the given sum.

9. When would the formula $S_n = \frac{n}{2}[2a_1 + (n - 1)d]$ be preferred to the formula $S_n = \frac{n}{2}(a_1 + a_n)$?

### LESSON 19-2 PRACTICE

10. Find the partial sum $S_{10}$ of the arithmetic series with $a_1 = 4$, $d = 5$.

11. Find the partial sum $S_{12}$ of the arithmetic series $26 + 24 + 22 + 20 + \ldots$.

12. Find the sum of the first 10 terms of an arithmetic sequence with an eighth term of 8.2 and a common difference of 0.4.

13. **Model with mathematics.** An auditorium has 12 seats in the first row, 15 in the second row, and 18 in the third row. If this pattern continues, what is the total number of seats for the first eight rows?

**My Notes**

### Learning Targets:

- Identify the index, lower and upper limits, and general term in sigma notation.
- Express the sum of a series using sigma notation.
- Find the sum of a series written in sigma notation.

> **SUGGESTED LEARNING STRATEGIES:** Look for a Pattern, Think-Pair-Share, Create Representations

In the Binomial Theorem activity in Unit 3, you were introduced to a shorthand notation called **sigma notation** ($\Sigma$). It is used to express the sum of a series.

The expression $\displaystyle\sum_{n=1}^{4}(2n+5)$ is read "the sum from $n = 1$ to $n = 4$ of $2n + 5$."

To expand the series to show the terms of the series, substitute 1, 2, 3, and 4 into the expression for the general term. To find the sum of the series, add the terms.

$$\sum_{n=1}^{4}(2n+5) = (2 \cdot 1 + 5) + (2 \cdot 2 + 5) + (2 \cdot 3 + 5) + (2 \cdot 4 + 5)$$

$$= 7 + 9 + 11 + 13 = 40$$

**MATH TIP**

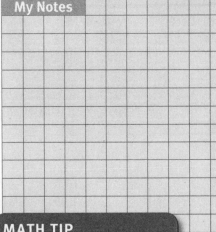

upper limit of summation

$$\sum_{n=1}^{4}(2n+5)$$

general term

index of summation     lower limit of summation

### Example A

Evaluate $\displaystyle\sum_{j=1}^{6}(2j-3)$.

**Step 1:** The values of $j$ are 1, 2, 3, 4, 5, and 6. Write a sum with six addends, one for each value of the variable.
$$= [2(1) - 3] + [2(2) - 3] + [2(3) - 3] + [2(4) - 3] + [2(5) - 3] + [2(6) - 3]$$

**Step 2:** Evaluate each expression.
$$= -1 + 1 + 3 + 5 + 7 + 9$$

**Step 3:** Simplify.
$$= 24$$

**MATH TIP**

To find the first term in a series written in sigma notation, substitute the value of the lower limit into the expression for the general term.

To find subsequent terms, substitute consecutive integers that follow the lower limit, stopping at the upper limit.

### Try These A

a. **Use appropriate tools strategically.** Write the terms in the series $\displaystyle\sum_{n=1}^{8}(3n-2)$. Then find the indicated sum.

b. Write the sum of the first 10 terms of $80 + 75 + 70 + 65 + \ldots$ using sigma notation.

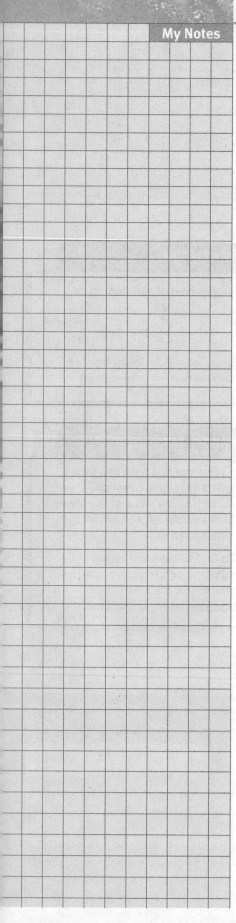

### Check Your Understanding

Summarize the following formulas for an arithmetic series.

**1.** common difference    $d =$ _____

**2.** $n$th term    $a_n =$ _____

**3.** sum of first $n$ terms    $S_n =$ _____

or

$S_n =$ _____

## LESSON 19-3 PRACTICE

Find the indicated partial sum of each arithmetic series.

**4.** $\displaystyle\sum_{n=1}^{15} (3n - 1)$

**5.** $\displaystyle\sum_{k=1}^{20} (2k + 1)$

**6.** $\displaystyle\sum_{j=5}^{10} 3j$

**7.** Identify the index, upper and lower limits, and general term of Item 4.

**8. Attend to precision.** Express the following sum using sigma notation: $3 + 7 + 11 + 15 + 19 + 23 + 27$

## ACTIVITY 19 PRACTICE

Write your answers on notebook paper.
Show your work.

### Lesson 19-1

1. Determine whether or not each sequence is arithmetic. If the sequence is arithmetic, state the common difference.
   a. $4, 5, 7, 10, \ldots$
   b. $5, 7, 9, 11, \ldots$
   c. $12, 9, 6, 3, \ldots$

2. Determine whether or not each sequence is arithmetic. If the sequence is arithmetic, use the explicit formula to write a general expression for $a_n$ in terms of $n$.
   a. $4, 12, 20, 28, \ldots$
   b. $5, 10, 20, 40, \ldots$
   c. $4, 0, -4, -8, \ldots$

3. Determine whether or not each sequence is arithmetic. If the sequence is arithmetic, use the recursive formula to write a general expression for $a_n$ in terms of $a_{n-1}$.
   a. $7, 7.5, 8, 8.5, \ldots$
   b. $6, 7, 8, 9, \ldots$
   c. $-2, 4, -8, \ldots$

4. Find the indicated term of each arithmetic sequence.
   a. $a_1 = 4, d = 5; a_{15}$
   b. $14, 18, 22, 26, \ldots; a_{20}$
   c. $45, 41, 37, 33, \ldots; a_{18}$

5. Find the sequence for which $a_8$ does NOT equal 24.
   A. $3, 6, 9, \ldots$
   B. $-32, -24, -16, \ldots$
   C. $108, 96, 84, \ldots$
   D. $-8, -4, 0, \ldots$

6. A radio station offers a $100 prize on the first day of a contest. Each day that the prize money is not awarded, $50 is added to the prize amount. If a contestant wins on the 17th day of the contest, how much money will be awarded?

7. If $a_4 = 20$ and $a_{12} = 68$, find $a_1$, $a_2$, and $a_3$.

8. Find the indicated term of each arithmetic sequence.
   a. $a_1 = -2, d = 4; a_{12}$
   b. $15, 19, 23, 27, \ldots; a_{10}$
   c. $46, 40, 34, 28, \ldots; a_{20}$

9. What is the first value of $n$ that corresponds to a positive value? Explain how you found your answer.

| $n$ | 1 | 2 | 3 | 4 | 5 |
|-----|------|------|------|------|------|
| $a_n$ | $-42.5$ | $-37.8$ | $-33.1$ | $-28.4$ | $-23.7$ |

10. Find the first four terms of the sequence with $a_1 = \frac{2}{3}$ and $a_n = a_{n-1} + \frac{1}{6}$.

11. If $a_1 = 3.1$ and $a_5 = -33.7$, write an expression for the sequence and find $a_2$, $a_3$, and $a_4$.

### Lesson 19-2

12. Find the indicated partial sum of each arithmetic series.
   a. $a_1 = 4, d = 5; S_{10}$
   b. $14 + 18 + 22 + 26 + \ldots; S_{12}$
   c. $45 + 41 + 37 + 33 + \ldots; S_{18}$

13. Find the indicated partial sum of each arithmetic series.
   a. $1 + 3 + 5 + \ldots; S_6$
   b. $1 + 3 + 5 + \ldots; S_{10}$
   c. $1 + 3 + 5 + \ldots; S_{12}$
   d. Explain the relationship between $n$ and $S_n$ in parts a–c.

14. Find the indicated partial sum of the arithmetic series.

   $0 + (x + 2) + (2x + 4) + (3x + 6) + \ldots; S_{10}$

   A. $9x + 18$
   B. $10x + 20$
   C. $45x + 90$
   D. $55x + 110$

15. Two companies offer you a job. Company A offers you a $40,000 first-year salary with an annual raise of $1500. Company B offers you a $38,500 first-year salary with an annual raise of $2000.
   a. What would your salary be with Company A as you begin your sixth year?
   b. What would your salary be with Company B as you begin your sixth year?
   c. What would be your total earnings with Company A after 5 years?
   d. What would be your total earnings with Company B after 5 years?

**16.** If $S_{12} = 744$ and $a_1 = 40$, find $d$.

**17.** In an arithmetic series, $a_1 = 47$ and $a_7 = -13$, find $d$ and $S_7$.

**18.** In an arithmetic series, $a_9 = 9.44$ and $d = 0.4$, find $a_1$ and $S_9$.

**19.** The first prize in a contest is $500, the second prize is $450, the third prize is $400, and so on.
   **a.** How many prizes will be awarded if the last prize is $100?
   **b.** How much money will be given out as prize money?

**20.** Find the sum of $13 + 25 + 37 + \ldots + 193$.
   **A.** 1339
   **B.** 1648
   **C.** 1930
   **D.** 2060

**21.** Find the sum of the first 150 natural numbers.

**22.** A store puts boxes of canned goods into a stacked display. There are 20 boxes in the bottom layer. Each layer has two fewer boxes than the layer below it. There are five layers of boxes. How many boxes are in the display? Explain your answer.

**Lesson 19-3**

**23.** Find the indicated partial sum of each arithmetic series.

   **a.** $\sum_{j=1}^{5}(5 - 6j)$

   **b.** $\sum_{j=1}^{20}5j$

   **c.** $\sum_{j=5}^{15}(5 - j)$

**24.** Does $\sum_{j=1}^{10}(2j+1) = \sum_{j=1}^{5}(2j+1) + \sum_{j=6}^{10}(2j+1)$? Verify your answer.

**25.** Does $\sum_{j=4}^{9}(j-7) = \sum_{j=1}^{9}(j-7) - \sum_{j=1}^{3}(j-7)$? Verify your answer.

**26.** Which statement is true for the partial sum $\sum_{j=1}^{n}(4j+3)$?
   **A.** For $n = 5$, the sum is 35.
   **B.** For $n = 7$, the sum is 133.
   **C.** For $n = 10$, the sum is 230.
   **D.** For $n = 12$, the sum is 408.

**27.** Evaluate.

   **a.** $\sum_{j=1}^{6}(j+3)$

   **b.** $\sum_{j=10}^{15}(j-12)$

   **c.** $\sum_{j=1}^{8}(4j)$

**28.** Which is greater: $\sum_{j=4}^{8}(-3j+29)$ or $\sum_{j=4}^{8}-3j+29$?

**29.** Which expression is the sum of the series $7 + 10 + 13 + \ldots + 25$?

   **A.** $\sum_{j=1}^{7}4+3j$

   **B.** $\sum_{j=1}^{7}(4-3j)$

   **C.** $\sum_{j=1}^{7}(3+4j)$

   **D.** $\sum_{j=1}^{7}(4+3j)$

**30.** Evaluate $\sum_{j=1}^{5}\left(\dfrac{j \bullet \pi}{2}\right)$.

**MATHEMATICAL PRACTICES**
**Look For and Make Use of Structure**

**31.** How does the common difference of an arithmetic sequence relate to finding the partial sum of an arithmetic series?

# Geometric Sequences and Series

## Squares with Patterns
### Lesson 20-1 Geometric Sequences

**Learning Targets:**

- Determine whether a given sequence is geometric.
- Find the common ratio of a geometric sequence.
- Write an expression for a geometric sequence, and calculate the *n*th term.

**SUGGESTED LEARNING STRATEGIES:** Summarizing, Paraphrasing, Create Representations

Meredith is designing a mural for an outside wall of a warehouse that is being converted into the Taylor Modern Art Museum. The mural is 32 feet wide by 31 feet high. The design consists of squares in five different sizes that are painted black or white as shown below.

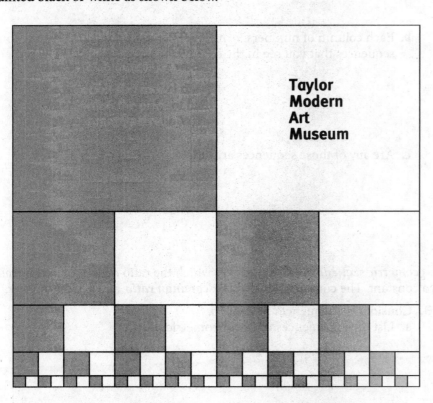

1. Let Square 1 be the largest size and Square 5 be the smallest size. For each size, record the length of the side, the number of squares of that size in the design, and the area of the square.

| Square # | Side of Square (ft) | Number of Squares | Area of Square (ft²) |
|----------|---------------------|-------------------|----------------------|
| 1        |                     |                   |                      |
| 2        |                     |                   |                      |
| 3        |                     |                   |                      |
| 4        |                     |                   |                      |
| 5        |                     |                   |                      |

2. Work with your group. Refer to the table in Item 1. As you share your ideas, be sure to use mathematical terms and academic vocabulary precisely. Make notes to help you remember the meaning of new words and how they are used to describe mathematical concepts.

   **a.** Describe any patterns that you notice in the table.

   **b.** Each column of numbers forms a sequence of numbers. List the four sequences that you see in the columns of the table.

   **c.** Are any of those sequences arithmetic? Why or why not?

A **geometric sequence** is a sequence in which the ratio of consecutive terms is a constant. The constant is called the **common ratio** and is denoted by $r$.

3. Consider the sequences in Item 2b.
   **a.** List those sequences that are geometric.

   **b.** State the common ratio for each geometric sequence.

**MATH TIP**

To find the common difference in an arithmetic sequence, subtract the preceding term from the following term.

To find the common ratio in a geometric sequence, divide any term by the preceding term.

**4.** Use $a_n$ and $a_{n-1}$ to write a general expression for the common ratio $r$.

**5.** Consider the sequences in the columns of the table in Item 1 that are labeled Square # and Side of Square.
   **a.** Plot the Square # sequence by plotting the ordered pairs (term number, square number).
   **b.** Using another color or symbol, plot the Side of Square sequence by plotting the ordered pairs (term number, side of square).
   **c.** Is either sequence a linear function? Explain why or why not.

### Check Your Understanding

**6.** Determine whether each sequence is arithmetic, geometric, or neither. If the sequence is arithmetic, state the common difference. If it is geometric, state the common ratio.
   **a.** 3, 9, 27, 81, 243, . . .
   **b.** 1, −2, 4, −8, 16, . . .
   **c.** 4, 9, 16, 25, 36, . . .
   **d.** 25, 20, 15, 10, 5, . . .

**7.** Use $a_{n+1}$ and $a_{n+2}$ to write an expression for the common ratio $r$.

**8.** Describe the graph of the first 5 terms of a geometric sequence with the first term 2 and the common ratio equal to 1.

**9. Reason abstractly.** Use the expression from Item 4 to write a *recursive formula* for the term $a_n$ and describe what the formula means.

The terms in a geometric sequence also can be written as the product of the first term and a power of the common ratio.

**10.** For the geometric sequence $\{4, 8, 16, 32, 64, \dots\}$, identify $a_1$ and $r$. Then fill in the missing exponents and blanks.

$a_1 = $ _____ $\qquad\qquad r = $ _____

$a_2 = 4 \cdot 2^{-} = 8$

$a_3 = 4 \cdot 2^{-} = 16$

$a_4 = 4 \cdot 2^{-} = $ _____

$a_5 = 4 \cdot 2^{-} = $ _____

$a_6 = 4 \cdot 2^{-} = $ _____

$a_{10} = 4 \cdot 2^{-} = $ _____

**11.** Use $a_1$, $r$, and $n$ to write an *explicit formula* for the $n$th term of any geometric sequence.

**12.** Use the formula from Item 11 to find the indicated term in each geometric sequence.

**a.** $1, 2, 4, 8, 16, \dots ; a_{16}$

**b.** $4096, 1024, 256, 64, \dots ; a_9$

My Notes

## Check Your Understanding

**13. a.** Complete the table for the terms in the sequence with $a_1 = 3$; $r = 2$.

| Term | Recursive $a_n = a_{n-1} \cdot r$ | Explicit $a_n = a_1 \cdot r^{n-1}$ | Value of Term |
|---|---|---|---|
| $a_1$ | 3 | $3 \cdot 2^{1-1} = 3$ | 3 |
| $a_2$ | $3 \cdot 2$ | $3 \cdot 2^{2-1} = 3 \cdot 2$ | 6 |
| $a_3$ | $(3 \cdot 2) \cdot 2$ | $3 \cdot 2^{3-1} = 3 \cdot 2^2$ | 12 |
| $a_4$ | | | |
| $a_5$ | | | |

**b.** What does the product $(3 \cdot 2)$ represent in the recursive expression for $a_3$?

**c. Express regularity in repeated reasoning.** Compare the recursive and explicit expressions for each term. What do you notice?

## LESSON 20-1 PRACTICE

**14.** Write a formula that will produce the sequence that appears on the calculator screen below.

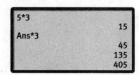

```
5*3
            15
Ans*3
            45
           135
           405
```

**15.** Determine whether each sequence is arithmetic, geometric, or neither. If the sequence is arithmetic, state the common difference, and if it is geometric, state the common ratio.
 **a.** $3, 5, 7, 9, 11, \ldots$

 **b.** $5, 15, 45, 135, \ldots$

 **c.** $6, -4, \dfrac{8}{3}, -\dfrac{16}{9}, \ldots$

 **d.** $1, 2, 4, 7, 11, \ldots$

**16.** Find the indicated term of each geometric sequence.
 **a.** $a_1 = -2, r = 3; a_8$

 **b.** $a_1 = 1024, r = -\dfrac{1}{2}; a_{12}$

**17. Attend to precision.** Given the data in the table below, write both a recursive formula and an explicit formula for $a_n$.

| $n$ | 1 | 2 | 3 | 4 |
|---|---|---|---|---|
| $a_n$ | 0.25 | 0.75 | 2.25 | 6.75 |

## Learning Targets:

- Derive the formula for the sum of a finite geometric series.
- Calculate the partial sums of a geometric series.

> **SUGGESTED LEARNING STRATEGIES:** Close Reading, Vocabulary Organizer, Think-Pair-Share, Create Representations

The sum of the terms of a geometric sequence is a **geometric series**. The sum of a **finite geometric series** where $r \neq 1$ is given by these formulas:

$$S_n = a_1 + a_1r + a_1r^2 + a_1r^3 + \ldots + a_1r^{n-1}$$

$$S_n = a_1\left(\frac{1-r^n}{1-r}\right)$$

**MATH TERMS**

A **finite series** is the sum of a finite sequence and has a specific number of terms.

An **infinite series** is the sum of an infinite sequence and has an infinite number of terms. You will work with infinite series later in this Lesson.

1. To derive the formula, Step 1 requires multiplying the equation of the sum by $-r$. Follow the remaining steps on the left to complete the derivation of the sum formula.

   **Step 1** $S_n = a_1 + a_1r + a_1r^2 + a_1r^3 + \ldots + a_1r^{n-1}$
   $-rS_n = -a_1r - a_1r^2 - a_1r^3 - \ldots - a_1r^{n-1} - a_1r^n$

   **Step 2** Combine terms on each side of the equation (most terms will cancel out).

   **Step 3** Factor out $S_n$ on the left side of the equation and factor out $a_1$ on the right.

   **Step 4** Solve for $S_n$.

**MATH TIP**

When writing out a *sequence*, separate the terms with commas. A *series* is written out as an expression and the terms are separated by addition symbols. If a series has negative terms, then the series may be written with subtraction symbols.

## Example A

Find the total of the Area of Square column in the table in Item 1 from the last lesson. Then use the formula developed in Item 1 of this lesson to find the total area and show that the result is the same.

**Step 1:** Add the areas of each square from the table.

$$256 + 64 + 16 + 4 + 1 = 341$$

| Square # | 1 | 2 | 3 | 4 | 5 |
|----------|-----|-----|-----|-----|-----|
| Area | 256 | 64 | 16 | 4 | 1 |

**Step 2:** Find the common ratio.

$$\frac{64}{256} = 0.25, \frac{16}{64} = 0.25, \frac{4}{16} = 0.25; r = 0.25$$

**Step 3:** Substitute $n = 5$, $a_1 = 256$, and $r = 0.25$ into the formula for $S_n$.

$$S_n = a_1\left(\frac{1-r^n}{1-r}\right); S_5 = 256\left(\frac{1-0.25^5}{1-0.25}\right)$$

**Step 4:** Evaluate $S_5$.

$$S_5 = 256\left(\frac{1-0.25^5}{1-0.25}\right) = 341$$

## Lesson 20-2
### Geometric Series

### Try These A

Find the indicated sum of each geometric series. Show your work.

**a.** Find $S_5$ for the geometric series with $a_1 = 5$ and $r = 2$.

**b.** $256 + 64 + 16 + 4 + \ldots;\ S_6$

**c.** $\displaystyle\sum_{n=1}^{10} 2 \cdot 3^{n-1}$

> **MATH TIP**
>
> Recall that *sigma notation* is a shorthand notation for a series. For example:
>
> $$\sum_{n=1}^{3} 8 \cdot 2^{n-1}$$
> $$= 8(2)^{(1-1)} + 8(2)^{(2-1)} + 8(2)^{(3-1)}$$
> $$= 8 \cdot 1 + 8 \cdot 2 + 8 \cdot 4$$
> $$= 8 + 16 + 32$$
> $$= 56$$

### Check Your Understanding

**2. Reason quantitatively.** How do you determine if the common ratio in a series is negative?

**3.** Find the sum of the series $2 + 8 + 32 + 128 + 512$ using sigma notation.

Recall that the sum of the first $n$ terms of a series is a *partial sum*. For some geometric series, the partial sums $S_1, S_2, S_3, S_4, \ldots$ form a sequence with terms that approach a limiting value. The limiting value is called the **sum of the infinite geometric series**.

To understand the concept of an infinite sum of a geometric series, follow these steps.

- Start with a square piece of paper, and let it represent one whole unit.
- Cut the paper in half, place one piece of the paper on your desk, and keep the other piece of paper in your hand. The paper on your desk represents the first partial sum of the series, $S_1 = \frac{1}{2}$.
- Cut the paper in your hand in half again, adding one of the pieces to the paper on your desk and keeping the other piece in your hand. The paper on your desk now represents the second partial sum.
- Repeat this process as many times as you are able.

**4. Use appropriate tools strategically.** Each time you add a piece of paper to your desk, the paper represents the next term in the geometric series.

**a.** As you continue the process of placing half of the remaining paper on your desk, what happens to the amount of paper on your desktop?

> **MATH TIP**
>
> If the terms in the sequence $a_1, a_2, a_3, \ldots, a_n, \ldots$ get close to some constant as $n$ gets very large, the constant is the limiting value of the sequence. For example, in the sequence $1, \frac{1}{2}, \frac{1}{3}, \frac{1}{4}, \frac{1}{5}, \ldots, \frac{1}{n}, \ldots,$ the terms get closer to a limiting value of 0 as $n$ gets larger.

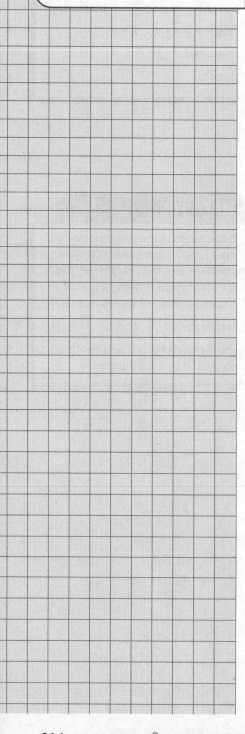
**CONNECT TO AP**

An infinite series whose partial sums continually get closer to a specific number is said to *converge*, and that number is called the *sum of the infinite series*.

**4. b.** Fill in the blanks to complete the partial sums for the infinite geometric series represented by the pieces of paper on your desk.

$$S_1 = \frac{1}{2}$$

$$S_2 = \frac{1}{2} + \underline{\quad} = \underline{\quad}$$

$$S_3 = \frac{1}{2} + \underline{\quad} + \underline{\quad} = \underline{\quad}$$

$$S_4 = \frac{1}{2} + \underline{\quad} + \underline{\quad} + \underline{\quad} = \underline{\quad}$$

$$S_5 = \frac{1}{2} + \underline{\quad} + \underline{\quad} + \underline{\quad} + \underline{\quad} = \underline{\quad}$$

$$S_6 = \frac{1}{2} + \underline{\quad} + \underline{\quad} + \underline{\quad} + \underline{\quad} + \underline{\quad} = \underline{\quad}$$

**c.** Plot the first six partial sums.

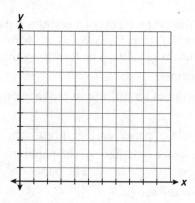

**d.** Do the partial sums appear to be approaching a limiting value? If so, what does the value appear to be?

**5.** Consider the geometric series $2 + 4 + 8 + 16 + 32 + \ldots$.
   **a.** List the first five partial sums for this series.

   **b.** Do these partial sums appear to have a limiting value?

   **c.** Does there appear to be a sum of the infinite series? If so, what does the sum appear to be? If not, why not?

**6.** Consider the geometric series $3 - 1 + \dfrac{1}{3} - \dfrac{1}{9} + \dfrac{1}{27} - \dfrac{1}{81} + \dfrac{1}{243} - \ldots$
   **a.** List the first seven partial sums for this series.

   **b.** Do these partial sums appear to have a limiting value?

   **c.** Does there appear to be a sum of the infinite series? If so, what does the sum appear to be? If not, why not?

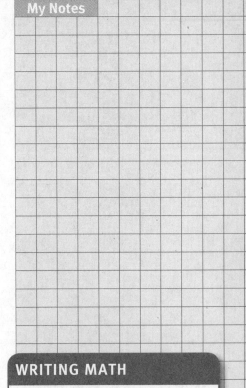

**WRITING MATH**

You can write the sum of an infinite series by using summation, or sigma, notation and using an infinity symbol for the upper limit. For example,

$$\sum_{n=1}^{\infty} 3\left(-\frac{1}{3}\right)^{n-1}$$

$$= 3 - 1 + \frac{1}{3} - \ldots$$

### Check Your Understanding

Find the indicated partial sums of each geometric series. Do these partial sums appear to have a limiting value? If so, what does the infinite sum appear to be?

**7.** First 8 partial sums of the series $1 + 2 + 4 + 8 + \ldots$

**8.** First 6 partial sums of the series $\dfrac{2}{5} + \dfrac{2}{15} + \dfrac{2}{45} + \dfrac{2}{135} + \ldots$

### LESSON 20-2 PRACTICE

Find the indicated partial sum of each geometric series.

**9.** $1 - 3 + 9 - 27 + \ldots; S_7$

**10.** $\dfrac{1}{625} - \dfrac{1}{125} + \dfrac{1}{25} - \dfrac{1}{5} + \ldots; S_9$

Consider the geometric series $-1 + 1 - 1 + 1 - 1 + \ldots$

**11.** Find $S_4$ and $S_6$. Generalize the partial sum when $n$ is an even number.

**12.** Find $S_5$ and $S_7$. Generalize the partial sum when $n$ is on odd number.

**13.** Describe any conclusions drawn from Items 11 and 12.

**14. Construct viable arguments.** What conclusions if any can you draw from this lesson about the partial sums of geometric series where $r \geq 1$ or $r \leq -1$?

**My Notes**

## Learning Targets:

- Determine if an infinite geometric sum converges.
- Find the sum of a convergent geometric series.

**SUGGESTED LEARNING STRATEGIES:** Create Representations, Look for a Pattern, Quickwrite

Recall the formula for the sum of a finite series $S_n = \dfrac{a_1(1 - r^n)}{1 - r}$. To find the sum of an infinite series, find the value that $S_n$ gets close to as $n$ gets very large. For any infinite geometric series where $-1 < r < 1$, as $n$ gets very large, $r^n$ gets close to 0.

$$S_n = \frac{a_1(1 - r^n)}{1 - r}$$

$$S \approx \frac{a_1(1 - 0)}{1 - r}$$

$$\approx \frac{a_1}{1 - r}$$

An infinite geometric series $\displaystyle\sum_{n=0}^{\infty} a_1 r^n$ converges to the sum $S = \dfrac{a_1}{1 - r}$ if and only if $|r| < 1$ or $-1 < r < 1$. If $|r| \geq 1$, the infinite sum does not exist.

1. Consider the three series from Items 4–6 of the previous lesson. Decide whether the formula for the sum of an infinite geometric series applies. If so, use it to find the sum. Compare the results to your previous answers.

   **a.** $\dfrac{1}{2} + \dfrac{1}{4} + \dfrac{1}{8} + \dfrac{1}{16} + \dfrac{1}{32} + \ldots$

   **b.** $2 + 4 + 8 + 16 + 32 + \ldots$

   **c.** $3 - 1 + \dfrac{1}{3} - \dfrac{1}{9} + \dfrac{1}{27} - \dfrac{1}{81} + \dfrac{1}{243} - \ldots$

> **MATH TIP**
>
> $S_n$ represents the sum of a finite series. Use $S$ to indicate the sum of an infinite series.

> **MATH TIP**
>
> $-1 < r < 1$ can be written as $|r| < 1$. As $n$ increases, $r^n$ gets close to, or *approaches*, 0. It is important to realize that as $r^n$ approaches 0, you can say that $|r^n|$, but not $r^n$, is getting "smaller."

### Check Your Understanding

Find the infinite sum if it exists or tell why it does not exist. Show your work.

2. $64 + 16 + 4 + 1 + \ldots$

3. $\dfrac{1}{3} + \dfrac{5}{12} + \dfrac{25}{48} + \dfrac{125}{192} + \ldots$

4. $\displaystyle\sum_{n=1}^{\infty} 3\left(\dfrac{2}{5}\right)^{n-1}$

**My Notes**

5. Consider the arithmetic series $2 + 5 + 8 + 11 + \ldots$.
   a. Find the first four partial sums of the series.

   b. Do these partial sums appear to have a limiting value?

   c. Does the arithmetic series appear to have an infinite sum? Explain.

6. Summarize the following formulas for a geometric series.

   common ratio          $r = \underline{\hspace{3cm}}$

   $n$th term          $a_n = \underline{\hspace{3cm}}$

   Sum of first $n$ terms    $S_n = \underline{\hspace{3cm}}$

   Infinite sum         $S = \underline{\hspace{3cm}}$

---

**Check Your Understanding**

Consider the series $0.2 + 0.02 + 0.002 + \ldots$.

7. Find the common ratio between the terms of the series.

8. Does this series have an infinite sum? If yes, use the formula to find the sum.

9. **Construct viable arguments.** Make a conjecture about the infinite sum $0.5 + 0.05 + 0.005 + \ldots$. Then verify your conjecture with the formula.

---

## LESSON 20-3 PRACTICE

Find the infinite sum if it exists, or tell why it does not exist.

10. $18 - 9 + \dfrac{9}{2} - \dfrac{9}{4} + \ldots$

11. $729 + 486 + 324 + 216 + \ldots$

12. $81 + 108 + 144 + 192 + \ldots$

13. $-33 - 66 - 99 - 132 - \ldots$

14. **Reason quantitatively.** At the beginning of the lesson it is stated that "for any infinite geometric series where $-1 < r < 1$, as $n$ gets very large, $r^n$ gets close to 0." Justify this statement with an example, using a negative value for $r$.

## ACTIVITY 20 PRACTICE
Write your answers on notebook paper.
Show your work.

### Lesson 20-1

1. Write *arithmetic, geometric,* or *neither* for each sequence. If arithmetic, state the common difference. If geometric, state the common ratio.
   **a.** 4, 12, 36, 108, 324, . . .
   **b.** 1, 2, 6, 24, 120, . . .
   **c.** 4, 9, 14, 19, 24, . . .
   **d.** 35, −30, 25, −20, 15, . . .

2. Find the indicated term of each geometric series.
   **a.** $a_1 = 1, r = -3; a_{10}$
   **b.** $a_1 = 3072, r = \frac{1}{4}; a_8$

3. If $a_n$ is a geometric sequence, express the quotient of $\frac{a_7}{a_4}$ in terms of $r$.

4. The first three terms of a geometric series are $\frac{1}{81}, \frac{1}{27}, \frac{1}{9} \dots$. What is $a_6$?
   **A.** $\frac{3}{81}$
   **B.** 3
   **C.** $\frac{364}{81}$
   **D.** 9

5. Determine the first three terms of a geometric sequence with a common ratio of 2 and defined as follows:
   $$x - 1, x + 6, 3x + 4$$

6. Determine whether each sequence is geometric. If it is a geometric sequence, state the common ratio.
   **a.** $x, x^2, x^4, \dots$
   **b.** $(x + 3), (x + 3)^2, (x + 3)^3, \dots$
   **c.** $3^x, 3^{x+1}, 3^{x+2}, \dots$
   **d.** $x^2, (2x)^2, (3x)^2, \dots$

7. If $a_3 = \frac{9}{32}$ and $a_5 = \frac{81}{512}$, find $a_1$ and $r$.

8. The 5 in the expression $a_n = 4(5)^{n-1}$ represents which part of the expression?
   **A.** $n$
   **B.** $a_1$
   **C.** $r$
   **D.** $S_n$

9. A ball is dropped from a height of 24 feet. The ball bounces to 85% of its previous height with each bounce. Write an expression and solve to find how high (to the nearest tenth of a foot) the ball bounces on the sixth bounce.

10. Write the recursive formula for each sequence.
    **a.** 4, 2, 1, 0.5, . . .
    **b.** 2, 6, 18, 54, 162, . . .
    **c.** $\frac{4}{5}, \frac{4}{25}, \frac{4}{125}, \dots$
    **d.** $-45, 5, -\frac{5}{9}, \dots$

11. Write the explicit formula for each sequence.
    **a.** 4, 2, 1, 0.5, . . .
    **b.** 2, 6, 18, 54, 162, . . .
    **c.** $\frac{4}{5}, \frac{4}{25}, \frac{4}{125}, \dots$
    **d.** $-45, 5, -\frac{5}{9}, \dots$

### Lesson 20-2

12. Find the indicated partial sum of each geometric series.
    **a.** $5 + 2 + \frac{4}{5} + \frac{8}{25} + \dots; S_7$
    **b.** $\frac{1}{8} + \frac{1}{4} + \frac{1}{2} + \dots; S_{15}$

13. For the geometric series $2.9 + 3.77 + 4.90 + 6.37 + \dots$, do the following:
    **a.** Find $S_9$ (to the nearest hundredth).
    **b.** How many more terms have to be added in order for the sum to be greater than 200?

14. George and Martha had two children by 1776, and each child had two children. If this pattern continued to the 12th generation, how many descendants do George and Martha have?

15. A finite geometric series is defined as $0.6 + 0.84 + 1.18 + 1.65 + \dots + 17.36$. How many terms are in the series?
    **A.** $n = 5$
    **B.** $n = 8$
    **C.** $n = 10$
    **D.** $n = 11$

16. Evaluate $\displaystyle\sum_{j=1}^{6} 3(2)^j$

**17.** During a 10-week summer promotion, a baseball team is letting all spectators enter their names in a weekly drawing each time they purchase a game ticket. Once a name is in the drawing, it remains in the drawing unless it is chosen as a winner. Since the number of names in the drawing increases each week, so does the prize money. The first week of the contest the prize amount is $10, and it doubles each week.
   **a.** What is the prize amount in the fourth week of the contest? In the tenth week?
   **b.** What is the total amount of money given away during the entire promotion?

**18.** In case of a school closing due to inclement weather, the high school staff has a calling system to make certain that everyone is notified. In the first round of phone calls, the principal calls three staff members. In the second round of calls, each of those three staff members calls three more staff members. The process continues until all of the staff is notified.
   **a.** Write a rule that shows how many staff members are called during the $n$th round of calls.
   **b.** Find the number of staff members called during the fourth round of calls.
   **c.** If all of the staff has been notified after the fourth round of calls, how many people are on staff at the high school, including the principal?

## Lesson 20-3

**19.** Find the infinite sum if it exists. If it does not exist, tell why.
   **a.** $24 + 12 + 6 + 3 + \ldots$
   **b.** $\frac{1}{12} + \frac{1}{6} + \frac{1}{3} + \frac{2}{3} + \ldots$
   **c.** $1296 - 216 + 36 - 6 + \ldots$

**20.** Write an expression in terms of $a_n$ that means the same as $\displaystyle\sum_{j=1}^{\infty} 2\left(\frac{1}{3}\right)^j$

**21.** Express $0.2727\ldots$ as a fraction.

**22.** Use the common ratio to determine if the infinite series converges or diverges.
   **a.** $36 + 24 + 12 + \ldots$
   **b.** $-4 + 2 + (-1) + \ldots$
   **c.** $3 + 4.5 + 6.75 + \ldots$

**23.** The infinite sum $0.1 + 0.05 + 0.025 + 0.0125 + \ldots$
   **A.** diverges.
   **B.** converges at 0.2.
   **C.** converges at 0.5.
   **D.** converges at 1.0.

**24.** An infinite geometric series has $a_1 = 3$ and a sum of 4. Find $r$.

**25.** The graph depicts which of the following?

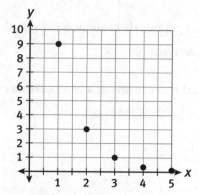

   **A.** converging arithmetric series
   **B.** converging geometric series
   **C.** diverging arithmetic series
   **D.** diverging geometric series

**26.** True or false? No arithmetic series with a common difference that is not equal to zero has an infinite sum. Explain.

## MATHEMATICAL PRACTICES
**Make Sense of Problems and Persevere in Solving Them**

**27.** Explain how knowing any two terms of a geometric sequence is sufficient for finding the other terms.

In a classic math problem, a king wants to reward a knight who has rescued him from an attack. The king gives the knight a chessboard and plans to place money on each square. He gives the knight two options. Option 1 is to place a thousand dollars on the first square, two thousand on the second square, three thousand on the third square, and so on. Option 2 is to place one penny on the first square, two pennies on the second, four on the third, and so on.

Think about which offer sounds better and then answer these questions.

1. List the first five terms in the sequences formed by the given options. Identify each sequence as arithmetic, geometric, or neither.
   a. Option 1
   b. Option 2

2. For each option, write a rule that tells how much money is placed on the $n$th square of the chessboard and a rule that tells the total amount of money placed on squares 1 through $n$.
   a. Option 1
   b. Option 2

3. Find the amount of money placed on the 20th square of the chessboard and the total amount placed on squares 1 through 20 for each option.
   a. Option 1
   b. Option 2

4. There are 64 squares on a chessboard. Find the total amount of money placed on the chessboard for each option.
   a. Option 1
   b. Option 2

5. Which gives the better reward, Option 1 or Option 2? Explain why.

| Scoring Guide | Exemplary | Proficient | Emerging | Incomplete |
|---|---|---|---|---|
| | The solution demonstrates these characteristics: | | | |
| **Mathematics Knowledge and Thinking** (Items 1, 3, 4) | • Fluency in determining specified terms of a sequence or the sum of a specific number of terms of a series | • A functional understanding and accurate identification of specified terms of a sequence or the sum of a specific number of terms of a series | • Partial understanding and partially accurate identification of specified terms of a sequence or the sum of a specific number of terms of a series | • Little or no understanding and inaccurate identification of specified terms of a sequence or the sum of a specific number of terms of a series |
| **Problem Solving** (Items 3, 4) | • An appropriate and efficient strategy that results in a correct answer | • A strategy that may include unnecessary steps but results in a correct answer | • A strategy that results in some incorrect answers | • No clear strategy when solving problems |
| **Mathematical Modeling / Representations** (Items 1, 2) | • Fluency in accurately representing real-world scenarios with arithmetic and geometric sequences and series | • Little difficulty in accurately representing real-world scenarios with arithmetic and geometric sequences and series | • Some difficulty in representing real-world scenarios with arithmetic and geometric sequences and series | • Significant difficulty in representing real-world scenarios with arithmetic and geometric sequences and series |
| **Reasoning and Communication** (Item 5) | • Clear and accurate explanation of which option provides the better reward | • Adequate explanation of which option provides the better reward | • Misleading or confusing explanation of which option provides the better reward | • Incomplete or inadequate explanation of which option provides the better reward |

# Exponential Functions and Graphs

## Sizing Up the Situation
### Lesson 21-1 Exploring Exponential Patterns

### Learning Targets:
- Identify data that grow exponentially.
- Compare the rates of change of linear and exponential data.

> **SUGGESTED LEARNING STRATEGIES:** Create Representations, Look for a Pattern, Quickwrite

Ramon Hall, a graphic artist, needs to make several different-sized draft copies of an original design. His original graphic design sketch is contained within a rectangle with a width of 4 cm and a length of 6 cm. Using the office copy machine, he magnifies the original 4 cm × 6 cm design to 120% of the original design size, and calls this his first draft. Ramon's second draft results from magnifying the first draft to 120% of its new size. Each new draft is 120% of the previous draft.

1. Complete the table with the dimensions of Ramon's first five draft versions, showing all decimal places.

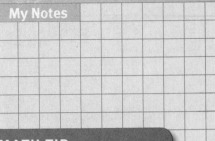

**MATH TIP**

Magnifying a design creates similar figures. The ratio between corresponding lengths of similar figures is called the *constant of proportionality*, or the *scale factor*. For a magnification of 120%, the scale factor is 1.2.

| Number of Magnifications | Width (cm) | Length (cm) |
|:---:|:---:|:---:|
| 0 | 4 | 6 |
| 1 | | |
| 2 | | |
| 3 | | |
| 4 | | |
| 5 | | |

2. **Make sense of problems.** The resulting draft for each magnification has a unique width and a unique length. Thus, there is a functional relationship between the number of magnifications *n* and the resulting width *W*. There is also a functional relationship between the number of magnifications *n* and the resulting length *L*. What are the reasonable domain and range for these functions? Explain.

3. Plot the ordered pairs (*n*, *W*) from the table in Item 1. Use a different color or symbol to plot the ordered pairs (*n*, *L*).

4. Use the data in Item 1 to complete the table.

| Increase in Number of Magnifications | Change in the Width | Change in the Length |
|---|---|---|
| 0 to 1 | $4.8 - 4 = 0.8$ | $7.2 - 6 = 1.2$ |
| 1 to 2 | | |
| 2 to 3 | | |
| 3 to 4 | | |
| 4 to 5 | | |

5. From the graphs in Item 3 and the data in Item 4, do these functions appear to be linear? Explain why or why not.

6. **Express regularity in repeated reasoning.** Explain why each table below contains data that can be represented by a linear function. Write an equation to show the linear relationship between $x$ and $y$.

   a.

   | x | −3 | −1 | 1 | 3 | 5 |
   |---|---|---|---|---|---|
   | y | 8 | 5 | 2 | −1 | −4 |

   b.

   | x | 2 | 5 | 11 | 17 | 26 |
   |---|---|---|---|---|---|
   | y | 3 | 7 | 15 | 23 | 35 |

7. Consider the data in the table below.

   | x | 0 | 1 | 2 | 3 | 4 |
   |---|---|---|---|---|---|
   | y | 24 | 12 | 6 | 3 | 1.5 |

   a. Can the data in the table be represented by a linear function? Explain why or why not.

   b. Describe any patterns that you see in the consecutive $y$-values.

**My Notes**

8. Consider the data in the table in Item 1. How does the relationship of the data in this table compare to the relationship of the data in the table in Item 7?

**Check Your Understanding**

9. Complete the table so that the function represented is a linear function.

| x | 1 | 2 | 3 | 4 | 5 |
|---|---|---|---|---|---|
| f(x) | 16 | 22 | | | 40 |

10. **Reason quantitatively.** Explain why the function represented in the table cannot be a linear function.

| x | 1 | 2 | 3 | 4 | 5 |
|---|---|---|---|---|---|
| f(x) | 7 | 12 | 16 | 19 | 21 |

## LESSON 21-1 PRACTICE

**Model with mathematics.** Determine whether each function is linear or nonlinear. Explain your answers.

11. $x$ = number of equally sized pans of brownies; $f(x)$ = number of brownies

12. $x$ = cost of an item; $f(x)$ = price you pay in a state with a 6% sales tax

13. $x$ = number of months; $f(x)$ = amount of money in a bank account with interest compounded monthly

14.

| x | 2 | 4 | 6 | 8 | 10 |
|---|---|---|---|---|---|
| y | 2.6 | 3.0 | 3.8 | 4.8 | 6.0 |

15.

| x | 5 | 10 | 15 | 20 | 25 |
|---|---|---|---|---|---|
| y | 1.25 | 1.00 | 0.75 | 0.50 | 0.25 |

16. Identify if there is a constant rate of change or constant multiplier. Determine the rate of change or constant multiplier.

| x | 1 | 2 | 3 | 4 |
|---|---|---|---|---|
| y | 6 | 4.8 | 3.84 | 3.072 |

## MATH TERMS

An **exponential function** is a function of the form $f(x) = a \cdot b^x$, where $a$ and $b$ are constants, $x$ is the domain, $f(x)$ is the range, $a \neq 0$, $b \neq 0$, and $b \neq 1$.

## MATH TERMS

In an exponential function, the multiplicative constant is called an **exponential decay factor** when it is between 0 and 1.

When the multiplicative constant is greater than 1, it is called an **exponential growth factor**.

## MATH TIP

To compare change in size, you could also use the *growth rate*, or *percent increase*. This is the percent that is equal to the ratio of the increase amount to the original amount.

## CONNECT TO TECHNOLOGY

Confirm the reasonableness of your function in Item 2b by using a graphing calculator to make a scatter plot of the data in the table in Item 8 in Lesson 21-1. Then graph the function to see how it compares to the scatter plot.

**Learning Targets:**
- Identify and write exponential functions.
- Determine the decay factor or growth factor of an exponential function.

**SUGGESTED LEARNING STRATEGIES:** Vocabulary Organizer, Create Representations, Look for a Pattern, Quickwrite, Think-Pair-Share

The data in the tables in Items 7 and 8 of the previous lesson were generated by *exponential functions*. In the special case when the change in the input variable $x$ is constant, the output variable $y$ of an exponential function changes by a *multiplicative constant*. For example, in the table in Item 7, the increase in the consecutive $x$-values results from repeatedly adding 1, while the decrease in $y$-values results from repeatedly multiplying by the constant $\frac{1}{2}$, known as the *exponential decay factor*.

1. In the table in Item 1 in Lesson 21-1, what is the *exponential growth factor*?

2. You can write an equation for the exponential function relating $W$ and $n$.
   a. Complete the table below to show the calculations used to find the width of each magnification.

| Number of Magnifications | Calculation to Find Width (cm) |
|---|---|
| 0 | 4 |
| 1 | 4(1.2) |
| 2 | 4(1.2)(1.2) |
| 3 | 4(1.2)(1.2)(1.2) |
| 4 | |
| 5 | |
| 10 | |
| $n$ | |

   b. **Express regularity in repeated reasoning.** Write a function that expresses the resulting width $W$ after $n$ magnifications of 120%.

   c. Use the function in part b to find the width of the 11th magnification.

## Lesson 21-2
## Exponential Functions

The general form of an exponential function is $f(x) = a(b^x)$, where $a$ and $b$ are constants and $a \neq 0$, $b > 0$, $b \neq 1$.

3. For the exponential function written in Item 2b, identify the value of the parameters $a$ and $b$. Then explain their meaning in terms of the problem situation.

4. Starting with Ramon's original 4 cm × 6 cm rectangle containing his graphic design, write an exponential function that expresses the resulting length $L$ after $n$ magnifications of 120%.

Ramon decides to print five different reduced draft copies of his original design rectangle. Each one will be reduced to 90% of the previous size.

5. Complete the table below to show the dimensions of the first five draft versions. Include all decimal places.

| Number of Reductions | Width (cm) | Length (cm) |
|---|---|---|
| 0 | 4 | 6 |
| 1 | | |
| 2 | | |
| 3 | | |
| 4 | | |
| 5 | | |

6. Write the exponential decay factor and the *decay rate* for the data in the table in Item 5.

7. **Model with mathematics.** Use the data in the table in Item 5.
   a. Write an exponential function that expresses the width $w$ of a reduction in terms of $n$, the number of reductions performed.

   b. Write an exponential function that expresses the length $l$ of a reduction in terms of $n$, the number of reductions performed.

   c. Use the functions to find the dimensions of the design if the original design undergoes ten reductions.

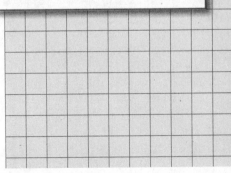

**MATH TIP**

To compare change in size, you could also use the *decay rate*, or *percent decrease*. This is the percent that is equal to the ratio of the decrease amount to the original amount.

**My Notes**

### Check Your Understanding

8. Why is it necessary to place restrictions that $a \neq 0$, $b > 0$, and $b \neq 1$ in the general form of an exponential function?

9. An exponential function contains the ordered pairs $(3, 6)$, $(4, 12)$, and $(5, 24)$.
    a. What is the scale factor for this function?
    b. Does the function represent exponential decay or growth? Explain your reasoning.

10. **Make sense of problems.** For the equation $y = 2000(1.05)^x$, identify the value of the parameters $a$ and $b$. Then explain their meaning in terms of a savings account in a bank.

### LESSON 21-2 PRACTICE

**Construct viable arguments.** Decide whether each table of data can be modeled by a linear function, an exponential function, or neither, and justify your answers. If the data can be modeled by a linear or exponential function, give an equation for the function using regression methods available through technology.

11.

| x | 0 | 1 | 2 | 3 | 4 |
|---|---|---|---|---|---|
| y | 1 | 3 | 9 | 27 | 81 |

12.

| x | 0 | 1 | 2 | 3 | 4 |
|---|---|---|---|---|---|
| y | 4 | 8 | 14 | 22 | 32 |

13. Given that the function has an exponential decay factor of 0.8, complete the table.

| x | 0 | 1 | 2 | 3 | 4 |
|---|---|---|---|---|---|
| y | 64 | | | | |

14. What is the decay rate for the function in Item 13?

15. Write the function represented in Item 13.

**My Notes**

### Learning Targets:

- Determine when an exponential function is increasing or decreasing.
- Describe the end behavior of exponential functions.
- Identify asymptotes of exponential functions.

> **SUGGESTED LEARNING STRATEGIES:** Create Representations, Activating Prior Knowledge, Close Reading, Vocabulary Organizer, Think-Pair-Share, Group Presentation

1. Graph the functions $y = 6(1.2)^x$ and $y = 6(0.9)^x$ on a graphing calculator or other graphing utility. Sketch the results.

2. Determine the domain and range for each function. Use interval notation.

   Domain                    Range

   **a.** $y = 6(1.2)^x$    _____

   **b.** $y = 6(0.9)^x$    _____

A function is said to *increase* if the $y$-values increase as the $x$-values increase. A function is said to *decrease* if the $y$-values decrease as the $x$-values increase.

3. Describe each function as increasing or decreasing.
   **a.** $y = 6(1.2)^x$




   **b.** $y = 6(0.9)^x$

**CONNECT TO AP**

Not all functions increase or decrease over the entire domain of the function. Functions may increase, decrease, or remain constant over various intervals of the domain. Functions that either increase or decrease over the entire domain are called *strictly monotonic*.

As you learned in a previous activity, the *end behavior* of a graph describes the $y$-values of the function as $x$ increases without bound and as $x$ decreases without bound. If the end behavior approaches some constant $a$, then the graph of the function has a horizontal *asymptote* at $y = a$.

When $x$ increases without bound, the values of $x$ approach positive infinity, $\infty$. When $x$ decreases without bound, the values of $x$ approach negative infinity, $-\infty$.

4. Describe the end behavior of each function as $x$ approaches $\infty$. Write the equation for any horizontal asymptotes.
   **a.** $y = 6(1.2)^x$




   **b.** $y = 6(0.9)^x$

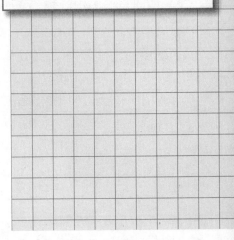

**MATH TERMS**

If the graph of a relation gets closer and closer to a line, the line is called an **asymptote** of the graph.

**My Notes**

5. Describe the end behavior of each function as $x$ approaches $-\infty$. Write the equation for any horizontal asymptotes.
   a. $y = 6(1.2)^x$

   b. $y = 6(0.9)^x$

6. Identify any $x$- or $y$-intercepts of each function.
   a. $y = 6(1.2)^x$

   b. $y = 6(0.9)^x$

7. **Reason abstractly.** Consider how the parameters $a$ and $b$ affect the graph of the general exponential function $f(x) = a(b)^x$. In parts a–c, use a graphing calculator to graph each of the following functions. Compare and contrast the graphs.

   a. $f(x) = 2^x$; $g(x) = 3(2)^x$; $h(x) = -3(2)^x$; $j(x) = \frac{1}{4}(2)^x$; $k(x) = -\frac{1}{4}(2)^x$

   b. $f(x) = 10^x$; $g(x) = 2(10)^x$; $h(x) = -3(10)^x$; $j(x) = \frac{1}{4}(10)^x$; $k(x) = -\frac{1}{4}(10)^x$

   c. $f(x) = \left(\frac{1}{2}\right)^x$; $g(x) = 4\left(\frac{1}{2}\right)^x$; $h(x) = -6\left(\frac{1}{4}\right)^x$; $j(x) = \frac{1}{2}\left(\frac{1}{4}\right)^x$;

   $k(x) = -\frac{1}{4}\left(\frac{1}{10}\right)^x$

   d. Describe the effects of different values of $a$ and $b$ in the general exponential function $f(x) = a(b)^x$. Consider attributes of the graph such as the $y$-intercept, horizontal asymptotes, and whether the graph is increasing or decreasing.

### Check Your Understanding

Graph the functions $f(x) = -6(1.2)^x$ and $g(x) = -6(0.9)^x$ on a graphing calculator or other graphing utility.

8. Determine the domain and range for each function.

9. Describe the end behavior of each function as $x$ approaches $\infty$.

10. Describe the end behavior of each function as $x$ approaches $-\infty$.

## LESSON 21-3 PRACTICE

**Make use of structure.** For each exponential function, state whether the function increases or decreases, and give the $y$-intercept. Use the general form of an exponential function to explain your answers.

11. $y = 8(2)^x$

12. $y = 0.3(0.25)^x$

13. $y = -2(10)^x$

14. $y = -(0.3)^x$

15. **Construct viable arguments.** What is true about the asymptotes and $y$-intercepts of the functions in this lesson? What conclusions can you draw?

## Learning Targets:

- Explore how changing parameters affects the graph of an exponential function.
- Graph transformations of exponential functions.

> **SUGGESTED LEARNING STRATEGIES:** Close Reading, Create Representations, Quickwrite

You can use transformations of the graph of the function $f(x) = b^x$ to graph functions of the form $g(x) = a(b)^{x-c} + d$, where $a$ and $b$ are constants, and $a \neq 0$, $b > 0$, $b \neq 1$. Rather than having a single parent graph for all exponential functions, there is a different parent graph for each base $b$.

1. Graph the parent graph $f$ and the function $g$ by applying the correct vertical stretch, shrink, and/or reflection over the $x$-axis. Write a description of each transformation.

**a.** $f(x) = \left(\frac{1}{2}\right)^x$ \qquad $g(x) = 4\left(\frac{1}{2}\right)^x$

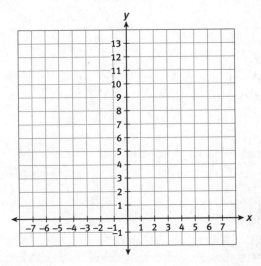

**b.** $f(x) = 3^x$ \qquad $g(x) = -\frac{1}{2}(3)^x$

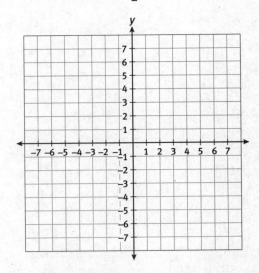

> **MATH TIP**
>
> You can draw a quick sketch of the parent graph for any base $b$ by plotting the points $\left(-1, \frac{1}{b}\right)$, $(0, 1)$, and $(1, b)$.

> **CONNECT TO AP**
>
> Exponential functions are important in the study of calculus.

**My Notes**

**CONNECT TO TECHNOLOGY**

You can use a graphing calculator to approximate the range values when the *x*-coordinates are not integers. For $f(x) = 2^x$, use a calculator to find $f\left(\frac{1}{2}\right)$ and $f\left(\sqrt{3}\right)$.

$$2^{\frac{1}{2}} \approx 1.414$$
$$2^{\sqrt{3}} \approx 3.322$$

Then use a graphing calculator to verify that the points $\left(\frac{1}{2}, 2^{\frac{1}{2}}\right)$ and $\left(\sqrt{3}, 2^{\sqrt{3}}\right)$ lie on the graph of $f(x) = 2^x$.

2. Sketch the parent graph *f* and the graphs of *g* and *h* by applying the correct horizontal or vertical translation. Write a description of each transformation and give the equations of any asymptotes.

  **a.** $f(x) = 2^x$
   $g(x) = 2^{(x-3)}$
   $h(x) = 2^{(x+2)}$

  **b.** $f(x) = 10^x$
   $g(x) = 10^{(x-1)}$
   $h(x) = 10^{(x+3)}$

  **c.** $f(x) = 10^x$
   $g(x) = 10^x - 1$
   $h(x) = 10^x + 3$

  **d.** $f(x) = \left(\frac{1}{3}\right)^x$
   $g(x) = \left(\frac{1}{3}\right)^x - 2$

3. **Attend to precision.** Describe how each function results from transforming a parent graph of the form $f(x) = b^x$. Then sketch the parent graph and the given function on the same axes. Give the domain and range of each function in interval notation. Give the equations of any asymptotes.

a. $g(x) = 3^{x+4} + 1$

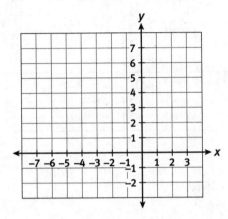

b. $g(x) = 2\left(\frac{1}{3}\right)^x - 4$

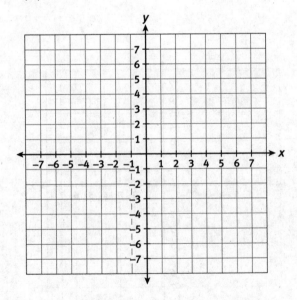

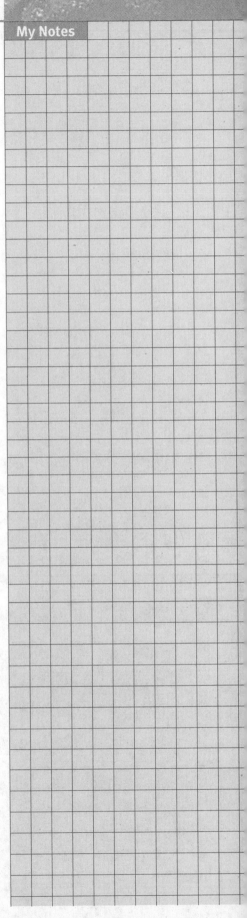

**My Notes**

c. $g(x) = \frac{1}{2}(4)^{x-4} - 2$

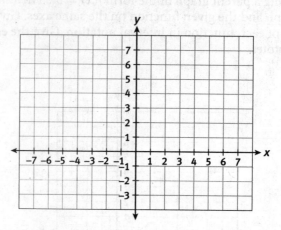

4. Describe how the function $g(x) = -3(2)^{x-6} + 5$ results from transforming a parent graph $f(x) = 2^x$. Sketch both graphs on the same axes. Give the domain and range of each function in interval notation. Give the equations of any asymptotes. Use a graphing calculator to check your work.

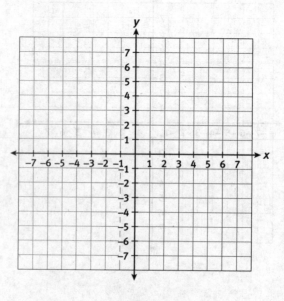

**My Notes**

## Check Your Understanding

5. **Reason quantitatively.** Explain how to change the equation of a parent graph $f(x) = 4^x$ to a translation that is left 6 units and a vertical shrink of 0.5.

6. Write the parent function $f(x)$ of $g(x) = -3(2)^{(x+2)} - 1$ and describe how the graph of $g(x)$ is a translation of the parent function.

## LESSON 21-4 PRACTICE

Describe how each function results from transforming a parent graph of the form $f(x) = b^x$. Then sketch the parent graph and the given function on the same axes. State the domain and range of each function and give the equations of any asymptotes.

7. $g(x) = 10^{x-2} - 3$

8. $g(x) = \frac{1}{2}(2)^{x-4} + 1$

9. $g(x) = -2\left(\frac{1}{3}\right)^{x+4}$

**Make use of structure.** Write the equation that indicates each transformation of the parent equation $f(x) = 2^x$. Then use the graph below and draw and label each transformation.

10. For $g(x)$, the $y$-intercept is at $(0, 3)$.

11. For $h(x)$, the exponential growth factor is 0.5.

12. For $k(x)$, the graph of $f(x)$ is horizontally translated to the right 3 units.

13. For $l(x)$, the graph of $f(x)$ is vertically translated upward 2 units.

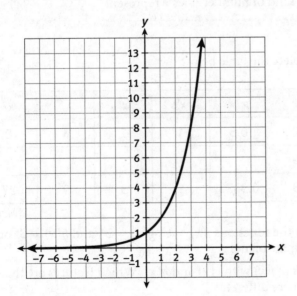

### Learning Targets:
- Graph the function $f(x) = e^x$.
- Graph transformations of $f(x) = e^x$.

**SUGGESTED LEARNING STRATEGIES:** Quickwrite, Group Presentation, Debriefing

1. **Use appropriate tools strategically.** On a graphing calculator, set $Y_1 = x$ and $Y_2 = \left(1 + \frac{1}{x}\right)^x$. Let $x$ increase by increments of 100. Describe what happens to the table of values for $Y_2$ as $x$ increases.

This irrational constant is called $e$ and is often used in exponential functions.

2. **a.** On a graphing calculator, enter $Y_1 = e^x$. Using the table of values associated with $Y_1$, complete the table below.

| $x$ | $Y_1 = e^x$ |
|-----|-------------|
| 0   |             |
| 1   |             |
| 2   |             |
| 3   |             |

**b. Reason quantitatively.** Which row in the table gives the approximate value of $e$? Explain.

**c.** What kind of number does $e$ represent?

3. **a.** Complete the table below.

| $x$ | $x^{-1}$ | $x^0$ | $x^1$ | $x^2$ | $x^3$ |
|-----|----------|-------|-------|-------|-------|
| 2   | 0.5      | 1     | 2     | 4     | 8     |
| $e$ |          |       |       |       |       |
| 3   | 0.3333   | 1     | 3     | 9     | 27    |

**b.** Graph the functions $f(x) = e^x$, $g(x) = 2^x$, and $h(x) = 3^x$ on the same coordinate plane.

**c.** Compare $f(x)$ with $g(x)$ and $h(x)$. Which features are the same? Which are different?

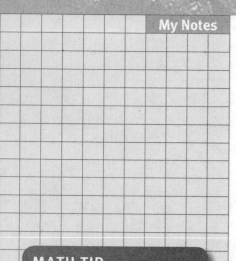

**MATH TIP**

Exponential functions that describe examples of (continuous) exponential growth or decay use $e$ for the base. You will learn more about the importance of $e$ in Precalculus.

**4.** Graph the parent function $f(x) = e^x$ and the function $g(x)$ by applying the correct vertical stretch, shrink, reflection over the $x$-axis, or translation. Write a description for the transformation. State the domain and range of each function. Give the equation of any asymptotes.

**a.** $f(x) = e^x$

$g(x) = -\frac{1}{2}(e^x)$

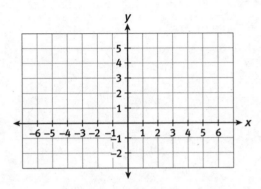

**b.** $f(x) = e^x$

$g(x) = e^{x-4} + 1$

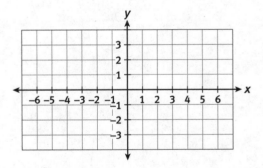

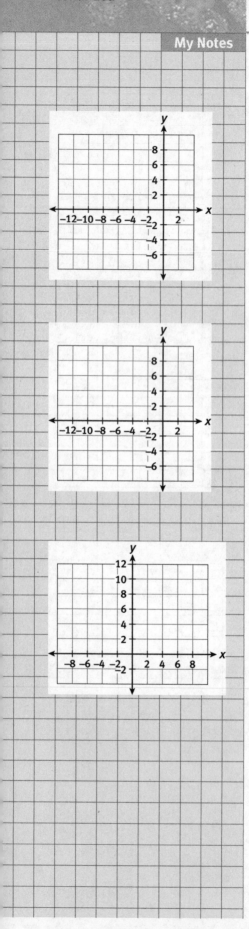

**5.** Graph the parent graph *f* and the function *g* by applying the correct transformation. Write a description of each transformation. State the domain and range of each function. Give the equation of any asymptotes.

**a.** $f(x) = e^x$

$g(x) = 2e^x - 5$

**b.** $f(x) = e^x$

$g(x) = 2e^{x+1}$

**c.** $f(x) = e^x$

$g(x) = \frac{1}{2}(e^{x-4}) - 2$

**6.** Explain how the parameters $a$, $c$, and $d$ transform the parent graph $f(x) = b^x$ to produce the graph of the function $g(x) = a(b)^{x-c} + d$.

## Check Your Understanding

Match each exponential expression with its graph.

**7.** $f(x) = 3e^x$

**A.**

**8.** $f(x) = -0.4e^x$

**B.**

**9.** $f(x) = e^x + 2$

**C.**
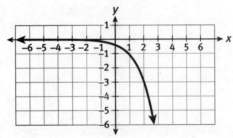

**10.** $f(x) = -e^x$

**D.**
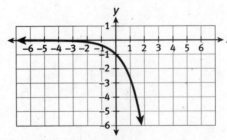
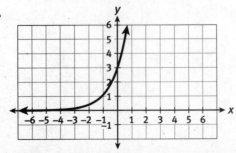

## LESSON 21-5 PRACTICE

**Model with mathematics.** Describe how each function results from transforming a parent graph of the form $f(x) = e^x$. Then sketch the parent graph and the given function on the same axes. State the domain and range of each function and give the equations of any asymptotes.

**11.** $g(x) = \frac{1}{4}e^x + 5$

**12.** $g(x) = e^{x-3} - 4$

**13.** $g(x) = -4e^{x-3} + 3$

**14.** $g(x) = 2e^{x+4}$

**15. Critique the reasoning of others.** On Cameron's math test, he was asked to describe the transformations from the graph of $f(x) = e^x$ to the graph of $g(x) = e^{x-2} - 2$. Cameron wrote "translation left 2 units and down 2 units." Do you agree or disagree with Cameron? Explain your reasoning.

**16.** What similarities, if any, are there between the functions studied in this lesson and the previous lesson?

## Exponential Functions and Graphs
### Sizing Up the Situation

## ACTIVITY 21 PRACTICE
Write your answers on notebook paper.
Show your work.

### Lesson 21-1

1. a. Complete the table so that the function represented is a linear function.

| x | 1 | 2 | 3 | 4 | 5 |
|---|---|---|---|---|---|
| f(x) | 5.4 | 6.7 | | | 10.6 |

   b. What function is represented in the data?

2. a. How do you use a table of values to determine if the relationship of $y = 3x + 2$ is a linear relationship?
   b. How do you use a graph to determine if the relationship in part a is linear?

3. Which relationship is nonlinear?
   **A.** (2, 12), (5, 18), (6.5, 21)
   **B.** (6, x + 2), (21, x + 7), (−9, x − 3)
   **C.** (0.25, 1.25), (1.25, 2.50), (2.50, 5.00)
   **D.** (−5, 20), (−3, 12), (−1, 4)

4. Determine if the table of data can be modeled by a linear function. If so, give an equation for the function. If not, explain why not.

| x | 0 | 1 | 2 | 3 | 4 |
|---|---|---|---|---|---|
| y | $\frac{1}{5}$ | $\frac{3}{5}$ | 1 | $1\frac{2}{5}$ | $1\frac{4}{5}$ |

5. Which relationship has the greatest value for $x = 4$?
   **A.** $y = 5(3)^x + 2$
   **B.** $y = 5(2^x + 3)$
   **C.** $y = 5(3x + 2)$
   **D.** $y = 5(2)^{x+3}$

6. Ida paints violets onto porcelain plates. She paints a spiral that is a sequence of violets, the size of each consecutive violet being a fraction of the size of the preceding violet. The table below shows the width of the first three violets in the continuing pattern.

| Violet Number | 1 | 2 | 3 |
|---|---|---|---|
| Width (cm) | 4 | 3.2 | 2.56 |

   a. Is Ida's shrinking violet pattern an example of an exponential function? Explain.
   b. Find the width of the fourth and fifth violets in the sequence.

   c. Write an equation to express the size of the smallest violet in terms of the number of violets on the plate.
   d. If a plate has a total of 10 violets, explain two different ways to determine the size of the smallest violet.

### Lesson 21-2

7. Which statement is NOT true for the exponential function $f(x) = 4(0.75)^x$?
   **A.** Exponential growth factor is 75%.
   **B.** Percent of decrease is 25%.
   **C.** The scale factor is 0.75.
   **D.** The decay rate is 25%.

8. For the exponential function $f(x) = 3.2(1.5)^x$, identify the value of the parameters $a$ and $b$. Then explain their meaning, using the vocabulary from the lesson.

9. Decide whether each table of data can be modeled by a linear function, an exponential function, or neither. If the data can be modeled by a linear or exponential function, give an equation for the function.
   a.

| x | 0 | 1 | 2 | 3 | 4 |
|---|---|---|---|---|---|
| y | 24 | 18 | 12 | 6 | 0 |

   b.

| x | 0 | 1 | 2 | 3 | 4 |
|---|---|---|---|---|---|
| y | 36 | 18 | 9 | 4.5 | 2.25 |

10. Sixteen teams play in a one-game elimination match. The winners of the first round go on to play a second round until only one team remains undefeated and is declared the champion.
   a. Make a table of values for the number of rounds and the number of teams participating.
   b. What is the reasonable domain and the range of this function? Explain.
   c. Find the rate of decay.
   d. Find the decay factor.

## Lesson 21-3

**11.** Which of the following functions have the same graph?

**A.** $f(x) = \left(\frac{1}{4}\right)^x$

**B.** $f(x) = 4^x$

**C.** $f(x) = 4^{-x}$

**D.** $f(x) = x^4$

**12.** Which function is modeled in the graph below?

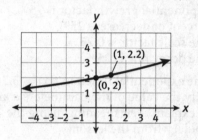

**A.** $y = (2)^x$

**B.** $y = 2(1.1)^x$

**C.** $y = (2)^{1.1x}$

**D.** $y = 2.1x$

**13.** For each exponential function, state the domain and range, whether the function increases or decreases, and the $y$-intercept.

**a.** $y = 2(4)^x$
**b.** $y = 3\left(\frac{1}{2}\right)^x$

**c.** $y = -(0.3)^x$
**d.** $y = -3(5.2)^x$

**14.** The *World Factbook* produced by the Central Intelligence Agency estimates the July 2012 United States population as 313,847,465. The following rates are also reported as estimates for 2012.

**Birth rate: 13.7 births/1000 population**

**Death rate: 8.4 deaths/1000 population**

**Net migration rate: 3.62 migrant(s)/1000 population**

**a.** Write a percent for each rate listed above.
**b.** Combine the percents from part a to find the overall growth rate for the United States.
**c.** The exponential growth factor for a population is equal to the growth rate plus 100%. What is the exponential growth rate for the United States?
**d.** Write a function to express the United States population as a function of years since 2012.
**e.** Use the function from part d to predict the United States population in the year 2050.

**15.** Under what conditions is the function $f(x) = a(3)^x$ increasing?

## Lesson 21-4

**16.** Describe how each function results from transforming a parent graph of the form $f(x) = b^x$. Then sketch the parent graph and the given function on the same axes. State the domain and range of each function and give the equations of any asymptotes.

**a.** $g(x) = 2^{x+3} - 4$

**b.** $g(x) = -3\left(\frac{1}{2}\right)^x + 2$

**c.** $g(x) = \frac{1}{2}(3)^{x+3} - 4$

**17. a.** Explain why a change in $c$ for the function $a(b)^{x-c} + d$ causes a horizontal translation.
**b.** Explain why a change in $d$ for the function $a(b)^{x-c} + d$ causes a vertical translation.

**18.** Which transformation maps the graph of $f(x) = 3^x$ to $g(x) = \left(\frac{1}{3}\right)^x$?

**A.** horizontal translation
**B.** shrink
**C.** reflection
**D.** vertical translation

## Lesson 21-5

**19.** Is $f(x) = e^x$ an increasing or a decreasing function? Explain your reasoning.

**20.** Which function has a $y$-intercept of $(0, 0)$?
**A.** $y = e^x + 1$
**B.** $y = -e^x + 1$
**C.** $y = e^x - 1$
**D.** $y = e^x$

**21.** What ordered pair do $f(x) = e^x$ and $g(x) = 2^x$ have in common?

## MATHEMATICAL PRACTICES
### Attend to Precision

**22.** Explain the difference between $y = x^2$ and $y = 2^x$.

# Logarithms and Their Properties

Earthquakes and Richter Scale

Lesson 22-1 Exponential Data

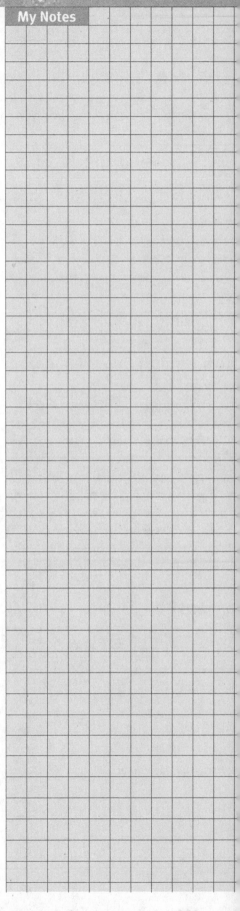

**Learning Targets:**

- Complete tables and plot points for exponential data.
- Write and graph an exponential function for a given context.
- Find the domain and range of an exponential function.

SUGGESTED LEARNING STRATEGIES: Summarizing, Paraphrasing, Create Representations, Quickwrite, Close Reading, Look for a Pattern

In 1935, Charles F. Richter developed the Richter magnitude test scale to compare the size of earthquakes. The Richter scale is based on the amplitude of the seismic waves recorded on seismographs at various locations after being adjusted for distance from the epicenter of the earthquake.

Richter assigned a magnitude of 0 to an earthquake whose amplitude on a seismograph is 1 micron, or $10^{-4}$ cm. According to the Richter scale, a magnitude 1.0 earthquake causes 10 times the ground motion of a magnitude 0 earthquake. A magnitude 2.0 earthquake causes 10 times the ground motion of a magnitude 1.0 earthquake. This pattern continues as the magnitude of the earthquake increases.

1. **Reason quantitatively.** How does the ground motion caused by earthquakes of these magnitudes compare?
   **a.** magnitude 5.0 earthquake compared to magnitude 4.0

   **b.** magnitude 4.0 earthquake compared to magnitude 1.0

   **c.** magnitude 4.0 earthquake compared to magnitude 0

The sign below describes the effects of earthquakes of different magnitudes. Read through this sign with your group and identify any words that might be unfamiliar. Find their meanings to aid your understanding.

---

**Typical Effects of Earthquakes of Various Magnitudes**
1.0  Very weak, no visible damage
2.0  Not felt by humans
3.0  Often felt, usually no damage
4.0  Windows rattle, indoor items shake
5.0  Damage to poorly constructed structures, slight damage to well-designed buildings
6.0  Destructive in populated areas
7.0  Serious damage over large geographic areas
8.0  Serious damage across areas of hundreds of miles
9.0  Serious damage across areas of hundreds of miles
10.0 Extremely rare, never recorded

---

**My Notes**

2. Complete the table to show how many times as great the ground motion is when caused by each earthquake as compared to a magnitude 0 earthquake.

| Magnitude | Ground Motion Compared to Magnitude 0 |
|---|---|
| 1.0 | 10 |
| 2.0 | 100 |
| 3.0 | |
| 4.0 | |
| 5.0 | |
| 6.0 | |
| 7.0 | |
| 8.0 | |
| 9.0 | |
| 10.0 | |

3. In parts a–c below, you will graph the data from Item 2. Let the horizontal axis represent the magnitude of the earthquake and the vertical axis represent the amount of ground motion caused by the earthquake as compared to a magnitude 0 earthquake. Alternatively, use technology to perform an exponential regression.

   a. Plot the data using a grid that displays $-10 \leq x \leq 10$ and $-10 \leq y \leq 10$. Explain why this grid is or is not a good choice.

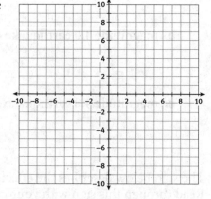

   b. Plot the data using a grid that displays $-10 \leq x \leq 100$ and $-10 \leq y \leq 100$. Explain why this grid is or is not a good choice.

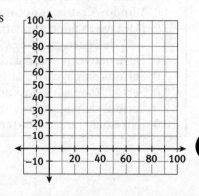

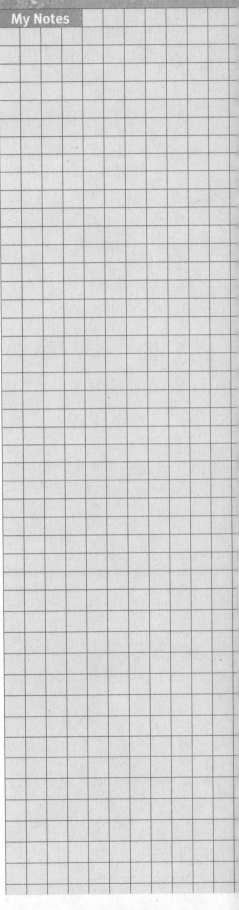

**My Notes**

**c.** Scales may be easier to choose if only a subset of the data is graphed and if different scales are used for the horizontal and vertical axes. Determine an appropriate subset of the data and a scale for the graph. Plot the data and label and scale the axes. Draw a function that fits the plotted data.

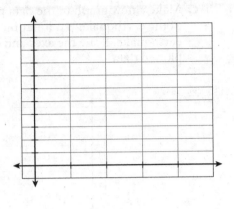

**d.** Write a function $G(x)$ for the ground motion caused compared to a magnitude 0 earthquake by a magnitude $x$ earthquake.

## Check Your Understanding

**4.** What is the domain of the function in Item 3d? Is the graph of the function continuous?

**5.** Use the graph from Item 3c to estimate how many times greater the ground motion of an earthquake of magnitude 3.5 is than a magnitude 0 earthquake. Solve the equation you wrote in Item 3d to check that your estimate is reasonable.

**6. Make sense of problems.** In Item 3, the data were plotted so that the ground motion caused by the earthquake was a function of the magnitude of the earthquake.
   **a.** Is the ground motion a result of the magnitude of an earthquake, or is the magnitude of an earthquake the result of ground motion?

   **b.** Based your answer to part a, would you choose ground motion or magnitude as the independent variable of a function relating the two quantities? What would you choose as the dependent variable?

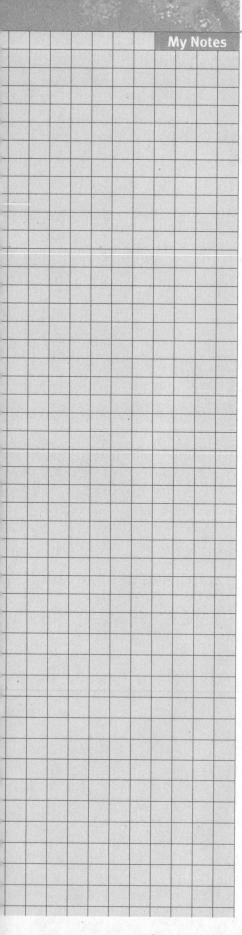

**My Notes**

**c.** Make a new graph of the data plotted Item 3c so that the magnitude of the earthquake is a function of the ground motion caused by the earthquake. Scale the axes and draw a function that fits the plotted data.

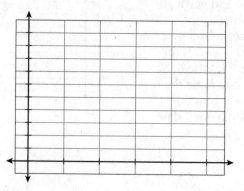

**7.** Let the function you graphed in Item 6c be $y = M(x)$, where $M$ is the magnitude of an earthquake for which there is $x$ times as much ground motion as a magnitude 0 earthquake.

**a.** Identify a reasonable domain and range of the function $y = G(x)$ from Item 3d and the function $y = M(x)$ in this situation. Use interval notation.

|  | **Domain** | **Range** |
|---|---|---|
| $y = G(x)$ | _____ | _____ |
| $y = M(x)$ | _____ | _____ |

**b.** In terms of the problem situation, describe the meaning of an ordered pair on the graphs of $y = G(x)$ and $y = M(x)$.

$y = G(x)$ _____ , _____

$y = M(x)$ _____ , _____

**c.** A portion of the graphs of $y = G(x)$ and $y = M(x)$ is shown on the same set of axes. Describe any patterns you observe.

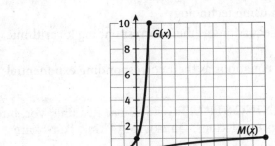

### Check Your Understanding

**8.** How did you choose the scale of the graph you drew in Item 6c?

**9.** What is the relationship between the functions $G$ and $M$?

## LESSON 22-1 PRACTICE

How does the ground motion caused by earthquakes of these magnitudes compare?

**10.** magnitude 5.0 compared to magnitude 2.0

**11.** magnitude 7.0 compared to magnitude 0

**12.** magnitude 6.0 compared to magnitude 5.0

**13.** A 1933 California earthquake had a Richter scale reading of 6.3. How many times more powerful was the Alaska 1964 earthquake with a reading of 8.3?

**14. Critique the reasoning of others.** Garrett said that the ground motion of an earthquake of magnitude 6 is twice the ground motion of an earthquake of magnitude 3. Is Garrett correct? Explain.

## Learning Targets:

- Use technology to graph $y = \log x$.
- Evaluate a logarithm using technology.
- Rewrite exponential equations as their corresponding logarithmic equations.
- Rewrite logarithmic equations as their corresponding exponential equations.

SUGGESTED LEARNING STRATEGIES: Close Reading, Vocabulary Organizer, Create Representations, Quickwrite, Think-Pair-Share

The Richter scale uses a base 10 *logarithmic* scale. A base 10 logarithmic scale means that when the ground motion is expressed as a power of 10, the magnitude of the earthquake is the exponent. You have seen this function $G(x) = 10^x$, where $x$ is the magnitude, in Item 3d of the previous lesson.

The function $M$ is the inverse of an exponential function $G$ whose base is 10. The algebraic rule for $M$ is a *common logarithmic* function. Write this function as $M(x) = \log x$, where $x$ is the ground motion compared to a magnitude 0 earthquake.

**MATH TERMS**

A **logarithm** is an exponent to which a base is raised that results in a specified value.

A **common logarithm** is a base 10 logarithm, such as $\log 100 = 2$, because $10^2 = 100$.

**1.** Graph $M(x) = \log x$ on a graphing calculator.

  **a.** Make a sketch of the calculator graph. Be certain to label and scale each axis.

  **b.** Use $M$ to estimate the magnitude of an earthquake that causes 120,000 times the ground motion of a magnitude 0 earthquake. Describe what would happen if this earthquake were centered beneath a large city.

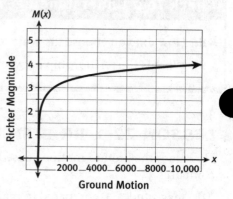

**TECHNOLOGY TIP**

The $\boxed{\text{LOG}}$ key on your calculator is for common, or base 10, logarithms.

  **c.** Use $M$ to determine the amount of ground motion caused by the 2002 magnitude 7.9 Denali earthquake compared to a magnitude 0 earthquake.

**2.** Complete the tables below to show the relationship between the exponential function base 10 and its inverse, the common logarithmic function.

**MATH TIP**

You can also write the equation $y = \log x$ as $y = \log_{10} x$. In the equation $y = \log x$, 10 is understood to be the base. Just as exponential functions can have bases other than 10, **logarithmic functions** can also be expressed with bases other than 10.

| $x$ | $y = 10^x$ |
|------|------------|
| 0 | $10^0 = 1$ |
| 1 | |
| 2 | |
| 3 | |
| $\log x$ | |

| $x$ | $y = \log x$ |
|------|--------------|
| $1 = 10^0$ | $\log 1 = 0$ |
| $10 = 10^1$ | |
| $100 = 10^2$ | |
| $1000 = 10^3$ | |
| $10^x$ | |

3. Use the information in Item 2 to write a logarithmic statement for each exponential statement.
   a. $10^4 = 10,000$
   b. $10^{-1} = \dfrac{1}{10}$

4. Use the information in Item 2 to write each logarithmic statement as an exponential statement.
   a. $\log 100,000 = 5$
   b. $\log\left(\dfrac{1}{100}\right) = -2$

5. Evaluate each logarithmic expression without using a calculator.
   a. $\log 1000$
   b. $\log \dfrac{1}{10,000}$

**MATH TIP**

Recall that two functions are inverses when $f(f^{-1}(x)) = f^{-1}(f(x)) = x$.

The exponent $x$ in the equation $y = 10^x$ is the common logarithm of $y$. This equation can be rewritten as $\log y = x$.

**Check Your Understanding**

6. What function has a graph that is symmetric to the graph of $y = \log x$ about the line $y = x$? Graph both functions and the line $y = x$.

7. Evaluate $\log 10^x$ for $x = 1, 2, 3,$ and 4.

8. Let $f(x) = 10^x$ and let $g(x) = f^{-1}(x)$. What is the algebraic rule for $g(x)$? Describe the relationship between $f(x)$ and $g(x)$.

**LESSON 22-2 PRACTICE**

9. Evaluate without using a calculator.
   a. $\log 10^6$
   b. $\log 1,000,000$
   c. $\log \dfrac{1}{100}$

10. Write an exponential statement for each.
    a. $\log 10 = 1$
    b. $\log \dfrac{1}{1,000,000} = -6$
    c. $\log a = b$

11. Write a logarithmic statement for each.
    a. $10^7 = 10,000,000$
    b. $10^0 = 1$
    c. $10^m = n$

12. **Model with mathematics.** The number of decibels $D$ of a sound is modeled with the equation $D = 10 \log\left(\dfrac{I}{10^{-12}}\right)$ where $I$ is the intensity of the sound measured in watts. Find the number of decibels in each of the following:
    a. whisper with $I = 10^{-10}$
    b. normal conversation with $I = 10^{-6}$
    c. vacuum cleaner with $I = 10^{-4}$
    d. front row of a rock concert with $I = 10^{-1}$
    e. military jet takeoff with $I = 10^2$

My Notes

## Learning Targets:
- Make conjectures about properties of logarithms.
- Write and apply the Product Property and Quotient Property of Logarithms.
- Rewrite logarithmic expressions by using properties.

**SUGGESTED LEARNING STRATEGIES:** Activating Prior Knowledge, Create Representations, Look for a Pattern, Quickwrite, Guess and Check

You have already learned the properties of exponents. Logarithms also have properties.

**1.** Complete these three properties of exponents.

$a^m \cdot a^n =$ _____

$\dfrac{a^m}{a^n} =$ _____

$(a^m)^n =$ _____

**2. Use appropriate tools strategically.** Use a calculator to complete the tables below. Round each answer to the nearest thousandth.

| x | y = log x |
|---|-----------|
| 1 | 0 |
| 2 | |
| 3 | |
| 4 | |
| 5 | |

| x | y = log x |
|----|-----------|
| 6 | |
| 7 | |
| 8 | |
| 9 | |
| 10 | |

**3.** Add the logarithms from the tables in Item 2 to see if you can develop a property. Find each sum and round each answer to the nearest thousandth.

$\log 2 + \log 3 =$ _____

$\log 2 + \log 4 =$ _____

$\log 2 + \log 5 =$ _____

$\log 3 + \log 3 =$ _____

**My Notes**

4. Compare the answers in Item 3 to the tables of data in Item 2.

   a. **Express regularity in repeated reasoning.** Is there a pattern or property when these logarithms are added? If yes, explain the pattern that you have found.

   b. State the property of logarithms that you found by completing the following statement.

   $\log m + \log n = $ _____

5. Explain the connection between the property of logarithms stated in Item 4 and the corresponding property of exponents in Item 1.

6. Graph $y_1 = \log 2 + \log x$ and $y_2 = \log 2x$ on a graphing calculator. What do you observe? Explain.

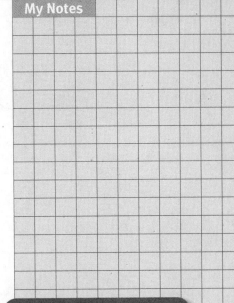

### TECHNOLOGY TIP

When using the ⃞LOG key on a graphing calculator, a leading parenthesis is automatically inserted. The closing parenthesis for logarithmic expressions must be entered manually. So entering $\log 2 + \log x$ without closing the parenthesis that the calculator will place before the 2 will NOT give the correct result.

### Check Your Understanding

Identify each statement as true or false. Justify your answers.

7. $\log mn = (\log m)(\log n)$

8. $\log xy = \log x + \log y$

9. Make a conjecture about the property of logarithms that relates to the property of exponential equations that states the following:
$$\frac{a^m}{a^n} = a^{m-n}.$$

10. Use the information from the tables in Item 2 to provide examples that support your conjecture in Item 9.

11. Graph $y_1 = \log x - \log 2$ and $y_2 = \log \frac{x}{2}$ on a graphing calculator. What do you observe?

### Check Your Understanding

Use the information from the tables in Item 2 and the properties in Items 4b and 9.

**12.** Write two different logarithmic expressions to find a value for log 36.

**13.** Write a logarithmic expression that contains a quotient and simplifies to 0.301.

**14. Construct viable arguments.** Show that $\log (3 + 4) \neq \log 3 + \log 4$.

### LESSON 22-3 PRACTICE

Use the table of logarithmic values at the beginning of the lesson to evaluate the logarithms in Items 15 and 16. Do not use a calculator.

**15. a.** $\log\left(\dfrac{8}{3}\right)$

   **b.** $\log 24$

   **c.** $\log 64$

   **d.** $\log 27$

**16. a.** $\log\left(\dfrac{4}{9}\right)$

   **b.** $\log 2.25$

   **c.** $\log 144$

   **d.** $\log 81$

**17.** Rewrite $\log 7 + \log x - (\log 3 + \log y)$ as a single logarithm.

**18.** Rewrite $\log\left(\dfrac{8m}{9n}\right)$ as a sum of four logarithmic terms.

**19. Make use of structure.** Rewrite $\log 8 + \log 2 - \log 4$ as a single logarithm and evaluate the result using the table at the beginning of the lesson.

**Learning Targets:**

- Make conjectures about properties of logarithms.
- Write and apply the Power Property of Logarithms.
- Rewrite logarithmic expressions by using their properties.

**SUGGESTED LEARNING STRATEGIES:** Think-Pair-Share, Create Representations

1. Make a conjecture about the property of logarithms that relates to the property of exponents that states the following: $(a^m)^n = a^{mn}$.

2. Use the information from the tables in Item 2 in the previous lesson and the properties developed in Items 4 and 9 in the previous lesson to support your conjecture in Item 1.

3. **Use appropriate tools strategically.** Graph $y_1 = 2 \log x$ and $y_2 = \log x^2$ on a graphing calculator. What do you observe?

**Check Your Understanding**

Identify each statement as true or false. Justify your answer.

4. $2 \log \sqrt{m} = \log m$
5. $\log 10^2 = \log 2^{10}$

6. **Express regularity in repeated reasoning.** The logarithmic properties that you conjectured and then verified in this lesson and the previous lesson are listed below. State each property.

Product Property: _____

Quotient Property: _____

Power Property: _____

**7.** Use the properties from Item 6 to rewrite each expression as a single logarithm. Assume all variables are positive.
   **a.** $\log x - \log 7$

   **b.** $2 \log x + \log y$

**8.** Use the properties from Item 6 to expand each expression. Assume all variables are positive.
   **a.** $\log 5xy^4$

   **b.** $\log \dfrac{x}{y^3}$

**9.** Rewrite each expression as a single logarithm. Then evaluate.
   **a.** $\log 2 + \log 5$

   **b.** $\log 5000 - \log 5$

   **c.** $2 \log 5 + \log 4$

### Check Your Understanding

**10.** Explain why $\log (a + 10)$ does not equal $\log a + 1$.

**11.** Explain why $\log (-100)$ is not defined.

## LESSON 22-4 PRACTICE

**Attend to precision.** Rewrite each expression as a single logarithm. Then evaluate the expression without using a calculator.

**12.** $\log 5 + \log 20$

**13.** $\log 3 - \log 30$

**14.** $2 \log 400 - \log 16$

**15.** $\log \dfrac{1}{400} + 2 \log 2$

**16.** $\log 100 + \log \left( \dfrac{1}{100} \right)$.

**17.** Expand the expression $\log bc^3 d^2$.

# Logarithms and Their Properties
## Earthquakes and Richter Scale

## ACTIVITY 22 PRACTICE
Write your answers on notebook paper.
Show your work.

### Lesson 22-1

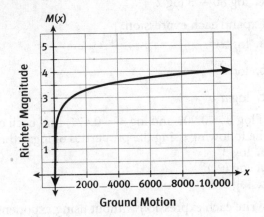

M(x)

Richter Magnitude

Ground Motion

1. What is the $y$-intercept of the graph?

2. What is the $x$-intercept of the graph?

3. Is $M(x)$ an increasing or decreasing function?

4. Which of these statements are NOT true regarding the graph above?
   **A.** The graph contains the point $(1, 0)$.
   **B.** The graph contains the point $(10, 1)$.
   **C.** The domain is $x > 0$.
   **D.** The $x$-axis is an asymptote.

### Lesson 22-2

5. Use a calculator to find a decimal approximation rounded to three decimal places.
   **a.** $\log 47$
   **b.** $\log 32.013$
   **c.** $\log\left(\dfrac{5}{7}\right)$
   **d.** $\log -20$

6. A logarithm is a(n)
   **A.** variable.
   **B.** constant.
   **C.** exponent.
   **D.** coefficient.

7. Write an exponential statement for each logarithmic statement below.
   **a.** $\log 10,000 = 4$
   **b.** $\log \dfrac{1}{1,000,000,000} = -9$
   **c.** $\log a = 6$

8. Write a logarithmic statement for each exponential statement below.
   **a.** $10^{-2} = \dfrac{1}{100}$
   **b.** $10^1 = 10$
   **c.** $10^4 = n$

9. Evaluate without using a calculator.
   **a.** $\log 10^5$
   **b.** $\log 100$
   **c.** $\log \dfrac{1}{100,000}$

10. If $\log a = x$, and $10 < a < 100$, what values are acceptable for $x$?
    **A.** $0 < x < 1$
    **B.** $1 < x < 2$
    **C.** $2 < x < 3$
    **D.** $10 < x < 100$

### Lesson 22-3

11. If $\log 2 = 0.301$ and $\log 3 = 0.447$, find each of the following using only these values and the properties of logarithms. Show your work.
    **a.** $\log 6$
    **b.** $\log\left(\dfrac{2}{3}\right)$
    **c.** $\log 1.5$
    **d.** $\log 18$

12. Which expression does NOT equal 3?

    A. $\log 10^3$

    B. $\dfrac{\log 10^5}{\log 10^2}$

    C. $\log\left(\dfrac{10^7}{10^4}\right)$

    D. $\log 10^4 - \log 10$

13. Explain the connection between the exponential equation $(10^3 \cdot 10^5 = 10^8)$ and the logarithmic equation $(\log 10^3 + \log 10^5 = \log 10^8)$.

14. Rewrite each expression as a single logarithm.

    a. $\log 2 + \log x - (\log 3 + \log y)$

    b. $\log 5 - \log 7$

    c. $(\log 24 + \log 12) - \log 6$

15. Expand each expression.

    a. $\log\left(\dfrac{3x}{8y}\right)$

    b. $\log\left(\dfrac{m+v}{3}\right)$

    c. $\log\left(\dfrac{4}{9-u}\right)$

16. If $\log 2 = 0.301$ and $\log 3 = 0.477$, find each of the following using the properties of logarithms.

    a. $\log 4$

    b. $\log 27$

    c. $\log \sqrt{2}$

    d. $\log \sqrt{12}$

**Lesson 22-4**

17. Complete each statement to illustrate a property for logarithms.

    a. Product Property      $\log uv = ?$

    b. Quotient Property     $\log \dfrac{u}{v} = ?$

    c. Power Property        $\log u^v = ?$

18. Rewrite each expression as a single logarithm. Then evaluate without using a calculator.

    a. $\log 500 + \log 2$

    b. $2\log 3 + \log \dfrac{1}{9}$

    c. $\log 80 - 3\log 2$

19. Expand each expression.

    a. $\log xy^2$

    b. $\log \dfrac{xy}{z}$

    c. $\log a^3 b^2$

20. If $\log 8 = 0.903$ and $\log 3 = 0.477$, find each of the following using the properties of logarithms.

    a. $\log 3^8$

    b. $\log (2^3)^3$

    c. $\log 8(3^2)$

21. Write each expression without using exponents.

    a. $m \log n + \log n^m$

    b. $\log (mn)^0$

    c. $\log 2^4 + \log 2^3$

22. Which of the following statements is TRUE?

    A. $\log \dfrac{x}{y} = \dfrac{\log x}{\log y}$

    B. $\log \dfrac{x}{y} = y \log x$

    C. $\log (x + y) = \log x + \log y$

    D. $\log \sqrt{x} = \dfrac{1}{2} \log x$

**MATHEMATICAL PRACTICES**
**Reason Abstractly and Quantitatively**

23. Verify using the properties of logarithms that $\log 10^x - \log 10^4 = x - 4$. Then evaluate for $x = \pi$, using 3.14 for $\pi$.

**WHETHER OR NOT**

1. **Reason quantitatively.** Tell whether or not each table contains data that can be modeled by an exponential function. Provide an equation to show the relationship between $x$ and $y$ for the sets of data that are exponential.

   **a.**

   | x | 0 | 1 | 2 | 3 |
   |---|---|---|---|---|
   | y | 3 | 6 | 12 | 24 |

   **b.**

   | x | 0 | 1 | 2 | 3 |
   |---|---|---|---|---|
   | y | 2 | 4 | 6 | 8 |

   **c.**

   | x | 0 | 1 | 2 | 3 |
   |---|---|---|---|---|
   | y | 108 | 36 | 12 | 4 |

2. Tell whether or not each function is increasing. State *increasing* or *decreasing*, and give the domain, range, and $y$-intercept of the function.

   **a.** $y = 4\left(\dfrac{2}{3}\right)^x$       **b.** $y = -3(4)^x$

3. Let $g(x) = 2(4)^{x+3} - 5$.
   **a.** Describe the function as a transformation of $f(x) = 4^x$.
   **b.** Graph the function using your knowledge of transformations.
   **c.** What is the horizontal asymptote of the graph of $g$?

4. Rewrite each exponential equation as a common logarithmic equation.

   **a.** $10^3 = 1000$      **b.** $10^{-4} = \dfrac{1}{10,000}$      **c.** $10^7 = 10,000,000$

5. **Make use of structure.** Rewrite each common logarithmic equation as an exponential equation.

   **a.** $\log 100 = 2$      **b.** $\log 100,000 = 5$      **c.** $\log \dfrac{1}{100,000} = -5$

6. Evaluate each expression without using a calculator.
   **a.** $\log 1000$      **b.** $\log 1$      **c.** $\log 2 + \log 50$

7. Evaluate using a calculator. Then rewrite each expression as a single logarithm without exponents and evaluate again as a check.
   **a.** $\log 5 + \log 3$      **b.** $\log 3^4$      **c.** $\log 3 - \log 9$

| Scoring Guide | Exemplary | Proficient | Emerging | Incomplete |
|---|---|---|---|---|
| | The solution demonstrates these characteristics: | | | |
| **Mathematics Knowledge and Thinking**<br><br>(Items 1, 2, 3c, 4–7) | • Clear and accurate understanding of how to determine whether a table of data represents an exponential function<br><br>• Clear and accurate understanding of the features of exponential functions and their graphs including domain and range<br><br>• Fluency in evaluating and rewriting exponential and logarithmic equations and expressions | • Largely correct understanding of how to determine whether a table of data represents an exponential function<br><br>• Largely correct understanding of the features of exponential functions and their graphs including domain and range<br><br>• Little difficulty when evaluating and rewriting exponential and logarithmic equations and expressions | • Partial understanding of how to determine whether a table of data represents an exponential function<br><br>• Partial understanding of the features of exponential functions and their graphs including domain and range<br><br>• Some difficulty when evaluating and rewriting logarithmic and exponential equations and expressions | • Little or no understanding of how to determine whether a table of data represents an exponential function<br><br>• Inaccurate or incomplete understanding of the features of exponential functions and their graphs including domain and range<br><br>• Significant difficulty when evaluating and rewriting logarithmic and exponential equations and expressions |
| **Problem Solving**<br><br>(Item 1) | • An appropriate and efficient strategy that results in a correct answer | • A strategy that may include unnecessary steps but results in a correct answer | • A strategy that results in some incorrect answers | • No clear strategy when solving problems |
| **Mathematical Modeling / Representations**<br><br>(Items 1, 3b) | • Fluency in recognizing exponential data and modeling it with an equation<br><br>• Effective understanding of how to graph an exponential function using transformations | • Little difficulty in accurately recognizing exponential data and modeling it with an equation<br><br>• Largely correct understanding of how to graph an exponential function using transformations | • Some difficulty with recognizing exponential data and modeling it with an equation<br><br>• Partial understanding of how to graph an exponential function using transformations | • Significant difficulty with recognizing exponential data and model it with an equation<br><br>• Mostly inaccurate or incomplete understanding of how to graph an exponential function using transformations |
| **Reasoning and Communication**<br><br>(Items 1a, 3a) | • Clear and accurate justification of whether or not data represented an exponential model<br><br>• Precise use of appropriate math terms and language to describe a function as a transformation of another function | • Adequate justification of whether or not data represented an exponential model<br><br>• Adequate and correct description of a function as a transformation of another function | • Misleading or confusing justification of whether or not data represented an exponential model<br><br>• Misleading or confusing description of a function as a transformation of another function | • Incomplete or inadequate justification of whether or not data represented an exponential model<br><br>• Incomplete or mostly inaccurate description of a function as a transformation of another function |

# Inverse Functions: Exponential and Logarithmic Functions

## Undoing It All
### Lesson 23-1 Logarithms in Other Bases

**Learning Targets:**
- Use composition to verify two functions as inverse.
- Define the logarithm of $y$ with base $b$.
- Write the Inverse Properties for logarithms.

**SUGGESTED LEARNING STRATEGIES:** Close Reading, Create Representations

In the first unit, you studied inverses of linear functions. Recall that two functions $f$ and $g$ are *inverses* of each other if and only if $f(g(x)) = x$ for all $x$ in the domain of $g$, and $g(f(x)) = x$ for all $x$ in the domain of $f$.

1. Find the inverse function $g(x)$ of the function $f(x) = 2x + 1$. Show your work.

**MATH TIP**

To find the inverse of a function algebraically, interchange the $x$ and $y$ variables and then solve for $y$.

2. Use the definition of inverse functions to prove that $f(x) = 2x + 1$ and the $g(x)$ function you found in Item 1 are inverse functions.

3. Graph $f(x) = 2x + 1$ and its inverse $g(x)$ on the grid below. What is the line of symmetry between the graphs?

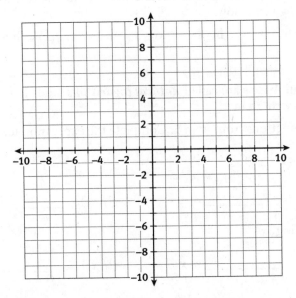

In a previous activity, you investigated exponential functions with a base of 10 and their inverse functions, the common logarithmic functions. Recall in the Richter scale situation that $G(x) = 10^x$, where $x$ is the magnitude of an earthquake. The inverse function is $M(x) = \log x$, where $x$ is the ground motion compared to a magnitude 0 earthquake.

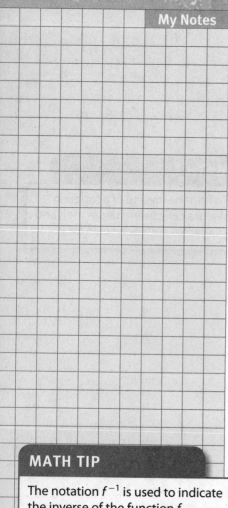

4. A part of each of the graphs of $y = G(x)$ and $y = M(x)$ is shown below. What is the line of symmetry between the graphs? How does that line compare with the line of symmetry in Item 3?

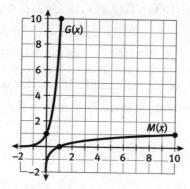

Logarithms with bases other than 10 have the same properties as common logarithms.

> The logarithm of $y$ with base $b$, where $y > 0$, $b > 0$, $b \neq 1$, is defined as: $\log_b y = x$ if and only if $y = b^x$.

The exponential function $y = b^x$ and the logarithmic function $y = \log_b x$, where $b > 0$ and $b \neq 1$, are inverse functions. The (restricted) domain of one function is the (restricted) range of the other function. Likewise, the (restricted) range of one function is the (restricted) domain of the other function.

**MATH TIP**

The notation $f^{-1}$ is used to indicate the inverse of the function $f$.

5. Let $g(x) = f^{-1}(x)$, the inverse of function $f$. Write the rule for $g$ for each function $f$ given below.

   **a.** $f(x) = 5^x$      **b.** $f(x) = \log_4 x$      **c.** $f(x) = \log_e x$

Logarithms with base $e$ are called ***natural logarithms***, and "$\log_e$" is written **ln**. So, $\log_e x$ is written $\ln x$.

6. Use the functions from Item 5. Complete the expression for each composition.

   **a.** $f(x) = 5^x$

   $f(g(x)) = $ _____ $= x$      $g(f(x)) = $ _____ $= x$

   **b.** $f(x) = \log_4 x$

   $f(g(x)) = $ _____ $= x$      $g(f(x)) = $ _____ $= x$

   **c.** $f(x) = e^x$

   $f(g(x)) = $ _____ $= x$      $g(f(x)) = $ _____ $= x$

**7.** Use what you learned in Item 6 to complete these *Inverse Properties of Logarithms*. Assume $b > 0$ and $b \neq 1$.

**a.** $b^{\log_b x} = $ _____

**b.** $\log_b b^x = $ _____

**8.** Simplify each expression.

**a.** $6^{\log_6 x}$

**b.** $\log_3 3^x$

**c.** $7^{\log_7 x}$

**d.** $\log 10^x$

**e.** $\ln e^x$

**f.** $e^{\ln x}$

**Check Your Understanding**

**9.** Describe the process you use to find the inverse function $g(x)$ if $f(x) = 7x + 8$.

**10.** **Construct viable arguments.** Look at the graphs in Items 3 and 4. What can you conclude about the line of symmetry for a function and its inverse?

**11.** Answer each of the following as true or false. If false, explain your reasoning.
**a.** The "$-1$" in function notation $f^{-1}$ means $\frac{1}{f}$.

**b.** Exponential functions are the inverse of logarithmic functions.
**c.** If the inverse is a function, then the original must be a function.

## LESSON 23-1 PRACTICE

Let $g(x) = f^{-1}(x)$, the inverse of function $f$. Write the rule for $g$ for each function $f$ given below.

**12.** $f(x) = 3x - 8$

**13.** $f(x) = \frac{1}{2}x + 5$

**14.** $f(x) = 5x - 6$

**15.** $f(x) = -x + 7$

**16.** $f(x) = 7^x$

**17.** $f(x) = e^x$

**18.** $f(x) = \log_{12} x$

**19.** $f(x) = \ln x$

Simplify each expression.

**20.** $\log_9 9^x$

**21.** $15^{\log_{15} x}$

**22.** $\ln e^x$

**23.** $8^{\log_8 x}$

**My Notes**

**Learning Targets:**
- Apply the properties of logarithms in any base.
- Compare and expand logarithmic expressions.
- Use the Change of Base Formula.

> **SUGGESTED LEARNING STRATEGIES:** Create Representations, Close Reading

When rewriting expressions in exponential and logarithmic form, it is helpful to remember that a *logarithm is an exponent*. The exponential statement $2^3 = 8$ is equivalent to the logarithmic statement $\log_2 8 = 3$.

Notice that the logarithmic expression is equal to 3, which is the exponent in the exponential expression.

**1.** Express each exponential statement as a logarithmic statement.

    **a.** $3^4 = 81$         **b.** $6^{-2} = \dfrac{1}{36}$         **c.** $e^0 = 1$

**2.** Express each logarithmic statement as an exponential statement.

    **a.** $\log_4 16 = 2$     **b.** $\log_5 125 = 3$     **c.** $\ln 1 = 0$

**3.** Evaluate each expression without using a calculator.

    **a.** $\log_2 32$                     **b.** $\log_4\left(\dfrac{1}{64}\right)$

    **c.** $\log_3 27$                     **d.** $\log_{12} 1$

> **MATH TIP**
>
> Remember that a logarithm is an exponent. To evaluate the expression $\log_6 36$, find the exponent for 6 that gives the value 36. $6^2 = 36$. Therefore, $\log_6 36 = 2$.

### Check Your Understanding

**4.** Why is the value of $\log_{-2} 16$ undefined?

**5.** **Critique the reasoning of others.** Mike said that the $\log_3$ of $\dfrac{1}{9}$ is undefined, because $3^{-2} = \dfrac{1}{9}$, and a log cannot have a negative value. Is Mike right? Why or why not?

The *Product, Quotient,* and *Power Properties* of common logarithms also extend to bases other than base 10.

**6.** Use the given property to rewrite each expression as a single logarithm. Then evaluate each logarithm in the equation to see that both sides of the equation are equal.

    **a. Product Property:** $\log_2 4 + \log_2 8 = \underline{\hspace{2cm}}$

                       $\underline{\hspace{1.5cm}} + \underline{\hspace{1.5cm}} =$

    **b. Quotient Property:** $\log_3 27 - \log_3 3 = \underline{\hspace{2cm}}$

                       $\underline{\hspace{1.5cm}} - \underline{\hspace{1.5cm}} = \underline{\hspace{1.5cm}}$

    **c. Power Property:** $2\log_5 25 = \underline{\hspace{2cm}}$

                       $2 \cdot \underline{\hspace{1.5cm}} = \underline{\hspace{1.5cm}}$

7. Expand each expression. Assume all variables are positive.

   **a.** $\log_7\left(\dfrac{x}{y^3}\right)$

   **b.** $\log_4 x^2 y$

   **c.** $\ln\left(\dfrac{x^2}{y^3}\right)$

8. Assume that $x$ is any real number, and decide whether the statement is *always true, sometimes true,* or *never true*. If the statement is sometimes true, give the conditions for which it is true.

   **a.** $\log 7 - \log 5 = \dfrac{\log 7}{\log 5}$

   **b.** $\log_5 5^x = x$

   **c.** $2^{\log_2 x^2} = x^2$

   **d.** $\log_4 3 + \log_4 5 - \log_4 x = \log_4 15$

   **e.** $2 \ln x = \ln x + \ln x$

### Check Your Understanding

9. **Attend to precision.** Why is it important to specify the value of the variables as positive when using the Product, Quotient, and Power Properties of logarithms? Use Item 7 to state an example.

10. Simplify the following expression:
    $\log 7 - \log 5$

Sometimes it is useful to change the base of a logarithmic expression. For example, the log key on a calculator is for common, or base 10, logs. Changing the base of a logarithm to 10 makes it easier to work with logarithms on a calculator.

11. Use the common logarithm function on a calculator to find the numerical value of each expression. Write the value in the first column of the table. Then write the numerical value using logarithms in base 2 in the second column.

| | Numerical Value | $\log_2 a$ |
|---|---|---|
| $\dfrac{\log 2}{\log 2}$ | 1 | $\log_2 2$ |
| $\dfrac{\log 4}{\log 2}$ | | |
| $\dfrac{\log 8}{\log 2}$ | | |
| $\dfrac{\log 16}{\log 2}$ | | |
| $\dfrac{\log N}{\log 2}$ | | |

**12.** The patterns observed in the table in Item 11 illustrate the **Change of Base Formula**. Make a conjecture about the Change of Base Formula of logarithms.

$$\log_b x = \underline{\hspace{3cm}}$$

**13.** Consider the expression $\log_2 12$.

    **a.** The value of $\log_2 12$ lies between which two integers?

    **b.** Write an equivalent common logarithm expression for $\log_2 12$, using the Change of Base Formula.

    **c.** Use a calculator to find the value of $\log_2 12$ to three decimal places. Compare the value to your answer from part a.

---

### Check Your Understanding

**14.** Change each expression to a logarithmic expression in base 10. Use a calculator to find the value to three decimal places.

    **a.** $\log_5 32$                  **b.** $\log_3 104$

**15.** In Item 13, how do you find out which values the value of $\log_2 12$ lies between?

---

### LESSON 23-2 PRACTICE

Write a logarithmic statement for each exponential statement.

**16.** $7^3 = 343$

**17.** $3^{-2} = \frac{1}{9}$

**18.** $e^m = u$

Write an exponential statement for each logarithmic statement.

**19.** $\log_6 1296 = 4$

**20.** $\log_{\frac{1}{2}} 4 = -2$

**21.** $\ln x = t$

Evaluate each expression without using a calculator.

**22.** $\log_4 64$

**23.** $\log_2 \left( \frac{1}{32} \right)$

Change each expression to a logarithmic expression in base 10. Use a calculator to find the value to three decimal places.

**24.** $\log_3 7$

**25.** $\log_2 18$

**26.** $\log_{25} 4$

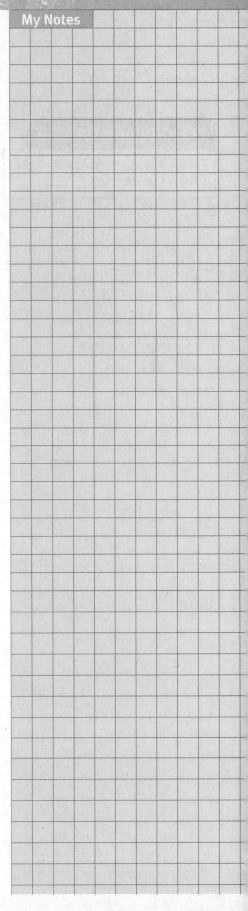

**Learning Targets:**
- Find intercepts and asymptotes of logarithmic functions.
- Determine the domain and range of a logarithmic function.
- Write and graph transformations of logarithmic functions.

**SUGGESTED LEARNING STRATEGIES:** Create Representations, Look for a Pattern, Close Reading, Quickwrite

1. Examine the function $f(x) = 2^x$ and its inverse, $g(x) = \log_2 x$.

   a. Complete the table of data for $f(x) = 2^x$. Then use that data to complete a table of values for $g(x) = \log_2 x$.

| $x$ | $f(x) = 2^x$ |
|---|---|
| −2 | |
| −1 | |
| 0 | |
| 1 | |
| 2 | |

| $x$ | $g(x) = \log_2 x$ |
|---|---|
| | |
| | |
| | |
| | |
| | |

   b. Graph both $f(x) = 2^x$ and $g(x) = \log_2 x$ on the same grid.

   c. What are the $x$- and $y$-intercepts for $f(x) = 2^x$ and $g(x) = \log_2(x)$?

   d. What is the line of symmetry between the graphs of $f(x) = 2^x$ and $g(x) = \log_2 x$?

   e. State the domain and range of each function using interval notation.

   f. What is the end behavior of the graph of $f(x) = 2^x$?

   g. What is the end behavior of the graph of $g(x) = \log_2(x)$?

**My Notes**

**h.** Write the equation of any asymptotes of each function.

$f(x) = 2^x$ _____

$g(x) = \log_2 x$ _____

**TECHNOLOGY TIP**

The LN key on your calculator is the natural logarithm key.

**2.** Examine the function $f(x) = e^x$ and its inverse, $g(x) = \ln x$.

**a.** Complete the table of data for $f(x) = e^x$. Then use those data to complete a table of values for $g(x) = \ln x$.

| x | $f(x) = e^x$ |
|---|---|
| −2 | |
| −1 | |
| 0 | |
| 1 | |
| 2 | |

| x | $g(x) = \ln x$ |
|---|---|
| | |
| | |
| | |
| | |
| | |

**b.** Graph both $f(x) = e^x$ and $g(x) = \ln x$ on the same grid.

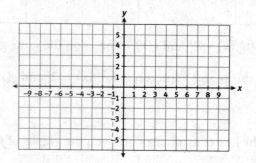

**c.** What are the x- and y-intercepts for $f(x) = e^x$ and $g(x) = \ln x$?

**d.** What is the line of symmetry between the graphs of $f(x) = e^x$ and $g(x) = \ln x$?

**e.** State the domain and range of each function using interval notation.

**f.** What is the end behavior of the graph of $f(x) = e^x$?

**g.** What is the end behavior of the graph of $g(x) = \ln x$?

**h.** Write the equation of any asymptotes of each function.
$f(x) = e^x$_____
$g(x) = \ln x$_____

**Lesson 23-3**
**Graphs of Logarithmic Functions**

**Check Your Understanding**

3. **Make sense of problems.** From the graphs you drew for Items 1 and 2, draw conclusions about the behavior of inverse functions with respect to:
   **a.** the intercepts
   **b.** the end behavior
   **c.** the asymptotes

4. If a function has an intercept of (0, 0), what point, if any, will be an intercept for the inverse function?

Transformations of the graph of the function $f(x) = \log_b x$ can be used to graph functions of the form $g(x) = a \log_b (x - c) + d$, where $b > 0$, $b \neq 1$. You can draw a quick sketch of each parent graph, $f(x) = \log_b x$, by plotting the points $\left(\frac{1}{b}, -1\right)$, $(1, 0)$, and $(b, 1)$.

5. Sketch the parent graph $f(x) = \log_2 x$ on the axes below. Then, for each transformation of $f$, provide a verbal description and sketch the graph, including asymptotes.
   **a.** $g(x) = 3 \log_2 x$

   **b.** $h(x) = 3 \log_2 (x + 4)$

   **c.** $j(x) = 3 \log_2 (x + 4) - 2$

   **d.** $k(x) = \log_2 (8x)$

   **e.** $m(x) = -3 \log_2 x$

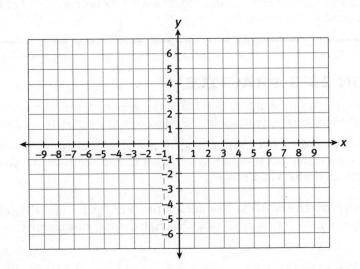

**MATH TIP**

Recall that a graph of the exponential function $f(x) = b^x$ can be drawn by plotting the points $\left(-1, \frac{1}{b}\right)$, $(0, 1)$, and $(1, b)$.

Switching the x- and y-coordinates of these points gives you three points on the graph of the inverse of $f(x) = b^x$, which is $f(x) = \log_b x$.

6. Explain how the function $j(x) = 3 \log_2 (x + 4) - 2$ can be entered on a graphing calculator using the common logarithm key. Then graph the function on a calculator and compare the graph to your answer in Item 5c.

**My Notes**

7. Consider how the parameters $a$, $c$ and $d$ transform the graph of the general logarithmic function $y = a\log_b(x - c) + d$.
   a. Use a graphing calculator to graph the parent function $f(x) = \log x$. Then, for each transformation of $f$, provide a verbal description of the transformation and the equation of the asymptote.

      i.   $y = -\log x$
      ii.  $y = 2 \log x$
      iii. $y = \log (x + 1)$
      iv.  $y = -3 \log(x - 2) + 1$
      v.   $y = \frac{1}{2}\log x - 3$

   b. Use a graphing calculator to graph the parent graph $f(x) = \ln x$. Then, for each transformation of $f$, provide a verbal description of the transformation and the equation of the asymptote.

      i.   $y = -\frac{1}{2}\ln(x + 1)$
      ii.  $y = 2 \ln x + 1$
      iii. $y = 3 \ln(x - 1)$
      iv.  $y = -\ln x - 2$

   c. Explain how the parameters $a$, $c$, and $d$ transform the parent graph $f(x) = \log_b x$ to produce a graph of the function $g(x) = a \log_b (x - c) + d$.

### Check Your Understanding

8. **Look for and make use of structure.**
   a. Compare the effect of $a$ in a logarithmic function $a \log_b x$ to $a$ in a quadratic function $ax^2$ (assume $a$ is positive).
   b. Compare the effect of $c$ in a logarithmic function $\log_b (x - c)$ to $c$ in a quadratic function $(x - c)^2$.

## LESSON 23-3 PRACTICE

9. Given an exponential function that has a $y$-intercept of 1 and no $x$-intercept, what is true about the intercepts of the function's inverse?

10. **Make sense of problems.** The inverse of a function has a domain of $(-\infty, \infty)$ and a range of $(0, \infty)$. What is true about the original function's domain and range?

**Model with mathematics.** Graph each function, using a parent graph and the appropriate transformations. Describe the transformations.

11. $f(x) = 2 \log_2 (x) - 6$

12. $f(x) = \log (x - 5) + 1$

13. $f(x) = \frac{1}{2}\ln x$

14. $f(x) = \log_2 (x + 4) - 3$

15. $f(x) = 2 \log (x - 1)$

16. $f(x) = -\log_2 (x + 2)$

## ACTIVITY 23 PRACTICE

Write your answers on notebook paper.
Show your work.

### Lesson 23-1

Let $g(x) = f^{-1}(x)$, the inverse of function $f$. Write the
rule for $g$ for each function $f$ given below.

1. $f(x) = 7x - 9$
2. $f(x) = \left(\frac{1}{3}\right)^x$
3. $f(x) = 2x - 8$
4. $f(x) = -x + 3$
5. $f(x) = 5^x$
6. $f(x) = e^x$
7. $f(x) = \log_{20} x$
8. $f(x) = \ln x$

Simplify each expression.

9. $\log_3 3^x$
10. $12^{\log_{12} x}$
11. $\ln e^x$
12. $7^{\log_7 x}$

### Lesson 23-2

Express each exponential statement as a logarithmic
statement.

13. $12^2 = 144$
14. $2^{-3} = \frac{1}{8}$
15. $e^n = m$
16. $e^{3x} = 2$
17. $10^2 = 100$
18. $e^0 = 1$

Express each logarithmic statement as an
exponential statement.

19. $\log_3 9 = 2$
20. $\log_2 64 = 6$
21. $\ln 1 = 0$
22. $\ln x = 6$
23. $\log_2 64 = 6$
24. $\ln e = 1$

Expand each expression. Assume all variables are
positive.

25. $\log_2 x^2 y^5$
26. $\log_4 \left(\frac{x^8}{5}\right)$
27. $\ln ex$
28. $\ln \left(\frac{1}{x}\right)$
29. Which is an equivalent form of the expression
$\ln 5 + 2 \ln x$?
A. $5 \ln x^2$
B. $\ln 2x^5$
C. $\ln 5x^2$
D. $2 \ln x^5$

Rewrite each expression as a single, simplified logarithmic term. Assume all variables are positive.

**30.** $\log_2 32 + \log_2 2$

**31.** $\log_3 x^2 - \log_3 y$

**32.** $\ln x + \ln 2$

**33.** $3 \ln x$

Evaluate each expression without using a calculator.

**34.** $\log_{12} 12$

**35.** $\log_7 343$

**36.** $\log_7 49$

**37.** $\log_3 81$

Change each expression to a logarithmic expression in base 10. Use a calculator to find the value to three decimal places.

**38.** $\log_4 20$

**39.** $\log_{20} 4$

**40.** $\log_5 45$

**41.** $\log_3 18$

**Lesson 23-3**

**42.** If the domain of a logarithmic function is $(0, \infty)$ and the range is $(-\infty, \infty)$, what are the domain and range of the inverse of the function?
   **A.** domain: $(-\infty, \infty)$, range: $(-\infty, \infty)$
   **B.** domain: $(0, \infty)$, range: $(-\infty, \infty)$
   **C.** domain: $(-\infty, \infty)$, range: $(-\infty, \infty)$
   **D.** domain: $(-\infty, \infty)$, range: $(0, \infty)$

Graph each function, using a parent graph and the appropriate transformations. Describe the transformations.

**43.** $f(x) = 3 \log_2 (x) - 1$

**44.** $f(x) = \log_3 (x - 4) + 2$

**45.** $f(x) = \frac{1}{4} \log_4 x$

**46.** $f(x) = \log_2 (x + 3) - 4$

**47.** $f(x) = -2\log(x + 3) - 1$

**48.** $f(x) = -3\ln(x - 4) + 2$

**MATHEMATICAL PRACTICES**
**Model with Mathematics**

**49.** Given the function $f(x) = 2^x + 1$
   **a.** Give the domain, range, $y$-intercept, and any asymptotes for $f(x)$. Explain.
   **b.** Draw a sketch of the graph of the function on a grid. Describe the behavior of the function as $x$ approaches $\infty$ and as $x$ approaches $-\infty$.

## College Costs
## Lesson 24-1 Exponential Equations

● **Learning Targets:**
- Write exponential equations to represent situations.
- Solve exponential equations.

> **SUGGESTED LEARNING STRATEGIES:** Summarizing, Paraphrasing, Create Representations, Vocabulary Organizer, Note Taking, Group Presentation

Wesley is researching college costs. He is considering two schools: a four-year private college where tuition and fees for the current year cost about $24,000, and a four-year public university where tuition and fees for the current year cost about $10,000. Wesley learned that over the last decade, tuition and fees have increased an average of 5.6% per year in four-year private colleges and an average of 7.1% per year in four-year public colleges.

To answer Items 1–4, assume that tuition and fees continue to increase at the same average rate per year as in the last decade.

1. Complete the table of values to show the estimated tuition for the next four years.

| Years from Present | Private College Tuition and Fees | Public College Tuition and Fees |
|---|---|---|
| 0 | $24,000 | $10,000 |
| 1 | | |
| 2 | | |
| 3 | | |
| 4 | | |

2. **Express regularity in repeated reasoning.** Write two functions to model the data in the table above. Let $R(t)$ represent the private tuition and fees and $U(t)$ represent the public tuition and fees, where $t$ is the number of years from the present.

3. Wesley plans to be a senior in college six years from now. Use the models above to find the estimated tuition and fees at both the private and public colleges for his senior year in college.

4. **Use appropriate tools strategically.** Write an equation that can be solved to predict the number of years that it will take for the public college tuition and fees to reach the current private tuition and fees of $24,000. Find the solution using both the graphing and table features of a calculator.

> **MATH TIP**
>
> To solve an equation graphically on a calculator, enter each side of the equation as a separate function and find the intersection point of the two functions.

My Notes

Solving a problem like the one in Item 4 involves solving an exponential equation. An *exponential equation* is an equation in which the variable is in the exponent. Sometimes you can solve an exponential equation by writing both sides of the equation in terms of the same base. Then use the fact that when the bases are the same, the exponents must be equal:

$$b^m = b^n \text{ if and only if } m = n$$

### Example A
Solve $6 \cdot 4^x = 96$.

$$6 \cdot 4^x = 96$$

| | | |
|---|---|---|
| **Step 1:** | $4^x = 16$ | Divide both sides by 6. |
| **Step 2:** | $4^x = 4^2$ | Write both sides in terms of base 4. |
| **Step 3:** | $x = 2$ | If $b^m = b^n$, then $m = n$. |

### Example B
Solve $5^{4x} = 125^{x-1}$.

$$5^{4x} = 125^{x-1}$$

| | | |
|---|---|---|
| **Step 1:** | $5^{4x} = (5^3)^{x-1}$ | Write both sides in terms of base 5. |
| **Step 2:** | $5^{4x} = 5^{3x-3}$ | Power of a Power Property: $(a^m)^n = a^{mn}$ |
| **Step 3:** | $4x = 3x - 3$ | If $b^m = b^n$, then $m = n$. |
| **Step 4:** | $x = -3$ | Solve for $x$. |

### Try These A–B
Solve for $x$. Show your work.

**a.** $3^x - 1 = 80$  **b.** $2^x = \dfrac{1}{32}$  **c.** $6^{3x-4} = 36^{x+1}$  **d.** $\left(\dfrac{1}{7}\right)^x = \left(\dfrac{1}{49}\right)$

**MATH TIP**

Check your work by substituting your solutions into the original problem and verifying the equation is true.

### Check Your Understanding

**5.** When writing both sides of an equation in terms of the same base, how do you determine the base to use?

**6.** How could you check your solution to an exponential equation? Show how to check your answers to Try These part a.

## LESSON 24-1 PRACTICE

**Make use of structure.** Solve for $x$ by writing both sides of the equation in terms of the same base.

**7.** $2^{10x} = 32$

**8.** $4^x - 5 = 11$

**9.** $2^{4x-2} = 4^{x+2}$

**10.** $8^x = \dfrac{1}{64}$

**11.** $4 \cdot 5^x = 100$

**12.** $3 \cdot 2^x = 384$

**13.** $\left(\dfrac{1}{3}\right)^{2x} = \left(\dfrac{1}{9}\right)^{4-x}$

**14.** $\left(\dfrac{1}{2}\right)^{2x} = \left(\dfrac{1}{8}\right)^{10-x}$

**15.** Can you apply the method used in this lesson to solve the equation $2^{4x} = 27$? Explain why or why not.

**Learning Targets:**
- Solve exponential equations using logarithms.
- Estimate the solution to an exponential equation.
- Apply the compounded interest formula.

> **SUGGESTED LEARNING STRATEGIES:** Note Taking, Group Presentation, Create Representations, Close Reading, Vocabulary Organizer

For many exponential equations, it is not possible to rewrite the equation in terms of the same base. In this case, use the concept of inverses to solve the equation symbolically.

### Example A

Estimate the solution of $3^x = 32$. Then solve to three decimal places.
Estimate that $x$ is between 3 and 4, because $3^3 = 27$ and $3^4 = 81$.

$$3^x = 32$$

| | | |
|---|---|---|
| **Step 1:** | $\log_3 3^x = \log_3 32$ | Take the log base 3 of both sides. |
| **Step 2:** | $x = \log_3 32$ | Use the Inverse Property to simplify the left side. |
| **Step 3:** | $x = \dfrac{\log 32}{\log 3}$ | Use the Change of Base Formula. |
| **Step 4:** | $x \approx 3.155$ | Use a calculator to simplify. |

### Try These A

Estimate each solution. Then solve to three decimal places. Show your work.

**a.** $6^x = 12$   **b.** $5^x = 610$   **c.** $4^x = 0.28$   **d.** $e^x = 91$

### Example B

Find the solution of $4^{x-2} = 35.6$ to three decimal places.

$$4^{x-2} = 35.6$$
$$\log_4 4^{x-2} = \log_4 35.6 \qquad \text{Take the log base 4 of both sides.}$$

| | | |
|---|---|---|
| **Step 1:** | $x - 2 = \log_4 35.6$ | Use the Inverse Property to simplify the left side. |
| **Step 2:** | $x = \log_4 35.6 + 2$ | Solve for $x$. |
| **Step 3:** | $x = \dfrac{\log 35.6}{\log 4} + 2$ | Use the Change of Base Formula. |
| **Step 4:** | $x \approx 4.577$ | Use a calculator to simplify. |

### Try These B

Find each solution to three decimal places. Show your work.

**a.** $12^{x+3} = 240$   **b.** $4.2^{x+4} + 0.8 = 5.7$   **c.** $e^{2x-4} = 148$

---

**My Notes**

> **MATH TIP**
>
> Recall that the *Inverse Properties* of logarithms state that for $b > 0, b \neq 1$:
> $$\log_b b^x = x$$
> and
> $$b^{\log_b x} = x$$

1. Rewrite the equation you wrote in Item 4 of Lesson 24-1. Then show how to solve the equation using the Inverse Property.

## MATH TERMS

**Compound interest** is interest that is earned or paid not only on the principal but also on previously accumulated interest. At specific periods of time, such as daily or annually, the interest earned is added to the principal and then earns additional interest during the next period.

## MATH TIP

When interest is compounded annually, it is paid once a year. Other common compounding times are shown below.

**Times per Year**

| | |
|---|---|
| Semiannually | 2 |
| Quarterly | 4 |
| Monthly | 12 |
| Weekly | 52 |
| Daily | 365 |

Wesley's grandfather gave him a birthday gift of $3000 to use for college. Wesley plans to deposit the money in a savings account. Most banks pay *compound interest*, so he can use the formula below to find the amount of money in his savings account after a given period of time.

**Compound Interest Formula**

$$A = P\left(1 + \frac{r}{n}\right)^{nt}$$

$A$ = amount in account
$P$ = principal invested
$r$ = annual interest rate as a decimal
$n$ = number of times per year that interest is compounded
$t$ = number of years

## Example C

If Wesley deposits the gift from his grandfather into an account that pays 4% annual interest compounded quarterly, how much money will Wesley have in the account after three years?

Substitute into the compound interest formula. Use a calculator to simplify.

$$A = P\left(1 + \frac{r}{n}\right)^{nt} = 3000\left(1 + \frac{0.04}{4}\right)^{4(3)} \approx \$3380.48$$

Solution: Wesley will have $3380.48 in the account after three years.

## Try These C

How long would it take an investment of $5000 to earn $1000 interest if it is invested in a savings account that pays 3.75% annual interest compounded monthly?

Wesley's grandfather recommends that Wesley deposit his gift into an account that earns interest compounded continuously, instead of at a fixed number of times per year.

**Continuously Compounded Interest Formula**

$A = Pe^{rt}$

$A$ = amount in account
$P$ = principal invested
$r$ = annual interest rate as a decimal
$t$ = number of years

### Example D

If Wesley deposits the gift from his grandfather into an account that pays 4% annual interest compounded continuously, how much money will Wesley have in the account after three years?

Substitute into the continuously compounded interest formula. Use a calculator to simplify.

$$A = Pe^{rt} = 3000e^{0.04(3)} \approx \$3382.49$$

Solution: Wesley will have $3382.49 in the account after three years.

### Try These D

How long would it take an investment of $5000 to earn $1000 interest if it is invested in a savings account that pays 3.75% annual interest compounded continuously?

### Check Your Understanding

2. How is solving exponential and logarithmic equations similar to other equations that you have solved?
3. **Attend to precision.** In Examples C and D, why are the answers rounded to two decimal places?
4. A bank advertises an account that pays a monthly interest rate of 0.3% compounded continuously. What value do you use for $r$ in the continuously compounded interest formula? Explain.

### LESSON 24-2 PRACTICE

Solve for $x$ to three decimal places.

5. $8^x = 100$
6. $3^{x-4} = 85$
7. $3e^{x+2} = 87$
8. $2^{3x-2} + 7 = 25$
9. $2 \cdot 4^{3x} - 3 = 27$
10. $e^{2x} - 1.5 = 6.7$

11. **Make sense of problems.** A deposit of $4000 is made into a savings account that pays 2.48% annual interest compounded quarterly.
   a. How much money will be in the account after three years?
   b. How long will it take for the account to earn $500 interest?
   c. How much more money will be in the account after three years if the interest is compounded continuously?

### Learning Targets:
- Solve logarithmic equations.
- Identify extraneous solutions to logarithmic equations.
- Use properties of logarithms to rewrite logarithmic expressions.

> **SUGGESTED LEARNING STRATEGIES:** Create Representations, Vocabulary Organizer, Note Taking, Group Presentation

Equations that involve logarithms of variable expressions are called *logarithmic equations*. You can solve some logarithmic equations symbolically by using the concept of functions and their inverses. Since the domain of logarithmic functions is restricted to the positive real numbers, it is necessary to check for *extraneous solutions* when solving logarithmic equations.

**MATH TERMS**

An **extraneous solution** is a solution that arises from a simplified form of the equation that does not make the original equation true.

### Example A

Solve $\log_4 (3x - 1) = 2$.

$$\log_4 (3x - 1) = 2$$

**Step 1:** $4^{\log_4 (3x-1)} = 4^2$     Write in exponential form using 4 as the base.

**Step 2:** $3x - 1 = 16$     Use the Inverse Property to simplify the left side.

**Step 3:** $x = \dfrac{17}{3}$     Solve for $x$.

**Check:** $\log_4 (3 \cdot \dfrac{17}{3} - 1) = \log_4 16 = 2$

### Try These A

Solve for $x$. Show your work.

**a.** $\log_3 (x - 1) = 5$     **b.** $\log_2 (2x - 3) = 3$     **c.** $4 \ln (3x) = 8$

To solve other logarithmic equations, use the fact that when the bases are the same, $m > 0$, $n > 0$, and $b \neq 1$, the logarithmic values must be equal:

$$\log_b m = \log_b n \text{ if and only if } m = n$$

**My Notes**

### Example B

Solve $\log_3 (2x - 3) = \log_3 (x + 4)$.

$$\log_3 (2x - 3) = \log_3 (x + 4)$$

**Step 1:**     $2x - 3 = x + 4$       If $\log_b m = \log_b n$, then $m = n$.

**Step 2:**          $x = 7$          Solve for $x$.

**Check:** $\log_3 (2 \cdot 7 - 3) \stackrel{?}{=} \log_3 (7 + 4)$

$$\log_3 11 = \log_3 11$$

### Try These B

Solve for $x$. Check for extraneous solutions. Show your work.

**a.** $\log_6 (3x + 4) = 1$        **b.** $\log_5 (7x - 2) = \log_5 (3x + 6)$

**c.** $\ln 10 - \ln (4x - 6) = 0$

Sometimes it is necessary to use properties of logarithms to simplify one side of a logarithmic equation before solving the equation.

### Example C

Solve $\log_2 x + \log_2 (x + 2) = 3$.

$$\log_2 x + \log_2 (x + 2) = 3$$

**Step 1:**     $\log_2 [x(x + 2)] = 3$       Product Property of Logarithms

**Step 2:**     $2^{\log_2 [x(x+2)]} = 2^3$       Write in exponential form using 2 as the base.

**Step 3:**         $x(x + 2) = 8$       Use the Inverse Property to simplify.

**Step 4:**     $x^2 + 2x - 8 = 0$       Write as a quadratic equation.

**Step 5:**    $(x + 4)(x - 2) = 0$       Solve the quadratic equation.

**Step 6:**     $x = -4$ or $x = 2$       Check for extraneous solutions.

**Check:** $\log_2 (-4) + \log (-4 + 2) \stackrel{?}{=} 3$      $\log_2 2 + \log (2 + 2) \stackrel{?}{=} 3$

$\log_2 (-4) + \log (-2) \stackrel{?}{=} 3$        $\log_2 2 + \log 4 \stackrel{?}{=} 3$

$$\log_2 8 \stackrel{?}{=} 3$$

$$3 = 3$$

Because $\log_2 (-4)$ and $\log (-2)$ are not defined, $-4$ is not a solution of the original equation; thus it is extraneous.

The solution is $x = 2$.

### Try These C

Solve for $x$, rounding to three decimal places if necessary. Check for extraneous solutions.

**a.** $\log_4 (x + 6) - \log_4 x = 2$

**b.** $\ln (2x + 2) + \ln 5 = 2$

**c.** $\log_2 2x + \log_2 (x - 3) = 3$

Some logarithmic equations cannot be solved symbolically using the previous methods. A graphing calculator can be used to solve these equations.

### Example D

Solve $-x = \log x$ using a graphing calculator.
$$-x = \log x$$

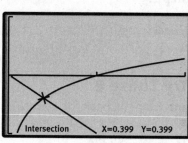

**Step 1:** Enter $-x$ for Y1.

**Step 2:** Enter $\log x$ for Y2.

**Step 3:** Graph both functions.

**Step 4:** Find the $x$-coordinate of the point of intersection: $x \approx 0.399$

**Solution:** $x \approx 0.399$

### Try These D

Solve for $x$.

a. $x \log x = 3$

b. $\ln x = -x^2 - 1$

c. $\ln (2x + 4) = x^2$

### Check Your Understanding

1. Explain how it is possible to have more than one solution to a simplified logarithmic equation, only one of which is valid.

2. **Critique the reasoning of others.** Than solves a logarithmic equation and gets two possible solutions, $-2$ and 4. Than immediately decides that $-2$ is an extraneous solution, because it is negative. Do you agree with his decision? Explain your reasoning.

## LESSON 24-3 PRACTICE

Solve for $x$, rounding to three decimal places if necessary. Check for extraneous solutions.

3. $\log_5 (3x + 4) = 2$

4. $\log_3 (4x + 1) = 4$

5. $\log_{12} (4x - 2) = \log_{12} (x + 10)$

6. $\log_2 3 + \log_2 (x - 4) = 4$

7. $\ln (x + 4) - \ln (x - 4) = 4$

8. **Construct viable arguments.** You saw in this lesson that logarithmic equations may have extraneous solutions. Do exponential equations ever have extraneous solutions? Justify your answer.

## Learning Targets:

- Solve exponential inequalities.
- Solve logarithmic inequalities.

**SUGGESTED LEARNING STRATEGIES:** Note Taking, Group Presentation, Create Representations

You can use a graphing calculator to solve exponential and logarithmic inequalities.

### Example A

Use a graphing calculator to solve the inequality $4.2^{x+3} > 9$.

**Step 1:** Enter $4.2^{x+3}$ for Y1 and 9 for Y2.

**Step 2:** Find the $x$-coordinate of the point of intersection: $x \approx -1.469$

**Step 3:** The graph of $y = 4.2^{x+3}$ is above the graph of $y = 9$ when $x > -1.469$.

**Solution:** $x > -1.469$

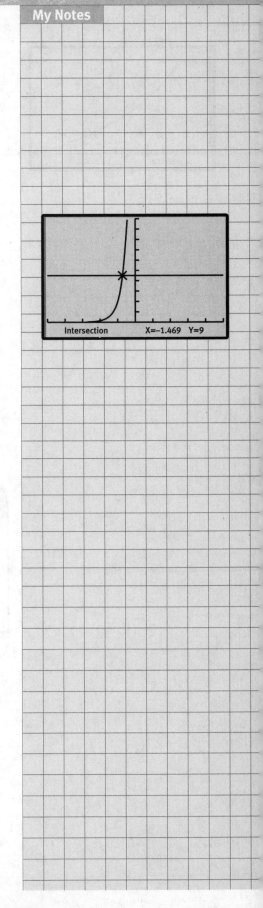

### Try These A

Use a graphing calculator to solve each inequality.

**a.** $3 \cdot 5.1^{1-x} < 75$   **b.** $\log 10x \geq 1.5$   **c.** $7.2 \ln x + 3.9 \leq 12$

### Example B

Scientists have found a relationship between atmospheric pressure and altitudes up to 50 miles above sea level that can be modeled by $P = 14.7(0.5)^{\frac{a}{3.6}}$. $P$ is the atmospheric pressure in lb/in.$^2$ Solve the equation $P = 14.7(0.5)^{\frac{a}{3.6}}$ for $a$. Use this equation to find the atmospheric pressure when the altitude is greater than 2 miles.

**Step 1:** Solve the equation for $a$.

$$\frac{P}{14.7} = 0.5^{\frac{a}{3.6}}$$   Divide both sides by 14.7.

$$\log_{0.5}\left(\frac{P}{14.7}\right) = \log_{0.5}\left(0.5^{\frac{a}{3.6}}\right)$$   Take the log base 0.5 of each side.

$$\log_{0.5}\left(\frac{P}{14.7}\right) = \frac{a}{3.6}$$   Simplify.

$$3.6\log_{0.5}\left(\frac{P}{14.7}\right) = a$$   Multiply both sides by 3.6.

$$\frac{3.6\log\left(\frac{P}{14.7}\right)}{\log 0.5} = a$$   Use the Change of Base Formula.

**My Notes**

Intersection     X=10.002   Y=2

**Step 2:** Use your graphing calculator to solve the inequality

$$\frac{3.6 \log\left(\frac{P}{14.7}\right)}{\log 0.5} > 2.$$

The graph of $y = \dfrac{3.6 \log\left(\frac{x}{14.7}\right)}{\log 0.5}$ is above the graph of $y = 2$ when

$0 < x < 10.002$.

**Solution:** When the altitude is greater than 2, the atmospheric pressure is between 0 and 10.002 lb/in.$^2$.

## Try These B

Suppose that the relationship between $C$, the number of digital cameras supplied, and the price $x$ per camera in dollars is modeled by the function $C = -400 + 180 \cdot \log x$.

**a.** Find the range in the price predicted by the model if there are between 20 and 30 cameras supplied.

**b.** Solve the equation for $x$. Use this equation to find the number of cameras supplied when the price per camera is more than \$300.

### Check Your Understanding

**2.** How are exponential and logarithmic inequalities different from exponential and logarithmic equations?

**3.** Describe how to find the solution of an exponential or logarithmic inequality from a graph. What is the importance of the intersection point in this process?

## LESSON 24-4 PRACTICE

Use a graphing calculator to solve each inequality.

**4.** $16.4(0.87)^{x-1.5} \geq 10$

**5.** $30 < 25 \log (3.5x - 4) + 12.6 < 50$

**6.** $4.5e^x \leq 2$

**7.** $\ln (x - 7.2) > 1.35$

## ACTIVITY 24 PRACTICE
**Write your answers on notebook paper.**
**Show your work.**

### Lesson 24-1

1. Which exponential equation can be solved by rewriting both sides in terms of the same base?
   **A.** $4^x = 12$
   **B.** $6 \cdot 2^{x-3} = 256$
   **C.** $3^{x+2} - 5 = 22$
   **D.** $e^x = 58$

2. Solve for $x$.
   **a.** $16^x = 32^{x-1}$
   **b.** $8 \cdot 3^x = 216$
   **c.** $5^x = \dfrac{1}{625}$
   **d.** $7^{2x} = 343^{x-4}$
   **e.** $4^x + 8 = 72$
   **f.** $e^x = 3$
   **g.** $e^{3x} = 2$
   **h.** $3e^{5x} = 42$

### Lesson 24-2

3. Solve for $x$ to three decimal places.
   **a.** $7^x = 300$
   **b.** $5^{x-4} = 135$
   **c.** $3^{2x+1} - 5 = 80$
   **d.** $3 \cdot 6^{3x} = 0.01$
   **e.** $5^x = 212$
   **f.** $3(2^{x+4}) = 350$

4. A deposit of $1000 is made into a savings account that pays 4% annual interest compounded monthly.
   **a.** How much money will be in the account after 6 years?
   **b.** How long will it take for the $1000 to double?

5. June invests $7500 at 12% interest for one year.
   **a.** How much would she have if the interest is compounded yearly?
   **b.** How much would she have if the interest is compounded daily?

6. If $4000 is invested at 7% interest per year compounded continuously, how long will it take to double the original investment?

7. At what annual interest rate, compounded continuously, will money triple in nine years?
   **A.** 1.3%
   **B.** 7.3%
   **C.** 8.1%
   **D.** 12.2%

### Lesson 24-3

8. Compare the methods of solving equations in the form of $log = log$ (such as $\log_3 (2x - 3) = \log_3 (x + 4)$) and $log = number$ (such as $\log_4 (3x - 1) = 2$).

9. Solve for $x$. Check for extraneous solutions.
   **a.** $\log_2 (5x - 2) = 3$
   **b.** $\log_4 (2x - 3) = 2$
   **c.** $\log_7 (5x + 3) = \log_7 (3x + 11)$
   **d.** $\log_6 4 + \log_6 (x + 2) = 1$
   **e.** $\log_3 (x + 8) = 2 - \log_3 (x)$
   **f.** $\log_2 (x + 6) - \log_2(x) = 3$
   **g.** $\log_2 x - \log_2 5 = \log_2 10$
   **h.** $5 \ln 3x = 40$
   **i.** $\ln 4x = 30$

**10.** If an equation contains
   **a.** $\log(x - 2)$, how do you know the solutions must be greater than 2?
   **b.** $\log(x + 3)$, how do you know solutions must be greater than $-3$?

**11.** Solve for $x$ to three decimal places using a graphing calculator.
   **a.** $\ln 3x = x^2 - 2$
   **b.** $\log(x + 7) = x^2 - 6x + 5$

## Lesson 24-4

**12.** Use a graphing calculator to solve each inequality.
   **a.** $2000 < 1500(1.04)^{12x} < 3000$
   **b.** $4.5 \log(2x) + 8.4 \geq 9.2$
   **c.** $\log_3(3x - 5) \geq \log_3(x + 7)$
   **d.** $\log_2 2x \leq \log_4(x + 3)$
   **e.** $5^{x+3} \leq 2^{x+4}$

## MATHEMATICAL PRACTICES
### Look For and Make Use of Structure

**13.** Explore how the compounded interest formula is related to the continuously compounded interest formula.
   **a.** Consider the expression $\left(1 + \dfrac{1}{m}\right)^m$, where $m$ is a positive integer. Enter the expression in your calculator as $y_1$. Then find the value of $y_1(1000)$, $y_1(10,000)$, and $y_1(1,000,000)$.
   **b.** As $m$ increases, what happens to the value of the expression?
   **c.** The compounded interest formula is
   $A = P\left(1 + \dfrac{r}{n}\right)^{nt}$. Let $m = \dfrac{n}{r}$. Explain why the formula may be written as
   $A = P\left[\left(1 + \dfrac{1}{m}\right)^m\right]^{rt}$.

   **d.** As the number of compounding periods, $n$, increases, so does the value of $m$. Explain how your results from parts b and c show the connection between the compounded interest formula and the continuously compounded interest formula.

1. **Make use of structure.** Express each exponential statement as a logarithmic statement.

   **a.** $5^{-3} = \dfrac{1}{125}$

   **b.** $7^2 = 49$

   **c.** $20^2 = 400$

   **d.** $3^6 = 729$

2. Express each logarithmic statement as an exponential statement.

   **a.** $\log_8 512 = 3$

   **b.** $\log_9 \left(\dfrac{1}{729}\right) = -3$

   **c.** $\log_2 64 = 6$

   **d.** $\log_{11} 14{,}641 = 4$

3. Evaluate each expression without using a calculator.

   **a.** $25^{\log_{25} x}$

   **b.** $\log_3 3^x$

   **c.** $\log_3 27$

   **d.** $\log_8 1$

   **e.** $\log_2 40 - \log_2 5$

   **f.** $\dfrac{\log 25}{\log 5}$

4. Solve each equation symbolically. Give approximate answers rounded to three decimal places. Check your solutions. Show your work.

   **a.** $4^{2x-1} = 64$

   **b.** $5^x = 38$

   **c.** $3^{x+2} = 98.7$

   **d.** $2^{3x-4} + 7.5 = 23.6$

   **e.** $\log_3 (2x + 1) = 4$

   **f.** $\log_8 (3x - 2) = \log_8 (x + 1)$

   **g.** $\log_2 (3x - 2) + \log_2 8 = 5$

   **h.** $\log_6 (x - 5) + \log_6 x = 2$

5. Let $f(x) = \log_2 (x - 1) + 3$.

   **a.** Sketch a parent graph and a series of transformations that result in the graph of $f$. How would the graph of $y = \log(x - 1) + 3$ and $y = \ln(x - 1) + 3$ compare?

   **b.** Give the equation of the vertical asymptote of the graph of $f$.

6. **Make sense of problems.** Katie deposits $10,000 in a savings account that pays 8.5% interest per year, compounded quarterly. She does not deposit more money and does not withdraw any money.

   **a.** Write the formula to find the amount in the account after 3 years.

   **b.** Find the total amount she will have in the account after 3 years.

7. How long would it take an investment of $6500 to earn $1200 interest if it is invested in a savings account that pays 4% annual interest compounded quarterly? Show the solution both graphically and symbolically.

| Scoring Guide | Exemplary | Proficient | Emerging | Incomplete |
|---|---|---|---|---|
| | The solution demonstrates these characteristics: | | | |
| **Mathematics Knowledge and Thinking** (Items 1–7) | • Fluency and accuracy in evaluating and rewriting exponential and logarithmic equations and expressions<br>• Effective understanding of and accuracy in solving logarithmic and exponential equations algebraically and graphically<br>• Effective understanding of logarithmic functions and their key features as transformations of a parent graph | • Largely correct work when evaluating and rewriting exponential and logarithmic equations and expressions<br>• Adequate understanding of how to solve logarithmic and exponential equations algebraically and graphically leading to solutions that are usually correct<br>• Adequate understanding of logarithmic functions and their key features as transformations of a parent graph | • Difficulty when evaluating and rewriting logarithmic and exponential equations and expressions<br>• Partial understanding of how to solve logarithmic and exponential equations algebraically and graphically<br>• Partial understanding of logarithmic functions and their key features as transformations of a parent graph | • Mostly inaccurate or incomplete work when evaluating and rewriting logarithmic and exponential equations and expressions<br>• Inaccurate or incomplete understanding of how to solve exponential and logarithmic equations algebraically and graphically<br>• Little or no understanding of logarithmic functions and their key features as transformations of a parent graph |
| **Problem Solving** (Items 6, 7) | • An appropriate and efficient strategy that results in a correct answer | • A strategy that may include unnecessary steps but results in a correct answer | • A strategy that results in some incorrect answers | • No clear strategy when solving problems |
| **Mathematical Modeling / Representations** (Items 5–7) | • Fluency in modeling a real-world scenario with an exponential equation or graph<br>• Effective understanding of how to graph a logarithmic function using transformations | • Little difficulty in accurately modeling a real-world scenario with an exponential equation or graph<br>• Largely correct understanding of how to graph a logarithmic function using transformations | • Some difficulty in modeling a real-world scenario with an exponential equation or graph<br>• Partial understanding of how to graph a logarithmic function using transformations | • Significant difficulty with modeling a real-world scenario with an exponential equation or graph<br>• Mostly inaccurate or incomplete understanding of how to graph a logarithmic function using transformations |
| **Reasoning and Communication** (Items 6, 7) | • Clear and accurate use of mathematical work to justify an answer | • Correct use of mathematical work to justify an answer | • Partially correct justification of an answer using mathematical work | • Incorrect or incomplete justification of an answer using mathematical work |

# Radical and Rational Functions

## Unit Overview

In this unit, you will extend your study of functions to radical, rational, and inverse functions. You will graph radical and rational functions using transformations and by analyzing key features of the graph, and you will examine the domain and range of the functions. You will solve rational equations and inequalities as well as equations with rational exponents. You will also solve inverse and combined variation problems, average cost per unit problems, and work problems that are modeled using rational functions.

## Key Terms

As you study this unit, add these and other terms to your math notebook. Include in your notes your prior knowledge of each word, as well as your experiences in using the word in different mathematical examples. If needed, ask for help in pronouncing new words and add information on pronunciation to your math notebook. It is important that you learn new terms and use them correctly in your class discussions and in your problem solutions.

### Math Terms

- square root regression
- one-to-one function
- rational function
- horizontal asymptote
- vertical asymptote
- inverse variation
- constant of variation
- combined variation
- joint variation
- complex fraction
- discontinuity
- removable point of discontinuity

## ESSENTIAL QUESTIONS

**?** Why is it important to consider the domain and range of a function?

**?** How are rational functions useful in everyday life?

## EMBEDDED ASSESSMENTS

This unit has three embedded assessments, following Activities 26, 28, and 30. The first will give you the opportunity to demonstrate what you have learned about radical functions and their inverses. The second assessment focuses on inverse and combined variation. You will also graph rational functions using transformations of the parent function, and you will use rational functions to model average cost per unit. In the third assessment, you will graph rational functions by analyzing key features, such as asymptotes and intercepts, and you will solve rational equations and inequalities.

**Embedded Assessment 1:**

Radical Functions: Square Roots, Cube Roots, and Their Inverses    p. 415

**Embedded Assessment 2:**

Rational Functions and Variation    p. 443

**Embedded Assessment 3:**

Rational Expressions, Equations, and Inequalities    p. 473

# Getting Ready

Write your answers on notebook paper.
Show your work.

1. Evaluate each of the expressions.
   a. $3\sqrt{49}$

   b. $2\sqrt[3]{64}$

   c. $\left(\sqrt{x+2}\right)^2$

2. Perform the indicated operation.
   a. $\dfrac{2x}{5} - \dfrac{3x}{10}$

   b. $\dfrac{2x+1}{x+3} + \dfrac{4x-3}{x+3}$

   c. $\dfrac{2}{x} + \dfrac{5}{x+1}$

   d. $\dfrac{2x}{7} \cdot \dfrac{21}{x^2}$

   e. $\dfrac{x^3}{6} \div \dfrac{x}{12}$

3. Simplify each expression.
   a. $(2x^2 y)(3xy^3)$

   b. $(4ab^3)^2$

   c. $\dfrac{16x^3}{4x}$

   d. $\dfrac{2x+12}{x+6}$

4. What values are not possible for the variable $x$ in each expression below? Explain your reasoning.
   a. $\dfrac{2}{x}$     b. $\dfrac{2}{x-1}$

5. Factor each expression.
   a. $81x^2 - 25$
   b. $2x^2 - 5x - 3$

6. Which of the following is the inverse of $h(x) = 3x - 7$?
   A. $7 - 3x$          B. $3x + 7$
   C. $\dfrac{x+7}{3}$          D. $\dfrac{1}{3x-7}$

7. Write each inequality in interval notation.
   a. $x > -5$
   b. $x \le 2$
   c. $-3 < x \le 7$

8. If $y$ varies directly as $x$ and $y = 24$ when $x = 16$, what is $y$ when $x = 50$?

# Square Root and Cube Root Functions

## Go, Boat, Go!
### Lesson 25-1 Square Root Functions

**Learning Targets:**
- Graph and describe transformations of the square root function $y = \sqrt{x}$.
- Interpret key features of a graph that models a relationship between two quantities.

> **SUGGESTED LEARNING STRATEGIES:** Create Representations, Note Taking, Think-Pair-Share, Look for a Pattern, Work Backward

The hull speed $H$, in knots, of a boat is given by the function $H(x) = 1.34\sqrt{x}$, where $x$ is the length of the boat in feet at the waterline.

1. The hull speed function is a transformation of the parent square root function $f(x) = \sqrt{x}$.
   a. Graph $H$ and $f$ on the same axes. How do these graphs compare to each other?

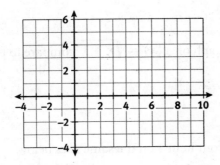

   b. What are the domain and the range of $f$? Write your answers as inequalities, in set notation, and in interval notation.

   c. **Model with mathematics.** Given that $x$ represents the length of the boat, should the domain of $H(x)$ be more restricted than $f(x)$? Can you determine the domain precisely? Explain your reasoning.

> **CONNECT TO TRANSPORTATION**
>
> The speed of a boat is measured in knots (nautical miles per hour). The distance it travels in water is measured in nautical miles. A nautical mile is equal to 1.15 statute miles.

> **MATH TIP**
>
> To graph the parent square root function, use key points with $x$-values that are perfect squares, such as 0, 1, 4, and 9.

**MATH TIP**

Recall that the function
$y = a \cdot f(x)$ represents a *vertical stretch or shrink* of the original function $y = f(x)$ after the $y$-values have been multiplied by $a$.

2. Explain how you could use transformations of the graph of $f(x) = \sqrt{x}$ to graph $g(x) = 2\sqrt{x}$.

3. Consider the functions $f(x) = \sqrt{x}$ and $g(x) = \sqrt{2x}$.
   a. Write $g(x)$ as a product in the form $a\sqrt{x}$.

   b. Explain how you could use transformations of the graph of $f(x) = \sqrt{x}$ to graph $g(x) = \sqrt{2x}$.

4. How does the graph of $g(x) = \sqrt{x-3}$ compare to the graph of $f(x) = \sqrt{x}$?

**MATH TIP**

Recall that the function $y = f(x \pm c)$ results in a *horizontal translation* of the original function while $y = f(x) \pm c$ results in a *vertical translation* of the original function.

5. Sketch $g$ and $f$ from Item 4 on the same axes below.

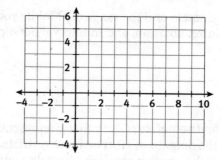

6. What are the domain and range of $g$?

**Check Your Understanding**

7. What does the graph in Item 1 tell us about the relationship between the length of a boat and its hull speed?

8. The $x$-intercept of the parent function $f(x) = \sqrt{x}$ is $(0, 0)$. Without using transformations, how would you find the $x$-intercept, also known as the root, of $f(x) = \sqrt{x-3}$?

Multiple transformations can be applied to the basic function to create a new function. Transformations might include translations, reflections, stretching, or shrinking.

9. Describe the transformations of $f(x) = \sqrt{x}$ that result in the functions listed below.

   **a.** $g(x) = -\sqrt{x} + 2$

   **b.** $h(x) = \sqrt{x - 3} + 4$

**MATH TIP**

Recall that the function $y = -f(x)$ represents a *reflection over the x-axis* of the original function $y = f(x)$ after the $y$-values have been multiplied by $-1$.

10. Sketch the graph of each function in Item 9 as well as the parent function. Use a calculator to check your results. Then state the domain and range for each function. Write your answers as inequalities, in set notation, and in interval notation.

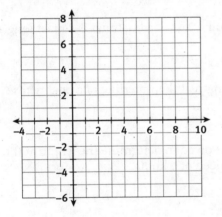

**TECHNOLOGY TIP**

One way to enter a square root equation into a graphing calculator is to write it using a fractional exponent. Recall that $\sqrt{x}$ can be written as $x$ raised to the $\frac{1}{2}$ power. So, you could enter $\sqrt{x - 3} + 4$ as $(x - 3)^{\left(\frac{1}{2}\right)} + 4$. Make sure to place parentheses around the fractional exponent.

11. Without graphing, determine the domain and range of the function $f(x) = \sqrt{x + 5} - 1$.

**Check Your Understanding**

12. Describe $f(x) = 2\sqrt{x - 3}$ as a transformation of $f(x) = \sqrt{x}$. State the domain and range.

13. Graph $f(x) = \sqrt{x + 2} - 1$ using your knowledge of transformations.

14. Give a transformation of the square root function that has a range that approaches negative infinity as $x$ approaches infinity.

15. Use the graph of $h(x)$ in Item 10 to make a conjecture about the solution of the equation $\sqrt{x - 3} + 4 = 0$.

The graph of the hull speed of a boat $H$ is shown below. You also sketched this graph in Item 1a.

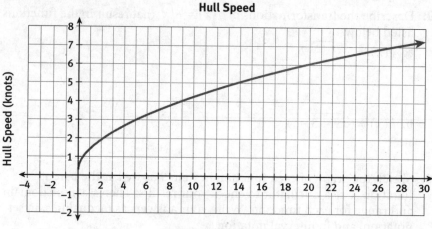

**Hull Speed**

*Hull Speed (knots)* (y-axis)

*Length at Waterline (ft)* (x-axis)

**16.** Use the graph to estimate the hull speed of a boat that is 24 feet long at the waterline.

**17.** Use the graph to estimate the length at the waterline of a boat whose hull speed is 6 knots.

**18.** Write an equation that could be solved to determine the length at the waterline of a boat with a hull speed of 6 knots.

### Check Your Understanding

**19.** Use the graph at the top of the page to estimate the hull speed of a boat that is 9 feet long at the waterline.

**20.** Explain how you can tell from the graph above that the equation relating the hull speed and the length of the boat is not $H(x) = \sqrt{x}$.

### LESSON 25-1 PRACTICE

**21.** Graph $f(x) = \sqrt{x}$ and $g(x) = \frac{1}{2}\sqrt{x}$ on the same axes.

**22.** Describe $g(x)$ as a transformation of $f(x)$. What are the domain and range of each function?

**23.** Graph $p(x) = \sqrt{x}$ and $q(x) = \sqrt{x+4} - 2$ on the same axes.

**24.** Describe $q(x)$ as a transformation of $p(x)$. What are the domain and range of each function?

**25.** **Reason abstractly.** Write a square root function that has a domain of $x \geq 7$ and a range of $y \geq 2$. Use a graphing calculator to confirm that your function meets the given requirements.

## Learning Targets:

- Solve square root equations.
- Identify extraneous solutions.

**SUGGESTED LEARNING STRATEGIES:** Note Taking, Identify a Subtask, Marking the Text, Predict and Confirm, Create Representations

To solve *square root equations*, follow these steps.

**Step 1:** Isolate the radical term.

**Step 2:** Square both sides of the equation.

**Step 3:** Solve for the unknown(s).

**Step 4:** Check for extraneous solutions.

> **MATH TIP**
>
> An *extraneous solution* can be introduced when you square both sides of an equation to eliminate the square root. The resulting equation may not be equivalent to the original for all values of the variable.

### Example A

Solve the equation $\sqrt{x-3}+4=9$.

**Step 1:** Isolate the radical.

**Step 2:** Square both sides.

**Step 3:** Solve the equation.

**Step 4:** Check the solution.

$$\sqrt{x-3}+4=9$$
$$\sqrt{x-3}=5$$
$$(\sqrt{x-3})^2=(5)^2$$
$$x-3=25, \text{ so } x=28$$
$$\sqrt{28-3}+4\overset{?}{=}9$$
$$5+4=9$$

### Example B

Solve the equation $x=(x+1)^{\frac{1}{2}}+5$.

**Step 1:** Isolate the radical.

**Step 2:** Square both sides.

**Step 3:** Solve for $x$.

possible solutions

**Step 4:** Check the possible solutions.

$$x=(x+1)^{\frac{1}{2}}+5$$
$$x-5=(x+1)^{\frac{1}{2}}$$
$$(x-5)^2=\left[(x+1)^{\frac{1}{2}}\right]^2$$
$$x^2-10x+25=x+1$$
$$x^2-11x+24=0$$
$$(x-3)(x-8)=0$$
$$x=3, 8$$
$$3\overset{?}{=}\sqrt{3+1}+5$$
$$3\neq 2+5$$
$$8\overset{?}{=}\sqrt{8+1}+5$$
$$8=3+5$$

> **WRITING MATH**
>
> You can write $\sqrt{x}$ as "$x$ to the $\frac{1}{2}$ power," namely, $x^{\frac{1}{2}}$.

Only $x=8$ is a solution; $x=3$ is an extraneous solution.

## Try These A–B

Solve each equation.

a. $2 - \sqrt{x+1} = -5$

b. $\sqrt{x+4} = x - 8$

c. $(x+6)^{\frac{1}{2}} = -x$

d. $(x+4)^{\frac{1}{2}} + 1 = 0$

1. Solve the hull speed equation you wrote in Item 18 of the previous lesson.

2. **Construct viable arguments.** Maggie claims that her sailboat *My Hero* has a hull speed of 7 knots. The length of her boat at the waterline is 24 feet. Is Maggie's claim reasonable? Explain why or why not.

### Check Your Understanding

3. Solve each equation.
   a. $(x-1)^{\frac{1}{2}} = 4$      b. $x + \sqrt{2x+3} = 0$
4. Solve the equation $0 = \sqrt{x+5}$, and then use transformations to sketch the graph of $f(x) = \sqrt{x+5}$. Make a connection between graphing $y = \sqrt{x+5}$ and solving the equation $0 = \sqrt{x+5}$.
5. Use your solution to the equation in Try These A–B part d to predict where the graph of $f(x) = (x+4)^{\frac{1}{2}} + 1$ will intersect the $x$-axis. Explain your reasoning.

You can also use technology to help you solve equations.

6. Solve the equation $2\sqrt{x+4} = 6$ using a graphing calculator. Enter the left side as one function and the right side as another function. Label the point where the graphs intersect.

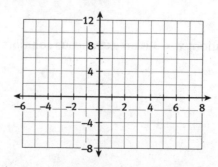

My Notes

**7.** Solve the equation $\sqrt{x-1} = 5$ using the same method as in Item 6.

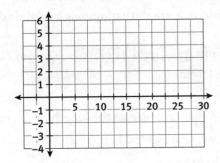

### Check Your Understanding

**8.** Solve the equation $2\sqrt{x+1} = 4$ using a graphing calculator. Include a sketch of the graph to support your answer.

**9.** In Example B, one of the two possible solutions found to the equation was an extraneous solution. Use a graphing calculator to solve the equation in Example B. Does the graph support the algebraic conclusion? Explain your reasoning.

**10.** In Item 6, you entered the left side of the equation as one function and the right side as another function and then found the point of intersection. Why is the $x$-coordinate of the point of intersection the solution to the equation?

### LESSON 25-2 PRACTICE

Solve each equation algebraically. Identify any extraneous solutions. Check your solutions using a graphing calculator.

**11.** $(x-6)^{\frac{1}{2}} = 4$

**12.** $3\sqrt{x+2} - 7 = 5$

**13.** $x + \sqrt{x+3} = 3$

**14.** $\sqrt{x-2} + 7 = 4$

**15.** Explain how graphing $f(x) = \sqrt{x-2} + 7$ and $g(x) = 4$ supports your algebraic solution to the equation in Item 14.

**16. Make sense of problems.** The approximate intersection of the graphs of $f(x) = \sqrt{x+7}$ and $g(x) = x - 1$ is (4.4, 3.4). Therefore, $x = 4.4$ is the approximate solution to what equation?

### Learning Targets:

● Graph transformations of the cube root function $y = \sqrt[3]{x}$.
● Identify key features of a graph that models a relationship between two quantities.

> **SUGGESTED LEARNING STRATEGIES:** Create Representations, Note Taking, Look for a Pattern

**MATH TIP**

The function for the radius used here is the inverse of the formula for the volume of a sphere, $V = \frac{4}{3}\pi r^3$, with $V$ represented by $x$.

**MATH TIP**

$\sqrt[3]{x}$ can be written as "$x$ to the $\frac{1}{3}$ power," or $x^{\frac{1}{3}}$.

The function $r(x) = \sqrt[3]{\dfrac{3}{4\pi}x}$ represents the length of the radius of a sphere as a function of its volume, represented here by $x$. An approximation of this function is $r(x) = \sqrt[3]{0.24x}$.

1. The radius function is a transformation of the parent cube root function $f(x) = \sqrt[3]{x}$.

   a. Write $r(x)$ as a product in the form $r(x) = a\sqrt[3]{x}$ or $r(x) = ax^{\frac{1}{3}}$ so that it is easier to see the relationship between it and the parent function. Round $a$ to one decimal place.

   b. Graph $r(x)$ and $f(x)$ on the same axes. How do these graphs compare to each other? How would the graphs of $h(x) = x^3$ and $j(x) = 0.6x^3$ compare?

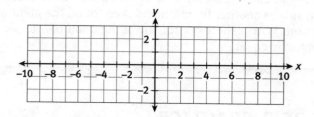

   c. What are the domain and the range of $f(x)$? Of $r(x)$? Write your answers as inequalities, in set notation, and in interval notation.

   d. Describe the transformations of $h(x) = x^3$ that result in the following functions.

   **i.** $j(x) = (-2x)^3$

   **ii.** $k(x) = (x - 5)^3$

   **iii.** $m(x) = x^3 - 4$

   **iv.** $n(x) = 2(0.5x + 4)^3 - 6$

2. How does the graph of $g(x) = \sqrt[3]{-x+1} + 3$ compare to the graph of $f(x) = \sqrt[3]{x}$? How would the graphs of $h(x) = x^3$ and $j(x) = (-x+1)^3 + 3$ compare?

3. Sketch $g(x)$ and $f(x)$ from Item 2 on the same axes below.

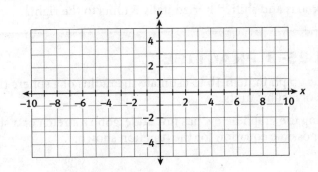

4. What are the domain and range of each function?

### Check Your Understanding

5. Why is the domain of a cube root function all real numbers, while the domain of a square root function is restricted to only nonnegative numbers?

6. **Attend to precision.** In Item 1, $x$ represents the volume of a sphere and $r(x)$ the radius. Given this context, should the domain and range of $r(x)$ be restricted? Explain your reasoning.

7. Write an equation that could be solved to find the volume of a sphere that has a radius of 2 inches. Write your equation two ways using a rational exponent and a radical.

8. Describe the transformations of $f(x) = \sqrt[3]{x}$ and $h(x) = x^3$ that result in the functions listed below.

   a. $g(x) = -\sqrt[3]{x} - 3$ and $j(x) = -(x-3)^3$

   b. $p(x) = 4\sqrt[3]{-x} - 1$ and $q(x) = 0.25(-4x)^3 - 1$

9. Without graphing, state the domain and range of the functions in Item 8.

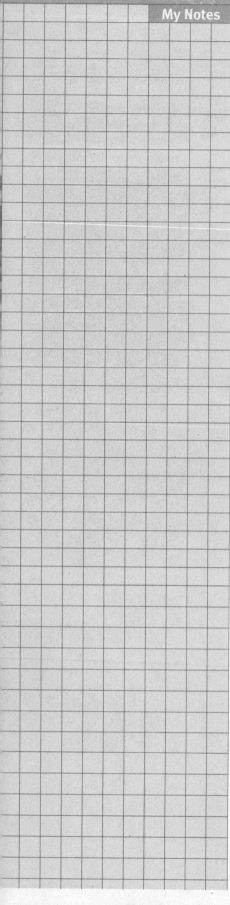

**Check Your Understanding**

10. Describe the transformations of $f(x) = \sqrt[3]{x}$ that result in the function $f(x) = 2\sqrt[3]{x+4} - 7$. Also, describe the transformations of $h(x) = x^3$ that result in the function $h(x) = 2(x+4)^3 - 7$.

11. **a.** Write an equation for a cube root function that has been reflected across the $x$-axis and shifted horizontally 5 units to the right.
    **b.** Write an equation for a cubic function that has been reflected across the $x$-axis and shifted horizontally 5 units to the right.

## LESSON 25-3 PRACTICE

12. Use your graph in Item 1b to estimate the radius of a sphere that has a volume of 6 cubic units.

13. Assuming the graph below has not undergone a stretch or a shrink, write a possible equation for the function shown.

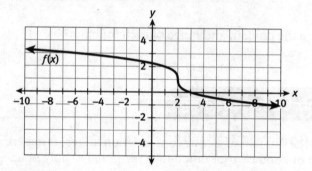

14. Sketch the graph of $h(x) = \sqrt[3]{x} - 4$. Describe the transformations. Then state the domain and range.

15. Sketch the graph of $p(x) = \sqrt[3]{x+5} + 2$. Describe the transformations. Then state the domain and range.

16. Consider the statement below.

    *If a cube root function is reflected across the x-axis and then across the y-axis, the resulting graph is the same as the graph of the original cube root function before the transformations.*

    Do you agree with the statement? If not, explain why. If you agree, write an algebraic expression that represents the relationship described in the statement.

17. **Make use of structure.** If you solve the equation $\sqrt[3]{x} = 0$, you find that the graph of $f(x) = \sqrt[3]{x}$ intersects the $x$-axis at $x = 0$. Where does the graph of $f(x) = \sqrt[3]{x+6}$ intersect the $x$-axis? Explain your reasoning.

18. Describe the transformations of $f(x) = x^3$ that result in the following functions.
    **a.** $f(x) = (-3x)^3$　　　　**b.** $f(x) = \left(\frac{1}{3}x\right)^3$
    **c.** $f(x) = 4\left(-\frac{1}{2}x\right)^3 - 5$

### Learning Targets:
- Solve cube root equations.
- Check the reasonableness of solutions.

The steps for solving *cube root equations* are very similar to those for solving square root equations.

**Step 1:** Isolate the radical term.

**Step 2:** Cube both sides of the equation.

**Step 3:** Solve for the unknown(s).

### Example A
Solve the equation $4\sqrt[3]{2x-1} - 5 = 3$.

$$4\sqrt[3]{2x-1} - 5 = 3$$

**Step 1:** Isolate the radical.

Add 5 to both sides, and then divide both sides by 4.

$$4\sqrt[3]{2x-1} = 8$$
$$\sqrt[3]{2x-1} = 2$$

**Step 2:** Cube both sides.

**Step 3:** Solve the equation.

$$\left(\sqrt[3]{2x-1}\right)^3 = (2)^3$$
$$2x - 1 = 8$$
$$2x = 9$$
$$x = \frac{9}{2}$$

### Example B
Use a graphing calculator to solve the equation in Example A.

**Step 1:** Enter the left side of the equation as one function and the right side as a second function.

**Step 2:** Find the point of intersection.

**Step 3:** The *x*-coordinate of the point of intersection is the solution.

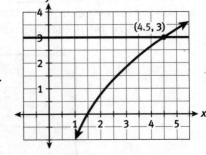

**Solution:** $x = 4.5$

### Try These A–B

Solve each equation. Use algebraic techniques or a graphing calculator.

**a.** $4 + (x-1)^{\frac{1}{3}} = 2$  **b.** $7\sqrt[3]{2x+5} = 21$

### Check Your Understanding

1. Solve each equation.
   **a.** $\sqrt[3]{x-1} = 5$  **b.** $\sqrt[3]{3x-1} - 6 = -4$

2. **Reason quantitatively.** Kari graphed the functions $y_1 = \sqrt[3]{x} - 4$ and $y_2 = \dfrac{\sqrt[3]{x}}{2}$ on her graphing calculator and found that the intersection of the graphs is (512, 4). What does this tell you about the solution to the equation $\sqrt[3]{x} - 4 = \dfrac{\sqrt[3]{x}}{2}$?

3. In Item 2, Kari used a graphing calculator to solve the problem. In this particular case, is the use of a graphing calculator more efficient than the use of algebraic techniques? Explain your reasoning.

### LESSON 25-4 PRACTICE

For Items 4–6, solve each equation algebraically. Check your solutions using a graphing calculator.

4. $\sqrt[3]{x} + 3 = 5$
5. $2 + \sqrt[3]{x+5} = 3$
6. $3\sqrt[3]{2x} = 12$
7. Solving the equation $\sqrt[3]{x-1} = 5$ using a graphing calculator set to a standard 10-by-10 viewing window yields the following graph.

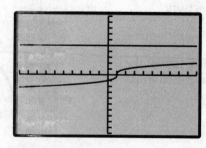

Does this graph contradict your solution to Item 1a? Explain your reasoning.

8. **Critique the reasoning of others.** Marcus claims that a softball with a radius of approximately 2 inches has a volume of 40 cubic inches. Is Marcus's claim reasonable? Solve the equation you wrote in Item 7 of the previous lesson to support your answer.

## ACTIVITY 25 PRACTICE

Write your answers on notebook paper.
Show your work.

### Lesson 25-1

1. The function $L(x) = \sqrt{\dfrac{x}{6}}$ represents the length of a side of a cube whose surface area is $x$ square units.
   a. Write $L(x)$ as a transformation of the parent square root function $f(x) = \sqrt{x}$.
   b. Graph $L(x)$ and $f(x)$ on the same axes. How do these graphs compare to each other?
   c. The $x$-intercept of $f(x)$ is $x = 0$. What is the $x$-intercept of $L(x)$?
   d. What is the domain of $L(x)$? Is the domain reasonable for this scenario?

2. Which of the following square root functions has a domain of $[3, \infty)$?
   A. $f(x) = \sqrt{x} + 3$
   B. $f(x) = \sqrt{x} - 3$
   C. $f(x) = \sqrt{x + 3}$
   D. $f(x) = \sqrt{x - 3}$

3. a. Explain why the range of $g(x) = -\sqrt{x}$ is $(-\infty, 0]$ rather than $[0, \infty)$. Draw a sketch to support your answer.
   b. Explain why the domain of $h(x) = \sqrt{-x}$ is $(-\infty, 0]$ rather than $[0, \infty)$. Draw a sketch to support your answer.

### Lesson 25-2

4. a. Solve the equation $4 = \sqrt{\dfrac{x}{6}}$ to find the surface area of a cube whose sides are 4 cm long. Show your work.
   b. Use the formula for finding the surface area of a cube, $S = 6s^2$, where $s$ is the length of the side of the cube, to check your results from part a. Is your answer reasonable?

5. Solve each equation algebraically. Identify any extraneous roots.
   a. $\sqrt{x - 2} + 5 = 8$
   b. $\sqrt{x + 2} + x = 0$
   c. $x = \sqrt{3x - 12} + 4$
   d. $\sqrt{x + 5} + 2 = 0$

6. Let $f(x) = \sqrt{x + 5} + 2$. Sketch the graph of $f(x)$ using what you know about transformations. Identify the $x$-intercepts, if any, and tell whether your graph supports your answer to Item 5d.

7. The screen shot below shows the solution to a square root equation.

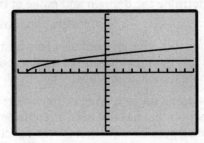

   Assuming that the radical term is of the form $\sqrt{x \pm a}$ and that the point of intersection is $(-5, 2)$, write an equation that the graph could be used to solve.

## Lesson 25-3

8. Which equation represents the following transformation?

   *the parent cube root function $f(x) = \sqrt[3]{x}$ vertically stretched by a factor of 2*

   **A.** $g(x) = \sqrt[3]{8x}$

   **B.** $h(x) = \sqrt[3]{2x}$

   **C.** $p(x) = \sqrt[3]{x} - 2$

   **D.** $q(x) = \sqrt[3]{x} + 2$

9. Sketch the graph of $f(x) = -\sqrt[3]{x} + 4$ using what you know about transformations.

10. Determine the domain and range of the function $f(x) = a\sqrt[3]{bx - c} + d$. Justify your answer.

11. If possible, give an example of a transformation that changes the domain of a cube root function. If not possible, explain why not.

12. Assuming the graph below represents a cube root function that has not been stretched or shrunk, write a possible equation for the function.

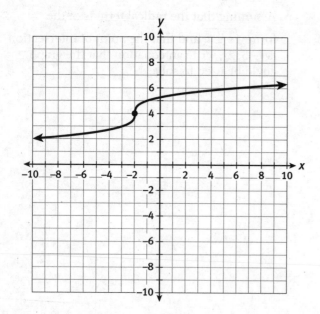

## Lesson 25-4

13. Solve each equation using algebraic techniques. Show your work.

    **a.** $\sqrt[3]{x} + 5 = 8$

    **b.** $5\sqrt[3]{x + 1} = 10$

14. To enter a cube root function into a graphing calculator, you can write the radical using an exponent of $\frac{1}{3}$. Use this fact to solve the equation $\sqrt[3]{x + 2} + 9 = 12$.

## MATHEMATICAL PRACTICES
### Use Appropriate Tools Strategically

15. You are given the option on a math quiz to solve only one problem using a graphing calculator. You must solve the other problems using algebraic techniques. Which of the following would you choose to solve with the graphing calculator, and why? Be specific. Then solve the equation using a calculator.

    *Problem 1*: $\sqrt{x} + 5 = 17$

    *Problem 2*: $\sqrt{x} + 5 = x$

    *Problem 3*: $\sqrt{x} + x = 5 + x$

# Inverses: Roots, Squares, and Cubes
## Swing, Swing, Swing
## Lesson 26-1 Square Root Functions and Regressions

### Learning Targets:
- Graph and write the inverse of square root functions.
- Find a square root model for a given table of data.

**SUGGESTED LEARNING STRATEGIES:** Create Representations, Note Taking, Think-Pair-Share

You have studied linear functions and their inverses as well as logarithmic and exponential functions that are inverse functions. Let's review what we know about inverse functions $f$ and $g$:

$$f(g(x)) = x \text{ for all } x \text{ in the domain of } g, \text{ and}$$
$$g(f(x)) = x \text{ for all } x \text{ in the domain of } f.$$

Now consider one of the radical functions you've just studied: square root functions.

### Example A

Graph the inverse of $f(x) = x^{\frac{1}{2}}$. Then give the domain and range of both the function and its inverse.

**Step 1:** List four points on the graph of $f$.

$(0, 0), (1, 1), (4, 2), (9, 3)$

**Step 2:** Interchange $x$ and $y$ for each point. These points will be on the graph of the inverse.

$(0, 0), (1, 1), (2, 4), (3, 9)$

**Step 3:** Connect the points.

**Step 4:** Consider the $x$- and $y$-values of the graphs to determine the domain and range of the functions.

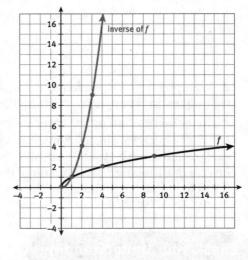

**Solution:** The blue graph is the inverse of $f$. The domain of both the function and its inverse is $x \geq 0$. The range of both the function and its inverse is $y \geq 0$.

### Example B

For $f(x) = x^{\frac{1}{2}}$, find $f^{-1}$ algebraically. Then give the domain and range of $f^{-1}$.

**Step 1:** Let $y$ represent $f(x)$.  $\qquad y = x^{\frac{1}{2}}$

**Step 2:** Interchange $x$ and $y$ to form the inverse relationship.  $\qquad x = y^{\frac{1}{2}}$

**Step 3:** Solve for $y$ to find the inverse.  $\qquad (x)^2 = \left(y^{\frac{1}{2}}\right)^2$

Assume the inverse is a function.  $\qquad x^2 = y$

**Solution:** $f^{-1} = x^2$. The domain of $f^{-1}$ is all real numbers and the range is $y \geq 0$.

**Try These A–B**

**a.** Graph $f(x) = (x - 3)^{\frac{1}{2}}$ using the values $x = 3, 4,$ and $7$. Then graph its inverse on the same axes.

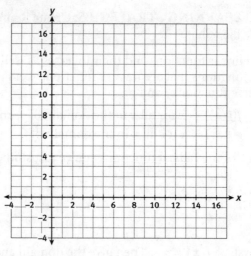

**b.** For the function in part a, find $f^{-1}$ algebraically.

In Examples A and B, we found the inverse of $f(x) = x^{\frac{1}{2}}$ using two different techniques. In Example A, graphing the inverse resulted in a domain of $x \geq 0$. However, finding the inverse algebraically resulted in the function $f^{-1} = x^2$, which we already know has a domain of all real numbers. The explanation for this is subtle but still very important when defining the inverse of a function: The domain of the inverse function $f^{-1}$ should be restricted to match the range of the original function.

## Check Your Understanding

**1.** Complete this statement about the inverse of $f(x) = x^{\frac{1}{2}}$:

$f^{-1}(x) = $ _____ for $x \geq$ _____.

**2.** Find the inverse of the function $h(x) = 1.34x^{\frac{1}{2}}$.

**3.** Give the domain and range for both $h$ and $h^{-1}$ in Item 2. Write your answers using inequalities, set notation, and interval notation.

In a previous lesson, you learned how to use a graphing calculator to find a quadratic regression based on real world data. Let's do the same for a square root function.

A physics class conducted an experiment comparing the period of a pendulum to the length of the pendulum. The results of the experiment are given in the table below.

CONNECT TO PHYSICS

The period of a pendulum is the length of time it takes to make one cycle, a complete swing back and forth. The period varies with the length of the pendulum, although other factors, which are not taken into account here, can affect the period.

| Length (in.) | 6 | 10 | 14 | 18 | 22 | 26 | 30 | 34 |
|---|---|---|---|---|---|---|---|---|
| Time (s) | 0.8 | 1.0 | 1.2 | 1.35 | 1.5 | 1.6 | 1.75 | 1.85 |

**4.** Make a scatter plot of the data on the coordinate grid below.

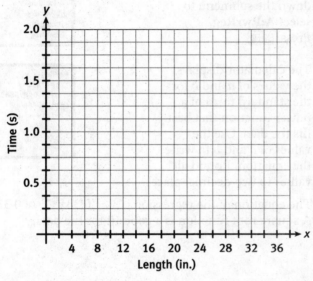

**5.** What parent function does the path of the data points resemble?

Recall that a quadratic regression is the process of finding a quadratic function that best fits a set of data. We used a graphing calculator to perform quadratic regressions. A ***square root regression*** is a similar process and can also be performed using a graphing calculator.

**6. Make use of structure.** If a square root function of the form $f(x) = a\sqrt{x}$ is the best fit for the data graphed in Item 4, make a conjecture about the value of $a$. Explain your reasoning.

MATH TERMS

A **square root regression** is the process of finding a square root function that best fits a set of data.

**TECHNOLOGY TIP**

**PwrReg** stands for *power regression*. It can be used for any regression of the form $y = ax^b$, when there are no translations.

## Example C

Use a graphing calculator to perform a regression for the pendulum data and determine the type of function that is the best fit.

**Step 1:** Press [STAT] to open the statistics menu. Choose **Edit** by pressing [ENTER]. Enter the data: the length data as L1 and the time data as L2.

| L1 | L2 | L3 | 1 |
|----|-----|-----|---|
| 6 | .8 | ------ | |
| 10 | 1 | | |
| 14 | 1.2 | | |
| 18 | 1.35 | | |
| 22 | 1.5 | | |
| 26 | 1.6 | | |
| 30 | 1.75 | | |

L1={6,10,14,18,...}

**Step 2:** Press [STAT] again. Move the cursor to highlight **Calc** and then scroll down the submenu to select **A:PwrReg**. Press [ENTER].

EDIT **CALC** TESTS
7↑QuartReg
8:LinReg(a+bx)
9:LnReg
0:ExpReg
**A:**PwrReg
B:Logistic
C:SinReg

**Step 3:** The calculator displays the values of *a* and *b* for the standard form of a power function that best fits the data. Use the values of *a* and *b* to write the equation. Round all values to two decimal places.

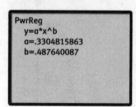

PwrReg
  y=a*x^b
  a=.3304815863
  b=.487640087

**Solution:** The equation of the regression is $y = 0.33x^{0.49} \approx 0.33\sqrt{x}$. A square root function is a good fit for the data.

**7.** Graph the square root model $y = 0.33\sqrt{x}$ on the coordinate grid in Item 4. Does your graph support a "good fit"? Explain your reasoning.

**8.** Give the domain and range for your square root regression. Write your answers using inequalities, set notation, and interval notation.

**9.** Use the square root model to predict the period of a pendulum that is 40 inches long. Round your answer to two decimal places.

**10.** Use the regression equation $y = 0.33\sqrt{x}$ to find the length of a pendulum that has a period of 3 seconds. Round your answer to the nearest half inch.

**Check Your Understanding**

11. The regression equation obtained from the calculator in Example C is $y = 0.33x^{0.49}$. Explain why it is acceptable to rewrite this equation as a square root, $y \approx 0.33\sqrt{x}$.

12. A power regression is only appropriate when there is no horizontal or vertical translation. How can you determine from the context of the pendulum problem that the parent function $f(x) = \sqrt{x}$ has not been translated?

## LESSON 26-1 PRACTICE

13. Graph the function $f(x) = 2x^{\frac{1}{2}}$. Then use at least four points from your graph to sketch $f^{-1}$ on the same coordinate grid.

14. Give the domain and range of the function and its inverse in Item 13. Write your answers using inequalities, set notation, and interval notation.

15. Find $f^{-1}$ for the function in Item 13 algebraically. Give restrictions for the inverse if there are any and explain.

16. Consider the data in the table below.

| x | 2 | 5 | 7 | 10 | 12 | 15 | 18 | 20 |
|---|---|---|---|----|----|----|----|----|
| y | 4.2 | 6.7 | 7.9 | 9.5 | 10.4 | 11.6 | 12.7 | 13.4 |

a. Assuming a square root function in the form $f(x) = a\sqrt{x}$ is a good fit for the data, make a conjecture about the value of $a$. Explain your reasoning.

b. Use a graphing calculator to perform a square root regression. Write your answer using a rational exponent and then using a radical. Round all values to hundredths.

17. **Model with mathematics.** Determine whether a square root function is a good model for the data shown in the table below. Explain your reasoning. If a square root model is not appropriate, offer an alternative model and explain how you arrived at this model.

| x | 1 | 2 | 5 | 10 | 12 | 20 | 24 | 31 | 36 |
|---|---|---|---|----|----|----|----|----|----|
| y | 2 | 2.5 | 3.4 | 4.3 | 4.6 | 5.4 | 5.8 | 6.3 | 6.6 |

**My Notes**

**MATH TIP**

Recall that a *relation* is a set of ordered pairs that may or may not be defined by a rule. Not all relations are functions, but all functions are relations.

**Learning Targets:**
- Graph and write the inverse of square root functions.
- Find the inverse relations of quadratic functions.

**SUGGESTED LEARNING STRATEGIES:** Vocabulary Organizer, Create Representations, Quickwrite, Look for a Pattern, Work Backward

All functions have an inverse *relation*, but the relation may or may not be a function.

1. Use the quadratic function *g* graphed below.
   **a.** Graph the inverse of *g*.

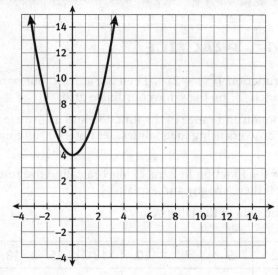

   **b.** Is the inverse of *g* a function? Explain your reasoning.

   **c.** What characteristic of the graph of a function can you use to determine whether its inverse relation is a function?

   **d.** Give the domain and range of the inverse relation in part a. Write your answers using inequalities, set notation, and interval notation.

### Example A

The quadratic function shown in the graph in Item 1 is $g(x) = x^2 + 4$. Find an equation for the inverse relation of this function.

**Step 1:** Let $y$ represent $g(x)$.      $y = x^2 + 4$

**Step 2:** Interchange $x$ and $y$ to form the inverse relationship.      $x = y^2 + 4$

**Step 3:** Solve for $y$ to find the inverse.      $x - 4 = y^2$

$$\pm(x-4)^{\frac{1}{2}} = y$$

**Solution:** $g^{-1}(x) = \pm(x-4)^{\frac{1}{2}} = \pm\sqrt{x-4}$

**MATH TIP**

When taking the square root of a variable, the result yields a positive and a negative value.

### Try These A

**a.** Find the inverse of the function $f(x) = -x^{\frac{1}{2}}$. State whether or not the inverse is a function.

**b.** Find the inverse of the function $g(x) = (x-5)^2$. State whether or not the inverse is a function.

### Check Your Understanding

**2.** In Try These A part a, why is it necessary to include a restriction on the domain in the definition of $g^{-1}$?

**3.** What specific part of the equation for $g^{-1}$ in Example A tells you that it is not a function? Explain your reasoning.

If desired, it is possible to restrict the domain of a function so that its inverse will also be a function. Consider the graph of $g(x) = x^2 + 4$ and its inverse from Item 1.

Imagine covering the right side of the graph of $g$ and then drawing the inverse. The result would be only the bottom half of the relation $g^{-1}$, which would be a function. So if we restrict the domain of $g$ to $x \leq 0$, the inverse of $g$ will be a function with a domain of $x \geq 4$ and a range of $y \leq 0$.

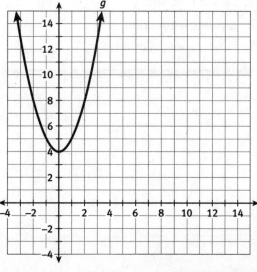

**MATH TIP**

The range of the inverse of a function is the same as the domain of the original function. You can use this fact to determine whether the inverse of a restricted quadratic function will be the top half or the bottom half of the inverse relation.

4. Give another possible restriction on the domain of the function $g(x) = x^2 + 4$ that ensures an inverse that is a function.

### Check Your Understanding

State whether the domain of each of the following functions must be restricted to ensure that its inverse is a function. Give an appropriate restriction where needed.

5. $f(x) = \sqrt{x + 3}$

6. $g(x) = x^{\frac{1}{2}} + 1$

7. $p(x) = (x - 5)^2$

8. $q(x) = x^2 + 6x + 9$

**MATH TIP**

The *horizontal line test* is similar to the vertical line test. It is a visual way to determine whether numbers in the range of a function have more than one corresponding number in the domain of the function.

A function is defined as ***one-to-one*** if, for each number in the range of the function, there is exactly one corresponding number in the domain of the function. If $f(x)$ is a one-to-one function, then it will pass both the vertical and *horizontal line test*.

9. Is $g$ from Item 1 a one-to-one function? Explain.

10. **Construct viable arguments.** Make a conjecture about a function whose inverse relation is a function.

### Check Your Understanding

Determine whether each type of function will *always*, *sometimes*, or *never* have an inverse that is a function, assuming the domain of the function has not been restricted. Explain your reasoning.

11. Linear function

12. Quadratic function

13. Square root function

# LESSON 26-2 PRACTICE

**14.** Graph the inverse of the function *f* on the coordinate grid.

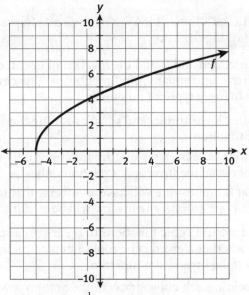

**15.** In Item 14, $f(x) = 2(x+5)^{\frac{1}{2}}$. Find $f^{-1}$ algebraically.

**16.** Find an equation for the inverse relation of $g(x) = 9x^2 - 4$. Then state the domain and range of *g* and $g^{-1}$. Write your answers using inequalities, set notation, and interval notation. State if *g* and $g^{-1}$ are one-to-one.

**17.** Restrict the domain of the function $h(x) = (x+7)^2$ so that its inverse will be a function. Then use the restriction to determine whether the graph of the inverse will be the top half or the bottom half of the inverse relation.

**18. Attend to precision.** Explain why an even function can never be a one-to-one function.

### MATH TIP

Recall that an *even function* is one in which $f(-x) = f(x)$ and is symmetrical across the *y*-axis. An *odd function* is one in which $f(-x) = -f(x)$ and is symmetrical around the origin.

## Learning Targets:

- Graph and write the inverse of cube root functions.
- Find the inverse relations of cubic functions.

> **SUGGESTED LEARNING STRATEGIES:** Create Representations, Look for a Pattern, Marking the Text

Thus far, we have graphed and found the inverses of linear, exponential, logarithmic, quadratic, and square root functions. We discovered a number of patterns related to these types of functions:

- Linear, exponential, logarithmic, and square root functions always have inverses that are functions.

- Quadratic functions have inverses that are functions only if the domain is restricted. Otherwise, the inverse is a relation only.

- Any function that is one-to-one will have an inverse that is a function. If a function is not one-to-one, the inverse will be a relation only.

Let's explore cube root and cubic functions to see if similar patterns exist. If we can determine whether a given cube root or cubic function is one-to-one, then we will know if the inverse is a function.

Study the graphs below. Each cubic graph in the bottom row is the inverse of the cube root graph above it in the top row. The graphs in the center and right-hand columns are translations of the graphs of the parent functions in the left-hand column.

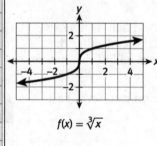

$f(x) = \sqrt[3]{x}$

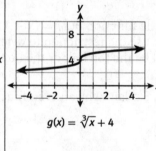

$g(x) = \sqrt[3]{x} + 4$

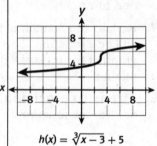

$h(x) = \sqrt[3]{x - 3} + 5$

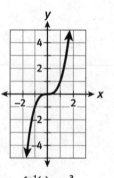

$f^{-1}(x) = x^3$

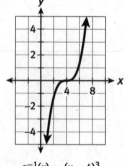

$g^{-1}(x) = (x - 4)^3$

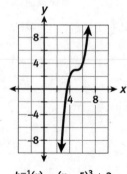

$h^{-1}(x) = (x - 5)^3 + 3$

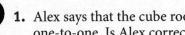
**My Notes**

1. Alex says that the cube root functions and cubic functions are not one-to-one. Is Alex correct? Explain your reasoning.

2. Give the domain and range for each of the functions and their inverses. You may write a general statement to describe the domain and range.

3. **Express regularity in repeated reasoning.** Make a conjecture about the inverses of cube root and cubic functions that are translations of the parent functions $f(x) = \sqrt[3]{x}$ and $f(x) = x^3$.

You may have noticed another pattern. The inverse of a translated cube root function is a translated cubic function. Since finding inverses involves interchanging the $x$- and $y$-values, the vertical and horizontal translations are also interchanged. Let's verify this with an example.

**Example A**

Find the inverse of the function $f(x) = \sqrt[3]{x - 6} + 1$.

**Step 1:** Let $y$ represent $f(x)$. $\qquad\qquad\qquad y = \sqrt[3]{x - 6} + 1$

**Step 2:** Interchange $x$ and $y$. $\qquad\qquad\qquad x = \sqrt[3]{y - 6} + 1$

**Step 3:** Solve for $y$ to find the inverse. $\qquad x - 1 = \sqrt[3]{y - 6}$

$$(x - 1)^3 = y - 6$$

$$(x - 1)^3 + 6 = y$$

**Solution:** $f^{-1}(x) = (x - 1)^3 + 6$

Not all cube root or cubic functions are translations of their parent functions, so we need to examine those as well.

**Try These A**

Find the inverse of the function.

a. $f(x) = \sqrt[3]{x + 3}$ $\qquad\qquad$ b. $f(x) = \sqrt[3]{x} + 5$

4. **Use appropriate tools strategically.** Use a graphing calculator to investigate the graph of $f(x) = \sqrt[3]{x^2 + 4x}$ in a standard 10-by-10 viewing window. Sketch the graph. Is $f$ a one-to-one function? Why or why not? Will the inverse of $f$ be a function?

5. Investigate the cubic function $g(x) = x^3 - 6x^2 + 8x + 5$. Use your calculator to graph $g$ in a standard 10-by-10 viewing window. Sketch the graph. Is $g$ a one-to-one function? Will the inverse of $g$ be a function?

### Check Your Understanding

6. Determine without graphing whether the function $f(x) = \sqrt[3]{x} + 2$ is a one-to-one function. Explain your reasoning.

7. Determine without graphing whether the inverse of the function $g(x) = (x + 5)^3$ will be a function. Explain your reasoning.

8. Make a conjecture as to whether cube root functions of the form $f(x) = a\sqrt[3]{x}$ or $f(x) = \sqrt[3]{ax}$ are one-to-one functions and will therefore have inverses that are functions. Explain your reasoning.

### LESSON 26-3 PRACTICE

9. The graph below shows the function $f(x) = \frac{1}{2}(x - 2)^3$. Sketch the graph of $f^{-1}$ on the same coordinate grid.

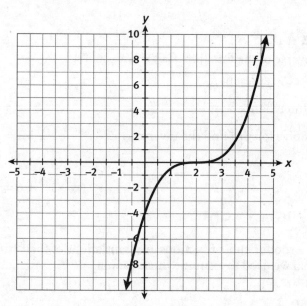

10. Give the domain and range of $f$ and $f^{-1}$. Write your answers using intervals, set notation, and interval notation.

11. Find the equation of $f^{-1}$ algebraically. Does the domain of $f$ need to be restricted to ensure that $f^{-1}$ is a function? Explain why or why not.

12. Use a graphing calculator to help you determine whether the function $p(x) = x^3 + 2x^2 - 4x + 2$ has an inverse that is a function. Explain how the calculator helps to determine the answer.

13. **Critique the reasoning of others.** Jiao claimed that the cubic function $f(x) = x^3 - 6x^2 + 12x - 8$ is a one-to-one function. She did not use a graphing calculator to make her determination. Steven looked at the function and immediately said Jiao was wrong. Who is correct? Justify your answer without using a graphing calculator.

## ACTIVITY 26 PRACTICE

Write your answers on notebook paper.
Show your work.

### Lesson 26-1

1. Magdalena collected the following data for the stopping distances of cars at various speeds.

| Stopping Distance (ft) | Speed (mph) |
|---|---|
| 30 | 25 |
| 43 | 30 |
| 59 | 35 |
| 97 | 45 |
| 145 | 55 |
| 172 | 60 |
| 202 | 65 |
| 234 | 70 |

She is aware that the data may be modeled by a square root function but she does not know the coefficient of the function.

a. Use the power regression feature of your calculator to find a square root function that fits this data. Round all values to two decimal places.

b. Explain how you could check your regression equation using one of the data points in the table.

c. Write and solve an equation to find the stopping distance of a car that is going 50 mph, assuming the same general road conditions as in Magdalena's study. Show your work.

d. Use the data points in the table to determine if your answer to part c is reasonable. Explain.

2. The domain of a function is $x \geq 2$ and its range is $y \geq 0$. Give the domain and range, using inequalities, of the inverse of the function.

3. The table below shows several points on the graph of $f(x) = 3x^{\frac{1}{2}}$.

| x | y |
|---|---|
| 0 | 0 |
| 1 | 3 |
| 4 | 6 |
| 9 | 9 |

Use this information to graph $f$ and its inverse on the same set of axes. Then give the domain and range of each using inequalities, set notation, and interval notation.

4. Find the inverse of $g(x) = (3x)^{\frac{1}{2}}$ algebraically.

5. For some function $g(x)$, $g(2) = 5$. Assuming that $g^{-1}$ is a function, which of the following is true?

A. $g^{-1}(2) = \frac{1}{5}$

B. $g^{-1}(2) = -5$

C. $g^{-1}(5) = 2$

D. $g^{-1}(5) = \frac{1}{2}$

### Lesson 26-2

6. Give an example of a function whose inverse is not a function.

7. Find the equation of the inverse of the function $h(x) = 5\sqrt{x-1}$. Then state whether the inverse is a function or a relation.

8. Graph the quadratic function $f(x) = x^2 - 4$ and its inverse relation on the same coordinate grid. Then give the domain and range of each using inequalities, set notation, and interval notation.

For Items 9–11, state whether the domain of the function must be restricted to ensure that its inverse is a function. Give an appropriate restriction where needed.

9. $f(x) = (x-5)^2 + 3$

10. $g(x) = \sqrt{2x + 4}$

11. $h(x) = 4x^2 + 20x + 25$

## Lesson 26-3

12. Use a graphing calculator to determine whether $g(x) = x^3 - 2x^2 - 7x - 4$ is a one-to-one function. Then explain what this tells you about the inverse of $g$.

13. Find the equation of the inverse of the function $f(x) = (2x + 3)^{\frac{1}{3}}$.

14. Draw a sketch to dispute the following statement:

    *Since an odd function is symmetric about the origin, it will be a one-to-one function.*

15. Which of the following cube root functions is NOT one-to-one?

    A. $f(x) = \sqrt[3]{3x + 5}$

    B. $f(x) = \dfrac{\sqrt[3]{x + 5}}{3}$

    C. $f(x) = \sqrt[3]{x + 5} + 3$

    D. $f(x) = \sqrt[3]{3x^2 + 5}$

## MATHEMATICAL PRACTICES
### Reason Abstractly and Quantitatively

16. When we restrict the domain of a quadratic function to ensure that its inverse will also be a function, we typically use the $x$-value of the vertex, mainly because it is convenient. However, we can restrict the domain in other ways that will also ensure an inverse that is a function.

    For the function $f(x) = x^2 - 8x + 16$, each of the following restrictions, except one, will ensure that the inverse of $f$ will be a function. Circle the restriction that does not ensure that the inverse will be a function. Explain your reasoning.

    A. $x \le 0$

    B. $x \le 2$

    C. $x \le 4$

    D. $x \ge 2$

    E. $x \ge 4$

1. The graph of a function $g$ is shown.
   a. Describe the graph as a transformation of $f(x) = \sqrt{x}$.
   b. Write the equation for $g$.
   c. State the domain and range of $g$.
   d. Find the inverse of $g$. Be sure to include any restrictions on the domain of the inverse.
   e. Use the graph or a table to solve the equation $g(x) = 7$.

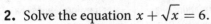

2. Solve the equation $x + \sqrt{x} = 6$.

3. Restrict the domain of the quadratic function $f(x) = x^2 - 2x - 15$ so that $f^{-1}$ is also a function.

4. The data below show the volume, $V$, of different-sized balls in relation to the length of the radius, $r$, of the ball.

| Ball | Volume (in.³) | Radius (in.) |
| --- | --- | --- |
| Ping Pong ball | 2.07 | 0.79 |
| Golf ball | 2.48 | 0.84 |
| Racketball | 6.04 | 1.13 |
| Tennis ball | 9.20 | 1.30 |
| Baseball | 12.77 | 1.45 |
| Softball | 69.46 | 2.55 |
| Volleyball | 321.56 | 4.25 |
| Basketball | 434.89 | 4.70 |

   a. Use the power regression feature of your calculator to determine whether a square root or cube root function best fits the data. Enter volume in one list and radius in another list.
   b. Write the equation of the regression two ways using a rational exponent and a radical function. Round all values to two decimal places.
   c. A cricket ball has a volume of 12.25 cubic inches. Use your regression equation to find the radius of a cricket ball. Round your answer to two decimal places.
   d. Most balls are in the general shape of a sphere. The formula for finding the volume of a sphere is $V = \frac{4}{3}\pi r^3$. Find the inverse of $V$ and compare it to your regression equation.

5. The table below gives several points on the graph of a cube root function, $h(x)$.

| $x$ | −6 | 1 | 2 | 3 | 10 |
| --- | --- | --- | --- | --- | --- |
| $y$ | 2 | 3 | 4 | 5 | 6 |

   a. Use the points in the table to graph the inverse of $h$.
   b. Use what you know about transformations and inverses to write the equation for $h^{-1}$.
   c. Use your equation for $h^{-1}$ to find the equation of the original function, $h(x)$, algebraically.

**Embedded Assessment 1**
*Use after Activity 26*

# Radical Functions: Square Roots, Cube Roots, and Their Inverses
## HOW BIG IS THAT BALL?

| Scoring Guide | Exemplary | Proficient | Emerging | Incomplete |
|---|---|---|---|---|
| | The solution demonstrates these characteristics: | | | |
| **Mathematics Knowledge and Thinking** (Items 1c, 1d, 1e, 2, 3, 4b, 4c, 5) | • Clear and accurate identification of key features of radical functions, including domain and range, and transformations of a parent function <br>• Fluency in solving equations (numerically or graphically, and algebraically) and rewriting expressions containing rational exponents or radicals <br>• Effective understanding of inverse functions, including producing an invertible function by restricting the domain | • Mostly accurate identification of key features of radical functions, including domain and range, and transformations of a parent function <br>• Little difficulty in solving equations (numerically or graphically, and algebraically) and rewriting expressions containing rational exponents or radicals <br>• Largely correct understanding of inverse functions, including producing an invertible function by restricting the domain | • Partially accurate identification of key features of radical functions, including domain and range, and transformations of a parent function <br>• Some difficulty in solving equations (numerically or graphically, and algebraically) and rewriting expressions containing rational exponents or radicals <br>• Partial understanding of inverse functions, including producing an invertible function by restricting the domain | • Incomplete or inaccurate identification of key features of radical functions, including domain and range, and transformations of a parent function <br>• Significant difficulty in solving equations (numerically or graphically, and algebraically) and rewriting expressions containing rational exponents or radicals <br>• Little or no understanding of inverse functions, including producing an invertible function by restricting the domain |
| **Problem Solving** (Item 4c) | • An appropriate and efficient strategy that results in a correct answer | • A strategy that may include unnecessary steps but results in a correct answer | • A strategy that results in some incorrect answers | • No clear strategy when solving problems |
| **Mathematical Modeling / Representations** (Items 1b, 4a, 4d, 5) | • Effective understanding of how to apply transformations to create an equation from a graph <br>• Fluency in writing expressions for the inverse of a function <br>• Effective understanding of modeling a real-world scenario with a power regression <br>• Clear and accurate understanding of how to rearrange a formula to highlight a quantity of interest | • Largely correct understanding of how to apply transformations to create an equation from a graph <br>• Little difficulty in writing expressions for the inverse of a function <br>• Largely correct understanding of modeling a real-world scenario with a power regression <br>• Mostly accurate understanding of how to rearrange a formula to highlight a quantity of interest | • Partial understanding of how to apply transformations to create an equation from a graph <br>• Some difficulty in writing expressions for the inverse of a function <br>• Partial understanding of modeling a real-world scenario with a power regression <br>• Partially accurate understanding of how to rearrange a formula to highlight a quantity of interest | • Little or no understanding of how to apply transformations to create an equation from a graph <br>• Significant difficulty in writing expressions for the inverse of a function <br>• Little or no understanding of modeling a real-world scenario with a power regression <br>• Incomplete or mostly inaccurate understanding of how to rearrange a formula to highlight a quantity of interest |
| **Reasoning and Communication** (Items 1a, 4a, 4d) | • Precise use of appropriate math terms and language to describe a function as a transformation of another function <br>• Clear and accurate description and comparison of equations that model real-world scenarios | • Adequate and largely correct description of a function as a transformation of another function <br>• Adequate description and comparison of equations that model real-world scenarios | • Misleading or confusing description of a function as a transformation of another function <br>• Misleading or confusing description and comparison of equations that model real-world scenarios | • Incomplete or mostly inaccurate description of a function as a transformation of another function <br>• Incomplete or inadequate description and comparison of equations that model real-world scenarios |

# Introduction to Rational Functions

## Planning a Summer Camp
### Lesson 27-1 Formulating and Graphing a Rational Function

**Learning Targets:**
- Formulate rational equations that model real-world situations.
- Graph equations on coordinate axes.

> **SUGGESTED LEARNING STRATEGIES:** Marking the Text, Summarizing, Paraphrasing, Create Representations, Look for a Pattern

The finance committee of a nonprofit summer camp for children is setting the cost for a 5-day camp. The fixed cost for the entire camp is $2400 per day, and includes things such as rent, salaries, insurance, and equipment. An outside food services company will provide meals at a cost of $3 per camper per meal. Campers will eat three meals a day.

As a nonprofit camp, the camp must cover its costs, but not make any profit. The committee must come up with a proposal for setting the fee for each camper, based on the number of campers who are expected to attend each week.

1. Initially, the committee decides to calculate camper fees based on the fixed cost of the camp alone, without meals for the campers.
   **a.** What is the total fixed cost for the five days?

   **b.** Complete the table below to determine the fee per camper that will guarantee the camp does not lose money.

| Number of Campers | Fee per Camper |
|-------------------|----------------|
|                   |                |
|                   |                |
|                   |                |
|                   |                |
|                   |                |
|                   |                |
|                   |                |
|                   |                |

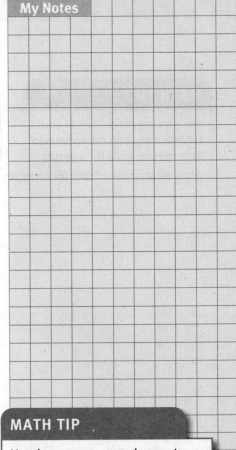

**MATH TIP**

Use the patterns you observe in the table to write an algebraic expression in the last row when there are *x* campers.

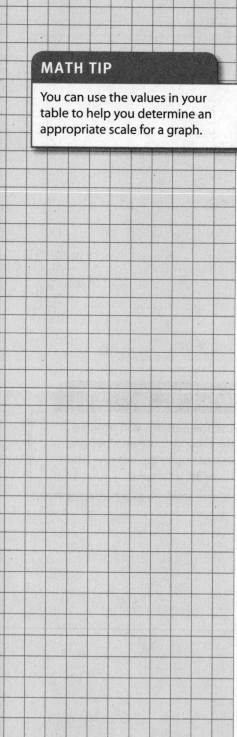

**MATH TIP**

You can use the values in your table to help you determine an appropriate scale for a graph.

**c.** Using an appropriate scale, make a graph showing the relationship between the fee per camper and the number of campers in attendance.

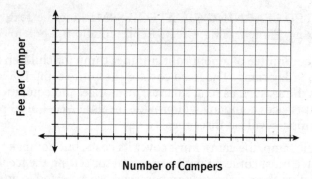

**Number of Campers**

**d.** Write an algebraic rule for the fee per camper as a function of the number of campers in attendance.

**2.** Describe the features of the graph in Item 1c.

**3. Reason abstractly.** Based on your work so far, is there a minimum camper fee, not counting the cost of meals? If so, what is it? Explain.

**Check Your Understanding**

**4.** What is the fee per camper if there are 2000 campers?

**5.** What relationship exists between the number of campers and the fee per camper?

**6.** Describe the domain and range of the function in the context of this problem.

**7.** The function developed in Item 1 did not account for meals. Campers eat three meals per day at a cost of $3 per camper per meal. The committee must determine a function that includes the cost of meals when setting the fee per camper.

**a.** What will be the total cost for meals per camper each 5-day week?

**b.** Complete the table below to determine the fee per camper that will guarantee the camp does not lose money.

| Number of Campers | Fixed Cost Plus the Cost of Meals | Fee per Camper |
|---|---|---|
| 25 | | |
| 50 | | |
| 75 | | |
| 100 | | |
| 200 | | |
| 500 | | |
| 1000 | | |
| $x$ | | |

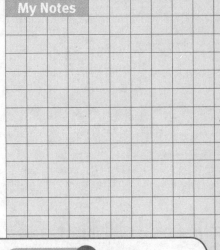

**CONNECT TO AP**

Describing the behavior of rational functions as they approach horizontal and vertical asymptotes provides an introduction to a more formal study of limits that will occur in calculus.

**c.** Using an appropriate scale, make a graph showing the relationship between the fee per camper, including meals, and the number of campers.

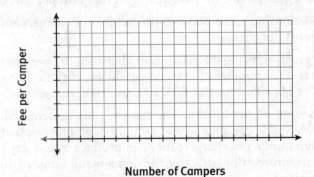

Number of Campers

**d.** Write an algebraic rule for the fee per camper, including meals, as a function of the number of children in attendance.

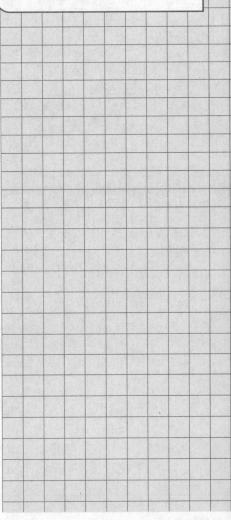

**8.** Based on your work so far, is there a minimum camper's fee? If so, what is it? Explain your reasoning.

**9.** How does your answer to Item 8 differ from the one you gave for Item 3?

### Check Your Understanding

**10.** What is the fee per camper if there are 2000 campers? Why is your answer different from what it was in Item 4?

**11.** Describe the domain and range of the function that includes the cost of meals in the context of this problem.

**12.** Describe the difference between the graphs in Items 1c and 7c.

## LESSON 27-1 PRACTICE

A new start-up company is going to produce cell phone chargers. The fixed cost for the company is $800 per day, which includes things such as rent, salaries, insurance, and equipment. The total daily cost, in dollars, to produce $x$ chargers is $C(x) = 4x + 800$.

**13.** Evaluate and interpret $C(100)$ and $\dfrac{C(100)}{100}$.

**14.** Write an algebraic rule for finding the average cost per charger.

**15.** What relationship exists between the number of chargers and the average cost per charger?

**16.** Make a graph showing the relationship between the average cost per charger and the number of chargers produced. Include data points for producing 50, 100, 200, 400, 600, 800, and 1000 chargers.

**17. Make sense of problems.** The company has determined, based on warehouse space, equipment, and number of employees, that the maximum number of chargers they can produce in one day is 6000. Given this information, describe the domain and range of the average cost function.

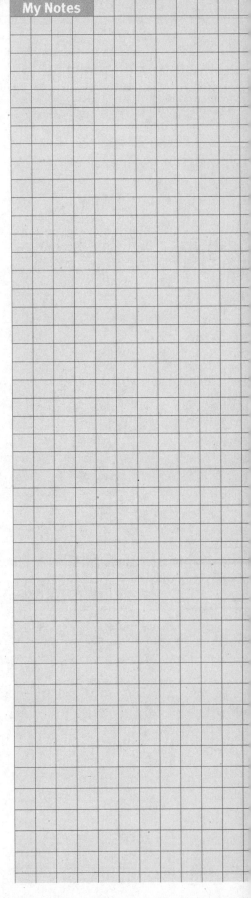

● **Learning Targets:**
- Formulate rational equations that model real-world situations.
- Graph equations on coordinate axes.

> **SUGGESTED LEARNING STRATEGIES:** Create Representations, Quickwrite, Self Revision/Peer Revision, Work Backward

Summer camp is a rewarding experience for many young children and teenagers. It is not unusual for nonprofit organizations to award scholarships to students.

1. The finance committee from the nonprofit summer camp in Lesson 27-1 decides to award 30 scholarships to students who otherwise could not afford the camp. These scholarships include full use of the facilities and all meals at no charge.

   **a.** To help account for the scholarships, complete the table below.

| Number of Campers | Fixed Cost Plus the Cost of Meals | Number of Paying Campers | Fee per Paying Camper |
|---|---|---|---|
| 50 | | | |
| 75 | | | |
| 100 | | | |
| 200 | | | |
| 500 | | | |
| 1000 | | | |
| *x* | | | |

   **b.** Using an appropriate scale, make a graph showing the relationship between the fee per paying camper and the number of campers.

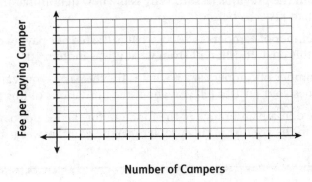

Number of Campers

**c.** Write an algebraic model for the fee per paying camper as a function of the number of campers in attendance.

**d.** What is the meaning of the numerator and the denominator in your model?

**2.** Based on your work so far, is there a minimum camper's fee? If so, what is it? Explain.

**3.** How does your answer to Item 2 differ from the one you gave for Item 8 in the previous lesson?

**4.** How does your graph in Item 1b compare to the one in Item 7c in the previous lesson?

### Check Your Understanding

**5.** Compare the model you wrote in Item 1c to the one you wrote in Item 7d in the previous lesson. Why is the new denominator $x - 30$, rather than just $x$ as before?

**6.** If the number of campers is 2000, what is the fee per paying camper? Why is this answer different from what it was in Item 10?

**7.** If the number of campers is 25, what is the fee per paying camper? What does your answer tell you about the limitations of this model?

**8.** Give the domain and range of the function for the fee per paying camper in the context of this problem. Write your answer using set notation.

Recall that as a nonprofit camp, the camp should not make any profit but still must cover its costs to stay in operation.

9. Last year the weekly camper fee was $80. If the camp charges the same amount and grants 30 scholarships, what is the minimum number of paying campers that must attend so the camp does not lose money?

10. Express the number of campers as a function of the fee for each paying camper.

11. What is the relationship between the function in Item 1c and the function in Item 10?

### Check Your Understanding

12. Explain how you could use the table of values you completed in Item 1a to check the reasonableness of your answer to Item 9.

13. Explain how you could use your answer to Item 10 to check the reasonableness of your answer to Item 9.

14. **Attend to precision.** Use the model $f(x) = \dfrac{12,000 + 45x}{x - 30}$ and a graphing calculator to find the minimum number of paying campers that must attend so the camp does not lose money if the weekly fee is $100. Describe the process you used to find your answer.

**My Notes**

## LESSON 27-2 PRACTICE

**15.** The summer camp can accommodate up to 300 campers, and market research indicates that campers do not want to pay more than $200 per week. Although the camp is nonprofit, it cannot afford to lose money. Write a proposal for setting the fee per camper. Be sure to include these items.
   - the proposed fee
   - the minimum number of campers needed to break even
   - the maximum possible income for the proposed fee
   - mathematics to support your reasoning

**Model with mathematics.** The population of grizzly bears in a remote area is modeled by the function $P(t) = \dfrac{200t - 120}{t + 0.5}$, where $t = 1$ represents the year 2001, $t = 2$ represents the year 2002, and so on. Use the model to answers Items 16–20.

**16.** Graph the grizzly bear population function.

**17.** Describe the features of the graph.

**18.** What are the domain and range of the function?

**19.** How many grizzly bears were there in 2005?

**20.** Predict the bear population in the year 2018.

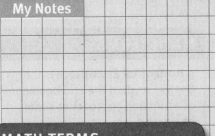

**Learning Targets:**
- Determine the horizontal and vertical asymptotes of a rational function.
- Graph a rational function on the coordinate plane.

**SUGGESTED LEARNING STRATEGIES:** Vocabulary Organizer, Interactive Word Wall, Create Representations, Note Taking

When using a function to model a situation like the fee per camper, you only use those values that make sense in the context of the situation. In Items 1–3, we will consider the ***rational function*** $f(x) = \dfrac{12,000 + 45x}{x - 30}$ over a broader range of values.

1. Graph the function on a graphing calculator, using the viewing window $[-450, 450]$ by $[-400, 400]$.
   a. Use your calculator to approximate the $x$- and $y$-intercepts.

   b. Find the exact values of the $x$- and $y$-intercepts, using the function. Show your work.

   c. Recall that division of a nonzero quantity by zero is *undefined*. Name the value(s) for which the function is not defined and explain how you determined the value(s).

   d. What is the domain of the function? Write your answer using set notation, interval notation, and inequalities.

   e. What is the range of the function? Write your answer using set notation, interval notation, and inequalities.

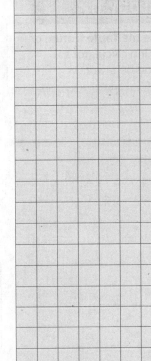

**MATH TERMS**

A **rational function** is a function that is the quotient of two polynomials. Its parent function is $f(x) = \dfrac{1}{x}$.

**TECHNOLOGY TIP**

Throughout this book, graphing calculator viewing window dimensions are given as [xmin, xmax] by [ymin, ymax].

**MATH TERMS**

A **horizontal asymptote** is the line $y = a$ when the end behavior of a function approaches some constant $a$.

A **vertical asymptote** is the line $x = b$ if the absolute value of a function increases without bound as $x$ approaches some number $b$.

If the values of a function $f$ approach some number $a$ as the absolute value of $x$ becomes large without bound, the line $y = a$ is called a **horizontal asymptote** of $f$. If the absolute value of a function $f$ increases without bound as $x$ approaches some number $b$, then the line $x = b$ is a **vertical asymptote** of $f$.

2. The graph below shows the function $f(x) = \dfrac{4x}{x-2}$.

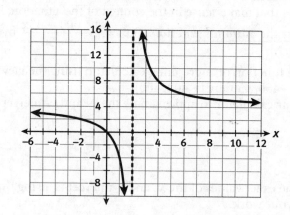

a. To examine the end behavior of the graph, use the function to complete the table. Round values to two decimal places.

| $x$ | $-300$ | $-100$ | $-50$ | $-20$ | $-10$ | $10$ | $20$ | $50$ | $100$ | $300$ |
|---|---|---|---|---|---|---|---|---|---|---|
| $f(x)$ | | | | | | | | | | |

b. Write the equations of the horizontal and vertical asymptotes.

c. What do you notice about the equation of the vertical asymptote in relation to the denominator of the function?

**TECHNOLOGY TIP**

You can use the **Table** feature of your graphing calculator to examine end behavior.

**Check Your Understanding**

3. In Items 1d and 1e, you found the domain and range of the rational function $\dfrac{12,000 + 45x}{x - 30}$. Compare your answer to the domain and range you found in the last lesson (Item 8) when the same function was used to model the paying camper fees.

4. Use the information you gathered in Item 1 to write the equations of the vertical and horizontal asymptotes of $f(x) = \dfrac{12,000 + 45x}{x - 30}$.

To graph a rational function, examine the equation and begin with key aspects, such as asymptotes and intercepts. Then fill in the "missing pieces" by plotting a few points around the asymptotes and intercepts.

5. Consider the function $R(x) = \dfrac{2x - 9}{x + 3}$.

   a. Is $R(x)$ a rational function? Explain your reasoning.

   b. For what value of $x$ is the function undefined? What does this tell you about the graph?

   c. Examine the end behavior of the function by completing the table. Then write the equation of the horizontal asymptote.

| $x$ | $-300$ | $-100$ | $-50$ | $-20$ | $-10$ | $-5$ | $10$ | $20$ | $50$ | $100$ | $300$ |
|---|---|---|---|---|---|---|---|---|---|---|---|
| $f(x)$ | | | | | | | | | | | |

   d. Find the exact values of the $x$- and $y$-intercepts. Show your work.

   e. Sketch the graph of $R(x)$ on the grid below. Include each piece of information you found in parts a–d. Use dotted lines to indicate asymptotes.

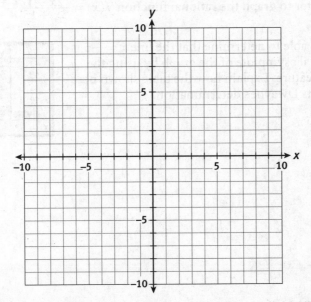

**MATH TIP**

The graph of a rational function will always approach (get very close to) its asymptotes.

**MATH TIP**

Use points that you have already found, such as intercepts and the points in the end behavior table, to fill in your graph.

**My Notes**

### Check Your Understanding

6. **Attend to precision.** Sketch the graph of the function in Item 1. Indicate the scale, label any intercepts, and include the horizontal and vertical asymptotes.

7. Given the function $f(x) = \dfrac{x+2}{x-3}$,

   a. Identify any asymptotes of $f$.
   b. Identify the $x$- and $y$-intercepts of $f$.
   c. Sketch the graph of $f$.

## LESSON 27-3 PRACTICE

8. Give the domain and range of the rational function in Item 5. Write your answers using set notation, interval notation, and inequalities.

9. Given the function $f(x) = \dfrac{2x+15}{x+3}$,

   a. Identify any asymptotes of $f$.
   b. Identify the $x$- and $y$-intercepts of $f$.
   c. Sketch the graph of $f$.

10. Write an equation of a rational function that has a numerator of 1 and a vertical asymptote at $x = 5$.

11. **Use appropriate tools strategically.** Dwayne used a graphing calculator to graph the rational function $f(x) = \dfrac{2x-1}{3x+15}$.

    He was able to determine that the line $x = -5$ is a vertical asymptote of the graph by using the **Table** feature. Explain how the table shown here supports Dwayne's determination.

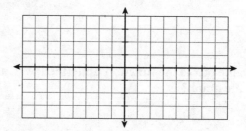

| X | Y1 | |
|----|--------|--|
| -7 | 2.5 | |
| -6 | 4.3333 | |
| -5 | ERROR | |
| -4 | -3 | |
| -3 | -1.167 | |
| -2 | -.5556 | |
| -1 | -.25 | |

X=-1

## ACTIVITY 27 PRACTICE
**Write your answers on notebook paper.**
**Show your work.**

### Lesson 27-1

Delaney decided to earn extra money by typing papers for people. Before she started her new endeavor, she had to purchase a printer. She paid $400 for the printer. She also determined that it would cost her approximately $0.05 per page in ink and paper.

1. Complete the table below to determine Delaney's average cost per page, including the cost of the printer.

| Number of Pages | Cost per Page |
|---|---|
| 20 | |
| 50 | |
| 100 | |
| 200 | |
| 400 | |
| $x$ | |

2. Using an appropriate scale, make a graph showing the relationship between the cost per page and the number of pages typed.

3. Write an algebraic rule for the cost per page as a function of the number of pages Delaney types.

4. What relationship exists between the number of pages typed and the cost per page?

5. What is the cost per page if Delaney types 1000 pages?

6. Based on your work so far, is there a minimum cost per page? Is this realistic in the context of the problem? Explain your answer.

### Lesson 27-2

Delaney wants to figure how much she should charge per page. She knows she needs to consider a variety of factors, such as what people are willing to pay, her costs, her time, and her profit. She has researched the issue and based on her research decides to charge $10 per page.

7. Complete the table below to determine Delaney's profit per page in relation to her cost per page.

| Number of Pages | Cost per Page | Profit per Page |
|---|---|---|
| 20 | | |
| 50 | | |
| 100 | | |
| 200 | | |
| 400 | | |
| $x$ | | |

8. Explain the meaning of any negative values in the table.

9. Using an appropriate scale, make a graph showing the relationship between the profit per page and the number of pages typed.

10. The algebraic rule $p(x) = 10 - \dfrac{400 + 0.05x}{x}$ can be used to model Delaney's profit per page. Use algebra to rewrite the rule as a single rational function, $p(x) = \dfrac{q(x)}{r(x)}$.

11. Use your answer from Item 10 to find Delaney's profit per page if she types 1000 pages and if she types 2000 pages.

12. Predict where the horizontal asymptote is for the graph of $p(x)$. Explain your reasoning.

## Lesson 27-3

**13.** Which of the following is the equation of the vertical asymptote for $f(x) = \frac{6x-1}{x+1}$?

A. $x = 6$
B. $x = 1$
C. $x = \frac{1}{6}$
D. $x = -1$

**14.** Given the function $f(x) = \frac{2x-9}{x+3}$,

a. Identify any asymptotes of $f$.
b. Identify the $x$- and $y$-intercepts of $f$.
c. Sketch the graph of $f$.

**15.** Which of the following is the range of the function in Item 14?

A. $(-\infty, -3) \cup (-3, \infty)$
B. $(-\infty, 2) \cup (2, \infty)$
C. $(-\infty, 3) \cup (3, \infty)$
D. $(-\infty, 4.5) \cup (4.5, \infty)$

**16.** Write an equation of a rational function that has a numerator of $x$ and a vertical asymptote at $x = -4$.

**17.** What is the domain of the function you created in Item 16? Write your answer in interval notation.

## MATHEMATICAL PRACTICES
### Look For and Make Use of Structure

**18.** Consider the graph of a rational function.

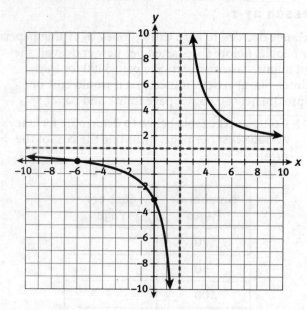

a. What is the $x$-intercept of the graph?
b. Write a linear equation with a leading coefficient of 1 which has the same $x$-intercept as this graph.
c. What is the equation of the vertical asymptote of the graph?
d. A vertical asymptote is the result of a 0 in the denominator of a rational function. Use this fact to write a linear expression that could be the denominator of the rational function.
e. Write a rational function using your answers to parts b and d to help you determine the numerator and denominator.
f. What is the $y$-intercept of your function from part e? Does it match the $y$-intercept of the graph?
g. Graph your function from part e on your graphing calculator. Does it match the graph at the beginning of the problem? What do this and your answer from part f tell you about your function?

# Inverse Variation and Rational Functions
## Stream Survival
## Lesson 28-1 Inverse Variation and Combined Variation

### Learning Targets:
- Create, solve, and graph an equation involving inverse variation.
- Solve an equation involving combined variation.

**SUGGESTED LEARNING STRATEGIES:** Marking the Text, Create Representations, Look for a Pattern, Vocabulary Organizer, Work Backward

The amount of dissolved oxygen in a body of water decreases as the water temperature increases. Dissolved oxygen needs to be at sufficient levels to sustain the life of aquatic organisms such as fish. The table shows the temperature $t$ and the corresponding amount of dissolved oxygen $D$ in a stream that flows into Lake Superior on several dates from May to August.

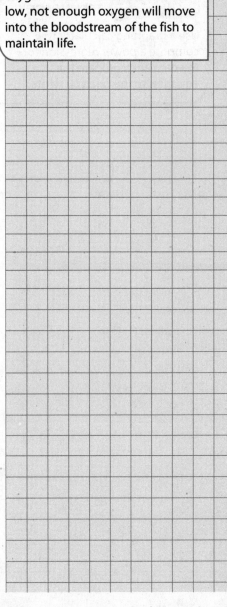

**CONNECT TO ECOLOGY**

Fish and other aquatic organisms need oxygen to live, just as mammals do. Dissolved oxygen in the water passes through fish gills and then is transferred into the bloodstream. When dissolved oxygen levels in the water are too low, not enough oxygen will move into the bloodstream of the fish to maintain life.

| Date | $t$ (° Celsius) | $D$ (mg $O_2$/L) | |
|------|-----------------|------------------|---|
| May 1 | 11.5 | 10.6 | |
| May 15 | 12.5 | 9.8 | |
| June 1 | 13.0 | 9.5 | |
| June 15 | 14.0 | 8.7 | |
| July 1 | 14.5 | 8.5 | |
| July 15 | 15.0 | 8.1 | |
| Aug 1 | 16.5 | 7.4 | |

1. Graph the data above as a set of points on the axes.

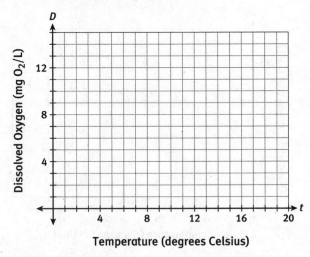

2. Are these data linear? Explain why or why not.

3. Add a fourth column to the table, showing the product of $t$ and $D$.

4. **Make use of structure.** What do you observe about the products of $t$ and $D$ that you recorded in the table?

**MATH TERMS**

**Inverse variation** is written in the form $y = \frac{k}{x}$, where $x$ and $y$ are the variables that vary inversely.

The **constant of variation** is the constant $k$ in the inverse variation equation. $k$ is equal to the product of $x$ and $y$.

**CONNECT TO TECHNOLOGY**

Use a graphing calculator to compute a power regression for the data and compare that equation to the one you wrote.

---

> **Inverse Variation Equation**
>
> When the product of two variable quantities $x$ and $y$ is constant, the two variables are said to vary inversely.
>
> If $xy = k$ and $x \neq 0$, then $y = \frac{k}{x}$, where $k$ is the **constant of variation**.

Although the products of $t$ and $D$ from Item 3 are not constant, the products are close in value. When you use mathematics to model a real-world situation, the functions do not always give exact results.

5. If you use inverse variation to model the dissolved oxygen and temperature relationship, what value would you choose for $k$?

6. Write an inverse variation equation relating $t$ and $D$ that shows a constant product. Then solve the equation for $D$.

7. **Use appropriate tools strategically.** Use your calculator to make a scatter plot of the points $(t, D)$ and graph the equation from Item 6 on the axes in Item 1.

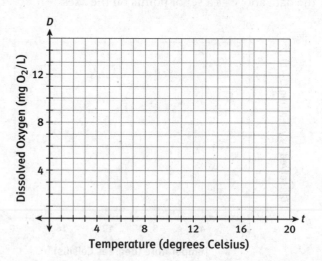

8. How well does the model that you created fit the data?

9. When dissolved oxygen is less than 6 mg $O_2$/L, salmon are in danger. Use the model to find the maximum safe temperature for salmon.

**My Notes**

### Check Your Understanding

Write and use an inverse variation equation to solve each problem.

**10.** $y$ varies inversely as $x$. When $x$ is 5, $y$ is 10. Find $y$ when $x$ is 18.

**11.** The length of a rectangle varies inversely as its width. If the area is 40 in.$^2$ and the width is 12.5 in., find the length of the rectangle.

**12.** Boyle's Law says that the volume of a gas in a closed container at constant temperature is inversely proportional to the pressure of the gas. Suppose 5 L of a gas are at a pressure of 2.0 atmospheres. What is the volume when the pressure is 3.0 atmospheres?

Another type of variation is ***combined variation***. Recall that two unknowns $x$ and $y$ vary *directly* if they are related by the equation $y = kx$ and *inversely* if $y = \dfrac{k}{x}$, where $k$, in both cases, is a nonzero constant.

Combined variation occurs when a variable varies directly with one variable and inversely with another variable. Combined variation is written in the form $y = \dfrac{kx}{z}$, where the constant of variation is $k$. $y$ varies directly with $x$ and inversely with $z$.

In Item 12, Boyle's Law results in an inverse variation as long as the temperature is constant. However, if both the pressure and the temperature vary, then the relationship between the volume, pressure, and temperature of a gas can be represented by a combined variation. This relationship is referred to as the combined gas law and states that the volume of a gas in a closed container varies directly with the temperature of the gas and inversely with the pressure of the gas.

### MATH TERMS

**Combined variation** is a combination of direct and inverse variation, written in the form $y = \dfrac{kx}{z}$, where $k$ is the constant of variation.

### MATH TERMS

**Joint variation** is another form of variation and is written in the form $y = kxz$.

### CONNECT TO CHEMISTRY

A common unit of pressure is the kilopascal, abbreviated kPa. A *torr* is a less common unit of pressure used in measuring partial vacuums. It is equal to approximately 133.32 pascals.

The kelvin, abbreviated K, is a unit of temperature often used in science. Unlike the more familiar Celsius and Fahrenheit scales, kelvin units are not referred to as "degrees." 300 K is about 27° C.

### Example A

If 2 liters of a gas have a pressure of 1,500 torr and a temperature of 300 kelvins, what is the volume when the temperature is 600 kelvins and the pressure is 750 torr?

**Step 1:** Write a combined variation formula. $\qquad V = \dfrac{kT}{P}$

**Step 2:** Substitute $V = 2$, $T = 300$, and $\qquad 2 = \dfrac{k(300)}{1500}$

$\qquad\qquad P = 1500$ to find $k$. $\qquad\qquad\qquad k = 10$

**Step 3:** Write the combined variation equation. $\quad V = \dfrac{10T}{P}$

**Step 4:** Find $V$ when $T = 600$ and $P = 750$. $\quad V = \dfrac{10(600)}{750} = 8$

**Solution:** The volume is 8 liters.

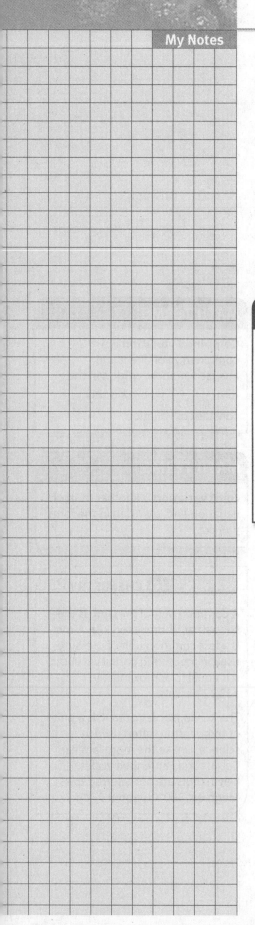

### Try These A

Find $k$, and then write and use a combined variation equation to solve each problem.

**a.** $y$ varies directly as $x$ and inversely as $z$. When $x = 3$ and $z = 4$, $y = 9$. Find $y$ when $x = 4$ and $z = 2$.

**b.** If 205 mL of a gas have a pressure of 30.8 kPa and a temperature of 451 kelvins, what is the volume when the temperature is reduced to 300 kelvins and the pressure is reduced to 100 kPa?

### Check Your Understanding

**13.** The electrical resistance $R$ of a wire varies directly as the length $l$ of the wire and inversely as the square of the wire's diameter, $d$. This relationship can be written as the combined variation equation $R = \dfrac{kl}{d^2}$. If a wire of length 50 feet and diameter 4 millimeters has a resistance of 2 ohms, what is the resistance of a wire made of the same metal that is twice as long but has a diameter of 2 millimeters?

**14.** Write a combined variation equation to represent the following relationship: $y$ varies directly as the square of $x$ and inversely as the cube root of $z$.

### LESSON 28-1 PRACTICE

**15.** Describe the relationship that exists between two variables that vary inversely.

**16.** The number of hours $h$ it takes for ice to melt completely varies inversely as the temperature $T$, assuming the temperature is above freezing. If it takes 2 hours for a square inch of ice to melt at 65° F, how long does it take the ice to melt if the temperature is 50° F? Explain your reasoning.

**17.** Write a combined variation equation to represent the following relationship: $y$ varies directly as the square root of $x$ and inversely as three times $z$.

**18.** Given the relationship in Item 17, if $y$ and $z$ both equal 2 when $x$ is 9, what is $y$ when $x$ is 36 and $z$ is 8?

**19.** **Reason quantitatively.** Use the combined variation equation you found for the resistance $R$ of the wire in Item 13 to determine which of the following wires (made of the same metal as in Item 13) has a greater resistance: a wire that is 100 feet long and 6 mm in diameter or a wire that is four times as long and twice as wide. Justify your answer.

## Learning Targets:

- Describe transformations of the parent function $f(x) = \frac{1}{x}$ and sketch the graphs.
- Identify the $x$-intercepts, $y$-intercepts, and asymptotes of transformations of the parent function $f(x) = \frac{1}{x}$.

**SUGGESTED LEARNING STRATEGIES:** Vocabulary Organizer, Create Representations, Look for a Pattern, Predict and Confirm, Note Taking

The rational function $f(x) = \frac{1}{x}$ is an example of an inverse variation equation whose constant of variation is 1.

**1.** Make a table of values and graph the parent rational function $f(x) = \frac{1}{x}$.

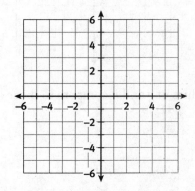

**2. Construct viable arguments.** Does your graph cross the $y$-axis? If so, give the $y$-intercept. If not, explain using algebra why it does not. Then answer the same questions about the $x$-axis.

**3.** Describe the key features of $f(x) = \frac{1}{x}$. Use appropriate mathematics vocabulary in your description.

---

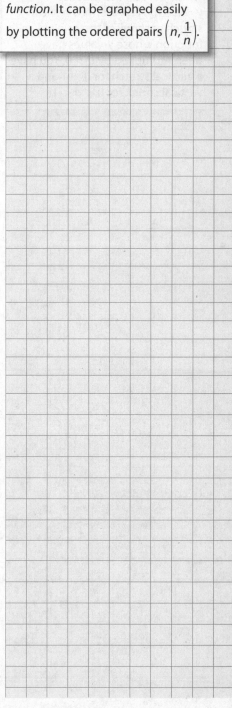

**MATH TIP**

The basic rational function is sometimes called the *reciprocal function*. It can be graphed easily by plotting the ordered pairs $\left(n, \frac{1}{n}\right)$.

My Notes

Functions like the one in the last lesson modeling dissolved oxygen and temperature are a *vertical stretch* of the parent function $f(x) = \frac{1}{x}$.

4. Enter the functions $f(x) = \frac{1}{x}$, $g(x) = \frac{2}{x}$, and $h(x) = \frac{5}{x}$ into your graphing calculator. Sketch the graphs on the axes below.

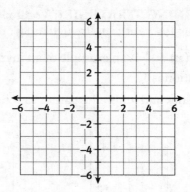

**MATH TIP**

Given $y = f(x)$, the function $y = a \cdot f(x)$ represents a *vertical stretch or shrink* of the original function whose *y*-values have been multiplied by $a > 0$. You have a vertical stretch for $a > 1$ and a vertical shrink for $0 < a < 1$.

5. How do the *y*-values of *g* and *h* compare to those of the parent function?

6. Describe the similarities and the differences in the graphs of those three functions.

7. Sketch the parent function $f(x) = \frac{1}{x}$ and the graph of $k(x) = \frac{3}{x}$ on the same axes without using your graphing calculator.

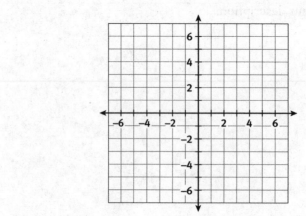

So far, we've sketched vertical stretches of the parent function $f(x) = \frac{1}{x}$. Now let's examine transformations of the form $h(x) = \frac{1}{bx}$.

8. Use algebra to write $h(x) = \frac{1}{bx}$ as a product of a coefficient and the parent function $f(x) = \frac{1}{x}$.

9. In Item 1, you made a table of values to graph the parent function $f(x) = \frac{1}{x}$. Use your answer to Item 8 to describe how to change the $y$-coordinates in the table to graph the function $h(x) = \frac{1}{2x}$.

10. Graph the parent function $f(x) = \frac{1}{x}$ and the function $h(x) = \frac{1}{2x}$ on the same axes without using your graphing calculator.

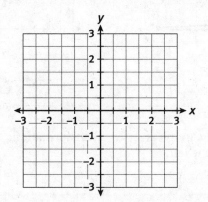

11. Without using your calculator, predict what the graph of $f(x) = -\frac{1}{x}$ will look like.

12. In Item 1, you made a table of values to graph the parent function $f(x) = \frac{1}{x}$. Describe how to change the $y$-coordinates of the points on the graph of the parent function to graph $g(x) = -\frac{2}{x}$.

**My Notes**

### Check Your Understanding

**13.** Sketch the graph of $k(x) = -\dfrac{2}{x}$.

**14.** Where are the horizontal and vertical asymptotes on the graphs of $g(x) = \dfrac{a}{x}$, $h(x) = \dfrac{1}{bx}$, and $k(x) = -\dfrac{1}{x}$ in relation to the asymptotes of the parent function $f(x) = \dfrac{1}{x}$? Explain your reasoning.

**15.** Sketch the graph of each function and then describe it as a transformation of the parent function $f(x) = \dfrac{1}{x}$. The first graph has been done for you.

**a.**
$$f(x) = \frac{1}{x+2}$$

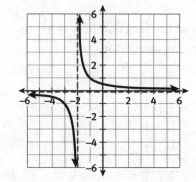

Transformation: The graph is translated 2 units to the left.

**b.**
$$f(x) = \frac{1}{x-2}$$

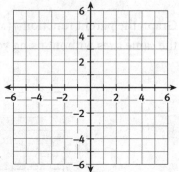

Transformation:

**c.**
$$f(x) = \frac{1}{x} + 2$$

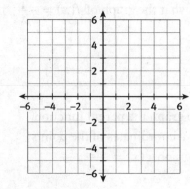

Transformation:

**d.**
$$f(x) = \frac{1}{x} - 2$$

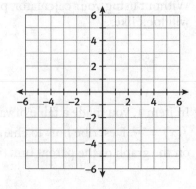

Transformation:

> **MATH TIP**
>
> Given $y = f(x)$, the function $y = f(x + c)$ results in a *horizontal translation* of the original function and $y = f(x) + c$ results in a *vertical translation* of the original function.

> **MATH TIP**
>
> A good strategy for translating rational functions is to first move the asymptotes and then fill in key points.

### Check Your Understanding

**16.** Describe each function as a transformation of $f(x) = \frac{1}{x}$.

    **a.** $f(x) = \frac{1}{x+1}$    **b.** $f(x) = \frac{1}{x} - 3$    **c.** $f(x) = \frac{1}{x-5} + 3$

**17. Make use of structure.** Without graphing, identify which functions in Item 16 cross the $x$-axis, $y$-axis, or both axes. Justify your answers.

### Example A

Describe the function $f(x) = \frac{2}{x-3} + 1$ as a transformation of $f(x) = \frac{1}{x}$.
Identify the $x$- and $y$-intercepts and the asymptotes. Sketch the graph.

| Transformations | Asymptotes |
|---|---|
| • vertical stretch by a factor of 2<br>• horizontal translation 3 units to the right<br>• vertical translation 1 unit up | $x = 3$<br>$y = 1$ |

| Intercepts |  |
|---|---|
| $y$-intercept: $f(0) = \frac{1}{3}$<br><br>$x$-intercept: Solve $f(x) = 0$.<br><br>$\quad\quad \frac{2}{x-3} + 1 = 0$<br><br>$\quad\quad\quad \frac{2}{x-3} = -1$<br><br>$\quad\quad\quad\quad 2 = -1(x-3)$<br><br>$\quad\quad\quad\quad x = 1$ | 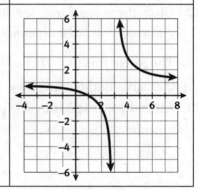 |

### Try These A

On a separate sheet of grid paper, describe each function as a transformation of $f(x) = \frac{1}{x}$. Identify the $x$- and $y$-intercepts and the asymptotes. Sketch the graph.

    **a.** $f(x) = \frac{3}{x} + 1$    **b.** $f(x) = -\frac{1}{x+1} - 2$    **c.** $f(x) = 3 + \frac{4}{x-2}$

**My Notes**

### Check Your Understanding

18. The rational function $R(x)$ is a transformation of the parent function $f(x) = \frac{1}{x}$. The parent function has been vertically shrunk by a factor of 3 and then translated down 5 units. What are the equations of the asymptotes of $R(x)$?

19. Describe the function $g(x) = \frac{4}{x+1} - 3$ as a transformation of $f(x) = \frac{1}{x}$. Identify the $x$- and $y$-intercepts and the asymptotes. Sketch the graph.

## LESSON 28-2 PRACTICE

20. Write a function that is $f(x) = \frac{1}{x}$ translated 3 units down and 5 units to the right.

21. Describe the graph of $g(x) = \frac{1}{4x}$ as a transformation of the parent function $f(x) = \frac{1}{x}$.

22. Given the rational function $R(x) = \frac{-2}{x} + 3$, identify the $x$- and $y$-intercepts and the asymptotes. Then sketch the graph.

23. The parent function $f(x) = \frac{1}{x}$ is translated 4 units up and 7 units to the right. Without graphing, identify the asymptotes.

24. **Attend to precision.** The point $(1, 1)$ lies on the graph of the parent function $f(x) = \frac{1}{x}$. Where does this point translate to on the graph of $g(x) = \frac{2}{x+1} - 5$?

## ACTIVITY 28 PRACTICE

Write your answers on notebook paper.
Show your work.

### Lesson 28-1

1. Given the inverse variation $y = \frac{10}{x}$, what is the constant of variation?
   - **A.** $k = -10$
   - **B.** $k = 1$
   - **C.** $k = 10$
   - **D.** $k = 100$

2. If $y$ varies inversely as $x$, and $y = 8$ when $x = 40$, which equation models this situation?
   - **A.** $y = \frac{5}{x}$
   - **B.** $y = \frac{32}{x}$
   - **C.** $y = \frac{48}{x}$
   - **D.** $y = \frac{320}{x}$

3. Evan's video game scores vary inversely as the number of games played without rest. If he scores 1,000 points after playing two games in a row, how much will he score after playing five games in a row?

4. The variable $y$ varies directly as $x$ and inversely as $z$. When $x = 4$ and $z = 14$, $y = 2$. Write a combined variation equation and find $y$ when $x = 6$ and $z = 3$.

5. Using the same relationship as in Item 4, find $z$ when $x = 14$ and $y = 49$.

### Lesson 28-2

6. Write a function that is $f(x) = \frac{1}{x}$ translated 2 units up and 6 units to the left.

7. Which function is a vertical translation and a vertical stretch of $f(x) = \frac{1}{x}$?
   - **A.** $f(x) = \frac{x}{2}$
   - **B.** $f(x) = \frac{1}{x+2}$
   - **C.** $f(x) = \frac{2}{x} + 1$
   - **D.** $f(x) = \frac{1}{2} + x$

Use $g(x) = \frac{2}{x+1} - 5$ to answer Items 8–10.

8. What is the vertical asymptote of $g$?
   - **A.** $x = -5$
   - **B.** $x = -1$
   - **C.** $x = 1$
   - **D.** $x = 2$

9. What is the vertical stretch of $g$?
   - **A.** 2
   - **B.** 1
   - **C.** $-5$
   - **D.** none

10. Identify the asymptotes of $g$.

11. The point $\left(8, \frac{1}{8}\right)$ lies on the graph of the parent function $f(x) = \frac{1}{x}$. Where does the image of this point lie on the graph of $h(x) = \frac{1}{3x}$?

12. Describe the graph of $g(x) = -\frac{1}{2x}$ as a transformation of the parent function $f(x) = \frac{1}{x}$.

For Items 13–15, identify the $x$- and $y$-intercepts and the asymptotes of the function. Then sketch the graph.

13. $f(x) = \frac{1}{x+2} - 2$

14. $g(x) = \frac{-2}{x} + 5$

15. $h(x) = \frac{1}{2x} - 4$

## MATHEMATICAL PRACTICES
### Model with Mathematics

16. Some satellites that orbit the earth travel in circular paths at extremely high velocities. The satellite's distance from the center of the earth is called the radius $r$ of the orbit. The time $T$, in hours, that it takes for a satellite to complete one full orbit around the earth varies directly as the radius of the orbit and inversely as the satellite's velocity $v$ in miles per hour. Suppose we know that it takes a satellite traveling at 11,340 mph 30 minutes to complete an orbit 900 miles above the earth.

   a. Write a combined variation equation to model this relationship.

   b. How many minutes will it take a satellite traveling at 12,600 mph to complete an orbit 1200 miles above the earth? Show your work.

1. **Model with mathematics.** KitKat Kondos makes kitty condos. They have $10,000 per week in fixed operating costs and each kitty condo costs $12 to make.
   a. Write a polynomial function that represents the cost of making $x$ kitty condos.
   b. Create a table to use with KitKat condos. Label the columns Number of Condos, Total Cost, and Cost per Condo. Use 25, 50, 75, 100, 125, 150, 200, 250, 300, 400, and $x$ for the number of condos.
   c. Write a rational function that represents the cost per condo of $x$ kitty condos.
   d. Draw a graph showing the relationship between the number of condos and the cost per condo. Use your table to determine an appropriate scale.
   e. If the cost per condo was $13, how many condos did the company make?

2. The following are two real-world applications that can be modeled by variation equations. Give the type of variation for each equation and the value of $k$, the constant of variation.

   a. $s = \dfrac{d}{t}$, where $s$ is the speed of a moving object that travels a distance $d$ in a given amount of time $s$

   b. $f = \dfrac{5}{3l}$, where $f$ is the force (pounds of pressure) needed to break a particular type of board $l$ feet long

3. If $y$ varies inversely as $x$ and $y = 8$ when $x = \dfrac{1}{2}$, write and use an inverse variation equation to find $y$ when $x = 2$.

4. The cost per person of renting a bus varies inversely with the number of people renting the bus. A particular bus can accommodate 56 people. If the bus is completely full, the cost per person is $15. Write and use an inverse variation equation to determine the cost per person if only 20 people rent the bus.

5. If $y$ varies directly as $x$ and inversely as $z$, and $y = 4$ when $x = 2$ and $z = 5$, write and use a combined variation equation to find $y$ when $x = 6$ and $z = 3$.

6. Use what you have learned about transformations to write an equation for the rational function whose graph is shown here. Pay close attention to the graph's scales. Check your equation by finding the $x$- and $y$-intercepts.

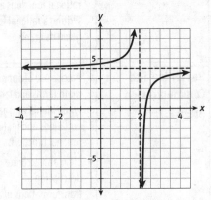

7. Given the rational function $r(x) = -\dfrac{2}{x + 3} - 1$.

   a. Describe $r(x)$ as a transformation of the parent function $f(x) = \dfrac{1}{x}$.
   b. Use what you know about transformations to identify the asymptotes of $r(x)$.
   c. Give the domain and range of $r(x)$. Write your answers in set notation and in interval notation.
   d. Find the $x$- and $y$-intercept of $r(x)$.
   e. Sketch the graph of $r(x)$. Include all of the key information from parts a to d and at least two additional points on the graph.

| Scoring Guide | Exemplary | Proficient | Emerging | Incomplete |
|---|---|---|---|---|
| | The solution demonstrates these characteristics: | | | |
| **Mathematics Knowledge and Thinking** (Items 3, 4, 5, 7b–d) | • Clear and accurate identification of key features of rational functions including domain and range, intercepts, and asymptotes and transformations of a parent function<br>• Fluency in recognizing, writing, and evaluating inverse and combined variation equations | • Mostly accurate identification of key features of rational functions including domain and range, intercepts, and asymptotes and transformations of a parent function<br>• Little difficulty in recognizing, writing, and evaluating inverse and combined variation equations | • Partially accurate identification of key features of rational functions including domain and range, intercepts, and asymptotes and transformations of a parent function<br>• Some difficulty in recognizing, writing, and evaluating inverse and combined variation equations | • Incomplete or inaccurate identification of key features of rational functions including domain and range, intercepts, and asymptotes and transformations of a parent function<br>• Significant difficulty in recognizing, writing, and evaluating inverse and combined variation equations |
| **Problem Solving** (Items 1, 4) | • An appropriate and efficient strategy that results in a correct answer | • A strategy that may include unnecessary steps but results in a correct answer | • A strategy that results in some incorrect answers | • No clear strategy when solving problems |
| **Mathematical Modeling / Representations** (Items 1, 2, 4, 6, 7e) | • Clear and accurate tables, graphs, equations, and rational functions to model a real-world scenario<br>• Clearly and accurately recognize real-world scenarios modeled by inverse or combined variation equations<br>• Fluency in applying transformations to graph rational functions and writing a rational function given its graph | • Mostly accurate tables, graphs, equations, and rational functions to model a real-world scenario<br>• Mostly accurate recognition of real-world scenarios modeled by inverse or combined variation equations<br>• Little difficulty in applying transformations to graph rational functions and writing a rational function given its graph | • Partially accurate tables, graphs, equations, and rational functions to model a real-world scenario<br>• Partial recognition of real-world scenarios modeled by inverse or combined variation equations<br>• Some difficulty in applying transformations to graph rational functions and writing a rational function given its graph | • Incomplete or mostly inaccurate tables, graphs, equations, and rational functions to model a real-world scenario<br>• Difficulty in recognizing real-world scenarios modeled by inverse or combined variation equations<br>• Significant difficulty in applying transformations to graph rational functions and writing a rational function given its graph |
| **Reasoning and Communication** (Items 2, 7) | • Precise use of appropriate math terms and language when identifying variation equations and features of rational functions<br>• Clear and accurate description of transformations of a parent function | • Adequate use of math terms and language when identifying variation equations and features of rational functions<br>• Adequate description of transformations of a parent function | • Misleading or confusing use of math terms and language when identifying variation equations and features of rational functions<br>• Misleading or confusing description of transformations of a parent function | • Incomplete or mostly inaccurate use of appropriate math terms and language when identifying variation equations and features of rational functions<br>• Incomplete or inadequate description of transformations of a parent function |

# Simplifying Rational Expressions

It's All Rational

## Lesson 29-1 Multiplying and Dividing Rational Expressions

### Learning Targets:

- Simplify rational expressions.
- Multiply and divide rational expressions.

**SUGGESTED LEARNING STRATEGIES:** Interactive Word Wall, Vocabulary Organizer, Note Taking, Marking the Text, Simplify the Problem

Rational expressions can be simplified and combined, using the operations of addition, subtraction, multiplication, and division.

Writing rational expressions in simpler forms and combining them helps you to understand and graph rational functions and solve equations.

To simplify a rational expression, factor the numerator and denominator. Identify the restrictions on the variable $x$ that make the denominator in the expression equal to zero. Then, divide out the common factors.

> **My Notes**

> **MATH TIP**
>
> The variable in a rational function must be restricted so that the denominator will not be equal to zero.

### Example A

Simplify each expression.

a. $\dfrac{x^2 + 5x - 14}{x^2 - 4}$   b. $\dfrac{2x^2 + 7x + 3}{x^2 + 7x + 12}$

**Step 1:** Identify the restrictions on $x$. Set the denominators equal to zero.

$x^2 - 4 = 0$
$(x + 2)(x - 2) = 0$
$x + 2 = 0$ or
$x - 2 = 0$
$x = -2$ or
$x = 2$

$x^2 + 7x + 12 = 0$
$(x + 3)(x + 4) = 0$

$x + 3 = 0$ or $x + 4 = 0$

$x = -3$ or $x = -4$

> **MATH TIP**
>
> Make sure that you use the original rational expression when identifying restrictions on the variable.

**Step 2:** Factor the numerators and denominators.

$\dfrac{x^2 + 5x - 14}{x^2 - 4}$
$= \dfrac{(x + 7)(x - 2)}{(x + 2)(x - 2)}$

$\dfrac{2x^2 + 7x + 3}{x^2 + 7x + 12}$
$= \dfrac{(2x + 1)(x + 3)}{(x + 4)(x + 3)}$

**Step 3:** Divide out common factors.

$= \dfrac{(x + 7)\cancel{(x - 2)}}{(x + 2)\cancel{(x - 2)}}$

$= \dfrac{(2x + 1)\cancel{(x + 3)}}{(x + 4)\cancel{(x + 3)}}$

$= \dfrac{x + 7}{x + 2}, x \neq 2, -2$

$= \dfrac{2x + 1}{x + 4}, x \neq -3, -4$

### Try These A

Simplify. Identify any restrictions on $x$. Show your work.

a. $\dfrac{x^2 + 20x + 36}{x^3 - 4x}$

b. $\dfrac{x^2 - 2x - 15}{2x^2 + 3x - 9}$

c. $\dfrac{x^3 - 9x}{3 - x}$

### Check Your Understanding

1. You are given a rational expression and told that the expression must be restricted so that $x \neq 3, -3$. What is the denominator of the expression you were given?

2. **Construct viable arguments.** Is it possible for a rational expression to have no restrictions? If so, give an example and explain why it has no restrictions. If not, explain why not.

To multiply rational expressions and express the product in lowest terms, factor the numerator and denominator of each expression. Then, divide out any common factors. Any restrictions on the value of $x$ in the original expressions will also apply to the simplified expression.

### Example B

Simplify the expression. Identify any restrictions on $x$.

Original expression $\qquad \dfrac{2x^2 - 8}{x^2 - 1} \cdot \dfrac{x^2 + 2x + 1}{x^3 - x^2 - 2x}$

**Step 1:** Factor the numerators and denominators.
$$\dfrac{2(x+2)(x-2)}{(x+1)(x-1)} \cdot \dfrac{(x+1)(x+1)}{x(x-2)(x+1)}$$

**Step 2:** Divide out common factors.
$$\dfrac{2(x+2)\cancel{(x-2)}\cancel{(x+1)}\cancel{(x+1)}}{\cancel{(x+1)}(x-1)x\cancel{(x-2)}\cancel{(x+1)}}$$

$$\dfrac{2(x+2)}{x(x-1)}, \ x \neq 2, 1, 0, -1$$

To divide rational expressions, write division as multiplication and then finish simplifying the expression using the same steps as in Example B.

### Example C

Simplify the expression. Identify any restrictions on $x$.

Original expression $\qquad \dfrac{x^2+5x+6}{x^2-4} \div \dfrac{5x+15}{3x^2-4x-4}$

**Step 1:** Write as multiplication. $\qquad \dfrac{x^2+5x+6}{x^2-4} \cdot \dfrac{3x^2-4x-4}{5x+15}$

**Step 2:** Factor the numerators and denominators. $\qquad \dfrac{(x+2)(x+3)}{(x+2)(x-2)} \cdot \dfrac{(3x+2)(x-2)}{5(x+3)}$

**Step 3:** Divide out common factors. $\qquad \dfrac{\cancel{(x+2)}\,\cancel{(x+3)}\,(3x+2)\,\cancel{(x-2)}}{\cancel{(x+2)}\,\cancel{(x-2)}\,(5)\,\cancel{(x+3)}}$

$$\dfrac{3x+2}{5}, \; x \neq -\dfrac{2}{3}, -2, 2, -3$$

> **MATH TIP**
>
> When dividing numerical fractions, write as multiplication.
>
> $$y = \dfrac{2x}{x+5}$$
>
> If $a$, $b$, $c$, and $d$ have any common factors, you can cancel them before you multiply.
>
> $$\dfrac{4}{15} \div \dfrac{8}{3} = \dfrac{4}{15} \cdot \dfrac{3}{8} =$$
>
> $$\dfrac{\cancel{4}}{\cancel{3} \cdot 5} \cdot \dfrac{\cancel{3}}{2 \cdot \cancel{4}} = \dfrac{1}{10}$$

### Try These B–C

Perform the indicated operation. Identify any restrictions on $x$. Write your answers on notebook paper. Show your work.

**a.** $\dfrac{2x+4}{x^2-25} \cdot \dfrac{x^2-5x-50}{4x^2-16}$ 
**b.** $\dfrac{6x^2}{3x^2-27} \div \dfrac{2x+2}{x^2-2x-3}$

---

### Check Your Understanding

3. **Reason quantitatively.** Explain the restrictions on $x$ for the expressions in Try These B–C.

4. Multiply the expression. Identify any restrictions on $x$.

$$\dfrac{x^2+3x-4}{x^2-1} \cdot \dfrac{x^2-4x-5}{2x+8}$$

5. Divide the expression. Identify any restrictions on $x$.

$$\dfrac{x^2-25}{x^2+6x-7} \div \dfrac{x^2+13x+40}{x^2+7x-8}$$

**My Notes**

## LESSON 29-1 PRACTICE

**6.** Simplify the expression. Identify any restrictions on $x$.

$$\frac{2x^2 - 5x - 12}{10x + 15}$$

**7.** Give a possible denominator for a rational expression that has restrictions $x \neq 4, -7$.

**8. Attend to precision.** Before graphing a rational function, you simplify the function and identify the restrictions on $x$. Explain what those restrictions tell you about the graph of the function.

**9.** Multiply the expression. Identify any restrictions on $x$.

$$\frac{4x - 4}{2x^2 - 9x - 5} \cdot \frac{x^2 - 5x}{x - 1}$$

**10.** Divide the expression. Identify any restrictions on $x$.

$$\frac{3x^2 - 3}{5x^2 + 9x + 4} \div \frac{21x - 21}{25x^2 - 16}$$

**11. Critique the reasoning of others.** Carmella simplified the following rational expression.

$$\frac{2x^2 + 7x + 3}{4x + 12} =$$

$$\frac{(2x + 1)(x + 3)}{4(x + 3)} =$$

$$\frac{(2x + 1)\cancel{(x + 3)}}{4\cancel{(x + 3)}} =$$

$$\frac{2x + 1}{4}$$

After simplifying the expression, she stated that there are no restrictions on $x$ since the denominator of her answer is a constant and cannot possibly equal 0. Did Carmella make any mistakes in her problem? If so, explain and correct her mistake(s).

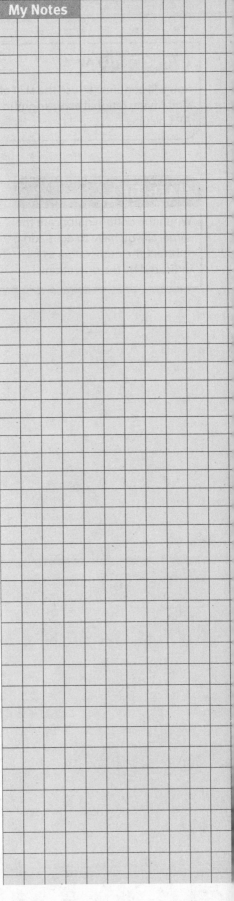

## Learning Targets:
- Add and subtract rational expressions.
- Simplify complex fractions.

**SUGGESTED LEARNING STRATEGIES:** Note Taking, Summarizing, Paraphrasing, Graphic Organizer, Simplify the Problem, Look for a Pattern

To add or subtract rational expressions with unlike denominators, find a common denominator. The easiest way to find the least common denominator is to factor the expressions. Then, the least common denominator is the product of each factor common to the expressions and any noncommon factors.

### Example A
Find the least common denominator of $\dfrac{1}{x^2 - 3x - 4}$ and $\dfrac{1}{x^2 - 16}$.

**Step 1:** Factor each denominator.
$$x^2 - 3x - 4 = (x + 1)(x - 4)$$
$$x^2 - 16 = (x + 4)(x - 4)$$

**Step 2:** Identify common factors and factors not in common.

Factors in Common: $x - 4$

Factors Not in Common:
$x + 4, x + 1$

**Step 3:** Write the least common denominator.

$(x + 4)(x + 1)(x - 4)$

### Try These A
Find the least common denominator of $\dfrac{1}{x^2 - 9}$ and $\dfrac{1}{3x^2 - 9x}$.

Now you are ready to add and subtract rational expressions with different denominators.

MATH TIP

When the denominators are the same, all you have to do is add or subtract the numerators as indicated by the operation.

## Example B

Simplify the expression. Identify any restrictions on $x$.

Original expression $\qquad$ $\dfrac{2}{x-2} - \dfrac{3}{x^2-2x} =$

**Step 1:** Factor the denominators. $\qquad \dfrac{2}{x-2} - \dfrac{3}{x(x-2)}$

**Step 2:** Find the least common denominator. $\qquad x(x-2)$

**Step 3:** Multiply the numerator and denominator of each term by the missing factor(s) of the least common denominator. $\qquad \dfrac{2(x)}{x(x-2)} - \dfrac{3}{x(x-2)} =$

**Step 4:** Subtract the like fractions to find the solution. $\qquad \dfrac{2x-3}{x(x-2)}, x \neq 2, 0$

## Try These B

Simplify each expression. Identify any restrictions on $x$. Write your answers on notebook paper. Show your work.

a. $\dfrac{3}{x+1} - \dfrac{x}{x-1}$

b. $\dfrac{2}{x} - \dfrac{3}{x^2-3x}$

c. $\dfrac{2}{x^2-4} + \dfrac{x}{x^2+4x+4}$

d. $\dfrac{x}{x+2} + \dfrac{4}{x-3}$

e. $\dfrac{1}{x} + \dfrac{2x}{x^2-3}$

f. $\dfrac{2}{x^2-9} - \dfrac{3}{x^2}$

## Check Your Understanding

1. **Reason quantitatively.** Why is it necessary to find a common denominator when adding rational expressions?

2. Simplify each expression. Identify any restrictions on $x$.

   a. $\dfrac{8}{x+5} + \dfrac{2x}{x+5} - \dfrac{x+3}{x+5}$

   b. $\dfrac{3x}{x^2-9} + \dfrac{1}{x+3}$

3. Find the least common denominator of $\dfrac{1}{5x+10}$ and $\dfrac{2}{x^2+4x+4}$.

4. Subtract: $\dfrac{2}{x^2-3x-4} - \dfrac{1}{x^2-1}$. Identify any restrictions on $x$.

## Lesson 29-2
## Adding and Subtracting Rational Expressions

You can simplify **complex fractions** if you treat them like a division problem. Simplify the numerator and denominator as much as possible, and then rewrite the problem using multiplication. Restricted values of $x$ include any values that make any of the denominators in the original expression or the simplified expression equal to 0.

### Example C

Simplify $\dfrac{1+\dfrac{1}{x+1}}{x-\dfrac{x}{x-1}}$. Identify any restrictions on $x$.

Original expression

$$\dfrac{1+\dfrac{1}{x+1}}{x-\dfrac{x}{x-1}} =$$

**Step 1:** Simplify the numerator and denominator using their least common denominators.

$$\dfrac{\dfrac{x+1}{x+1}+\dfrac{1}{x+1}}{\dfrac{x(x-1)}{(x-1)}-\dfrac{x}{x-1}} =$$

**Step 2:** Add or subtract fractions in the numerator and denominator. Combine like terms.

$$\dfrac{\dfrac{x+1+1}{x+1}}{\dfrac{x^2-x-x}{x-1}} = \dfrac{\dfrac{x+2}{x+1}}{\dfrac{x^2-2x}{x-1}} =$$

**Step 3:** Write division as multiplication of the reciprocal.

$$\dfrac{x+2}{x+1} \cdot \dfrac{x-1}{x^2-2x} =$$

**Step 4:** Factor and simplify if possible.

$$\dfrac{(x+2)(x-1)}{x(x+1)(x-2)}, x \neq 2, 1, 0, -1$$

### Try These C

Simplify. Identify any restrictions on $x$. Write your answers on notebook paper. Show your work.

**a.** $\dfrac{\dfrac{x^2-3x-4}{x^2-4}}{\dfrac{2x^2+2x}{x+2}}$

**b.** $\dfrac{\dfrac{x}{x+1}-\dfrac{1}{x-1}}{\dfrac{1}{x+1}+2}$

### Check Your Understanding

**5.** Why is 0 a restricted value for $x$ in Example C?

**6. Attend to precision.** Based on your work in this activity, do you think the set of rational expressions is closed under the operations of addition, subtraction, multiplication, and division by a nonzero rational expression? Explain.

**My Notes**

## LESSON 29-2 PRACTICE

7. Simplify. Identify any restrictions on $x$.

$$\frac{3x}{x-2} + \frac{x}{x-2} - \frac{8}{x-2}$$

8. Find the least common denominator:

$$\frac{2}{x+5}, \frac{x}{x^2+7x+10}, \text{ and } \frac{2x}{x^2-4}$$

9. Add the expressions. Identify any restrictions on $x$.

$$\frac{3}{x+2} + 2$$

10. Simplify. Identify any restrictions on $x$.

$$\frac{1}{x+1} + \frac{x}{x-6} - \frac{5x-2}{x^2-5x-6}$$

11. Simplify. Identify any restrictions on $x$.

$$\frac{\dfrac{2x^2-10x-28}{x^2-4}}{\dfrac{x+4}{x^2-9x+14}}$$

12. **Make sense of problems.** Consider the complex rational expression below.

$$\frac{3 - \dfrac{2}{x-4}}{5 + \dfrac{4}{x-4}}$$

   a. How is it different from the expression in Item 11?
   b. What is the first step in simplifying this expression?
   c. Simplify the expression. Identify any restrictions on $x$.

## Learning Targets:

- Identify the vertical asymptotes of rational functions by finding the domain values that make the functions undefined.
- Use the degrees of the numerator and denominator of rational functions to identify the horizontal asymptotes.

**SUGGESTED LEARNING STRATEGIES:** Vocabulary Organizer, Note Taking, Look for a Pattern, Marking the Text, Create Representations

In the graph of a rational function, a break in the graph often signals that a **discontinuity** has occurred. Algebraically, a discontinuity happens for values of $x$ that cause the function to be undefined and are therefore not in the domain of the function.

Common factors that are divided out of a function during the simplification process produce *holes* in the graph, rather than *asymptotes*. These holes are called **removable points of discontinuity**. The domain of a rational function does not include values of $x$ where there are holes or vertical asymptotes.

### Example A

Identify any vertical asymptotes and any holes in the graph.

$$f(x) = \frac{x^2 - 4}{x^2 + 5x + 6}$$

**Step 1:** Factor the numerator and denominator.

$$f(x) = \frac{(x+2)(x-2)}{(x+2)(x+3)}$$

**Step 2:** Divide out the common factors.

$$f(x) = \frac{x-2}{x+3}, \ x \neq -2$$

**Step 3:** Find the values that make the simplified denominator $= 0$.

$x + 3 = 0$ when $x = -3$
vertical asymptote $x = -3$

**Step 4:** Find other values that make the original denominator $= 0$.

$x + 2 = 0$ when $x = -2$
hole at $x = -2$

### Try These A

Identify any vertical asymptotes and any holes in the graph.

**a.** $f(x) = \dfrac{x^2 - x}{x^2 + 3x - 4}$

**b.** $f(x) = \dfrac{3 - x}{9 - x^2}$

**My Notes**

---

**MATH TIP**

If $f(x) = \dfrac{p(x)}{q(x)}$, where $p$ and $q$ are polynomial functions in standard form with no common factors other than 1, then the function $f$ has a *vertical asymptote* at each value of $x$ for which $q(x) = 0$.

---

**MATH TIP**

To find the vertical asymptote of a graph, determine the values of the variables that make the function undefined when it is in simplest form.

---

**TECHNOLOGY TIP**

Use a graphing calculator to graph the function and visually see the breaks where the asymptotes are located. The calculator does not show holes in a graph, but there is still an error message in the calculator's Table feature for those values of $x$.

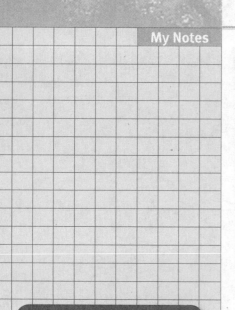

**My Notes**

### Check Your Understanding

1. Give the domain of the rational functions in Example A and Try These A. Write your answers in set notation and interval notation.

2. **Make use of structure.** Use the factored form of $f(x)$ below to identify any vertical asymptotes and any holes in the graph of the function.

$$f(x) = \frac{2x(x+4)}{x(x+4)(x-6)}$$

3. Give the domain of the rational function in Item 2. Write your answer in set notation and in interval notation.

---

**MATH TIP**

Since a horizontal asymptote describes end behavior, it is possible for a graph to cross the asymptote. There are algebraic techniques for determining if and when a graph crosses its horizontal asymptote.

---

A *horizontal asymptote* depends on the degrees of the numerator and denominator and describes the end behavior of a rational function.

- When the degrees are the same, the horizontal asymptote is the ratio of the leading coefficients.
- When the denominator degree is larger, the horizontal asymptote is equal to 0.
- When the numerator degree is larger, there is no horizontal asymptote.

### Example B
Identify the horizontal asymptote, if any.

a. $f(x) = \frac{2+x}{x^2-1}$

numerator degree = 1

denominator degree = 2

$2 > 1$

horizontal asymptote: $y = 0$

b. $f(x) = \frac{2x+2}{x-1}$

numerator degree = 1

denominator degree = 1

leading coefficients: 2, 1

ratio of leading coefficients: 2

horizontal asymptote: $y = 2$

### Try These B
Identify the horizontal asymptote, if any, of each function.

a. $f(x) = \frac{2-x}{x+4}$

b. $f(x) = \frac{x^2-1}{x+3}$

c. $\frac{x}{x^2-4}$

### Check Your Understanding

4. **Make sense of problems.** Give the range of the rational functions in Example B, part b, and Try These B, part a, given that neither of the graphs crosses its horizontal asymptote. Write your answers in set notation and interval notation.

5. Determine the degree and leading coefficient of the numerator and denominator of $f(x) = \dfrac{2x(x+4)}{x(x+4)(x-6)}$. Then give the equation of the horizontal asymptote, if any.

Now you are ready to use your knowledge of simplifying rational expressions to help you understand and graph rational functions.

To graph rational functions, follow these steps.

- Simplify the rational function.
- Express the numerator and denominator in factored form.
- Identify vertical asymptotes and holes.
- Identify $x$- and $y$-intercepts.
- Identify horizontal asymptote (end behavior).
- Make a sketch, using a graphing calculator as needed.

### Example C

Analyze and graph the rational function $f(x) = \dfrac{x^2 + 5x - 14}{x^2 - 4}$.

| Simplify. | Identify vertical asymptotes and holes. |
|---|---|
| $\dfrac{x^2 + 5x - 14}{x^2 - 4} =$ <br><br> $\dfrac{(x+7)(x-2)}{(x+2)(x-2)} =$ | vertical asymptote is $x = -2$ <br><br> hole at $x = 2$ |
| $\dfrac{(x+7)\cancel{(x-2)}}{(x+2)\cancel{(x-2)}} =$ <br><br> $\dfrac{x+7}{x+2}$ | **Identify intercepts.** <br> $x$-intercept: $x + 7 = 0$, so $x = -7$ <br> $y$-intercept: $f(0) = \dfrac{0+7}{0+2} = 3.5$ |
| **Identify horizontal asymptote.** <br><br> numerator degree $= 1$ <br> denominator degree $= 1$ <br><br> leading coefficients: 1, 1 <br> ratio of leading coefficients: 1 <br><br> horizontal asymptote: $y = 1$ | **Graph.** <br> 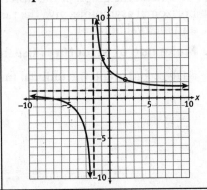 |

My Notes

### Try These C

Analyze and graph the rational function. Show your work.

$$f(x) = \frac{x^2 - 4}{x^3 - 3x^2 - 10x}$$

---

**Check Your Understanding**

6. Give the domain of the function in Try These C using set notation and interval notation.

7. **Reason abstractly.** Use your analysis of the function in Try These C to explain how you know that the graph does indeed cross its horizontal asymptote. Then give the range of $f$ using set notation and interval notation.

## LESSON 29-3 PRACTICE

8. Identify any vertical asymptotes or holes of $f(x) = \dfrac{x^2 - 25}{x^2 - 2x - 35}$.

9. Give the domain of the function in Item 8 using set notation and interval notation.

10. Identify any horizontal asymptotes of the function in Item 8.

11. Given that the graph of the function in Item 8 does not cross its horizontal asymptote, give the range of the function using set notation and interval notation.

12. **Make use of structure.** Use the steps demonstrated in Example C to analyze and graph the rational function $f(x) = \dfrac{x^2 + 2x}{x^2 - x - 6}$.

**Learning Targets:**

- Analyze and graph rational functions, identifying any asymptotes, intercepts, and holes.
- Analyze and graph rational functions representing real-world scenarios.

**SUGGESTED LEARNING STRATEGIES:** Graphic Organizer, Note Taking, Create Representations, Look for a Pattern, Marking the Text

To analyze and graph the sum or difference of two or more rational expressions, it is necessary to combine them into a single expression first. This makes it easier to identify the asymptotes and the intercepts.

### Example A

Analyze and graph the rational function $f(x) = \dfrac{2}{x-2} - \dfrac{3}{x^2 - 2x}$.

| **Simplify.** $\dfrac{2}{x-2} - \dfrac{3}{x^2 - 2x} =$ $\dfrac{2}{x-2} - \dfrac{3}{x(x-2)} =$ $\dfrac{2(x)}{x(x-2)} - \dfrac{3}{x(x-2)} =$ $\dfrac{2x-3}{x(x-2)}$ | **Identify vertical asymptotes and holes.** $x = 0$ and $x - 2 = 0$, so vertical asymptotes are $x = 0$ and $x = 2$ no holes |
|---|---|
| | **Identify intercepts.** $x$-intercept: $2x - 3 = 0$, so $x = 1.5$ $y$-intercept: none, because $f(x)$ is undefined when $x = 0$ |
| **Identify horizontal asymptote.** numerator degree $= 1$ denominator degree $= 2$ horizontal asymptote is $y = 0$ | **Graph.** 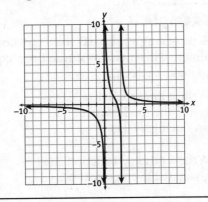 |

## Try These A

Analyze and graph the rational function. Write your answers on grid paper. Show your work.

$$f(x) = \frac{1}{x+1} - \frac{2}{x+3}$$

### Check Your Understanding

1. Does the graph in Example A cross the horizontal asymptote? How do you know?

2. Give the domain and range of the rational function in Example A. Write your answers in set notation and interval notation.

3. Analyze and graph the rational function $f(x) = \frac{x}{x+1} + \frac{1}{x-1}$.

A common business application involving rational functions is finding average cost per unit. Before deciding to make a new product, businesses conduct a very thorough cost analysis, with the primary question being whether their anticipated cost per unit will be small enough that they can make a reasonable profit.

### Example B

A recording studio has fixed costs of $18,000 to lay down tracks for a new album. This includes studio time, equipment, musicians, etc. It costs $1.20 to make each CD.

Write a linear function $C(x)$ giving the total cost of producing $x$ CDs.

Add the fixed cost and the per-unit cost.
$C(x) = 18,000 + 1.2x$

Write a rational function $A(x)$ giving the average cost per CD.

Divide by the number of units $x$.
$A(x) = \frac{C(x)}{x} = \frac{18,000 + 1.2x}{x}$

Find any vertical asymptotes.

Set the denominator $= 0$: $x = 0$

Find the horizontal asymptote for $A(x)$.

ratio of leading coefficients: 1.2
horizontal asymptote: $y = 1.2$

What is the domain of $A(x)$ in the context of the problem?

The domain is the set of counting numbers: $\{1, 2, 3, \ldots\}$

Graph $A(x) = \dfrac{18,000 + 1.2x}{x}$ using the analysis of the function above.

**Step 1:** Complete a table of values to help decide on an appropriate scale. Remember that the domain is determined by the context of the problem.

| x | 100 | 200 | 500 | 1000 | 1500 | 2000 | 2500 |
|---|------|------|------|------|------|------|------|
| A(x) | $181.20 | $91.20 | $37.20 | $19.20 | $13.20 | $10.20 | $8.40 |

**Step 2:** Decide on a scale and label the axes. Include titles for the axes. Then graph the points from the table of values.

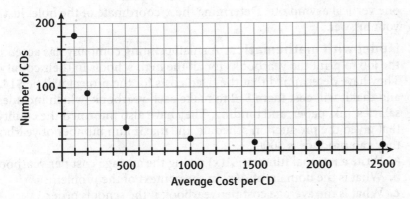

**Step 3:** Compare your graph to the analysis of the function.

The domain is discrete, so the data points are not connected by a curve. There appears to be a vertical asymptote at $x = 0$. As $x$ gets larger, the functional values get closer to the $x$-axis, which corresponds to the horizontal asymptote at $y = 1.2$.

## Check Your Understanding

**4.** Explain why the domain of $A(x)$ in Example B includes only the discrete values 1, 2, 3, … .

**5.** What is the average cost per CD if the studio produces 10,000 CDs? 15,000 CDs?

**6.** If the studio wants the average cost per CD to be $2, how many CDs must they make? Justify your answer.

**7. Reason abstractly.** What meaning does the horizontal asymptote have in the context of the problem in Example B?

## LESSON 29-4 PRACTICE

8. Analyze and graph the rational function. Write your answer on grid paper. Show your work.
$$f(x) = \frac{1}{x+2} + \frac{3}{x-3}$$

9. Give the domain of the function in Item 8 using set notation and interval notation.

10. Give the range of the function using set notation and interval notation. Be sure to consider whether or not the function crosses its horizontal asymptote.

11. The graph of the function $f(x) = \frac{4}{x+3} - \frac{2x-18}{x^2-9}$ has one hole and one vertical asymptote. Determine the $x$-coordinate of the hole. Justify your answer.

12. **Model with mathematics.** A small printing company has accepted the job to print the yearbooks for all the high schools in their county. They have determined that the fixed costs for the project will be $14,000 and that it will cost them $12 to make each yearbook, which includes salaries, ink, paper, and binding. They have also informed the county that given the production schedule, the maximum number of yearbooks they can produce is 3000.
   a. Write a rational function $A(x)$ giving the average cost per yearbook.
   b. What is the domain of $A(x)$ in the context of the problem?
   c. What is the average cost per yearbook if the schools order 1000 yearbooks?
   d. Give the equation of the horizontal asymptote for $A(x)$. What meaning does the asymptote have in the context of the problem?
   e. If together all the schools order 2000 yearbooks and the company charges them $40 for each one, what will the company's profit on this job be, assuming there were no unexpected costs? Explain your reasoning.

## ACTIVITY 29 PRACTICE
Write your answers on notebook paper.
Show your work.

### Lesson 29-1

1. What are the restrictions on $x$ in the rational expression $\dfrac{16-x^2}{4x+16}$?

   A. none
   B. $x \neq 0$
   C. $x \neq -4$
   D. $x \neq \pm 4$

2. Simplify $\dfrac{16-x^2}{4x+16}$. Identify any restrictions on $x$.

3. Give the restrictions on the expression $\dfrac{3}{x^2-5x-14}$ to determine where the graph of the rational function $f(x) = \dfrac{3}{x^2-5x-14}$ has vertical asymptotes.

4. Multiply $\dfrac{x^2-5x-6}{x^2-12x+36} \cdot \dfrac{x^2-36}{x^2-19x-20}$. Identify any restrictions on $x$.

5. Divide $\dfrac{4x+4}{x^2} \div \dfrac{x^2-1}{x^2-x}$. Identify any restrictions on $x$.

### Lesson 29-2

6. Find the least common denominator of $\dfrac{1}{x-3}$, $\dfrac{x}{x^2-6x+9}$, and $\dfrac{2x}{x^2+7x-30}$.

   A. $(x-3)$
   B. $(x-3)(x+10)$
   C. $(x-3)^2(x+10)$
   D. $(x-3)(x+3)(x+10)$

7. Simplify $\dfrac{6}{x-6} + \dfrac{x}{x+6}$.

   A. $-1$
   B. $\dfrac{x+6}{x-6}$
   C. $\dfrac{1}{x-6}$
   D. $\dfrac{x^2+36}{(x-6)(x+6)}$

8. Simplify $\dfrac{2}{x+3} - \dfrac{x}{x-1}$.

9. Simplify. Identify any restrictions on $x$.
   $$\dfrac{\frac{5}{x+6}}{\frac{10x}{x^2+3x-18}}$$

10. Simplify $\dfrac{\frac{1}{x-1}-\frac{1}{x}}{\frac{1}{x+1}-\frac{1}{x}}$. Identify any restrictions on $x$.

## Lesson 29-3

For Items 11–13, identify any vertical asymptotes, holes, and horizontal asymptotes for the function.

**11.** $f(x) = \dfrac{2x+4}{x^2-4}$

**12.** $f(x) = \dfrac{x^2}{x^2+x-12}$

**13.** $f(x) = \dfrac{3x^2}{x^2+16}$

**14.** Give the domain of each of the functions in Items 11–13. Write your answers in set notation and in interval notation.

**15.** Use your graphing calculator to help you determine the range of the function in Item 13. Write your answer in set notation and in interval notation.

**16.** Analyze and graph $f(x) = \dfrac{x^2-36}{x^2-5x-6}$.

## Lesson 29-4

For Items 17–20, use the rational function
$$f(x) = \frac{x-2}{x+5} + \frac{x^2+5x+6}{x^2+8x+15}.$$

**17.** Identify any vertical asymptotes, holes, and horizontal asymptotes by first simplifying the function.

**18.** State the domain of the function. Write your answers in set notation and interval notation.

**19.** Find the $x$- and $y$-intercepts of the graph.

**20.** Sketch the graph using your answers to Items 17–19.

**21.** A company making surfboards has fixed costs of $1600 per week. The cost to produce each surfboard is $24.
  **a.** Write a rational function $A(x)$ giving the average weekly cost per surfboard.
  **b.** The maximum number of surfboards that the company can produce per week is 2000. Given this restriction, what is the domain of $A(x)$ in the context of the problem?
  **c.** What is the average cost per surfboard if the company produces 1000 per week?
  **d.** What does the average cost per surfboard approach as production increases?
  **e.** What does your answer to part d tell you about the graph of the function?

## MATHEMATICAL PRACTICES
### Reason Abstractly and Quantitatively

Sometimes the graph of a rational function crosses its horizontal asymptote and sometimes it does not.

When the horizontal asymptote is $y = 0$, which is the $x$-axis, the graph will cross the asymptote wherever the simplified function has an $x$-intercept.

However, when the horizontal asymptote is not $y = 0$, you need to algebraically determine whether or not it crosses the asymptote. To do this, first find the horizontal asymptote and then set it equal to the original function. If you are able to find a solution for $x$, then you have found where the graph crosses the asymptote.

**22.** Determine whether the graphs of the functions in Items 11–13 cross their horizontal asymptotes. If so, tell where they cross. If not, explain how you determined that they do not cross.

# Rational Equations and Inequalities

## A Rational Pastime
## Lesson 30-1 Solving Rational Equations

### Learning Targets:

- Solve rational equations, identifying any extraneous solutions.
- Create and solve rational equations that represent work problems.

**SUGGESTED LEARNING STRATEGIES:** Marking the Text, Create Representations, Note Taking, Identify a Subtask, Guess and Check

Jesse pitches for the baseball team and wants to improve his batting average before the county all-stars are selected. To date, he has 10 hits out of 40 times at bat.

1. **Make sense of problems.** Batting average is the ratio of hits to at-bats. Write a ratio that represents Jesse's current batting average for this season and express the ratio in decimal form.

Jesse wants to improve his batting average to at least 0.320. If he gets a hit every time he bats, then his new batting average would be $\frac{10 + x}{40 + x}$, where $x$ is the number of future hits in as many times at bat.

2. Write an equation to determine how many consecutive hits he needs to bat 0.320.

To solve equations like the one you wrote in Item 2, multiply by an expression that eliminates all the denominators.

**CONNECT TO MEASUREMENT**

When a ratio is formed by two quantities with different units, it is also called a *rate*. Batting average is a rate, and even though we call it an average, it does not represent the mean of a set of numbers.

### Example A

Solve $\frac{x^2 - 4}{x + 1} = x + 5$

Original equation, undefined at $x = -1$

$$\frac{x^2 - 4}{x + 1} = x + 5$$

**Step 1:** Multiply both sides by $(x + 1)$ to cancel the denominator.

$$(x + 1)\left(\frac{x^2 - 4}{x + 1}\right) = (x + 5)(x + 1)$$

**Step 2:** Solve for $x$.

$$x^2 - 4 = x^2 + 6x + 5$$
$$-4 = 6x + 5$$
$$6x = -9$$
$$x = -1.5$$

**Step 3:** Check to see if the original equation is undefined at the solution.

**MATH TIP**

When checking your solutions, substitute the solution into the original equation.

**My Notes**

**3.** Solve the equation you wrote in Item 2 to find the number of consecutive hits that Jesse needs to increase his batting average.

### Example B

Solve $\dfrac{2}{x} - \dfrac{1}{x+2} = \dfrac{3}{x}$.

Original equation, undefined at $x = 0$ and $x = -2$

$$\dfrac{2}{x} - \dfrac{1}{x+2} = \dfrac{3}{x}$$

**Step 1:** Multiply both sides by $x(x+2)$ to cancel the denominators.

$$x(x+2)\left(\dfrac{2}{x} - \dfrac{1}{x+2}\right) = \left(\dfrac{3}{x}\right)x(x+2)$$

**Step 2:** Solve for $x$.

$$2(x+2) - 1(x) = 3(x+2)$$
$$2x + 4 - x = 3x + 6$$
$$x + 4 = 3x + 6$$
$$-2x = 2$$
$$x = -1$$

**Step 3:** Check to see if the original equation is undefined at the solution.

### Try These A–B

Solve each equation and check your solution.

**a.** $\dfrac{x+4}{x+5} = \dfrac{3}{5}$

**b.** $\dfrac{2x}{x+2} - \dfrac{x}{x-1} = 1$

When solving a rational equation, it is possible to introduce an *extraneous solution*. The extraneous solution is not valid in the original equation, although it satisfies the polynomial equation that results when you multiply by the simplest common denominator.

**4.** Solve the equation. Identify any extraneous solutions. $\dfrac{1}{x} - \dfrac{2x}{x+2} = \dfrac{x-6}{x(x+2)}$.

**My Notes**

### Check Your Understanding

Solve each equation. Identify any extraneous solutions. Show your work.

**5.** $\dfrac{x}{x-1} = \dfrac{1}{x-1} + \dfrac{2}{x}$

**6.** $\dfrac{1}{x} - \dfrac{x-1}{x^2+x} = \dfrac{x-1}{x+1}$

**7. Construct viable arguments.** Consider the equations in Try These A–B and Items 4–6. Compare the equations that did not have extraneous solutions to those that did. Make a conjecture about when a rational equation is likely to have an extraneous solution and what the extraneous solution might be.

Jesse's coach requires the team to help prepare the baseball diamond at school. Jesse and Cody, working together, can clean up the infield in 2 hours. If Jesse worked alone, it would take him 5 hours. To figure out how long it would take Cody to prepare the infield by himself, you must consider the portion of the job that can be completed in 1 hour.

**8.** If it takes Jesse 5 hours to complete the job, what fraction could he complete in 1 hour, assuming he works at an even pace?

**9.** If it takes Cody $t$ hours to complete the job, what fraction could he complete in 1 hour, assuming he works at an even pace?

**10.** Jesse and Cody, working together, can clean up the infield in 2 hours. What fraction of the job can they complete in 1 hour if they work together?

**11. Model with mathematics.** Now write an equation using the verbal model below.

| Jesse's work in 1 hour | + | Cody's work in 1 hour | = | Together work in 1 hour |

**12.** Solve the equation you wrote in Item 11 to determine how long it would take Cody to complete the job if he worked alone.

13. Use your answer to Item 12 to determine what fraction of the job Cody can complete in 1 hour.

14. Garrett has cleaned up the infield on his own before, and it took him 4 hours. How long will it take all three boys, working together, to prepare the infield for a game? Show your work.

### Check Your Understanding

15. **Reason quantitatively.** Describe how you might check the reasonableness of your answers to Items 12 and 14.

16. Working alone, Christine can put together a 500-piece puzzle in 4 hours. Christine's mom takes 2 hours to put together the same puzzle. Write and solve an equation to determine how long it will take to put the puzzle together if Christine and her mom work as a team.

## LESSON 30-1 PRACTICE

For Items 18–21, solve each equation. Identify any extraneous solutions.

17. $\frac{3}{x+2} - \frac{1}{5x} = \frac{1}{x}$

18. $\frac{4}{x} + 7 = \frac{2}{3x}$

19. $\frac{3}{x+1} + \frac{2}{x-4} = \frac{4x-11}{x^2-3x-4}$

20. $\frac{2}{x} - \frac{4}{x+1} = 3$

21. Working together, Aaron and Rosa can mow the lawn around the local library in 3 hours. Working alone, Aaron can mow the lawn in 5 hours. Write and solve an equation to determine how long it would take Rosa to mow the lawn by herself.

22. **Reason abstractly.** Working together, Pipe 1 and Pipe 2 can fill a tank in 12 hours. Pipe 1 takes twice as long as Pipe 2 to fill the tank. Write and solve an equation to determine how long it would take for Pipe 2, working by itself, to fill the tank.

**Learning Targets:**
- Solve rational inequalities by graphing.
- Solve rational inequalities by finding the sign of the inequality on either side of the numerator and denominator zeros.

**SUGGESTED LEARNING STRATEGIES:** Create Representations, Identify a Subtask, Look for a Pattern, Graphic Organizer, Note Taking

The rational inequality shown below can be solved graphically or numerically.

$$\frac{x^2 - 1}{x^2 - x - 12} < 0$$

1. First, factor the left side of the inequality and determine the zeros and the values of $x$ that are not in the domain of the function.

2. The graph of the left side of the inequality is shown below. The table shows the $x$- and $y$-coordinates and the sign of $y$.

| x | y | sign |
|---|---|---|
| −5 | 1.333 | + |
| −4 | 1.875 | + |
| −3 | undefined | |
| −2 | −0.5 | − |
| −1 | 0 | |
| 0 | 0.083 | + |
| 1 | 0 | |
| 2 | −0.3 | − |
| 3 | −1.333 | − |
| 4 | undefined | |
| 5 | 3 | + |

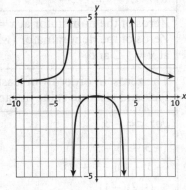

a. Identify the intervals of $x$ where the graph is below the $x$-axis.

b. **Attend to precision.** Look back to the original inequality. Why would the intervals of $x$ where the graph is below the $x$-axis be the solutions to the inequality?

**My Notes**

**MATH TIP**

To use this method, the inequality must be set up so that one side is a single rational expression and the other side is 0. If it is not, first transform the inequality into that form.

**MATH TIP**

You do not need to evaluate the inequality completely. Simply plug in the test values and figure out the sign of each factor and then the overall sign of the rational expression.

You can solve rational inequalities without using tables and graphs.

**Solving Rational Inequalities**

- Write the inequality in factored form.
- Identify the zeros of the numerator and the zeros of the denominator. (Note that the zeros of the denominator are the values where the rational function is not defined.)
- Pick one test value for $x$ that falls between each of the zeros.
- Evaluate the left-hand side of the inequality at these values to test the sign of the inequality in each interval and determine the solution.
- State the solution intervals, and graph them on the number line.

**Example A**

Solve the inequality $\dfrac{x^2-1}{x^2-2x-8} \le 0$

Factor:

$$\dfrac{(x+1)(x-1)}{(x-4)(x+2)} \le 0$$

Zeros of the numerator at $x = 1$ and $-1$
Zeros of the denominator (where function is undefined) at $x = -2$ and $4$

The zeros, in order from least to greatest, are: $-2, -1, 1, 4$
Pick and test one value in each interval: $-3, -1.5, 0, 2,$ and $5$

For $x = -3$:

$$\dfrac{(-3+1)(-3-1)}{(-3-4)(-3+2)}$$

$$= \dfrac{(-2)(-4)}{(-7)(-1)} > 0$$

For $x = -1.5$:

$$\dfrac{(-1.5+1)(-1.5-1)}{(-1.5-4)(-1.5+2)}$$

$$= \dfrac{(-0.5)(-2.5)}{(-5.5)(0.5)} < 0$$

Continue this process and record the results in a table.

| interval | $x < -2$ | $-2 < x \le -1$ | $-1 \le x \le 1$ | $1 \le x < 4$ | $x > 4$ |
|---|---|---|---|---|---|
| test value | $-3$ | $-1.5$ | $0$ | $2$ | $5$ |
| sign | $+$ | $-$ | $+$ | $-$ | $+$ |

The solution is the intervals of $x$ where the inequality is less than or equal to 0 (recall the "$\le 0$" in the original inequality). Therefore, $x$-values of the numerator zeros are included in the solution. $x$-values of the denominator are restricted and are not included in the solution.

Solution intervals: $-2 < x \le -1$ or $1 \le x < 4$

Graph the solution on a number line.

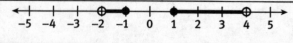

**Try These A**

Solve each inequality algebraically or graphically.

a. $\dfrac{x^2 - 5x - 6}{x^2 - 4x + 3} \geq 0$

b. $\dfrac{1}{x} - \dfrac{2}{x+2} < 0$

## Check Your Understanding

**3.** Use the graph of $f(x)$ below to solve the inequality $f(x) \geq 0$.

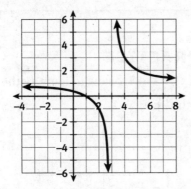

**4.** Solve the inequality algebraically or graphically.

$$\frac{x^2 + 2x - 15}{x - 1} < 0$$

A company making a new type of calculator has startup costs of $24,000. The cost to produce each calculator is $4.

**5. Model with mathematics.** Write an average cost function to represent the average cost per calculator.

**6.** The company's goal is to keep the average cost per calculator less than $9. Write an inequality to represent this scenario.

**7.** Will the average cost per calculator be less than $9 if the company makes 4000 calculators? Justify your answer.

**8.** Solve the inequality you wrote in Item 6 to determine the minimum number of calculators the company must make to meet their goal.

### Check Your Understanding

9. The company making the calculators finds that they are able to lower their per-calculator production cost from $4 to $3 by using a different material to make the casing. Given this change, what is the minimum number of calculators they must produce to keep the average cost below $9?

10. **Make sense of problems.** The company decides to sell the calculators for $20 each. The function $P(x) = 20 - \dfrac{24{,}000 + 3x}{x}$ represents the average profit per calculator. The company's goal is to make a profit of at least $15 per calculator. Write and solve an inequality to determine the minimum number of calculators they must produce to meet their goal.

### LESSON 30-2 PRACTICE

11. Use the graph of $f(x) = \dfrac{3}{x} + 1$ below to identify the intervals of $x$ where the graph is below the line $y = 1$.

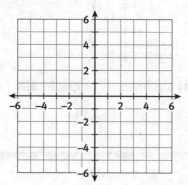

12. Use the graph to solve the inequality $\dfrac{3}{x} + 1 < 1$. Explain your reasoning.

13. Use the graph in Item 11 to solve the inequality $\dfrac{3}{x} + 1 < 0$.

14. Solve the inequality $\dfrac{x^2 + 5x - 14}{x^2 - 4} \geq 0$ algebraically or graphically.

15. **Make use of structure.** Ashton decided to combine the ideas of using a sign table and using a number line to solve an inequality. He made what he called the "sign line" below to solve the inequality $\dfrac{(x+3)(x-1)}{(x-4)(x+5)} < 0$.

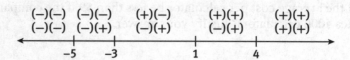

Given that Ashton's sign line is correct, what is the solution to the inequality? Explain your reasoning.

## ACTIVITY 30 PRACTICE
**Write your answers on notebook paper.**
**Show your work.**

### Lesson 30-1

1. Solve $\frac{x+3}{x-6} = \frac{2}{5}$.
   - **A.** $x = -1$
   - **B.** $x = -9$
   - **C.** $x = 9$
   - **D.** no solution

2. Solve $\frac{2x}{x-1} + \frac{x-3}{x-1} = 2$.
   - **A.** $x = 1$
   - **B.** $x = 0.5$
   - **C.** $x = 1, 0.5$
   - **D.** no solution

Solve each equation in Items 3–6. Identify any extraneous solutions.

3. $\frac{x+3}{2} = \frac{5}{x}$

4. $\frac{2}{x} + \frac{3}{x} = \frac{5}{x+1}$

5. $\frac{x-3}{x-1} - \frac{2}{x+1} = \frac{x-5}{x^2-1}$

6. $\frac{1}{x-3} = \frac{x}{9-3x}$

7. Raj, Ebony, and Jed paint houses during the summer. Raj takes 5 hours to paint a room by himself, while it takes Ebony 4 hours and Jed 3 hours. How long will it take them if they all work together?

8. When Joe and Jon work together, they can wire a room in 8 hours. Working alone, Joe needs 12 hours to wire a room. How long would it take Jon, working alone, to wire a room?

### Lesson 30-2

9. Use the graph below to determine which answer choice is the solution to the inequality $-\frac{1}{x+1} - 2 < 0$.

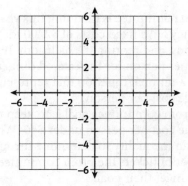

   - **A.** $x < -1$
   - **B.** $x < -1.5$
   - **C.** $-1.5 < x < -1$ or $x > -1$
   - **D.** $x < -1.5$ or $x > -1$

10. Use transformations to sketch the graph of $f(x) = -\frac{1}{x}$. Then solve the inequality $-\frac{1}{x} < 0$.

For Items 11–14, solve each inequality algebraically or graphically.

**11.** $\dfrac{x^2-9}{x^2-4x-5} < 0$

**12.** $\dfrac{1}{x+1} \geq \dfrac{2}{x-1}$

**13.** $\dfrac{x+7}{x^2-25} \leq 0$

**14.** $\dfrac{x^2-3x-18}{x^2-x-2} > 0$

**15.** The prom committee is planning this year's prom. They have fixed costs of $2200 for music, decorations, and renting the ballroom. It will also cost $25 per person for the catered dinner.

  **a.** Write a rational function that represents the average cost per person.

  **b.** The prom committee's goal is to keep the average cost per person under $40. Write and solve an inequality to determine the minimum number of tickets the prom committee must sell to meet their goal.

  **c.** The school principal reminds the prom committee that they must set aside 10 free tickets for the chaperones. The new average cost function is $A(x) = \dfrac{2200+25x}{x-10}$. How many more tickets must the committee sell to still keep the average cost per person under $40? Justify your answer.

## MATHEMATICAL PRACTICES
### Use Appropriate Tools Strategically

**16.** To solve rational inequalities using the method described in Lesson 30-2 Example A, the inequality must be set up so that one side is a single rational expression and the other side is 0. This often involves complex algebraic manipulation. You can use a graphing calculator as an alternate method to solve a rational inequality.

Consider the inequality $\dfrac{1}{x+5} + \dfrac{x}{x-3} < 2$.

On your graphing calculator, enter the left side of the inequality as $y_1$ and the right side as $y_2$. Be sure to use parentheses around the denominator of each expression.

Graph the equations. Set your window as follows:

$$\text{Xmin} = -15$$
$$\text{Xmax} = 15$$
$$\text{Ymin} = -5$$
$$\text{Ymax} = 5$$

  **a.** Draw a sketch of the graph you see on your calculator.

  **b.** Use the calculator's **Intersect** feature to find the point(s) of intersection between $y_1$ and $y_2$. Add the point(s) to your sketch.

  **c.** Explain how the point(s) of intersection help you solve the inequality.

  **d.** Shade the portions of the graph that represent the solution to the inequality.

  **e.** Solve the inequality.

1. Perform the indicated operation. Simplify your answer if necessary. Identify any restrictions on $x$.

   a. $\dfrac{2x-8}{x^2+5x-36} \cdot \dfrac{x^2+14x+45}{4x-12}$

   b. $\dfrac{1}{x} + \dfrac{x}{2x+4} - \dfrac{2}{x^2+2x}$

   c. $\dfrac{2-\dfrac{1}{x}}{4-\dfrac{1}{x^2}}$

2. For the rational function $f(x) = \dfrac{x^2+x}{x^2-x-2}$, give each of the following.

   a. vertical asymptotes and holes
   b. horizontal asymptotes
   c. $x$- and $y$-intercepts
   d. a sketch of the graph

3. **Make sense of problems.** A local contractor has three handymen that he always hires for remodeling bathrooms. Wayne is a very fast and competent worker who earns $24 per hour. Dashawn and Allen are not as experienced, take longer on projects, and earn $15 per hour.

   The contractor is working on a house that has two equally sized bathrooms. From past experience, he knows that Wayne can finish a bathroom in 10 hours working alone, Dashawn can finish one in 14 hours, and Allen can finish one in 15 hours. The contractor wants to pair up two of the handymen in such a way that he minimizes his payroll. This means that one of the handymen will be working alone on his bathroom. When the team of two finishes, they will move to another job rather than helping finish the other bathroom.

   a. Make a conjecture about which combination will minimize payroll: having Wayne work alone or having Wayne work with one of the slower handymen.

   b. Develop a plan for determining which combination will minimize the contractor's payroll for this project. Be sure to include these items:
   - the time it takes to complete each bathroom for each of the three possible combinations,
   - the total payroll for each combination,
   - which combination minimizes the payroll, and
   - mathematics to support your reasoning.

4. Solve the equation $\dfrac{1}{x+3} + \dfrac{2}{x} = \dfrac{-3}{x^2+3x}$. State any extraneous solutions.

5. Solve the inequality $\dfrac{x^2+4x-12}{x^2-x-20} \leq 0$ algebraically or graphically.

| Scoring Guide | Exemplary | Proficient | Emerging | Incomplete |
|---|---|---|---|---|
| | The solution demonstrates these characteristics: | | | |
| **Mathematics Knowledge and Thinking** (Items 1–5) | • Effective understanding and accuracy in simplifying rational expressions <br>• Clear and accurate identification of key features of the graph of a rational function <br>• Fluency in solving rational equations and inequalities | • Usually correct simplification of rational expressions <br>• Mostly accurate identification of key features of the graph of a rational function <br>• Little difficulty in solving rational equations and inequalities | • Difficulty when simplifying rational expressions <br>• Partially accurate identification of key features of the graph of a rational function <br>• Some difficulty in solving rational equations and inequalities | • Incomplete or mostly inaccurate simplification of rational expressions <br>• Incomplete or inaccurate identification of key features of the graph of a rational function <br>• Significant difficulty in solving rational equations and inequalities |
| **Problem Solving** (Item 3) | • An appropriate and efficient strategy that results in a correct answer | • A strategy that may include unnecessary steps but results in a correct answer | • A strategy that results in some incorrect answers | • No clear strategy when solving problems |
| **Mathematical Modeling / Representations** (Items 1d, 3) | • Effective understanding of how to graph a rational function <br>• Fluency in developing, applying, and interpreting a model of a real-world scenario | • Largely correct understanding of how to graph a rational function <br>• Little difficulty in developing, applying, and interpreting a model of a real-world scenario | • Partially correct understanding of how to graph a rational function <br>• Some difficulty in developing, applying, and interpreting a model of a real-world scenario | • Inaccurate or incomplete understanding of how to graph a rational function <br>• Significant difficulty in developing, applying, and interpreting a model of a real-world scenario |
| **Reasoning and Communication** (Item 3) | • Precise use of appropriate math terms and language to make and verify conjectures <br>• Clear and accurate description of a plan to model a real-world scenario | • Adequate use of math terms and language when making and verifying conjectures <br>• Adequate description of a plan to model a real-world scenario | • Misleading or confusing use of math terms and language when making and verifying conjectures <br>• Misleading or confusing description of a plan to model a real-world scenario | • Incomplete or mostly inaccurate use of appropriate math terms and language when making and verifying conjectures <br>• Incomplete or inadequate description of a plan to model a real-world scenario |

# Trigonometry

## Unit Overview

In this unit you will build on your understanding of right triangle trigonometry as you study angles in radian measure, trigonometric functions, and periodic functions. You will investigate in depth the graphs of the sine, cosine, and tangent functions as well as trigonometric identities and reciprocal identities.

## Key Terms

As you study this unit, add these and other terms to your math notebook. Include in your notes your prior knowledge of each word, as well as your experiences in using the word in different mathematical examples. If needed, ask for help in pronouncing new words and add information on pronunciation to your math notebook. It is important that you learn new terms and use them correctly in your class discussions and in your problem solutions.

### Academic Vocabulary
- constraint

### Math Terms
- arc length
- unit circle
- radian
- standard position
- initial side
- terminal side
- coterminal angles
- reference angle
- trigonometric function
- periodic function
- period
- amplitude
- midline
- phase shift

## ESSENTIAL QUESTIONS

**?** What types of real-world problems can be modeled and solved using trigonometry?

**?** How are trigonometric functions used to model real-world problems?

## EMBEDDED ASSESSMENTS

This unit has two embedded assessments, following Activities 33 and 35. By completing these embedded assessments, you will demonstrate your understanding of trigonometric and circular functions.

**Embedded Assessment 1:**

Radians, Unit Circles, and Trigonometry     p. 509

**Embedded Assessment 2:**

Trigonometric Functions     p. 549

**Write your answers on notebook paper.**
**Show your work.**

1. Find the length of the hypotenuse of a 30°-60°-90° triangle whose shorter leg is 3 units long.

2. Find the length of one of the legs of a 45°-45°-90° triangle whose hypotenuse is 6 units long.

3. Explain how the graph of $y = \frac{1}{4}(x+1)^2 + 2$ differs from the graph of $y = x^2$. Explain how you can determine the differences without graphing.

4. Identify the coordinates of point $C$.

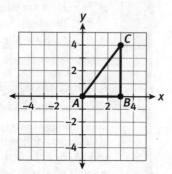

5. Identify the coordinates of point $F$.

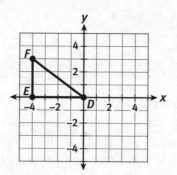

6. Determine the circumference of a circle with a 7.4-centimeter radius. Use 3.14 for $\pi$. Round to the nearest hundredth.

7. Determine the circumference of a circle with a 2-inch diameter. Write your answer in terms of $\pi$.

8. Write a function $C(t)$ to represent the cost of a taxicab ride, where the charge includes a fee of $2.75 plus $0.45 for each tenth of a mile $t$. Then give the slope and $y$-intercept of the graph of the function.

# Understanding Radian Measure

**Revolving Restaurant**

**Lesson 31-1 Radian Measure**

**Learning Targets:**

- Develop formulas for the length of an arc.
- Describe radian measure.

**SUGGESTED LEARNING STRATEGIES:** Visualization, Predict and Confirm, Look for a Pattern, Create Representations, Sharing and Responding

An architecture firm is designing a circular restaurant that has a radius of 50 feet. It will be situated on top of a tall building, where it will rotate.

The lead architect wants to determine how far people seated at different distances from the center of the restaurant will travel as the restaurant rotates through various angles. To start, he will determine how far a customer seated at the window has traveled after a 60° rotation.

1. **Attend to precision.** How far from the center is a customer seated at the window? Find the circumference of a circle with this distance as the radius. Give an exact answer in terms of π.

> **MATH TIP**
>
> Use the formula $C = 2\pi r$ to find circumference.

2. What portion of the circumference of the circle is generated by a 60° rotation of the radius?

3. Use the portion of the circle generated by a 60° rotation of the restaurant to find the approximate distance traveled by this customer.

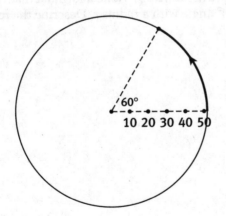

> **MATH TIP**
>
> π (*pi*) is an irrational number. If you need to provide the exact value of an expression that contains π, leave the symbol in the answer. We say that this answer is written *in terms of* π. Otherwise, simplify the expression using a numerical approximation for π. Use 3.14 for π in this unit unless otherwise indicated.

4. Complete the table by finding the circumference in terms of $\pi$ for diners at the specified distances in feet from the center of the restaurant. Also find the exact distances (in terms of $\pi$) and approximate distances traveled for diners when the restaurant rotates 60°.

| Radius (feet) | Circumference (feet) | Distance Traveled During a 60° Rotation (feet) |
|---|---|---|
| 50 | | |
| 40 | | |
| 30 | | |
| 20 | | |
| 10 | | |
| 1 | | |

5. Describe any pattern in the exact distance traveled.

The **arc length** is the length of a portion of the circumference of a circle. The arc length is determined by the radius of the circle and by the angle measure that defines the corresponding arc, or portion, of the circumference.

6. **Model with mathematics.** Write a formula that represents the arc length $s$ of a 60° angle with a radius $r$. Describe the relationship between $s$ and $r$.

**MATH TIP**

The variable $r$ is used to represent radius in formulas. The variable $s$ is often used to represent distance.

## Check Your Understanding

7. Identify the *constant of proportionality* in the formula in Item 6.

8. Use the formula in Item 6 to find the approximate distance a diner will travel when seated at each of the following distances from the center of the restaurant.
   **a.** 12 feet       **b.** 38 feet

9. How far has a diner, seated 25 feet from the restaurant center, traveled after rotating 120°? Explain how you found your answer.

10. Find the exact distances (in terms of $\pi$) and the approximate distances traveled by diners seated at the indicated distances from the center after the restaurant rotates 90°. Fill in the table.

| Radius (feet) | Distance Traveled During a 90° Rotation (feet) |
|---|---|
| 10 | |
| 20 | |
| 30 | |
| 40 | |
| 50 | |

11. **Reason quantitatively.** Write a formula that represents the arc length $s$ generated by a radius $r$ that rotates 90°. Compare and contrast this with the formula you wrote in Item 6.

12. In Item 9, you found the length of the arc $s$ generated by the 120° rotation of a 25-foot radius $r$. What is the constant of proportionality in a formula that defines $s$ in terms of $r$ for 120°? Give an exact answer in terms of $\pi$.

### MATH TIP

Recall that in the direct variation equation $y = kx$, $x$ and $y$ are proportional and $k$ is the *constant of proportionality*.

As you can see, the constant of proportionality used to find arc length *s* in terms of radius *r* is different for each angle of rotation.

When you find the arc length generated by a radius on a circle with radius 1, called a *unit circle*, you will find that the constant of proportionality takes on additional meaning.

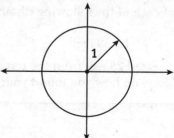

13. **Model with mathematics.** Write a formula for *s* in terms of *r* on a unit circle when the angle of rotation is 180°. Identify the constant of proportionality. Also identify the value of *s*.

On a unit circle, the constant of proportionality is the measure of the angle of rotation written in *radians*, which equals the length of the corresponding arc on the unit circle. For example, we say that 180° equals $\pi$ radians. We can use this fact about the relationship between *s* and *r* on the unit circle to convert degree measures to radian measures. It may be helpful to write these as proportions.

14. Convert each degree measure to radians. Give the answers in terms of $\pi$.
   a. 30°                 b. 45°                 c. 360°

**Check Your Understanding**

15. A circle has a radius of 15 feet. What is the length of the arc generated by a 45° angle?

16. What is the arc length generated by the 20° angle rotation on a circle that has a radius of 35 inches?

17. Convert each degree measure to radians.
   a. 135°                 b. 120°                 c. 270°

## LESSON 31-1 PRACTICE

18. What is the length of the arc formed by a 90° angle on a circle with a radius of 68 feet?

19. **Attend to precision.** What is the constant of proportionality for each angle measure? Write each answer in terms of $\pi$.
    **a.** 40°                **b.** 225°

20. Find the length of an arc formed by a 75° angle on a circle with a radius of 35 feet. Give the answer in terms of $\pi$.

21. Convert each degree measure to radians.
    **a.** 35°               **b.** 80°

Use the following information for Items 22–23. A diner has a circular dessert case in which the shelves inside rotate, but pause at set increments. Yesterday the restaurant manager decided to have the shelves pause every 60°.

22. How far did a lemon tart travel between each pause if it was placed on a shelf at a radius of 8 inches?

23. **Express regularity in repeated reasoning.** How far does a custard travel between each pause if it is placed at a radius of 12 inches?

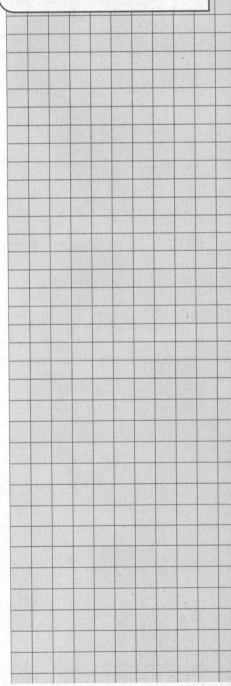

**My Notes**

CONNECT TO **AP**

In calculus, all angles are assumed to be measured in radians.

**My Notes**

### Learning Targets:
- Develop and apply formulas for the length of an arc.
- Apply radian measure.

**SUGGESTED LEARNING STRATEGIES:** Create a Plan, Look for a Pattern, Work Backward, Share and Respond, Create Representations

Angle measures can be given in degrees or radians. Angle measures in degrees are converted to radians to find arc length. Since we generally think of angles in degrees, it is useful to also know how to convert radian measures to degrees.

1. In Lesson 31-1, you found that $180° = \pi$ radians. What ratio can you multiply $\pi$ radians by to convert it back to $180°$?

2. Does this ratio also help you convert $\frac{\pi}{2}$ radians to $90°$? Show how you determined your answer.

3. **Make use of structure.** How can you convert an angle measure given in radians to degrees?

4. Convert the following angles in radians to degrees.

   a. $\frac{\pi}{5}$

   b. $\frac{\pi}{4}$

   c. $\frac{3\pi}{2}$

Sometimes angles greater than $360°$ are also given in radians.

5. Convert the following angles in radians to degrees.

   a. $\frac{7\pi}{3}$

   b. $\frac{6\pi}{2}$

   c. $\frac{11\pi}{4}$

**My Notes**

6. Given an angle in radian measure, how can you determine if the degree measure is less than or greater than 180° before doing the conversion?

7. Given an angle in radian measure, how can you tell if the degree measure is greater than 360° before you do the conversion?

**Check Your Understanding**

8. Convert the following angles in radians to degrees.
   a. $\dfrac{7\pi}{4}$                 b. $\dfrac{8\pi}{3}$

9. a. Is $\dfrac{6\pi}{5}$ radians greater than or less than 180°? Than 360°?

   b. Convert $\dfrac{6\pi}{5}$ radians to degrees.

10. **Construct viable arguments.** Before converting, how can you tell if a radian angle measure will be between 180° and 360°?

Let's think about the rotating restaurant from Lesson 31-1. You concluded that the distance traveled by a diner in the restaurant could be found using $S = \left(\dfrac{\pi}{3}\right)r$ for a 60° angle. You also now know that $\dfrac{\pi}{3}$ radian is equal to 60°.

11. **Express regularity in repeated reasoning.** Write a formula to find arc length *s* traveled by a diner in the restaurant for any radian angle measure $\theta$ and any radius *r*.

The designers decide that the restaurant should do one complete rotation every 40 minutes.

12. Approximately how far will a diner seated at a radius of 20 feet travel after dining for 1 hour, 20 minutes?

**MATH TIP**

The Greek symbol theta ($\theta$) is often used to represent an angle measure in a formula.

**13.** Approximately how far will a diner seated at a radius of 50 feet travel after dining for 1 hour 20 minutes?

### Check Your Understanding

**14.** How far will a diner seated 10 feet from the center of the restaurant travel in 1 hour?

**15.** How far will a diner seated 50 feet from the center travel in 1 hour?

**16.** How long does it take a diner seated 50 feet from the center to travel the distance that the diner seated 10 feet from the center travels in 1 hour?

## LESSON 31-2 PRACTICE

**17. Reason quantitatively.** Convert the following radians to degrees.

   **a.** $\dfrac{4\pi}{5}$            **b.** $\dfrac{3\pi}{4}$            **c.** $\dfrac{5\pi}{3}$

**18.** A diner in a rotating restaurant is seated and travels $\dfrac{2\pi}{5}$ radians before the waiter comes to the table. How many degrees does he travel before the waiter arrives?

**19.** A rotating dessert case does a full rotation every 9 minutes. How far will a dessert item travel in 30 minutes if placed at a radius of 6 inches?

**20.** The dessert case in Item 19 is sped up so that it does a complete rotation every 5 minutes. How far will a piece of dessert travel in 15 minutes if placed at a radius of 9 inches?

**21. Critique the reasoning of others.** Kyle says the radian angle measure $\dfrac{5\pi}{2}$ is between 180° and 360°. Is he correct? Explain your thinking. How many degrees is $\dfrac{5\pi}{2}$ radians?

# ACTIVITY 31 PRACTICE

Write your answers on notebook paper.
Show your work.

## Lesson 31-1

1. What is the approximate length of the arc formed by a 90° angle on a circle that has a radius of 70 feet?
   **A.** 55 ft          **B.** 110 ft
   **C.** 220 ft         **D.** 440 ft

2. A horse on a merry-go-round is positioned at a radius of 15 feet. How far will the horse travel after the merry-go-round rotates 60°?
   **A.** 15.7 ft          **B.** 23.6 ft
   **C.** 31.4 ft          **D.** 47.1 ft

3. A ticketholder is sitting on a bench that is on the merry-go-round. The ticketholder is sitting at a radius of 10 feet from the center. Approximately how far will the ticketholder travel after traveling 180° on the ride?

4. Several ticketholders are standing at various positions on the merry-go-round. Find the approximate distance ticketholders standing at the following radii will travel after the merry-go-round rotates 120°.
   **a.** 11 feet          **b.** 14 feet          **c.** 16 feet

5. Use the unit circle. What is the constant of proportionality for each of the following angles? Give your answer in terms of π.

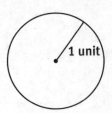

   **a.** 24°          **b.** 300°
   **c.** 72°          **d.** 270°

Find the arc lengths in Items 6 and 7.

6.

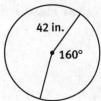

42 in.

160°

7.

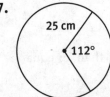

25 cm

112°

8. Find the length of the arc formed by each angle and the given radius.
   **a.** radius: 40 in., angle: 20°
   **b.** radius: 12 m, angle: 90°
   **c.** radius: 38 ft, angle: 75°

9. How many radians equal 225°?

10. Convert each degree measure to radians.
    **a.** 48°          **b.** 54°
    **c.** 160°          **d.** 120°

## Lesson 31-2

11. Convert the following radian angle measures to degrees:

   a. $\dfrac{\pi}{10}$        b. $\dfrac{5\pi}{6}$

   c. $\dfrac{8\pi}{3}$        d. $\dfrac{7\pi}{4}$

   e. $\dfrac{11\pi}{9}$       f. $\dfrac{10\pi}{3}$

   g. $\dfrac{3\pi}{5}$        h. $4\pi$

12. Is $\dfrac{\pi}{2}$ radians greater than, less than, or equal to 180°?

13. Is $\dfrac{3\pi}{4}$ radians greater than, less than, or equal to 180°?

14. Is $\dfrac{9\pi}{4}$ radians greater than, less than, or equal to 360°?

15. Is $2\pi$ radians greater than, less than, or equal to 360°?

16. A ticketholder on the merry-go-round is riding a horse that is at a radius of 12 feet. How far does she travel after the merry-go-round rotates $\dfrac{3\pi}{5}$ radians?

Use the following information for Items 17–20. A merry-go-round makes one complete rotation every 80 seconds.

17. Approximately how far will a ticketholder seated at a radius of 15 feet travel after 60 seconds?

18. Approximately how far will a ticketholder standing at a radius of 16 feet travel after 140 seconds?

19. Approximately how far will a ticketholder seated at a radius of 12 feet travel after 110 seconds?

## MATHEMATICAL PRACTICES
### Reason Abstractly and Quantitatively

20. A ticketholder seated at a radius of 14 feet rode the merry-go-round for 120 seconds. Find the distance the ticketholder traveled. What is the measure of the angle over which the ticketholder rotated in degrees? Explain how you found your answer.

# Trigonometric Functions

## Which Angle is Up?
### Lesson 32-1 Placing the Unit Circle on the Coordinate Plane

**Learning Targets:**
- Explore angles drawn in standard position on the coordinate plane.
- Find the sine of $\theta$ and the cosine of $\theta$.

> **SUGGESTED LEARNING STRATEGIES:** Vocabulary Organizer, Close Reading, Create Representations, Sharing and Responding, Look for a Pattern

In the last lesson you worked with angles formed by radii within a circle. In trigonometry, we work with angles on the coordinate plane. An angle is in **standard position** when the vertex is placed at the origin and the **initial side** is on the positive $x$-axis. The other ray that forms the angle is the **terminal side**.

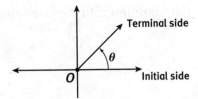

The terminal sides of angles with positive measures are formed by counterclockwise rotations. Angles with negative measures are formed by clockwise rotation of the terminal side.

### Example A

Draw an angle in standard position with a measure of $120°$.

Since $120°$ is $30°$ more than $90°$, the terminal side is $30°$ counterclockwise from the positive $y$-axis.

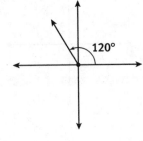

### Example B

Draw an angle in standard position with a measure of $-200°$.

Since $-200°$ is negative, the terminal side is $200°$ clockwise from the positive $x$-axis.

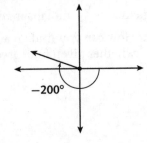

**My Notes**

### Example C

Draw an angle in standard position with a measure of $\frac{9\pi}{4}$ radians.

Since $\frac{9\pi}{4}$ is greater than $2\pi$ radians,
the terminal side makes one full rotation,
plus an additional $\frac{\pi}{4}$ radians.

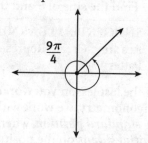

### Try These A–C

Draw an angle in standard position with the given angle measure.

**a.** $290°$

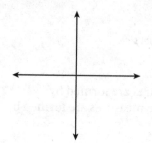

**b.** $-495°$

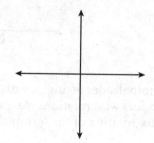

**c.** $\frac{5\pi}{6}$

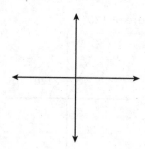

Angles can have different rotations but have the same initial and terminal sides. Such angles are ***coterminal angles***. In Example C, you can see that an angle that is $\frac{9\pi}{4}$ radians is coterminal with an angle that is $\frac{\pi}{4}$ radians.

**1.** How can you find an angle that is coterminal with a given angle, whether given in degrees or in radians?

### Example D

Find one positive and one negative angle that are coterminal with each given angle.

**a.** $225°$

$$225° + 360° = 585°$$

$$225° - 360° = -135°$$

**b.** $\frac{\pi}{3}$ radians

$$\frac{\pi}{3} + 2\pi = \frac{7\pi}{3}$$

$$\frac{\pi}{3} - 2\pi = -\frac{5\pi}{3}$$

### Try These D

Find one positive and one negative angle that are coterminal with each given angle.

**a.** $150°$

**b.** $320°$

**c.** $-270°$

**d.** $\frac{2\pi}{5}$

### Check Your Understanding

**2.** Draw an angle in standard position with a measure of $\frac{10\pi}{3}$ radians.

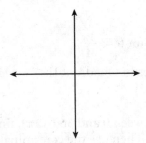

**3.** Find one positive and one negative angle that are coterminal with each of the given angles.

**a.** $-330°$      **b.** $480°$      **c.** $\frac{3\pi}{2}$

**4.** Are $520°$ and $-560°$ coterminal angles? Explain your answer.

**5.** Are $\frac{10\pi}{6}$ and $-\frac{28\pi}{6}$ coterminal angles? Explain your answer.

**6.** Is there a limit to the number of coterminal angles an angle can have? Explain.

**My Notes**

If $\theta$ is an angle in standard position, its ***reference angle*** $\alpha$ is the acute angle formed by the terminal side of $\theta$ and the $x$-axis. The graphs show the reference angle $\alpha$ for four different angles that have their terminal sides in different quadrants.

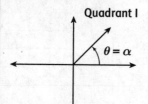
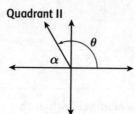
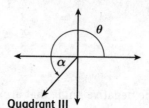
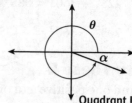

The relationship between $\theta$ and $\alpha$ is shown for each quadrant when $0° < \theta < 360°$ or $0 < \theta < 2\pi$.

|  | Quadrant I | Quadrant II | Quadrant III | Quadrant IV |
|---|---|---|---|---|
| Degrees: | $\alpha = \theta$ | $\alpha = 180° - \theta$ | $\alpha = \theta - 180°$ | $\alpha = 360° - \theta$ |
| Radians: | $\alpha = \theta$ | $\alpha = \pi - \theta$ | $\alpha = \theta - \pi$ | $\alpha = 2\pi - \theta$ |

### Example E

Find the reference angle for $\theta = 245°$.

The terminal side of $\theta$ lies in Quadrant III.

$\alpha = 245° - 180°$, so $\alpha = 65°$.

### Example F

Find the reference angle for $\theta = \dfrac{3\pi}{4}$.

The terminal side of $\theta$ lies in Quadrant II.

$\alpha = \pi - \dfrac{3\pi}{4}$, so $\alpha = \dfrac{\pi}{4}$.

When an angle is not between 0 and $360°(2\pi)$, find a coterminal angle that is within that range. Then use the coterminal angle to find the reference angle.

### Example G

Find the reference angle for $\theta = 435°$.

Since $435°$ is greater than $360°$, subtract.

$435 - 360 = 75°$

Now determine the reference angle for $75°$.

Since $75°$ is in Quadrant I, the reference angle is $75°$.

**My Notes**

### Example H
Find the reference angle for $\theta = \dfrac{13\pi}{4}$ radians.

Since $\dfrac{13\pi}{4}$ is greater than $2\pi$, subtract.

$$\dfrac{13\pi}{4} - 2\pi = \dfrac{13\pi}{4} - \dfrac{8\pi}{4} = \dfrac{5\pi}{4}$$

The terminal side of this angle is in Quadrant III.

$$\alpha = \dfrac{5\pi}{4} - \pi = \dfrac{5\pi}{4} - \dfrac{4\pi}{4}, \text{ so } \alpha = \dfrac{\pi}{4}.$$

### Try These E–H
Find the reference angle for each value of $\theta$.

**a.** $\theta = 325°$                  **b.** $\theta = \dfrac{4\pi}{9}$

**c.** $\theta = 515°$                 **d.** $\theta = \dfrac{7\pi}{6}$

**e.** $\theta = \dfrac{10\pi}{3}$               **f.** $\theta = 820°$

Coterminal and reference angles can be used to find trigonometric functions for angles in standard form. ***Trigonometric functions*** describe the relationships between sides and angles in a triangle.

We can look at these relationships on the unit circle. Since the radius of the unit circle is 1 unit, any right triangle with a hypotenuse formed by this radius has a hypotenuse length of 1 unit.

**MATH TIP**

You learned the trigonometric functions for sine and cosine in geometry.

$$\sin\theta = \dfrac{\text{opposite leg}}{\text{hypotenuse}}$$

$$\cos\theta = \dfrac{\text{adjacent leg}}{\text{hypotenuse}}$$

**Unit Circle**

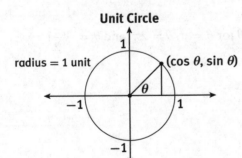

$$\sin\theta = \dfrac{y}{1} = y$$

$$\cos\theta = \dfrac{x}{1} = x$$

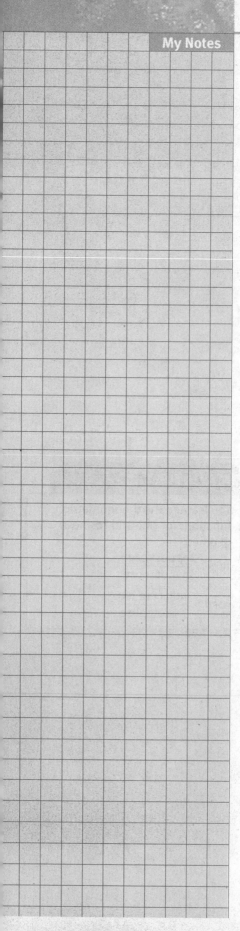

The cosine of $\theta$ (cos $\theta$) is the *x*-coordinate of the point at which the terminal side of the angle intersects the unit circle. The sine of $\theta$ (sin $\theta$) is the *y*-coordinate.

### Example I

Find the sine and cosine of 90°.

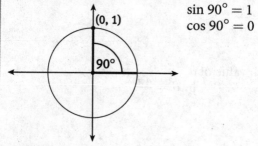

$$\sin 90° = 1$$
$$\cos 90° = 0$$

### Example J

Find the sine and cosine of 180°.

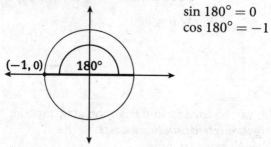

$$\sin 180° = 0$$
$$\cos 180° = -1$$

### Try These I–J

**a.** What are the sin $\theta$ and cos $\theta$ for $\theta = 270°$, $\theta = -270°$, and $\theta = 720°$?

**b.** What are the sin $\theta$ and cos $\theta$ for $\theta = \pi$, $\theta = 2\pi$, and $\theta = -\dfrac{\pi}{2}$?

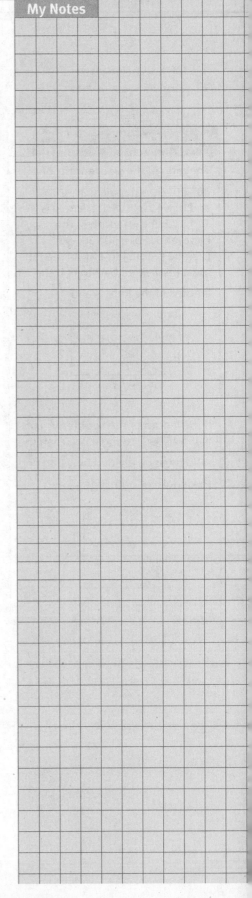

### Check Your Understanding

7. Find the reference angle for each value of $\theta$.
   a. $\theta = 135$          b. $\theta = 240°$
   c. $\theta = \dfrac{7\pi}{6}$          d. $\theta = \dfrac{5\pi}{3}$

8. Find the value of $\sin \theta$ and $\cos \theta$ for each angle.
   a. $\theta = 360°$          b. $\theta = -90°$          c. $\theta = -\dfrac{7\pi}{2}$

### LESSON 32-1 PRACTICE

9. Draw an angle in standard position with a measure of $-\dfrac{7\pi}{3}$ radians.

10. Give one positive and one negative angle that are coterminal with $-390°$.

11. What is the reference angle for each value of $\theta$?
    a. $\theta = \dfrac{17\pi}{6}$          b. $\theta = -250°$?

12. What are the sine and cosine for each value of $\theta$?
    a. $\theta = 270°$          b. $\theta = -5\pi$

13. **Attend to precision.** Refer to Examples I and J and Try These I–J. Do you notice anything about the sine and cosine of angles that are multiples of 90°?

**My Notes**

**Learning Targets:**
- Find the sine of $\theta$ and the cosine of $\theta$ using special right triangles.
- Find the tan of $\theta$.

**SUGGESTED LEARNING STRATEGIES:** Create Representations, Graphic Organizer, Look for a Pattern

You can use what you know about the ratios of side lengths of special right triangles to determine the sine and cosine of their angles. As shown in the last lesson, a right triangle whose hypotenuse is a radius of the unit circle has a hypotenuse length of 1 unit. The hypotenuse is the terminal side of an angle, $\theta$, and the sine and cosine of $\theta$ are the lengths of the legs of the right triangle.

**MATH TIP**

The ratio of the side lengths of a $30°$-$60°$-$90°$ triangle is $1 : \sqrt{3} : 2$, and of a $45°$-$45°$-$90°$ triangle is $1 : 1 : \sqrt{2}$. If the length of the hypotenuse of a $30°$-$60°$-$90°$ triangle is equal to 1, then the ratio must be divided by 2 to find the lengths of the legs, $\frac{1}{2}$ and $\frac{\sqrt{3}}{2}$.

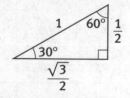

If the length of the hypotenuse of a $45°$-$45°$-$90°$ triangle is 1, then the ratio must be divided by $\sqrt{2}$ to find the length of both legs, $\frac{1}{\sqrt{2}} = \frac{\sqrt{2}}{2}$.

## Example A

What are the sine and cosine of $\theta$?

$$\theta = 30°$$

The sine and cosine are the lengths of the legs of a $30°$-$60°$-$90°$ triangle.

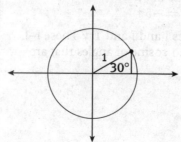

$$\sin 30° = y = \text{length of shorter leg} = \frac{1}{2}$$

$$\cos 30° = x = \text{length of longer leg} = \frac{\sqrt{3}}{2}$$

If $\theta$ is not in the first quadrant, use a reference angle.

## Example B

What are $\sin \theta$ and $\cos \theta$?

$$\theta = \frac{7\pi}{4} \text{ radians}$$

To find $\sin \theta$ and $\cos \theta$, draw the terminal side of the angle on the unit circle. Make a right triangle with one leg on the $x$-axis. Determine the reference angle, which is $\frac{\pi}{4}$, or $45°$. The triangle is a $45°$-$45°$-$90°$ triangle.

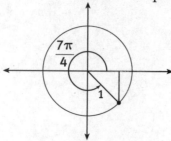

$$\sin \frac{7\pi}{4} = y = -\text{length of opposite leg} = -\frac{\sqrt{2}}{2}$$

$$\cos \frac{7\pi}{4} = x = \text{length of adjacent leg} = \frac{\sqrt{2}}{2}$$

## Try These A–B

What are sin $\theta$ and cos $\theta$ for each value of $\theta$?

**a.** $\theta = 300°$

**b.** $\theta = -225°$

**c.** $\theta = \dfrac{5\pi}{6}$

**d.** $\theta = -\dfrac{4\pi}{3}$

Sine and cosine are just two of the trigonometric functions. Next we will look at a third function, the tangent function.

Recall that the tangent function for a right triangle is $\tan \theta = \dfrac{\text{opposite leg}}{\text{adjacent leg}}$.

Looking at the unit circle on the coordinate plane, you can see that this can also be expressed as $\tan \theta = \dfrac{y}{x}$, where $y$ and $x$ are the coordinates at the point of intersection of the terminal side of $\theta$ and the unit circle.

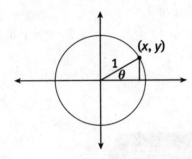

As with the relationships we saw with sine and cosine, this relationship is also true for all angles on the unit circle.

## Example C

What is $\tan \theta$ for $\theta = 60°$?

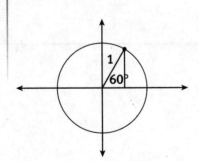

$$\tan 60° = \frac{y}{x} = \frac{\frac{\sqrt{3}}{2}}{\frac{1}{2}} = \sqrt{3}$$

**My Notes**

### Example D

What is $\tan \theta$ for $\theta = \dfrac{5\pi}{4}$?

Use the reference angle $\dfrac{\pi}{4}$.

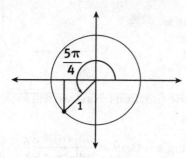

$$\tan \frac{5\pi}{4} = \tan \frac{\pi}{4} = \frac{\frac{\sqrt{2}}{2}}{\frac{\sqrt{2}}{2}} = 1$$

### Try These C–D

Find $\tan \theta$ for each value of $\theta$.

**a.** $\theta = 300°$          **b.** $\theta = 450°$

**c.** $\theta = \dfrac{2\pi}{3}$          **d.** $\theta = \dfrac{11\pi}{4}$

**MATH TIP**

When a ratio has a denominator of 0, the ratio is *undefined*.

**MATH TIP**

When a ratio has an irrational number in the denominator, the denominator needs to be rationalized.

Multiply the numerator and denominator by the irrational number.

For example, $\dfrac{2}{\sqrt{3}} \cdot \dfrac{\sqrt{3}}{\sqrt{3}} = \dfrac{2\sqrt{3}}{3}$.

### Check Your Understanding

1. Find $\sin \theta$ and $\cos \theta$.
   **a.** $\theta = 210°$    **b.** $\theta = \dfrac{2\pi}{3}$    **c.** $\theta = -\dfrac{\pi}{4}$

2. Find $\tan \theta$ for each value of $\theta$.
   **a.** $\theta = 240°$    **b.** $\theta = 690°$    **c.** $\theta = -585°$

3. What is $\tan \theta$ for these values of $\theta$?
   **a.** $\theta = \dfrac{7\pi}{6}$    **b.** $\theta = \dfrac{7\pi}{3}$    **c.** $\theta = -\dfrac{9\pi}{4}$

The terminal side of every angle in standard position has a point that intersects the unit circle. You have seen that a right triangle can be drawn with the terminal side of each angle as the hypotenuse. One leg of the triangle is the segment drawn from the point of intersection to the *x*-axis, and the other leg is the segment of the *x*-axis from the origin to the point of intersection with the vertical segment.

You have been looking at 30°-60°-90° triangles and 45°-45°-90° triangles. All of the angles that can form these two triangles are given on the unit circle below in degrees and radians.

4. Use the reference angle that can be formed to find the *x*- and *y*-coordinates for each point of intersection on the unit circle.

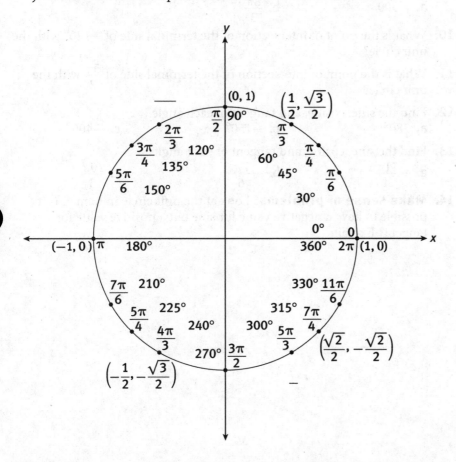

As you have seen in Lesson 32-1 and in the first part of this lesson, you can find the values of the trigonometric functions sine, cosine, and tangent using the coordinates of the point of intersection of the terminal side of each angle with the unit circle.

5. Use the coordinates you found in Item 4. What are the sine, cosine, and tangent of 210°?

6. What are the sine, cosine, and tangent of $\frac{5\pi}{4}$ radians?

**MATH TIP**

The coordinates of the intersection of the terminal side of an angle $\theta$ with the unit circle are $(\cos \theta, \sin \theta)$.

**My Notes**

---

**Check Your Understanding**

7. What are the sine, cosine, and tangent of 495°?

8. What are the sine, cosine, and tangent of $\frac{7\pi}{4}$ radians?

---

## LESSON 32-2 PRACTICE

9. Find the sine and cosine for each value of $\theta$.
   a. $-300$
   b. $\frac{8\pi}{3}$

10. What is the point of intersection of the terminal side of $-120°$ with the unit circle?

11. What is the point of intersection of the terminal side of $\frac{5\pi}{2}$ with the unit circle?

12. Find the sine, cosine, and tangent of each angle.
    a. 780°
    b. $-150°$
    c. $-405°$

13. Find the sine, cosine, and tangent of each angle.
    a. $-\frac{11\pi}{4}$
    b. $-\frac{7\pi}{6}$
    c. $\frac{10\pi}{3}$

14. **Make sense of problems.** Look at the unit circle in Item 4. Is it possible to have a negative value for sine but a positive value for tangent? Explain.

## ACTIVITY 32 PRACTICE
Write your answers on notebook paper.
Show your work.

### Lesson 32-1

1. Draw an angle in standard position for each of the following measures.
   **a.** $200°$          **b.** $575°$

   **c.** $-225°$          **d.** $-660°$

   **e.** $\frac{2\pi}{5}$          **f.** $-\frac{3\pi}{2}$

   **g.** $-\frac{9\pi}{4}$          **h.** $\frac{11\pi}{3}$

2. Which angle is a coterminal angle with $140°$?
   **A.** $-140°$          **B.** $40°$
   **C.** $400°$          **D.** $500°$

3. Which angle is a coterminal angle with $-75°$?
   **A.** $435°$          **B.** $-285°$
   **C.** $285°$          **D.** $-645°$

4. Which angle is *not* a coterminal angle with $\frac{5\pi}{4}$ radians?

   **A.** $-\frac{3\pi}{4}$          **B.** $-\frac{7\pi}{4}$

   **C.** $-\frac{11\pi}{4}$          **D.** $\frac{13\pi}{4}$

5. Give one positive and one negative angle that are coterminal with each of the following angles.
   **a.** $-65°$          **b.** $500°$

   **c.** $-\frac{6\pi}{5}$          **d.** $\frac{8\pi}{3}$

6. What is the reference angle for $\theta = 75°$?
   **A.** $15°$          **B.** $75°$
   **C.** $105°$          **D.** $255°$

7. What is the reference angle for $\theta = \frac{8\pi}{5}$?

   **A.** $\frac{\pi}{5}$          **B.** $\frac{2\pi}{5}$

   **C.** $\frac{3\pi}{5}$          **D.** $\frac{8\pi}{5}$

8. What is the reference angle for each value of $\theta$?
   **a.** $\theta = -325°$          **b.** $\theta = 530°$

   **c.** $\theta = -\frac{12\pi}{5}$          **d.** $\theta = \frac{7\pi}{4}$

9. In which quadrant is the reference angle $\alpha$ equal to $\theta$?

10. Find $\sin\theta$ and $\cos\theta$.
    **a.** $\theta = -180°$          **b.** $\theta = 450°$?

11. Find $\sin\theta$ and $\cos\theta$.
    **a.** $\theta = 6\pi$          **b.** $\theta = -\frac{7\pi}{2}$

12. What are the sine and cosine for each value of $\theta$?
    **a.** $\theta = 315°$          **b.** $\theta = -510°$

    **c.** $\theta = -\frac{11\pi}{6}$          **d.** $\theta = \frac{10\pi}{3}$

## Lesson 32-2

**13.** What is $\tan \theta$ for $\theta = -300°$?

 A. $-\dfrac{\sqrt{3}}{3}$  B. $\dfrac{\sqrt{3}}{2}$

 C. $\dfrac{1}{2}$  D. $\sqrt{3}$

**14.** What is $\tan \theta$ for $\theta = \dfrac{19\pi}{6}$?

 A. $-\sqrt{3}$  B. $\dfrac{\sqrt{3}}{3}$

 C. $\dfrac{\sqrt{3}}{2}$  D. $-\dfrac{1}{2}$

**15.** What is $\tan \theta$ for $\theta = 765°$?

 A. $\sqrt{2}$  B. $\dfrac{\sqrt{2}}{2}$

 C. $-1$  D. $1$

**16.** What is $\tan \theta$ for each value of $\theta$?

 **a.** $\theta = -495°$  **b.** $\theta = 690°$

 **c.** $\theta = \dfrac{14\pi}{3}$  **d.** $\theta = -\dfrac{7\pi}{2}$

**17.** Give an angle measure in degrees, between $0°$ and $360°$, whose terminal side has a point of intersection with the unit circle at $\left(-\dfrac{\sqrt{2}}{2}, -\dfrac{\sqrt{2}}{2}\right)$.

**18.** Give an angle measure in radians, between $\pi$ and $2\pi$, whose terminal side has a point of intersection with the unit circle at $\left(\dfrac{1}{2}, -\dfrac{\sqrt{3}}{2}\right)$.

**19.** What are the sine, cosine, and tangent of $390°$?

**20.** What are the sine, cosine, and tangent of $-510°$?

**21.** What are the sine, cosine, and tangent of $\dfrac{13\pi}{3}$?

**22.** What are the sine, cosine, and tangent of $-\dfrac{11\pi}{4}$?

## MATHEMATICAL PRACTICES
### Use Appropriate Tools Strategically

**23.** Use the unit circle in Item 4 of Lesson 32-2. Determine which trigonometric functions are positive and which are negative in each quadrant. Explain how you determined the signs for each quadrant. Summarize your findings on a coordinate plane like the one below.

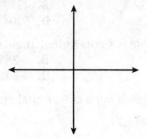

# Trigonometric Identities: Pythagorean Connection   ACTIVITY 33

**More Than Just Triangles**

**Lesson 33-1  The Pythagorean Identity**

## Learning Targets:

- Prove the Pythagorean identity.
- Use the Pythagorean identity to find sin $\theta$, cos $\theta$, or tan $\theta$, given the value of one of these functions and the quadrant of $\theta$.

> **SUGGESTED LEARNING STRATEGIES:** Close Reading, Look for a Pattern, Discussion Groups, Create Representations

The trigonometric functions of sine, cosine, and tangent are each a ratio relating two of the three sides of a right triangle. Any two of these trigonometric ratios have one side in common, and together they relate all three sides of a triangle.

We can use the definitions of sine, cosine, and tangent to explore these relationships.

Look at the ratios that were defined in the previous lesson for the unit circle, where the length of the hypotenuse is equal to 1:

$$\sin \theta = \frac{y}{1} \qquad \cos \theta = \frac{x}{1} \qquad \tan \theta = \frac{y}{x}$$

Since sin $\theta = y$ and cos $\theta = x$, we can write the tan $\theta$ in terms of sine and cosine.

$$\tan \theta = \frac{y}{x}, \text{ so } \tan \theta = \frac{\sin \theta}{\cos \theta}$$

In geometry, you studied a special relationship between the sides of a right triangle when you learned the Pythagorean Theorem.

Let's express the relationship between the sides of a triangle on the unit circle with the Pythagorean Theorem.

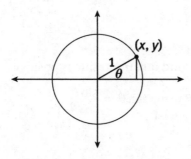

Here we can see that the legs are $x$ and $y$ and the hypotenuse is 1, so $x^2 + y^2 = 1^2$. Simplified, $x^2 + y^2 = 1$.

**My Notes**

> **MATH TIP**
>
> The Pythagorean Theorem shows the following relationship between the sides of a right triangle: $a^2 + b^2 = c^2$, where $a$ and $b$ are the legs and $c$ is the hypotenuse of a right triangle.

We can rewrite this equation with sine and cosine by substituting $\sin\theta$ for $y$ and $\cos\theta$ for $x$. Now we have the following equation:

$$(\sin\theta)^2 + (\cos\theta)^2 = 1$$

Using the notation $\sin^2\theta$ for $(\sin\theta)^2$ and $\cos^2\theta$ for $(\cos\theta)^2$, this equation can be rewritten as follows:

$$\sin^2\theta + \cos^2\theta = 1$$

This relationship is called a Pythagorean identity.

We can use all of these relationships between sine, cosine, and tangent to solve problems on the unit circle.

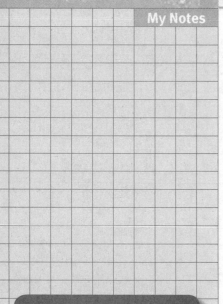

**MATH TIP**

The sign of each trigonometric function depends on the quadrant in which the terminal side of the angle lies.

### Example A

Given that $\cos\theta = -\dfrac{3}{5}$ and that $\dfrac{\pi}{2} < \theta < \pi$, find the value of $\sin\theta$ and $\tan\theta$.

Since we need $\sin\theta$ to calculate $\tan\theta$, let's first find $\sin\theta$.

Using $\sin^2\theta + \cos^2\theta = 1$, substitute any given information and solve.

$$\sin^2\theta + \left(-\frac{3}{5}\right)^2 = 1$$

$$\sin^2\theta + \left(\frac{9}{25}\right) = 1$$

$$\sin^2\theta = \frac{16}{25}$$

$$\sqrt{\sin^2\theta} = \sqrt{\frac{16}{25}}$$

$$\sin\theta = \frac{4}{5}$$

Because it is in the second quadrant, sine is positive.

Now we can find $\tan\theta$ using $\tan\theta = \dfrac{\sin\theta}{\cos\theta}$.

$$\tan\theta = \frac{\frac{4}{5}}{-\frac{3}{5}} = -\frac{4}{3}$$

### Try These A

**a.** Given that $\cos\theta = -\dfrac{8}{17}$ and that $\dfrac{\pi}{2} < \theta < \pi$, find the value of $\sin\theta$ and $\tan\theta$.

**b.** Given that $\cos\theta = -\dfrac{5}{13}$ and that $\pi < \theta < \dfrac{3\pi}{2}$, find the value of $\sin\theta$ and $\tan\theta$.

**My Notes**

### Check Your Understanding

1. Given that $\cos\theta = \frac{7}{25}$ and that $0 < \theta < \frac{\pi}{2}$, find the value of $\sin\theta$ and $\tan\theta$.

2. Given that $\sin\theta = \frac{3}{5}$ and that $\frac{\pi}{2} < \theta < \pi$, find the value of $\cos\theta$ and $\tan\theta$.

## LESSON 33-1 PRACTICE

3. Given that $\sin\theta = -\frac{40}{41}$ and that $\pi < \theta < \frac{3\pi}{2}$, find the value of $\cos\theta$ and $\tan\theta$.

4. Given that $\cos\theta = -\frac{5\sqrt{3}}{10}$ and that $\frac{\pi}{2} < \theta < \pi$, find the value of $\sin\theta$ and $\tan\theta$.

5. Given that $\sin\theta = -\frac{4\sqrt{2}}{8}$ and that $\frac{3\pi}{2} < \theta < 2\pi$, find the value of $\cos\theta$ and $\tan\theta$.

6. **Reason quantitatively.** If sine and cosine are both positive, in which quadrant is the terminal side of the angle?

7. **Reason abstractly.** When solving for a missing value of sine or cosine in the equation $\sin^2\theta + \cos^2\theta = 1$, is it possible that the answer may be negative? Explain.

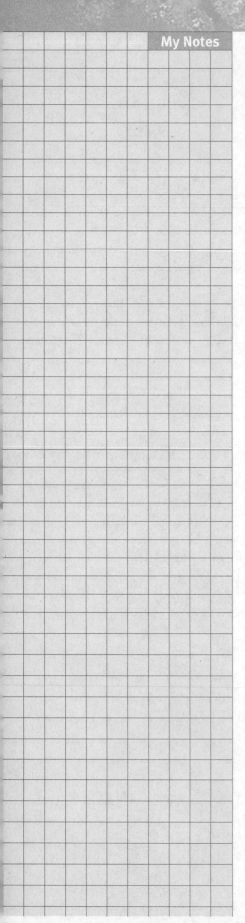

### Learning Targets:

- Define the three reciprocal trigonometric functions.
- Use the Pythagorean identity and the reciprocal trigonometric functions to prove other trigonometric identities.

**SUGGESTED LEARNING STRATEGIES:** Think Aloud, Discussion Groups, Note Taking

In addition to sine, cosine, and tangent, there are three more trigonometric functions. These functions are secant (sec), cosecant (csc) and cotangent (cot). Each of these is a reciprocal of one of the first three trigonometric functions you have learned. Similarly, the first three can be considered reciprocals of the second three. The reciprocal identities are shown here.

> **Reciprocal Identities**
>
> $\sin \theta = \dfrac{1}{\csc \theta}$  $\csc \theta = \dfrac{1}{\sin \theta}$
>
> $\cos \theta = \dfrac{1}{\sec \theta}$  $\sec \theta = \dfrac{1}{\cos \theta}$
>
> $\tan \theta = \dfrac{1}{\cot \theta}$  $\cot \theta = \dfrac{1}{\tan \theta}$

1. In Lesson 33-1 you learned the tangent quotient identity, $\tan \theta = \dfrac{\sin \theta}{\cos \theta}$.
   Given that cotangent and tangent are reciprocals of one another, express $\cot \theta$ in terms of $\sin \theta$ and $\cos \theta$.

In Lesson 33-1 you also learned about one Pythagorean identity, $\sin^2 \theta + \cos^2 \theta = 1$. There are three Pythagorean identities altogether. You can use the reciprocal and quotient identities to find the other two.

### Example A

Divide $\sin^2 \theta + \cos^2 \theta = 1$ by $\cos^2 \theta$ to find the second Pythagorean identity.

$$\frac{\sin^2 \theta}{\cos^2 \theta} + \frac{\cos^2 \theta}{\cos^2 \theta} = \frac{1}{\cos^2 \theta}$$

Simplify each ratio and substitute single trigonometric functions.

$$\tan^2 \theta + 1 = \sec^2 \theta$$

This is the second Pythagorean identity.

In a similar way, you can find the third Pythagorean identity.

### Try These A

Divide $\sin^2 \theta + \cos^2 \theta = 1$ by $\sin^2 \theta$ to find the third Pythagorean identity.

### Check Your Understanding

**2.** Simplify $\dfrac{1}{\cos\theta}$.

**3.** Show how $\sec^2\theta = \dfrac{1}{\cos^2\theta}$ is equivalent to $\sec\theta = \dfrac{1}{\cos\theta}$.

In addition to these trigonometric identities, there are other forms of the identities that you can derive by multiplying one identity by a trigonometric function.

### Example B

Multiply $1 + \cot^2\theta = \csc^2\theta$ by $\sin\theta$ to find another form of the trigonometric identity. Remember that if you multiply both sides of an equation by the same expression, it does not change the equation.

$1 + \cot^2\theta = \csc^2\theta$

$\sin\theta(1 + \cot^2\theta) = \sin\theta(\csc^2\theta)$

$\sin\theta + \sin\theta(\cot^2\theta) = \sin\theta\left(\dfrac{1}{\sin^2\theta}\right)$    Write parts you can in terms of sine.

$\sin\theta + \sin\theta\cot^2\theta = \csc\theta$    Simplify.

Other forms of trigonometric identities can be found this way as well.

### Try These B

**Make use of structure.** Multiply $\tan^2\theta + 1 = \sec^2\theta$ by $\cos\theta$ to find another form of the trigonometric identity.

My Notes

### Check Your Understanding

4. Multiply $\sin^2\theta + \cos^2\theta = 1$ by $\csc\theta$ to find another form of the trigonometric identity.
5. Divide $\sin^2\theta + \cos^2\theta = 1$ by $\cos\theta$ to find another form of the trigonometric identity.

## LESSON 33-2 PRACTICE

5. Simplify $\dfrac{1}{\csc^2\theta}$.

6. **Make use of structure.** Write $\dfrac{1}{\tan\theta}$ in two other ways.

7. Multiply $1 + \cot^2\theta = \csc^2\theta$ by $\sin^2\theta$ to find another form of the trigonometric identity.

8. Multiply $\tan^2\theta + 1 = \sec^2\theta$ by $\sin^2\theta$ to find another form of the trigonometric identity.

9. **Critique the reasoning of others.** Danielle says multiplying by $\cos\theta$ is the same as dividing by $\csc\theta$. Is she correct? Explain your reasoning.

# Trigonometric Identities: Pythagorean Connection
## More Than Just Triangles

## ACTIVITY 33 PRACTICE
**Write your answers on notebook paper.**
**Show your work.**

### Lesson 33-1

1. In which quadrant are sine, cosine, and tangent all positive?
   **A.** I    **B.** II    **C.** III    **D.** IV

2. In which quadrant are both sine and cosine negative?
   **A.** I    **B.** II    **C.** III    **D.** IV

3. Given that $\cos\theta = -\frac{11}{61}$ and that $\pi < \theta < \frac{3\pi}{2}$, what is the value of $\sin\theta$?

   **A.** $-\frac{11}{60}$      **B.** $\frac{11}{60}$

   **C.** $-\frac{60}{61}$      **D.** $\frac{60}{61}$

4. Given that $\cos\theta = \frac{15}{17}$ and that $\frac{3\pi}{2} < \theta < 2\pi$, find the value of $\sin\theta$ and $\tan\theta$.

5. Given that $\sin\theta = \frac{5}{13}$ and that $0 < \theta < \frac{\pi}{2}$, find the value of $\cos\theta$ and $\tan\theta$.

6. Given that $\sin\theta = -\frac{6\sqrt{2}}{12}$ and that $\frac{3\pi}{2} < \theta < 2\pi$, what is the value of $\cos\theta$?

   **A.** $\frac{6\sqrt{2}}{12}$      **B.** $-\frac{6\sqrt{2}}{12}$

   **C.** 1      **D.** $-1$

7. Given that $\sin\theta = \frac{2\sqrt{3}}{4}$ and that $\frac{\pi}{2} < \theta < \pi$, find the value of $\cos\theta$ and $\tan\theta$.

8. Given that $\cos\theta = -\frac{3\sqrt{2}}{6}$ and that $\pi < \theta < \frac{3\pi}{2}$, find the value of $\sin\theta$ and $\tan\theta$.

9. If the sine of an angle is positive and the cosine is negative, in which quadrant is the terminal side of the angle?
   **A.** I    **B.** II    **C.** III    **D.** IV

**Lesson 33-2**

10. Simplify $\dfrac{1}{\csc\theta}$.

11. Which is $\dfrac{1}{\cos^2\theta}$ simplified?

   **A.** $\sin^2\theta$      **B.** $\sec^2\theta$
   **C.** $\csc^2\theta$      **D.** $\cot^2\theta$

12. Write $\dfrac{1}{\cot\theta}$ in two other ways.

13. Which expression(s) equal $\sin\theta$?

   I. $\dfrac{1}{\csc\theta}$      III. $\dfrac{1}{\sec\theta}$

   II. $\csc\theta$      IV. $\tan\theta\cos\theta$

   **A.** I only
   **B.** III only
   **C.** I and IV
   **D.** II and IV

14. Which expression(s) are not equal to $\tan^2\theta$?

   I. $\sec^2\theta+1$      III. $\dfrac{\sin^2\theta}{\cos^2\theta}$

   II. $\sec^2\theta-1$      IV. $\dfrac{1}{\cot^2\theta}$

   **A.** I
   **B.** II
   **C.** III
   **D.** I and IV

15. Which is the product of $\tan^2\theta+1=\sec^2\theta$ and $\cos^2\theta$?
   **A.** $\csc^2\theta+\cos^2\theta=\cos^2\theta\sec^2\theta$
   **B.** $\sec^2\theta+\cos^2\theta=\cot^2\theta$
   **C.** $\sec^2\theta+\cos^2\theta=1$
   **D.** $\sin^2\theta+\cos^2\theta=1$

16. Multiply $1+\cot^2\theta=\csc^2\theta$ by $\sin^2\theta$ to find another form of the trigonometric identity.

17. Multiply $\sin^2\theta+\cos^2\theta=1$ by $\csc^2\theta$ to find another form of the trigonometric identity.

18. What is the product of $\tan\theta$ and $\cot\theta$?

## MATHEMATICAL PRACTICES
### Make Sense of Problems and Persevere in Solving Them

19. Is $\sin^2\theta+\cos^2\alpha=1$ a true equation? Explain.

# Radians, Unit Circles, and Trigonometry

## A FLORAL CLOCK

A landscape architect is designing a large, circular garden that looks like a clock for a local park.

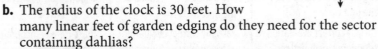

1. She wants to plant red dahlias in the sector between 7:00 and 9:00.
   a. How many degrees would an hour hand travel between 7:00 and 9:00? How many radians? What portion of the circumference is the arc between 7:00 and 9:00?
   b. The radius of the clock is 30 feet. How many linear feet of garden edging do they need for the sector containing dahlias?
   c. Suppose the architect uses a unit circle for her plans. What are the coordinates of the point showing 7:00? Showing 9:00?

2. The architect wants to locate a stone rabbit on the edge of the clock wherever $x = \pm 0.6$. How many stone rabbits does she need? What are the coordinates of the locations?

3. Mahesh walked around the completed floral clock. He started at 3:00, walked counterclockwise around the clock three times, continued walking to 10:00, and then stopped.
   a. How many degrees did he travel in all? How many radians?
   b. When Mahesh walked around the clock along a fixed pathway, he was 45 feet from its center. How far did he walk altogether?
   c. What angle between 0° and 360° is coterminal with his stopping place? What angle between 0 radians and $2\pi$ radians is coterminal with his stopping place?
   d. What is the reference angle of his stopping place in degrees? What is it in radians?

When Evan walked into his math class, the teacher announced that scientific calculators would not be allowed on the trigonometry exam. After thinking about it, Evan realized he could use what he already knew to find the value of the trigonometric functions.

4. How can he use 45°-45°-90° and 30°-60°-90° triangles to figure out the values sin 45° and cos 60°?

5. Evan used special right triangles to make a chart of the values of trigonometric functions for angles from 0° to 90°. Then he encountered a problem asking for $\tan \frac{\pi}{6}$. Explain how he can figure out its value.

6. Explain how he can use his chart to find the following values.
   a. $\sin(-45°)$
   b. $\cos \frac{2\pi}{3}$
   c. $\tan \frac{7\pi}{6}$
   d. $\sin 750°$

7. Given $\sec 18° \approx 1.05$ explain how he can use the reciprocal identities and Pythagorean identities to find the values of the other functions.
   a. $\tan 18°$
   b. $\cot 18°$
   c. $\cos 18°$
   d. $\sin 18°$
   e. $\csc 18°$

| Scoring Guide | Exemplary | Proficient | Emerging | Incomplete |
|---|---|---|---|---|
| | The solution demonstrates these characteristics: | | | |
| **Mathematics Knowledge and Thinking** (Items 1-7) | • Fluency in working with circles and angles measured in degrees and radians<br>• Effective understanding of the definitions of the trigonometric functions and the unit circle<br>• Clear and accurate evaluation of trigonometric functions using the unit circle, special right triangles, and trigonometric identities | • Little difficulty in working with circles and angles measured in degrees and radians<br>• Adequate understanding of the definitions of the trigonometric functions and the unit circle<br>• Largely correct evaluation of trigonometric functions using the unit circle, special right triangles, and trigonometric identities | • Some difficulty in working with circles and angles measured in degrees and radians<br>• Partial understanding of the definitions of the trigonometric functions and the unit circle<br>• Partially correct evaluation of trigonometric functions using the unit circle, special right triangles, and trigonometric identities | • Significant difficulty in working with circles and angles measured in degrees and radians<br>• Little or no understanding of the definitions of the trigonometric functions and the unit circle<br>• Inaccurate or incomplete evaluation of trigonometric functions using the unit circle, special right triangles, and trigonometric identities |
| **Problem Solving** (Items 1, 2, 3) | • An appropriate and efficient strategy that results in a correct answer | • A strategy that may include unnecessary steps but results in a correct answer | • A strategy that results in some incorrect answers | • No clear strategy when solving problems |
| **Mathematical Modeling / Representations** (Items 1, 2, 3) | • Effective understanding of how angles in circles, including the unit circle, relate to a real-world scenario | • Largely correct understanding of how angles in circles, including the unit circle, relate to a real-world scenario | • Partial understanding of how angles in circles, including the unit circle, relate to a real-world scenario | • Incomplete or inaccurate understanding of how angles in circles, including the unit circle, relate to a real-world scenario |
| **Reasoning and Communication** (Items 4, 5, 6, 7) | • Precise use of appropriate math terms and language when explaining how to evaluate trigonometric functions using a chart, the unit circle, or trigonometric identities | • Adequate use of math terms and language when explaining how to evaluate trigonometric functions using a chart, the unit circle, or trigonometric identities | • Misleading or confusing use of math terms and language when explaining how to evaluate trigonometric functions using a chart, the unit circle, or trigonometric identities | • Incomplete or mostly inaccurate use of math terms and language when explaining how to evaluate trigonometric functions using a chart, the unit circle, or trigonometric identities |

# Graphs of Trigonometric Functions

## Creation of a Mural
## Lesson 34-1 Periodic Functions

**Learning Targets:**
- Identify periodic functions.
- Find the period, midline, and amplitude of periodic functions.

**SUGGESTED LEARNING STRATEGIES:** Close Reading, Paraphrasing, Create Representations, Vocabulary Organizer, Discussion Groups, Think-Pair-Share

An artist created this design to decorate a wall of the new transit center. The painters wondered if there is a mathematical description for the pattern to make it easier for them to reproduce it accurately.

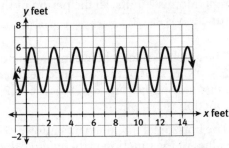

The pattern repeats at regular intervals, or *periods*, so it is called a ***periodic function***.

This graph shows a periodic function. You can extend it in both directions by repeating its shape.

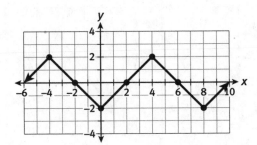

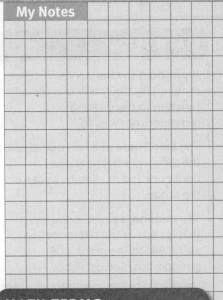

## MATH TERMS

A **periodic function** is a function that repeats its values in regular intervals called periods.

This graph does not show a periodic function. Although it extends in both directions, you cannot predict its shape, because it does not repeat at regular intervals.

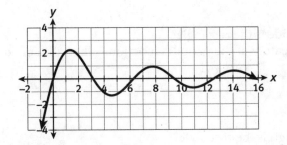

### Check Your Understanding

1. **Attend to precision.** Sketch the graph of a periodic function. Explain why it is periodic.

2. Sketch the graph of a function that is not periodic. Explain why it is not periodic.

**MATH TERMS**

A **period** is the horizontal distance required for the graph of a periodic function to complete one repetition, or *cycle*.

The **amplitude** of a function is half the difference between the minimum and maximum values of the range.

The **midline** is a horizontal axis that is used as the reference line about which the graph of a periodic function oscillates.

To describe the design shown for the transit center wall more precisely, you can define its *period*, *amplitude*, and *midline*. Study the graph shown here.

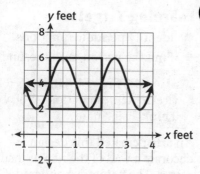

The portion of the design outlined by the rectangle shows one repetition, or *period*, of the function. The horizontal distance of one repetition is 2 units, so the period of the function is 2.

The graph oscillates between $y = 2$ and $y = 6$, so the range of the function is $2 \leq y \leq 6$. Half of that distance between these two values is called the *amplitude* of the function. Since $|6 - 2| \div 2 = 2$, the amplitude of the function is 2.

The horizontal line that runs midway between the maximum and minimum values of the function is the *midline*. Because 4 is midway between 6 and 2, the line $y = 4$ is the midline of the function.

3. Look at the following graph.

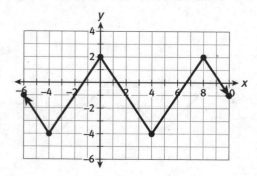

a. Draw a rectangle around exactly one repetition of the graph of the function.

b. How wide is the rectangle?
   What feature of the periodic function is the width of one repetition?

c. How high is the rectangle?
   How can you use the height to find the amplitude?

d. Draw the midline of the function.
   What is the equation of the midline?

Decide if each graph shows a periodic function. If it does, give its period, its amplitude, and the equation of its midline. If it does not, explain why not.

4.

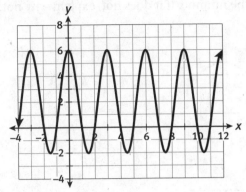

**MATH TIP**

Sketch a rectangle around one repetition of the function. Study the portion of the graph in the rectangle to find the period, amplitude, and midline.

5.

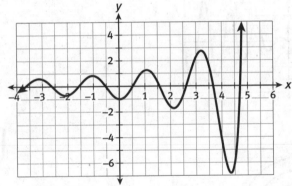

6.

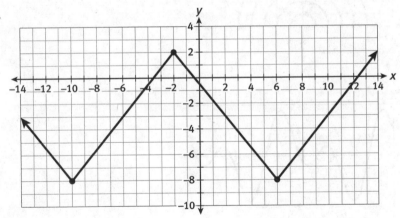

**Check Your Understanding**

7. Suppose you know the minimum and maximum values of a periodic function. How can you find its amplitude?

8. **Reason quantitatively.** How could you use the minimum and maximum values of a periodic function to find the equation of its midline?

**MATH TIP**

A *maximum* can be thought of as the greatest value of *y* or the *y*-value of the highest point on the graph.

A *minimum* is the least value of *y* or the *y*-value of the lowest point on the graph.

Periodic functions have more than one maximum and minimum.

My Notes

## LESSON 34-1 PRACTICE

Decide if each graph shows a periodic function. If it does, give the period, the amplitude, and the equation of the midline. If it does not, explain why not.

9.

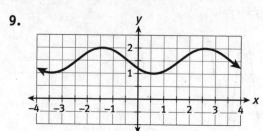

10.

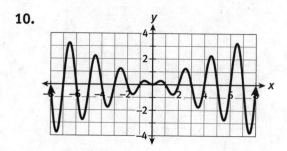

11.

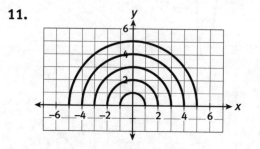

12.

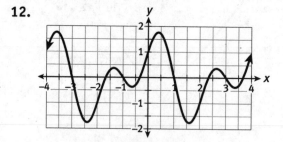

13. **Construct viable arguments.** Samir says that when the amplitude of a periodic function doubles, the maximum value of the function doubles. Do you agree or disagree? Justify your response.

**Learning Targets:**

- Graph the sine function, $y = a \sin b x$.
- Find the period, midline, and amplitude of sine functions.

> **SUGGESTED LEARNING STRATEGIES:** Chunking the Activity, Close Reading, Paraphrasing, Create Representations, Discussion Groups, Think-Pair-Share

The sine function is an example of a periodic function. It repeats every $2\pi$ radians, or $360°$. You can use a table of trigonometric values to plot the values you know and then connect them to show the graph of the sine function.

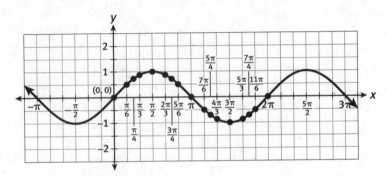

The graph of the sine function is symmetrical with respect to the origin, because it is unchanged rotated $180°$ around the origin. Therefore, it is an *odd function*. Another way to tell that it is an odd function is to see that the values for $\sin x$ and $\sin (-x)$ are additive inverses.

### Check Your Understanding

1. Name the period, the midline, and the amplitude of the sine function.

2. **Express regularity in repeated reasoning.** If $\sin \frac{\pi}{2} = .2588$, what is the value of $\sin\left(\frac{-\pi}{2}\right)$? How do you know?

3. **Make use of structure.** How can you use coterminal angles to explain why the sine function between $2\pi$ and $4\pi$ radians is the same as it is between 0 and $2\pi$ radians?

| $x$ | $\sin x$ |
|---|---|
| 0 | 0 |
| $\frac{\pi}{6}$ | $\frac{1}{2}$ |
| $\frac{\pi}{4}$ | $\frac{\sqrt{2}}{2}$ |
| $\frac{\pi}{3}$ | $\frac{\sqrt{3}}{2}$ |
| $\frac{\pi}{2}$ | 1 |
| $\frac{2\pi}{3}$ | $\frac{\sqrt{3}}{2}$ |
| $\frac{3\pi}{4}$ | $\frac{\sqrt{2}}{2}$ |
| $\frac{5\pi}{6}$ | $\frac{1}{2}$ |
| $\pi$ | 0 |
| $\frac{7\pi}{6}$ | $-\frac{1}{2}$ |
| $\frac{5\pi}{4}$ | $-\frac{\sqrt{2}}{2}$ |
| $\frac{4\pi}{3}$ | $-\frac{\sqrt{3}}{2}$ |
| $\frac{3\pi}{2}$ | $-1$ |
| $\frac{5\pi}{3}$ | $-\frac{\sqrt{3}}{2}$ |
| $\frac{7\pi}{4}$ | $-\frac{\sqrt{2}}{2}$ |
| $\frac{11\pi}{6}$ | $-\frac{1}{2}$ |
| $2\pi$ | 0 |

> **MATH TIP**
>
> Recall that an *odd function* is symmetric with respect to the origin. For each $x$, $f(-x) = -f(x)$.

**TECHNOLOGY TIP**

Be sure to set the calculator in radians before graphing in radians. Press MODE. Use the arrow keys to move the cursor over RADIAN, and press ENTER.

The parent sine function is $y = \sin x$. Changing the parent sine function transforms its graph. For example, a sine function may have a coefficient other than 1, written in the form $y = a \sin x$, where $a$ is the coefficient of the function.

4. Use a graphing calculator to sketch and compare the graphs of $y = \sin x$, $y = 3 \sin x$, and $y = \frac{1}{3} \sin x$.

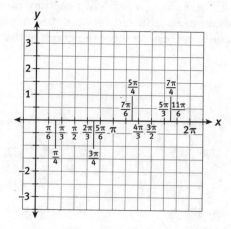

Notice that the periods, midlines, and $x$-intercepts are identical for all three graphs. However the amplitudes are different. The amplitude of $y = 3 \sin x$ is 3, and the graph is vertically stretched. The amplitude of $y = \frac{1}{3} \sin x$ is $\frac{1}{3}$ and the graph is vertically compressed. The amplitude of the function $y = a \sin \theta$ is $|a|$.

### Example A

Draw the graph of $y = \frac{3}{2} \sin x$.

Name its period, amplitude, and midline.

**Step 1:** Lightly sketch the parent sine function.

**Step 2:** Find several key points on the curve. Multiply the $y$ value of each point by $\frac{3}{2}$ and plot the new point. Connect the points.

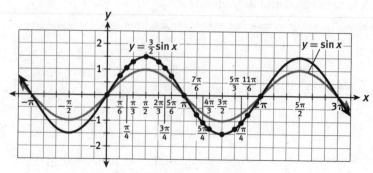

The period is $2\pi$, the amplitude is $\frac{3}{2}$, and the midline is $y = 0$.

**My Notes**

### Try These A
Graph each sine function on a separate coordinate plane. Name the period, amplitude, and midline for each.

**a.** $y = 2 \sin x$        **b.** $y = \frac{1}{2} \sin x$        **c.** $y = -1 \sin x$.

**d.** What is an equation of a sine function that has a period of $2\pi$, an amplitude of 4, and a midline of $y = 0$?

The graph of the parent sine function is also transformed when the angle has a coefficient other than 1, written as $y = \sin bx$, where $b$ is the coefficient of the angle.

5. **Use appropriate tools strategically.** Use a graphing calculator to compare the graphs of $y = \sin x$, $y = \sin 3x$, and $y = \sin \frac{1}{3} x$. Sketch and label the three graphs on the coordinate plane below.

**TECHNOLOGY TIP**

If the calculator does not show a full period, you can change the axes. Press [WINDOW] and change the *X*min, *X*max, *X*scl, *Y*min, *Y*max, and *Y*scl, as needed.

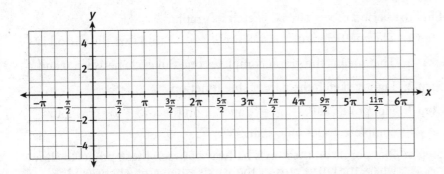

Notice that the amplitudes and midlines are identical for all three graphs. The periods are different. The graph of $y = \sin 3x$ is compressed horizontally, so that it shows three cycles between 0 and $2\pi$. It repeats every $\frac{2\pi}{3}$ units, so its period is $\frac{2\pi}{3}$. The graph of $y = \sin \frac{1}{3} x$ has $\frac{1}{3}$ of a cycle between 0 and $2\pi$. It is stretched horizontally and shows one full cycle between 0 and $6\pi$. Therefore, its period is $6\pi$.

The period of the function $y = \sin bx$ is $\frac{2\pi}{b}$. It is found by dividing $2\pi$ by the coefficient of the angle.

### Example B
Find the period of $y = \sin \frac{2}{3} x$. Sketch its graph.

**Step 1:** The coefficient of $x$ is $\frac{2}{3}$. Simplify $\frac{2\pi}{\frac{2}{3}}$. The period is $3\pi$. The graph completes one full cycle between 0 and $3\pi$.

**Step 2:** Lightly sketch the parent sine function from 0 to $3\pi$.

**Step 3:** Plot points at 0 and $3\pi$ on the $x$-axis to show the beginning and end of one cycle of $y = \sin \frac{2}{3}x$.

**Step 4:** Plot a point at $\frac{3\pi}{2}$ on the $x$-axis. It is the halfway point of the cycle. It shows where the curve crosses the $x$-axis when going between the maximum and minimum.

**Step 5:** Plot a maximum or minimum point at $\frac{3\pi}{4}$ and at $\frac{9\pi}{4}$. These points are halfway between two zeros of the function.

**Step 6:** Connect the points with a smooth curve. Label the function.

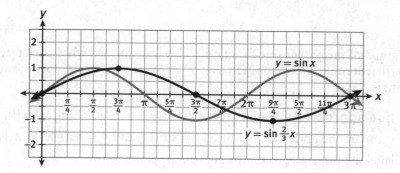

## Example C

Find the period of $y = \sin 4x$. Sketch its graph.

**Step 1:** The coefficient of $x$ is 4. Simplify $\frac{2\pi}{4}$ to find that the period is $\frac{\pi}{2}$. That means the graph completes one full cycle between 0 and $\frac{\pi}{2}$.

**Step 2:** Lightly sketch the parent sine function.

**Step 3:** Plot points at $0, \frac{\pi}{2}, \pi, \frac{3\pi}{2}$, and $2\pi$ on the $x$-axis to show four complete cycles of $y = \sin 4x$.

**Step 4:** Plot points on the $x$-axis halfway between those points to show where the curve crosses the $x$-axis when going between the maximum and minimum.

**Step 5:** Plot maximum or minimum points halfway between each two zeros of the function.

**Step 6:** Connect the points with a smooth curve. Label the function.

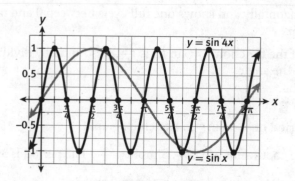

## Try These B–C

**Model with mathematics.** Find the period of each function. Graph at least one period of each function on a separate coordinate plane. Then state the amplitude and midline of each graph.

**a.** $y = \sin 2x$  **b.** $y = \sin \frac{1}{2} x$

**c.** What is an equation of a sine function that has a period of $\frac{\pi}{3}$, an amplitude of 1, and a midline of $y = 0$?

### Check Your Understanding

6. What is the difference between the graphs of $y = 2\sin x$ and $y = \sin 2x$?

7. **Reason quantitatively.** If $0 < a < 1$, how does the graph of $y = a \sin x$ differ from the graph of $y = \sin x$?

8. If $0 < b < 1$, how does the graph of $y = \sin bx$ differ from the graph of $y = \sin x$?

A sine function can have an amplitude that is different from 1 as well as a period that is different from $2\pi$. The equation of such a function is written in the form $y = a \sin bx$.

9. Name the period and amplitude of $y = 8 \sin \frac{1}{4} x$.

10. Name the period and amplitude of $y = -\frac{1}{4} \sin 8x$.

**MATH TIP**

The amplitude of $y = a \sin bx$, is $|a|$ and the period is $\frac{2\pi}{b}$.

### Example D

Find the period and amplitude of $y = 3 \sin 6x$. Sketch its graph.

**Step 1:** The coefficient of sine, $a$, is 3. The amplitude is 3, because $|3| = 3$.

**Step 2:** The coefficient of $x$, $b$, is 6. Simplify $\frac{2\pi}{6}$ to show that the period is $\frac{\pi}{3}$. That means the graph completes one full cycle between 0 and $\frac{\pi}{3}$.

**Step 3:** Lightly sketch the parent sine function from 0 to $2\pi$.

**Step 4:** Plot points at $0, \frac{\pi}{3}, \frac{2\pi}{3}, \pi, \frac{4\pi}{3}, \frac{5\pi}{3}$, and $2\pi$ on the $x$-axis to show six complete cycles of $y = 3 \sin 6x$.

**Step 5:** Plot points on the $x$-axis halfway between those points to show where the curve crosses the $x$-axis when going between the maximum and minimum.

**My Notes**

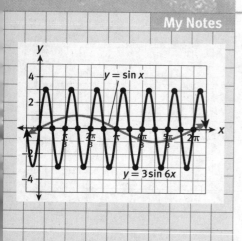

**Step 6:** Plot maximum or minimum points, 3 and −3, halfway between each two zeros of the function.

**Step 7:** Connect the points with a smooth curve. Label the function.

### Try These D

Name the period and amplitude of each function. Graph at least one period of each on a separate coordinate plane.

**a.** $y = -2 \sin \frac{2}{3} x$

**b.** $y = 3 \sin 3x$

**c.** $y = \frac{1}{4} \sin 4x$

**d.** $y = \frac{1}{2} \sin \frac{1}{2} x$

### Check Your Understanding

**11.** How far must you extend the $x$- and $y$-axes to show one period of $y = 3 \sin \frac{1}{3} x$?

**12. Reason quantitatively.** What is an equation for a sine function whose amplitude and period are both $\frac{3}{4}$ times the amplitude and period of $y = \sin \theta$? How did you find it?

**13. Construct viable arguments.** Suppose a classmate says that to stretch the parent sine function vertically so its amplitude is double, you would use the equation $y = 2 \sin x$. To stretch it horizontally so one period is twice as wide, you would use the equation $y = \sin 2x$. Do you agree or disagree? Explain.

### LESSON 34-2 PRACTICE

Name the period and amplitude of each function. Graph at least one period of each function on a separate coordinate plane.

**14.** $y = \frac{1}{2} \sin x$

**15.** $y = 2 \sin x$

**16.** $y = \sin \frac{1}{2} x$

**17.** $y = \sin 2x$

**18.** $y = \frac{2}{3} \sin 4x$

**19.** $y = 4 \sin \frac{2}{3} x$

**20. Reason abstractly.** How can you use the formula $period = \frac{2\pi}{b}$ to explain why the period decreases when $b > 1$ but increases when $0 < b < 1$?

## Learning Targets:

- Graph the cosine function, $y = a \cos bx$.
- Find the period, midline, and amplitude of cosine functions.

The cosine function is another example of a periodic function. It also repeats every $2\pi$ radians or $360°$. You can use a table of trigonometric values to plot the values you know and then connect them to show the graph of the cosine function.

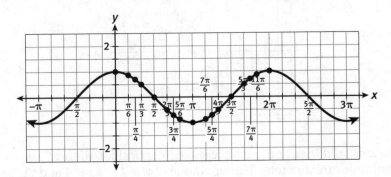

The graph of the cosine function is symmetrical with respect to the *y*-axis. Therefore, it is an *even function*. Another way to tell that it is an even function is to see that the values for $\cos x$ and $\cos(-x)$ are always the same.

### Check Your Understanding

1. Name the period, the midline, and the amplitude of the cosine function.
2. What is the maximum value of $\cos x$? List two *x*-values where the maximum occurs?
3. What is the minimum value of $\cos x$? List an *x* value where this minimum occurs.
4. Describe the similarities and differences between the maximums and minimums of the sine and cosine functions.

**TECHNOLOGY TIP**

Make sure your calculator is set to use radians instead of degrees.

Changes to the equation of the parent cosine function, $y = \cos x$, will transform its graph. One possible change is for the cosine function to have a coefficient other than 1, written as $y = a \cos x$ where $a$ is the coefficient of the function.

5. **Use appropriate tools strategically.** Use a graphing calculator to compare the graphs of $y = \cos x$, $y = 4 \cos x$, and $y = \frac{2}{3} \cos x$. Sketch and label the three graphs on the coordinate plane below.

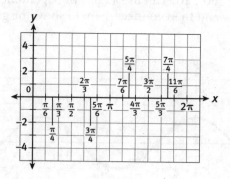

The periods, midlines, and $x$-intercepts are identical for all three graphs, but the amplitudes are different. The amplitude of $y = 4 \cos x$ is 4 and the graph is vertically stretched. The amplitude of $y = \frac{2}{3} \cos x$ is $\frac{2}{3}$ and the graph is vertically compressed. The amplitude of the function $y = a \cos x$ is $|a|$. As with the sine function, multiplying the cosine function by a coefficient changes the amplitude.

**Example A**

Draw the graph of $y = 3 \cos x$.
Name its period, amplitude, and midline.

**Step 1:** Lightly sketch the parent cosine function.

**Step 2:** Find several key points on the curve. Multiply the $y$ value of each by 3 and plot the new point. Connect the points.

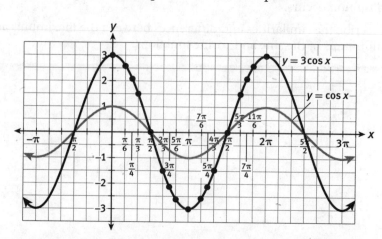

The period is $2\pi$, the amplitude is 3, and the midline is $y = 0$.

### Try These A

Graph each cosine function on a separate coordinate plane. Name the period, amplitude, and midline for each.

**a.** $y = 5 \cos x$  **b.** $y = \frac{3}{4} \cos x$  **c.** $y = -2\cos x$.

**d.** What is an equation of a cosine function that has a period of $2\pi$, an amplitude of $\frac{5}{2}$, and a midline of $y = 0$?

The graph of the parent cosine function is also transformed when the angle has a coefficient other than 1, written as $y = \cos bx$ where $b$ is the coefficient of the angle.

**6.** Use a graphing calculator to compare the graphs of $y = \cos x$, $y = \cos 5x$, and $y = \cos \frac{1}{4} x$. Sketch and label the 3 graphs on the coordinate plane below.

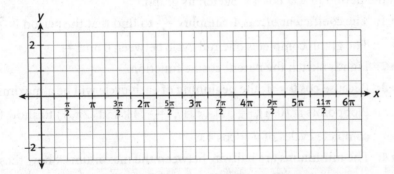

Notice that the amplitudes and midlines are identical for all three graphs. The periods are different. The graph of $y = \cos 5x$ is horizontally compressed so that it shows five cycles between 0 and $2\pi$. It repeats every $\frac{2\pi}{5}$ units so its period is $\frac{2\pi}{5}$. The graph of $y = \cos \frac{1}{4} x$ is horizontally stretched so that it shows one-fourth of a cycle between 0 and $2\pi$. It shows one full cycle between 0 and $8\pi$. Its period is $8\pi$.

The period of the function $y = \cos bx$ is $\frac{2\pi}{b}$. It is found by dividing $2\pi$ by the coefficient of the angle.

### Example B

Find the period of $y = \cos \frac{1}{3} x$. Sketch its graph.

**Step 1:** The coefficient of $x$ is $\frac{1}{3}$. Simplify $\frac{2\pi}{\frac{1}{3}}$ to find that the period is $6\pi$. The graph completes one full cycle between 0 and $6\pi$.

**Step 2:** Lightly sketch the parent cosine function from 0 to $6\pi$.

**Step 3:** A cycle of the cosine function begins and ends with its maximum. Plot points at $(0, 1)$ and $(6\pi, 1)$ to show the beginning and end of one cycle of $y = \cos\frac{1}{3}x$.

**Step 4:** Plot a point on $(3\pi, -1)$. It is the halfway point of the cycle. The minimum of the cosine is halfway through the cycle.

**Step 5:** The zeros of $y = \cos\frac{1}{3}x$ are halfway between the maximums and minimums of the function. Plot the points $\left(\frac{3\pi}{2}, 0\right)$ and $\left(\frac{9\pi}{2}, 0\right)$.

**Step 6:** Connect the points with a smooth curve. Label the function.

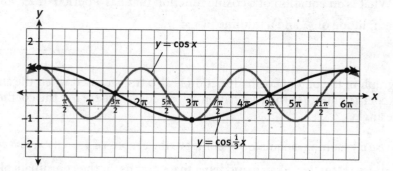

## Example C

Find the period of $y = \cos 4x$. Sketch its graph.

**Step 1:** The coefficient of $x$ is 4. Simplify $\frac{2\pi}{4}$ to find that the period is $\frac{\pi}{2}$. The graph completes one full cycle between 0 and $\frac{\pi}{2}$.

**Step 2:** Lightly sketch the parent cosine function.

**Step 3:** Because $\cos 0 = 1$, the beginning of each cycle will be a maximum. Plot points at $(0, 1)$, $\left(\frac{\pi}{2}, 1\right)$, $(\pi, 1)$, $\left(\frac{3\pi}{2}, 1\right)$, and $(2\pi, 1)$ to show four complete cycles of $y = \cos 4x$.

**Step 4:** The minimums are halfway between the maximums. Show these with points at $\left(\frac{\pi}{4}, -1\right)$, $\left(\frac{3\pi}{4}, -1\right)$, $\left(\frac{5\pi}{4}, -1\right)$, and $\left(\frac{7\pi}{4}, -1\right)$.

**Step 5:** The zeros occur between each maximum and minimum. Locate them at $\left(\frac{\pi}{8}, 0\right)$, $\left(\frac{3\pi}{8}, 0\right)$, $\left(\frac{5\pi}{8}, 0\right)$, $\left(\frac{7\pi}{8}, 0\right)$, $\left(\frac{9\pi}{8}, 0\right)$, $\left(\frac{11\pi}{8}, 0\right)$, $\left(\frac{13}{8}, 0\right)$, and $\left(\frac{15\pi}{8}, 0\right)$.

**Step 6:** Connect the points with a smooth curve. Label the function.

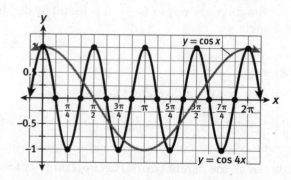

## Try These B–C

Find the period of the functions. Graph at least one period of each on a separate coordinate plane. Then name the amplitude and midline of each graph.

**a.** $y = \cos 2x$

**b.** $y = \cos \frac{1}{2}x$

**c.** What is an equation of a cosine function that has a period of $3\pi$, an amplitude of 1, and a midline of $y = 0$?

### Check Your Understanding

**7. Model with mathematics.** How is the graph of $y = \frac{3}{4}\cos 2x$ similar to the graph of $y = \frac{3}{4}\sin 2x$.

**8.** How is the graph of $y = \frac{3}{4}\cos 2x$ different from the graph of $y = \frac{3}{4}\sin 2x$.

Cosine functions can have both amplitudes and periods that are different from those of the parent function $y = \cos x$. Changes in the amplitude and period can be shown by the equation $y = a \cos bx$.

**9.** Name the period and amplitude of $y = 6\cos \frac{1}{3}x$.

**10.** Name the period and amplitude of $y = -\frac{1}{3}\cos 6x$.

**MATH TIP**

The amplitude of $y = a \cos bx$, is $|a|$ and the period is $\frac{2\pi}{b}$.

### Example D

Find the period and amplitude of $y = 2\cos 3x$. Sketch its graph.

**Step 1:** The coefficient of cosine, $a$, is 2. The amplitude is 2 because $|2| = 2$.

**Step 2:** The coefficient of $x$, $b$, is 3. The graph will have 3 cycles of $2\cos 3x$ between 0 and $2\pi$. The period is $\frac{2\pi}{3}$ which means the graph completes one full cycle between 0 and $\frac{2\pi}{3}$.

**Step 3:** Lightly sketch the parent cosine function from 0 to $2\pi$.

**Step 4:** The maximums, 2, will occur at $x = 0, \frac{2\pi}{3}, \frac{4\pi}{3}$, and $2\pi$. Locate them on the graph.

**Step 5:** The minimum, $-2$, will occur halfway between the maximums. Locate them on the graph.

**Step 6:** The zeros will fall between each maximum and minimum. Locate them on the graph.

**Step 7:** Connect the points with a smooth curve. Label the function.

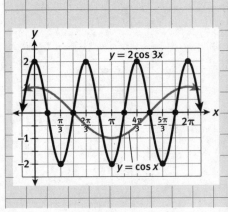

## Try These D

Name the period and amplitude of each function. Graph at least one period of each on a separate coordinate plane.

**a.** $y = 4 \cos 2x$

**b.** $y = -5 \cos \frac{1}{2} x$

**c.** $y = \frac{2}{3} \cos \frac{2}{3} x$

**d.** $y = 4 \cos 4x$

### Check Your Understanding

**11.** How does the parent cosine function change when it is stretched vertically? Stretched horizontally?

**12.** How does the parent cosine function change when it is compressed vertically? Compressed horizontally?

**13. Use appropriate tools strategically.** For what value(s) of $x$ does $\sin x = \cos x$ over the interval $0 \le x \le 2\pi$? Does $\sin 2x = \cos 2x$ for the same values of $x$ as $\sin x = \cos x$? Explain.

## LESSON 34-3 PRACTICE

Write your answers on notebook or graph paper.

Name the period and amplitude of each function. Graph at least one period of each on a separate coordinate plane.

**14.** $y = \frac{1}{2} \cos x$

**15.** $y = 2 \cos x$

**16.** $y = \cos \frac{1}{2} x$

**17.** $y = \cos 2x$

**18.** $y = \frac{2}{3} \cos 4x$

**19.** $y = 4 \cos \frac{2}{3} x$

**20. Make sense of problems.**
What is the equation of this graph in the form $y = a \cos bx$? How did you determine the values of $a$ and $b$?

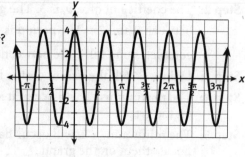

## Learning Targets:

● Graph the tangent function, $y = a \tan b x$.
● Find the period, and midline of tangent functions.

**SUGGESTED LEARNING STRATEGIES:** Chunking the Activity, Close Reading, Paraphrasing, Create Representations, Discussion Groups, Think-Pair-Share

The tangent function is another periodic function. You can use a table of trigonometric values to plot the values you know and then connect them to show the graph of the tangent function.

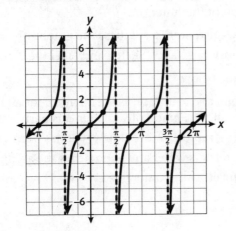

1. What is the shape of the graph?

2. What is the horizontal distance required for the graph of the tangent function to complete one cycle?

3. What is the range of the graph?

4. Are there any gaps in the graph? Where?

5. Is tangent an even or odd function? Explain.

To summarize, the tangent function is an odd periodic function with a period of $\pi$. It extends from negative to positive infinity so we do not refer to its amplitude. The curve approaches $x = -\dfrac{\pi}{2}$, $x = \dfrac{\pi}{2}$, and $x = \dfrac{3\pi}{2}$ but never intersects them and $x = -\dfrac{\pi}{2}$, $x = \dfrac{\pi}{2}$, and $x = \dfrac{3\pi}{2}$ are *asymptotes* of $y = \tan x$. Because the tangent function is undefined at these points, the domain of $\tan x$ is $x \neq \dfrac{\pi}{2}, \dfrac{3\pi}{2}, \dfrac{5\pi}{2}$ or any odd multiple of $\dfrac{\pi}{2}$. The midline is $y = 0$. The zeros are at multiples of $\pi$.

**MATH TIP**

Recall that an *asymptote* is a line that a graph approaches but does not intersect.

**My Notes**

**My Notes**

**MATH TIP**

$\tan x = \dfrac{\sin x}{\cos x}$

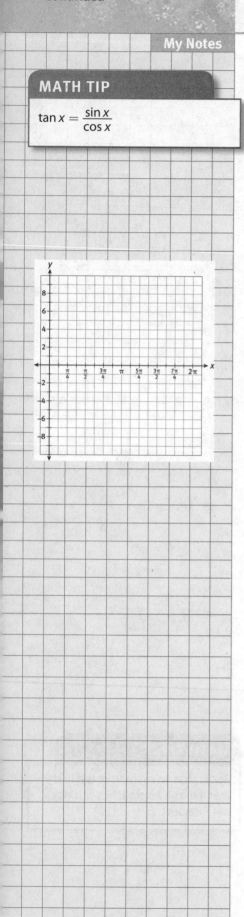

### Check Your Understanding

6. **Make use of structure.** What is tan $x$ when sin $x = 0$? Why?
7. What is tan $x$ when cos $x = 0$? Why? How is this shown on the graph?
8. What is tan $x$ when sin $x = \cos x$? Why? At what values of $x$ does this occur?

Multiplying the parent function $y = \tan x$ by a coefficient, $y = a \tan x$, transforms the graph of the function.

9. Use a graphing calculator to compare the graphs of $y = \tan x$, $y = 3 \tan x$, and $y = \dfrac{1}{3} \tan x$. Sketch and label the 3 graphs on the coordinate plane below.

The periods, midlines, and $x$-intercepts are identical for all three graphs, but the shapes are different. The graph of $y = 3 \tan x$ is narrower than $y = \tan x$ and approaches the asymptotes more slowly — it has been vertically stretched. The graph of $y = \dfrac{1}{3} \tan x$ is wider and approaches the asymptotes more quickly—it has been vertically compressed.

### Example A
Draw the graph of $y = \dfrac{3}{2} \tan x$.
Name its period, midline, and asymptotes.

**Step 1:** Lightly sketch the parent tangent function.
**Step 2:** Find several key points on the curve. Multiply the $y$ value of each by 3 and plot the new point. Connect the points.

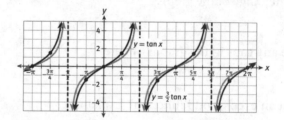

The period is $\pi$, the midline is $y = 0$ and the asymptotes are $x = -\dfrac{\pi}{2}$, $x = \dfrac{\pi}{2}$, and $x = \dfrac{3\pi}{2}$.

### Try These A
Graph each tangent function on a separate coordinate plane. State the period and state whether each function is vertically stretched or compressed relative to the parent function.

a. $y = 2 \tan x$    b. $y = \dfrac{5}{2} \tan x$    c. $y = \dfrac{1}{2} \tan x$.

The graph of the parent tangent function is also transformed when the coefficient of $x$ is a value other than 1, written as $y = \tan bx$. Changing the coefficient of $x$ changes the period of the function.

10. Use a graphing calculator to compare the graphs of $y = \tan x$, $y = \tan 3x$, and $y = \tan \frac{1}{3}x$. Sketch and label the 3 graphs on the coordinate plane below.

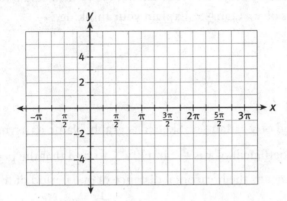

Notice that the midlines are identical for all three graphs. The periods and asymptotes are different. The graph of $y = \tan 3x$ completes 3 cycles in the same interval it takes $y = \tan x$ to complete 1 cycle. Its period is $\frac{\pi}{3}$, and it is horizontally compressed. The graph of $y = \tan \frac{1}{3}x$ completes one cycle in the same interval that $y = \tan x$ completes three cycles. Its period is $3\pi$, and it is horizontally stretched.

The period of the function $y = \tan b\theta$ is $\frac{\pi}{b}$. It is found by dividing $\pi$ by the coefficient of the angle.

The asymptotes of the functions are also different. Some asymptotes of $y = \tan x$ are $x = \frac{\pi}{2}$ and odd multiples of $\frac{\pi}{2}$. The asymptotes of $y = \tan 3x$ are closer together and are found at $x = \frac{\pi}{6}$ and odd multiples of $\frac{\pi}{6}$. The asymptotes of $y = \frac{1}{3}x$ are farther apart and are found at $x = \frac{3\pi}{2}$ and odd multiples of $\frac{3\pi}{2}$.

Discuss Items 11–14 with your group.

11. **Construct viable arguments.** How is the formula for finding the period of the tangent function different from the formulas for finding the periods of the sine and cosine functions? Why do you think this is?

12. **Make use of structure.** Compare the periods and asymptotes of $y = \tan x$ and $y = \tan 3x$. What pattern do you see?

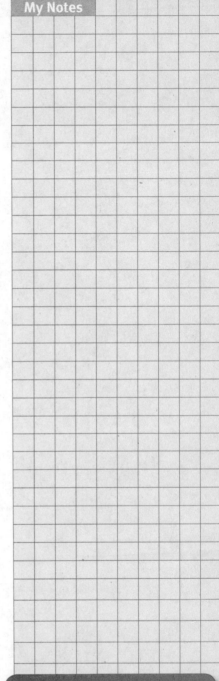

**DISCUSSION GROUP TIP**

As you share your ideas, be sure to use mathematical terms and academic vocabulary precisely. Make notes to help you remember the meaning of new words and how they are used to describe mathematical concepts.

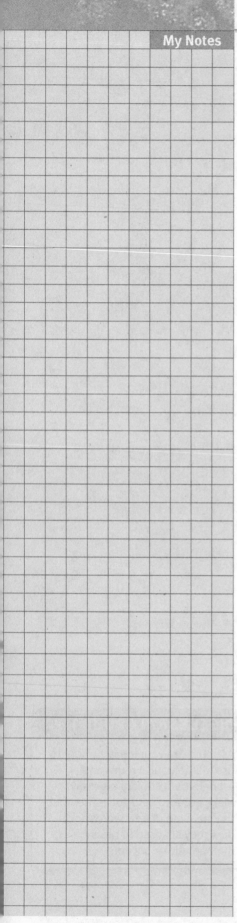

13. Compare the periods and asymptotes of $y = \tan$ and $y = \tan\frac{1}{3}x$ as well as their asymptotes. What pattern do you see?

14. **Reason abstractly.** Use your answers to Items 7 and 8 to predict the asymptotes of $y = \tan\frac{3}{2}x$. Explain your thinking.

### Example B

Find the period of $y = \tan\frac{3}{2}x$. Sketch its graph. Name its asymptotes.

**Step 1:** The coefficient of $x$ is $\frac{3}{2}$. Simplify $\frac{\pi}{\frac{3}{2}}$ to find that the period is $\frac{2}{3}\pi$. That means the horizontal distance of one period of the graph is $\frac{2}{3}\pi$.

**Step 2:** Lightly sketch the parent tangent function from $-\pi$ to $2\pi$.

**Step 3:** Find zeros of $y = \tan\frac{3}{2}x$ by dividing zeros of $y = \tan x$ by $\frac{3}{2}$. Some zeros of $y = \tan\frac{3}{2}x$ are $-\frac{2\pi}{3}, 0, \frac{2\pi}{3},$ and $\frac{4\pi}{3}$.

**Step 4:** Find the asymptotes of $y = \tan\frac{3}{2}x$ by dividing asymptotes of $y = \tan x$ by $\frac{3}{2}$. Some asymptotes of $y = \tan\frac{3}{2}x$ are $y = -\pi$, $y = -\frac{\pi}{3}, y = \frac{\pi}{3}, y = \pi,$ and $y = \frac{5\pi}{3}$. Sketch the asymptotes. Notice that the asymptotes are halfway between each pair of zeros.

**Step 5:** Draw the curves for $y = \tan\frac{3}{2}x$, having them cross the midline at the zeros and approach, but not touch, the asymptotes.

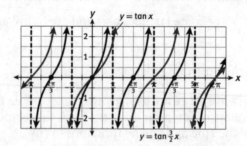

### Try These B

Find the period, some zeros, and some asymptotes of the functions. Graph at least one period of each on a separate coordinate plane.

a. $y = \tan 2x$

**b.** $y = \tan \frac{1}{2} x$

**c.** What is an equation of a tangent function with a period of $\frac{5}{2}\pi$?

**d.** What is an equation of a tangent function with a period of $\frac{2}{5}\pi$?

### Check Your Understanding

**15.** How could you use the function $y = \sin 2x$ to find the zeros of $y = \tan 2x$?

**16.** How could you use the function $y = \cos 2x$ to find the asymptotes of $y = \tan 2x$?

When you graph $y = a \tan bx$, the value of $a$ compresses or stretches the graph vertically. The value of $b$ compresses or stretches it horizontally.

### MATH TIP

The period of $y = a \tan bx$ is $\frac{\pi}{b}$. When $0 < a < 1$, the graph approaches the asymptotes more quickly than the graph of $y = \tan x$. When $a > 1$, the graph approaches the asymptotes more slowly than the graph of $y = \tan x$.

### Example C

Find the period and asymptotes of $y = \frac{1}{2} \tan \frac{1}{2} x$. Sketch its graph.

**Step 1:** Lightly sketch the parent tangent function.

**Step 2:** The coefficient of the angle, $b$, is $\frac{1}{2}$. The period is $\frac{\pi}{\frac{1}{2}}$ or $2\pi$.  The horizontal width of one period is $2\pi$.

**Step 3:** Divide zeros of $y = \tan x$, $-\pi$, 0, and $\pi$, by $\frac{1}{2}$ to find the zeros of $y = \frac{1}{2} \tan \frac{1}{2} x$. They are $-2\pi$, 0, and $2\pi$. Locate them on the graph.

**Step 4:** Divide asymptotes of $y = \tan x$, $x = -\frac{\pi}{2}$ and $x = \frac{\pi}{2}$, by $\frac{1}{2}$ to find the asymptotes of $y = \frac{1}{2} \tan \frac{1}{2} x$. They are $x = -\pi$ and $x = \pi$. Sketch them on the graph.

**Step 5:** Lightly sketch $y = \tan \frac{1}{2} x$ from $-2\pi$ to $2\pi$.

**Step 6:** Note that the value of $a$ on $y = \frac{1}{2} \tan \frac{1}{2} x$ is $\frac{1}{2}$. Locate some points on each portion of the curve of $y = \tan \frac{1}{2} x$. Multiply the $y$-values by $\frac{1}{2}$. Plot the points with the new $y$-values.

**Step 7:** Connect the points and zeros with a smooth curve. Do not let it intersect the asymptotes. Label the function.

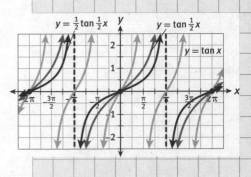

**MATH TIP**

The asymptotes of a tangent function are located halfway between the zeros of the function.

### Try These C

Name the period, zeros, and asymptotes of each function. Graph at least one period of each on a separate coordinate plane.

a. $y = \frac{2}{3}\tan\frac{3}{2}x$

b. $y = \frac{3}{2}\tan\frac{2}{3}x$

### Check Your Understanding

17. Write an equation of the tangent function where the curves of the tangent function will be closer together than in $y = \tan x$.

18. Write an equation of the tangent function where the curves of the tangent function approach the asymptotes more quickly than in $y = \tan x$.

### LESSON 34-4 PRACTICE

**Model with mathematics.** Name the period, zeros, and asymptotes of each function. Graph at least one period of each on a separate coordinate plane.

19. $y = \frac{5}{4}\tan x$

20. $y = \frac{4}{5}\tan x$

21. $y = \tan 4x$

22. $y = \tan\frac{1}{3}x$

23. $y = \frac{4}{3}\tan\frac{2}{3}x$

24. $y = \frac{2}{3}\tan\frac{4}{3}x$

25. **Critique the reasoning of others.** Dianne notices that the graphs of $y = 2\tan x$ and $y = \tan 2x$ are both narrower than the graph of $y = \tan x$. She concludes that they are equivalent graphs. Do you agree? Explain.

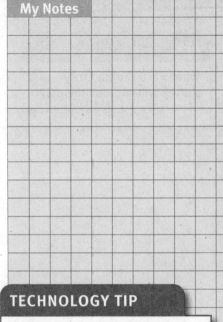

**Learning Targets:**

- Describe and graph functions of the form $y = a \sin b(x - h) + k$, $y = a \cos b(x - h) + k$, and $y = a \tan b(x - h) + k$.
- Find the period, amplitude, and midline of these trigonometric functions.

**SUGGESTED LEARNING STRATEGIES:** Close Reading, Paraphrasing, Create Representations, Discussion Groups, Identify a Subtask, Think-Pair-Share

The transformations in the previous lesson stretched or compressed the graphs of trigonometric functions. It is also possible to translate the graphs of trigonometric functions without changing their shapes.

1. **Use appropriate tools strategically.** For each item, use a graphing calculator to compare the three graphs. Sketch and label them on the coordinate plane. Then compare and contrast the graphs of the three functions

   **a.** $y = \sin x$, $y = \sin x + 3$, and $y = \sin x - 2$.

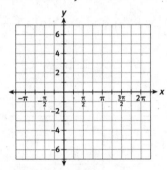

   **b.** $y = \cos x$, $y = \cos x + 4$, and $y = \cos x - 1$

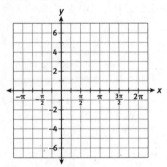

   **c.** $y = \tan x$, $y = \tan x + 3$, and $y = \tan x - 2$

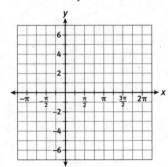

**TECHNOLOGY TIP**

Remember to set the WINDOW of your graphing period to show at least one full period of the function.

**MATH TIP**

When $k > 0$, the graph of $y = \sin x + k$ shifts $k$ units up, and the graph of $y = \sin x - k$ shifts $k$ units down.

The midline is the only feature that changes in each set of graphs. The amplitudes and periods stay the same. Adding or subtracting a constant causes the graph of the parent function to translate up or down. When you graph $y = \sin + k$, $y = \cos x + k$, and $y = \tan x + k$ the graph is translated $k$ units vertically. The midline is also vertically translated by $k$ units.

**Check Your Understanding**

**2.** Are the graphs of $y = 2\cos x$ and $y = \cos x + 2$ the same? Explain.

It is also possible to translate trigonometric functions horizontally.

**3. Use appropriate tools strategically.** For each item, use a graphing calculator to compare the three graphs. Sketch and label them on the coordinate plane. Then compare and contrast the graphs of the three functions
   **a.** $y = \sin x$, $y = \sin\left(x + \dfrac{\pi}{4}\right)$, and $y = \sin\left(x - \dfrac{\pi}{2}\right)$.

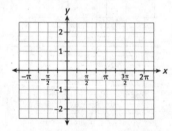

   **b.** $y = \cos x$, $y = \cos\left(x + \dfrac{\pi}{3}\right)$, and $y = \cos\left(x - \dfrac{2\pi}{3}\right)$.

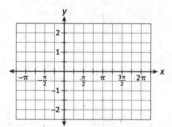

   **c.** $y = \tan x$, $y = \tan\left(x + \dfrac{\pi}{2}\right)$, and $y = \tan\left(x - \dfrac{\pi}{4}\right)$.

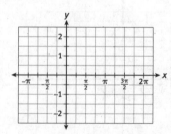

**MATH TIP**

When $h > 0$, the graph of $y = \sin(x - h)$ shifts $h$ units to the right, and the graph of $y = \sin(x + h)$ shifts $h$ units to the left.

The graphs in each set are the same except for their horizontal positions. Adding or subtracting a constant to the angle causes the graph of the parent function to translate left or right. When you graph $y = \sin(x - h)$, $y = \cos(x - h)$, and $y = \tan(x - h)$ the graph is translated $h$ units horizontally. Another name for a horizontal shift of a periodic function is a **_phase shift_**. The zeros also slide horizontally the same distance, as do the asymptotes of the tangent function.

**My Notes**

> **MATH TERMS**
>
> The **phase shift** of a periodic function is the distance it is translated horizontally from its parent function.

### Example A

Describe the vertical and horizontal shifts of $y = \cos(x - \pi) + 1$. Sketch its graph. Name its midline, at least one maximums, and at least one minimum.

**Step 1:** The vertical shift is 1 unit up. The horizontal shift is $\pi$ units to the right.

**Step 2:** Lightly sketch the parent cosine function from $-\pi$ to $2\pi$.

**Step 3:** Sketch and label the graph of $y = \cos(x - \pi) + 1$ one unit above and $\pi$ units to the right of the graph of $y = \cos x$.

**Step 4:** Locate and name one maximum and one minimum.

**Step 5:** Sketch the horizontal line $y = 1$ which is halfway between the minimums and maximums. This is the midline.

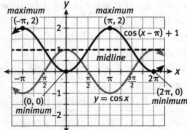

### Example B

Describe the vertical and horizontal shifts of $y = \tan\left(x + \dfrac{\pi}{4}\right) - 2$. Sketch its graph. Name its midline and at least one asymptote.

**Step 1:** The vertical shift is 2 units down. The horizontal shift is $\dfrac{\pi}{4}$ units to the left.

**Step 2:** Lightly sketch the parent tangent function from 0 to $2\pi$.

**Step 3:** Sketch and label the graph of $y = \tan\left(x + \dfrac{\pi}{4}\right) - 2$ two units below and $\dfrac{\pi}{4}$ units to the left of the graph of $y = \tan x$.

**Step 4:** Sketch the horizontal line $y = -2$. This is the midline.

**Step 5:** Sketch the asymptotes.

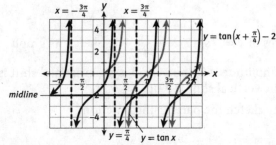

**My Notes**

**Try These A–B**

Describe the vertical and horizontal shifts of each function.
Graph at least one period of each on a separate coordinate plane. Draw and label the midline and any asymptotes.

**a.** $y = \sin\left(x + \dfrac{\pi}{3}\right) + 2$    **b.** $y = \tan\left(x - \dfrac{\pi}{2}\right) - 1$

The chart summarizes the transformations of the parent sine, cosine, and tangent functions that you have learned in this activity.

| $y = a\ sin\ b(x - h) + k$ |
|---|
| $y = a\ cos\ b(x - h) + k$ |
| $y = a\ tan\ b(x - h) + k$ |

| | |
|---|---|
| **a** | • The coefficient changes the amplitude of the sine and cosine functions.<br>• When $a > 1$, the amplitude increases and the graph is stretched vertically.<br>• When $0 < a < 1$, the amplitude decreases and the graph is compressed vertically.<br>• When $a < 0$, the graph is reflected across the $x$-axis. |
| **b** | • The coefficient changes the period.<br>• When $b > 1$, the period decreases and the graph is compressed horizontally.<br>• When $0 < b < 1$, the period increases and the graph is stretched horizontally.<br>• The period of $\sin bx$ and $\cos bx$ is $\dfrac{2\pi}{b}$.<br>• The period of $\tan bx$ is $\dfrac{\pi}{b}$. |
| **h** | • The constant shifts the graph horizontally.<br>• When $h > 0$, the graph shifts to the right.<br>• When $h < 0$, the graph shifts to the left. |
| **k** | • The constant shifts the graph vertically.<br>• When $k > 0$, the graph shifts up.<br>• When $k < 0$, the graph shifts down. |

**Example C**

List the features of $y = 2\sin 2\left(x + \dfrac{\pi}{4}\right) + 3$. Sketch its graph.

**Step 1:** The amplitude is 2, the period is $\pi$, horizontal shift is $\dfrac{\pi}{4}$ to the left, and the vertical shift is 3 up.

**Step 2:** Lightly sketch the parent sine function.

## Lesson 34-5
### Translating Trigonometric Functions

**Step 3:** Lightly sketch the graph of $y = 2 \sin 2x$. The amplitude is doubled by a factor of 2 and the period is compressed by a factor of $\frac{1}{2}$.

**Step 4:** Sketch that curve again, shifting it $\frac{\pi}{4}$ units to the left and 3 units up to show the graph of $y = 2 \sin 2\left(x + \frac{\pi}{4}\right) + 3$. Label it.

My Notes

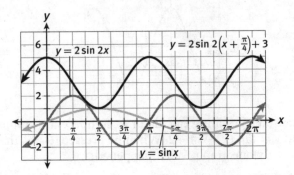

## Try These C

List the features of each function. Sketch its graph.

**a.** $y = \frac{4}{3} \cos \frac{1}{2}\left(x - \frac{\pi}{3}\right) + 2$     **b.** $y = \frac{3}{4} \tan 2\left(x + \frac{\pi}{3}\right) - 1$

**c.** What is an equation of a sine function with amplitude of 2, a period of $\pi$, a horizontal shift of $\frac{2\pi}{3}$ units to the right, and a vertical shift of 3 units down?

### Check Your Understanding

4. **Make sense of problems.** Find the amplitude, period, horizontal shift, and vertical shift of the graph below. Write its equation.

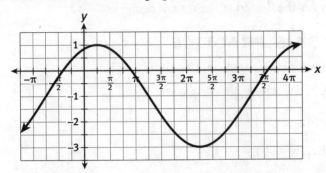

5. **Construct viable arguments.** When asked to write the equation of the graph shown below, Samara says it is $y = 2 \cos x$. Eduardo says it is $y = 2 \sin\left(x + \frac{\pi}{2}\right)$. Which student is correct? Why?

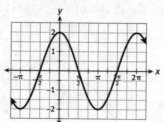

6. Dominic used a graphing calculator to compare the graphs of $y = \tan x - 2$ and $y = \tan(x - \pi) - 2$. When he pressed [GRAPH], the calculator displayed only one graph. What happened?

Look at the graph of the mural for the transit station that was presented at the beginning of the activity.

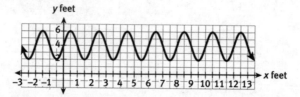

It is possible to write an equation that describes it accurately. Because it crosses the midline at $x = 0$, it would be easiest to use the sine function and write it in the form $y = a \sin b(x - h) + k$. Use information from the graph to find $a$, $b$, $h$, and $k$.

- The midline is $y = 4$. The function extends 2 feet above and 2 feet below the midline so the amplitude is 2.
- The graph completes one full cycle in 2 feet, so the period is 2. Solve $\frac{2\pi}{b} = 2$ for $b$.
- The graph has not been shifted horizontally, so the phase shift is 0. Because $h = 0$, it is not needed in the equation.
- The midline is $y = 4$ so the graph has been shifted 4 units up.

The equation for the design at the transit center is _____ .

## LESSON 34-5 PRACTICE

List the features of each function. Sketch its graph.

7. $y = \cos\frac{1}{2}(x - \pi) - 1$

8. $y = \frac{1}{3}\tan\left(x + \frac{2\pi}{3}\right) + 2$

9. $y = \frac{3}{2}\sin 2\left(x + \frac{\pi}{4}\right) + 1$

10. **Reason abstractly.** Why does adding a constant greater than zero to a trigonometric function move the graph up, but multiplying it by a coefficient greater than one stretches it?

# Graphs of Trigonometric Functions
## Creation of a Mural

**ACTIVITY 34**
*continued*

## ACTIVITY 34 PRACTICE

### Lesson 34-1

State whether each graph in Items 1–4 shows a periodic function. If periodic, give the period, amplitude, and the equation of the midline. If not periodic, explain why not.

**1.**

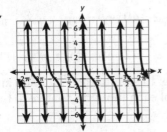

**2.**

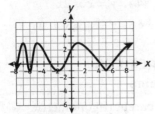

**3.**

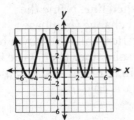

**4.**

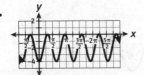

**5.** How can you use the maximum and minimum $y$-values of a periodic function to find the equation of the midline?

**6.** Draw the graph of a periodic function that has a period of 3, an amplitude of 2.5, and a midline of $y = 0.5$.

### Lesson 34-2

Name the period and amplitude of each function. Graph at least one period of each on a separate coordinate plane.

**7.** $y = 4 \sin x$

**8.** $y = \dfrac{1}{4} \sin x$

**9.** $y = \sin 4x$

**10.** $y = \sin \dfrac{1}{4} x$

**11.** $y = \dfrac{5}{2} \sin \dfrac{2}{5} x$

Refer to the graph below for Items 12–14.

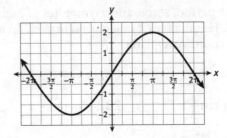

**12.** What is the period and amplitude of the graph?

**13.** What is the equation of the function?

**14.** What is the equation of a graph that is half as wide and twice as tall as the one shown?

### Lesson 34-3

Name the period and amplitude of each function. Graph at least one period of each on a separate coordinate plane.

**15.** $y = 3 \cos x$

**16.** $y = \dfrac{2}{3} \cos x$

**17.** $y = \cos 3x$

**18.** $y = \cos \dfrac{2}{3} x$

**19.** $y = \dfrac{3}{2} \cos \dfrac{1}{3} x$

Refer to the graph below for Items 20–21.

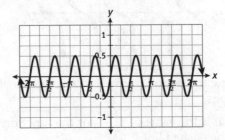

**20.** What is the period and amplitude of the graph?

**21.** What is the equation of the function?

Suppose a graphic designer wanted to use the cosine function to create a mural. However, she wanted it to appear three times narrower than the parent cosine function. She was not sure whether to use the graph of $y = 3 \cos x$ or the graph of $y = \cos 3x$.

**22.** Graph $y = \cos x$ and $y = 3 \cos x$ on the same coordinate axis. Compare and contrast the graphs of the two functions.

**23.** Graph $y = \cos x$ and $y = \cos 3x$ on the same coordinate axis. Compare and contrast the graphs of the two functions

**24.** Which equation results in a graph three times narrower than $y = \cos x$? Explain.

## Lesson 34-4

Name the period, zeros, and asymptotes of each function. Graph at least one period of each on a separate coordinate plane.

**25.** $y = \frac{3}{2} \tan x$      **26.** $y = \frac{1}{2} \tan x$

**27.** $y = \tan \frac{2}{3} x$      **28.** $y = \tan \frac{3}{2} x$

**29.** $y = 2 \tan \frac{1}{4} x$

Refer to the graph below for Items 30–31.

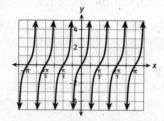

**30.** Name the period, zeros, and asymptotes of the graph.

**31.** What is the equation of the function?

Refer to the graph below for Items 32–34.

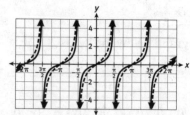

**32.** Name the period, zeros, and asymptotes of both graphs.

**33.** What is the value of $f\left(\frac{\pi}{4}\right)$ for the function shown by the dashed line?

**34.** What is the value of $f\left(\frac{\pi}{4}\right)$ for the function shown by the solid line?

**35.** What is the equation of the function shown by the dashed line? the solid line?

**36.** George graphed $y = \tan x$ as shown below. The teacher marked it wrong. He argued that the zeros and asymptotes were correct. He did not understand what was wrong with it. Explain why it is incorrect.

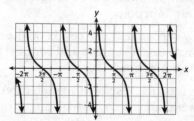

## Lesson 34-5

For each function, describe the phase (horizontal) shift and vertical shift relative to the parent function. Then graph it.

**37.** $y = \cos\left(x + \frac{\pi}{4}\right) + 2$    **38.** $y = \cos\left(x - \frac{2\pi}{3}\right) - 3$

**39.** $y = \tan\left(x - \frac{\pi}{3}\right) + 2$    **40.** $y = \tan\left(x + \frac{\pi}{2}\right) - 1$

**41.** $y = \sin\left(x - \frac{\pi}{2}\right) - 2$    **42.** $y = \sin(x + \pi) + 1$

Describe the meaning of the "2" in each function and its effect on the graph of each function relative to the parent function.

**43.** $y = 2 \cos x$      **44.** $y = \cos 2x$

**45.** $y = \cos(x + 2)$      **46.** $y = \cos x + 2$

## MATHEMATICAL PRACTICES
### Make Sense of Problems

In each graph below, the parent trigonometric function is shown with a dashed line. Name the amplitude change ($a$), period change ($b$), phase (horizontal) shift ($h$), and vertical shift ($k$) shown by the function graphed with a solid line. Then write its equation in the form $y = a \sin b(x - h) + k$, $y = a \cos b(x - h) + k$, or $y = a \tan b(x - h) + k$.

**47.**

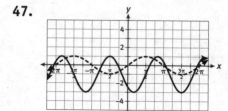

**48.**

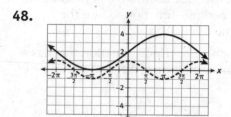

**49.**

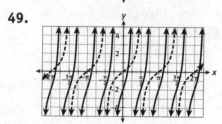

**The Sky Wheel**
## Lesson 35-1  Modeling Periodic Phenomena

### Learning Targets:

- Use trigonometric functions to model real-world periodic phenomena.
- Identify key features of these functions.

> **SUGGESTED LEARNING STRATEGIES:** Marking the Text, Visualization, Look for a Pattern, Think-Pair-Share, Group Presentation

Tyrell is an engineer at Rocket Rides. His job is to design amusement park rides that meet the needs of the company's clients. A new client has asked Rocket Rides to design a Ferris wheel, given the following *constraints*.

- The diameter of the wheel must be 88 feet.
- The highest point of the wheel must be 100 feet above ground.
- The wheel must make one rotation every 60 seconds.

Based on this information, Tyrell creates a preliminary sketch for a ride called The Sky Wheel, as shown.

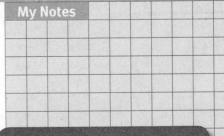

**ACADEMIC VOCABULARY**

A **constraint** is a condition or restriction that must be satisfied. For example, biologists might study the physical constraints that determine the possible sizes and shapes of insects.

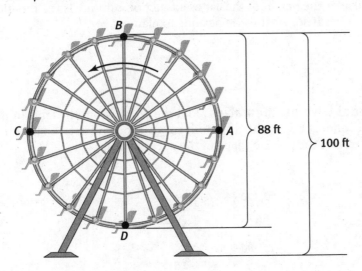

Tyrell wants to write a function that models the motion of the Ferris wheel. He starts by considering the motion of a car that begins at point *A*.

1. **Reason quantitatively.** What is the height of the car when it is at point *A*? Explain?

**2.** Tyrell makes a table showing the height of the car in feet at various times as the Ferris wheel rotates counterclockwise. Complete the table.

| Time (seconds) | 0 | 15 | 30 | 45 | 60 | 75 | 90 | 105 | 120 |
|---|---|---|---|---|---|---|---|---|---|
| Height (feet) | | | | | | | | | |

**3.** Describe any patterns you see in the table.

**4.** Consider the height of the car as a function of time. Is the function periodic? If so, what is the period? Explain.

**5. Model with mathematics.** Plot the points from the table in Item 2 and connect them with a smooth curve. (You will get a chance to determine the precise shape of the curve later.)

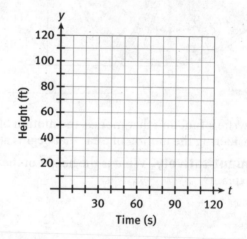

**6.** What is the amplitude of the function you graphed?

**7.** What is the equation of the midline?

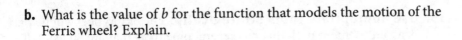

8. Tyrell plans to write an equation for the function in the form
   $f(t) = a \sin b(t - h) + k$.
   **a.** How is the value of $b$ related to the period of the function?

   **b.** What is the value of $b$ for the function that models the motion of the Ferris wheel? Explain.

9. Use the values from your answers in Items 6–8 to write an equation in the form $f(t) = a \sin b(t - h) + k$.

> **MATH TIP**
>
> The graph of the equation
> $y = a \sin b (x - h) + k$ has
> amplitude $|a|$ and midline $y = k$.

### Check Your Understanding

10. How can you check that the equation you wrote in Item 9 is reasonable?

11. How does the graph of the function $f(t)$ compare to the graph of the parent function, $y = \sin x$? Use the language of transformations in your answer.

12. Give a reasonable domain and range of the function $f(t)$.

13. **Make sense of problems.** Tyrell uses the function to make some predictions about the position of the car at various times.
    **a.** What does $f(20)$ represent?

    **b.** What is the value of $f(20)$ to the nearest tenth?

    **c.** How do you know that the value you found for $f(20)$ is reasonable?

**14.** During the first two complete rotations of The Sky Wheel, give the times when the car is moving upward and the times when the car is moving downward.

**15. Use appropriate tools strategically.** The Sky Wheel will be part of an amusement park that has several pine trees that are 80 feet tall. Tyrell wants to know the times when the car will be above the height of the treetops.
  **a.** Write an equation that Tyrell can solve to find the times when the car will be at the same height as the treetops.

  **b.** Use your calculator to find the times when the car will be at the same height as the treetops during the first two complete rotations of The Sky Wheel. Round to the nearest tenth of a second.

  **c.** During what intervals of time will the car be above the height of the treetops?

**16.** Tyrell wants to write a new function, $g(t)$, that models the motion of a car that starts at the bottom of The Sky Wheel (point $D$ in the figure at the beginning of the lesson).
  **a.** Modify the function $f(t)$ you wrote in Item 9 to write the new function $g(t)$.

  **b.** Sketch the graph of $g(t)$ below.

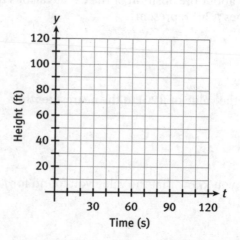

**My Notes**

## Check Your Understanding

17. How are the graphs of $f(t)$ and $g(t)$ similar? How are they different?

18. **Construct viable arguments.** Suppose the client decides that the highest point of The Sky Wheel should be 102 feet rather than 100 feet. The size of the wheel does not change. How would the function $f(t)$ need to be changed?

Tyrell wants to compare The Sky Wheel to some other Ferris wheels he has designed. He checks his files for information on The Round Robin and The Spin Cycle. The information he finds for these Ferris wheels is shown below.

### The Round Robin

| Time (seconds) | 0 | 12 | 24 | 36 | 48 | 60 |
|---|---|---|---|---|---|---|
| Height (feet) | 8 | 45 | 82 | 45 | 8 | 45 |

### The Spin Cycle

$$y = 33\cos\left(\frac{\pi}{45}t\right) + 43$$

19. Which of the three Ferris wheels (The Sky Wheel, The Round Robin or The Spin Cycle) rotates the fastest? Justify your answer.

20. Which of the three Ferris wheels is the tallest? Justify your answer.

21. Which of the three Ferris wheels has the greatest diameter? Justify your answer.

**CONNECT TO AP**

Periodic functions can be modeled by functions other than trigonometric functions. For example, the piecewise-defined function $f(x)$ shown below is periodic but not trigonometric.

$$f(x) = \begin{cases} 1 & x \text{ is an integer} \\ 0 & x \text{ is not an integer} \end{cases}$$

In calculus, you will explore these types of periodic functions when you study limits.

### Check Your Understanding

22. Explain how you can determine the height of the car on The Round Robin after 4 minutes.

23. Given the trigonometric equation that models the motion of a Ferris wheel, how can you determine the diameter of the Ferris wheel?

## LESSON 35-1 PRACTICE

24. Which of the three Ferris wheels in the activity (The Sky Wheel, The Round Robin, or The Spin Cycle) comes closest to the ground? What is this Ferris wheel's distance from the ground?

25. **Persevere in solving problems.** Refer to the table on the previous page that describes the motion of a car on The Round Robin.
   a. Write an equation that models the motion of the car.
   b. What is the height of the car after 15 seconds?
   c. During the first complete rotation of The Round Robin, at what time(s) is the car at a height of 65 feet? Round to the nearest tenth of a second.

26. Tyrell proposes to the client that The Sky Wheel rotate clockwise instead of counterclockwise. How should Tyrell modify the function $f(t)$ to model a clockwise rotation of the Ferris wheel?

27. The equation $y = 4\sin\left(\frac{\pi}{4}(x - 4)\right) + 7$ models the motion of a point on the edge of a circular gear, where $x$ is the number of seconds since the gear started turning and $y$ is the height of the point above the ground, in inches.
   a. How long does it take for the gear to make one complete rotation?
   b. What is the height of the point after 6 seconds?

28. **Model with mathematics.** The tide at a dock has a minimum height of 0.3 feet and a maximum height of 6.9 feet. It takes a total of 12.2 hours for the tide to come in and go back out. A fisherman wants to model the height $h$ of the tide in feet as a trigonometric function of the time $t$ in hours.
   a. What is the period of the function? What is the amplitude?
   b. Assume the low tide occurs at time $t = 0$. Write a function of the form $f(t) = a\sin b(t - h) + k$ that models the tide.
   c. Explain how you can check that your function is reasonable.
   d. What is the value of $f(15)$ to the nearest tenth? What does this represent?

## ACTIVITY 35 PRACTICE
Write your answers on notebook paper.
Show your work.

### Lesson 35-1

1. A Ferris wheel has a diameter of 94 feet, and the highest point of the wheel is 102 feet above the ground. The Ferris wheel makes one rotation every 80 seconds.
   a. Write a trigonometric function that models the motion of one car on the Ferris wheel.
   b. According to your model, what is the height of the car when the ride starts?
   c. What is the height of the car after 4 seconds?

2. A bicycle wheel has a diameter of 26 inches. Isabelle rides the bike so that the wheel makes two complete rotations per second. Which function models the height of a spot on the edge of the wheel?
   **A.** $h(t) = 13\sin(2\pi t) + 13$
   **B.** $h(t) = 13\sin(4\pi t)$
   **C.** $h(t) = 13\sin(4\pi t) + 13$
   **D.** $h(t) = 13\sin(2\pi t)$

3. The function $f(x)$ models the height in feet of the tide at a specific location $x$ hours after high tide.

   $$f(x) = 3.5\cos\left(\frac{\pi}{6}x\right) + 3.7$$

   a. What is the height of the tide at low tide?
   b. What is the period of the function? What does this tell you about the tides at this location?
   c. How many hours after high tide is the tide at a height of 3 feet for the first time?

4. An office building has a large clock on one face of the building. The minute hand of the clock is 12 feet long, and the center of the clock is 160 feet above the ground. The function $f(t)$ models the height of the tip of the minute hand above the ground in feet, with $t$ representing the time in minutes.
   a. What is the period of the function?
   b. Write an equation for $f(t)$ in the form $f(t) = a\sin b(t - h) + k$. Assume the minute hand points to the 12 on the clock at $t = 0$. (*Hint:* Be sure to write the function so that the minute hand is rotating clockwise!)
   c. Graph the function.
   d. What is the value of $f(15)$? Explain why this makes sense.
   e. Explain how you can find $f(180)$ without using a calculator.

5. Sonia and Jeremy turn a jump rope. The graph shows the height of a point at the middle of the rope. How many times do Sonia and Jeremy turn the rope each minute?

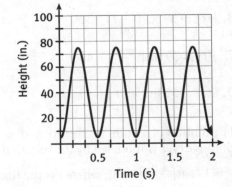

For Items 6–10, the height of an object, in centimeters, is modeled by the function $y = 42\sin\left(\frac{\pi}{10}(x - h)\right) + 55$. Determine whether each statement is always, sometimes, or never true.

**6.** The period of the function is 20.

**7.** The maximum height of the object is 55 centimeters.

**8.** The minimum height of the object occurs when $x = 0$.

**9.** The graph of the function has the midline $y = 55$.

**10.** The amplitude of the function is 84.

**11.** The function $f(t) = 40\sin\left(\frac{\pi}{45}t\right) + 48$ models the height in feet of one car of a Ferris wheel called The Colossus, where $t$ is the time in seconds. Each of the functions below models the motion of a different Ferris wheel. Which Ferris wheel has the same diameter as The Colossus?

**A.** $g(t) = 40\cos\left(\frac{\pi}{45}t\right) + 50$

**B.** $h(t) = 39\cos\left(\frac{\pi}{60}t\right) + 49$

**C.** $j(t) = 39\sin\left(\frac{\pi}{45}t\right) + 48$

**D.** $k(t) = 39\sin\left(\frac{\pi}{45}t\right) + 49$

**12.** The motion of a point on the drum of a clothes dryer is modeled by the function $y = 12\sin\left(\frac{4}{3}\pi t\right) + 20$, where $t$ is the time in seconds. How many times does the dryer rotate per minute?

**13.** The graph shows the height of a scratch on the edge of a circular gear.

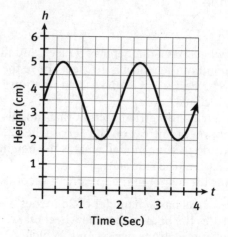

Which function is the best model for the height of the scratch?
**A.** $h(t) = 3.5\sin(\pi t) + 1.5$
**B.** $h(t) = 1.5\sin(\pi t) + 3.5$
**C.** $h(t) = 1.5\sin(2\pi t) + 3.5$
**D.** $h(t) = 1.5\sin\left(\frac{\pi}{2}t\right) + 3.5$

**14.** The height in feet of an object above the ground is modeled by the function $y = 3\cos(3\pi t) + 7.8$, where $t$ is the time in minutes. During the first complete cycle, at what times is the object closer than 6 feet to the ground? Use an inequality to express your answer.

## MATHEMATICAL PRACTICES
**Construct Viable Arguments and Critique the Reasoning of Others**

**15.** A student was asked to model the motion of one car of a Ferris wheel. The student claimed that it is possible to use the tangent function to model the motion, since the tangent function is periodic. Do you agree or disagree with the student's reasoning? Justify your answer.

Totally Tires sells tires and wheels for everything from bicycles to monster trucks. The front outside wall of the shop features a rotating tire to attract customers. The shop's owner has decided that the display needs to be improved. You have been hired to analyze the motion of the existing tire and to add another rotating tire to the display.

1.  According to the shop's owner, the motion of the existing tire can be modeled by the function $y = \cos\left(\frac{\pi}{15}x\right) + 5$, where $x$ is the time, in seconds, and $y$ is the height, in feet, of a point on the edge of the tire.
    a.  What are the reasonable domain and range of the function?
    b.  What is the period of the function? What does this represent?
    c.  Graph the function.
    d.  How does the graph compare to the graph of the parent function, $y = \cos x$?

2.  The shop's owner states that the new rotating tire that will be added to the display should have a diameter of 3 feet and that the top of the tire should be 7 feet above the ground. The owner would like this tire to make one complete rotation every 20 seconds. Write a function of the form $f(t) = a \sin b(t - h) + k$ to model the motion of a point on the edge of the new tire.

3.  **Reason abstractly.** Before the new tire is added to the display, the shop's owner wants a written statement so she can get a sense of what the completed display will look like. Write a summary comparing the existing rotating tire to the new one. Be sure to include answers to the following questions, with justifications.
    - Which tire rotates more quickly?
    - Which tire has a greater diameter?
    - Which tire comes closer to the ground?

| Scoring Guide | Exemplary | Proficient | Emerging | Incomplete |
|---|---|---|---|---|
| | The solution demonstrates these characteristics: | | | |
| **Mathematics Knowledge and Thinking** (Items 1, 2) | • Clear and accurate understanding of sinusoidal models including domain and range | • Largely correct understanding of sinusoidal models including domain and range | • Partial understanding of sinusoidal models including domain and range | • Incomplete or inaccurate understanding of sinusoidal models including domain and range |
| **Problem Solving** (Item 3) | • An appropriate and efficient strategy that results in a correct answer | • A strategy that may include unnecessary steps but results in a correct answer | • A strategy that results in some incorrect answers | • No clear strategy when solving problems |
| **Mathematical Modeling / Representations** (Items 1, 2, 3) | • Effective understanding of how features of an equation or graph relate to a real-world scenario <br> • Fluency in applying transformations to graph a function <br> • Fluency in writing a sinusoidal equation to model a real-world scenario | • Mostly accurate recognition of how features of an equation or graph relate to a real-world scenario <br> • Little difficulty in applying transformations to graph a function <br> • Little difficulty in writing a sinusoidal equation to model a real-world scenario | • Partial recognition of how features of an equation or graph relate to a real-world scenario <br> • Some difficulty in applying transformations to graph a function <br> • Some difficulty in writing a sinusoidal equation to model a real-world scenario | • Difficulty in recognizing how features of an equation or graph relate to a real-world scenario <br> • Significant difficulty in applying transformations to graph a function <br> • Significant difficulty in writing a sinusoidal equation to model a real-world scenario |
| **Reasoning and Communication** (Items 1d, 3) | • Precise use of appropriate math terms and language when interpreting and comparing models <br> • Clear and accurate description of transformations of a parent function | • Adequate use of math terms and language when interpreting and comparing models <br> • Adequate description of transformations of a parent function | • Misleading or confusing use of math terms and language when interpreting and comparing models <br> • Misleading or confusing description of transformations of a parent function | • Incomplete or mostly inaccurate use of appropriate math terms and language when interpreting and comparing models <br> • Incomplete or inadequate description of transformations of a parent function |

# Probability and Statistics

## Unit Overview

In this unit you will investigate whether a normal distribution is an appropriate model for data and, if it is, how to use the model to analyze and understand the data. You will learn the importance of impartiality in surveys and experiments, as well as use simulations to decide whether data are consistent or inconsistent with a conjecture. You will also investigate how to use data from a randomized experiment to compare two treatments and decide if an observed treatment effect is statistically significant.

## Key Terms

As you study this unit, add these and other terms to your math notebook. Include in your notes your prior knowledge of each word, as well as your experiences in using the word in different mathematical examples. If needed, ask for help in pronouncing new words and add information on pronunciation to your math notebook. It is important that you learn new terms and use them correctly in your class discussions and in your problem solutions.

### Academic Vocabulary

- placebo
- simulation

### Math Terms

- density curve
- $z$-score
- normal distribution
- normal curve
- sample
- survey
- response
- bias
- simple random sample
- experiment
- explanatory variable
- response variable
- completely randomized design
- randomized block design
- matched pairs design
- single-blind study
- double-blind study
- observational study
- confounding variable
- simulation
- statistic
- margin of error
- sample proportion
- sampling distribution
- critical value
- statistically significant

## ESSENTIAL QUESTIONS

**?** What role does a random process play when conducting a survey?

**?** What role does a random process play when conducting an experiment with two treatments?

**?** How can a simulation help you decide if a set of data is consistent or inconsistent with a conjecture about the world?

## EMBEDDED ASSESSMENTS

This unit has two embedded assessments, following Activities 37 and 40. These assessments will allow you to demonstrate your understanding of the relationships between data and models of real-world situations.

**Embedded Assessment 1:**

Normal Models, Surveys, and Experiments          p. 591

**Embedded Assessment 2:**

Simulations, Margin of Error, and Hypothesis Testing          p. 631

# Getting Ready

**Write your answers on notebook paper.**
**Show your work.**

1. The following are the lengths of time, in minutes, that it took each member of a group of 12 running buddies to complete a marathon.

| 241 | 229 | 230 | 234 | 215 | 231 |
|-----|-----|-----|-----|-----|-----|
| 239 | 229 | 221 | 231 | 220 | 238 |

   a. Make a stem-and-leaf plot of the data, using ten-minute intervals for the stems.
   b. Make a dot plot of the data.
   c. Make a histogram of the data using five-minute intervals.
   d. Describe the distribution of the data using everyday language.
   e. Use technology to determine the mean and median of the 12 marathon times.
   f. Suppose these 12 friends were joined by a thirteenth running buddy who completed the marathon in 205 minutes. Describe how that runner compares to the other twelve.

2. Suppose that 12 families with one child each were surveyed and asked these questions: "About how much time, in minutes, do you spend reading to your children each week?" and "How tall is your child, in inches?" If a strong negative correlation were observed in a scatter plot of (reading time, height), would that imply that reading to your children stunts their growth? Explain.

# Normal Distribution
## Take Me Out to the Ballgame
## Lesson 36-1 Shapes of Distributions

**Learning Targets:**
- Represent distribution with appropriate data plots.
- Interpret shape of a distribution and relate shape to measures of center and spread.

SUGGESTED LEARNING STRATEGIES: Marking the Text, Activating Prior Knowledge, Interactive Word Wall, Create Representations, Look for a Pattern, Think-Pair-Share, Group Presentation, Jigsaw, Quickwrite, Self Revision/Peer Revision

The sport of baseball has a long history of players, fans, and management maintaining and interpreting players' statistics. One of the most common statistics used to describe a hitter's effectiveness is the *batting average*. Batting average is defined as the number of hits a player achieves divided by the number of at-bats that the player needs to achieve those hits. Work with your group on Items 1–4.

1. A local recreational baseball club, the Cobras, has twelve players. The batting averages for those players are as follows. 0.265, 0.270, 0.275, 0.280, 0.280, 0.280, 0.285, 0.285, 0.285, 0.285, 0.290, 0.290.

   **a.** Create a dot plot for the batting averages.

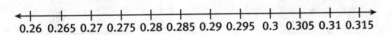

   **b.** Describe the shape of the dot plot.

   **c.** Find the mean and median of the data set. Which is larger?

   **d.** What is the connection between the shape of the distribution and the location of the mean and median in the distribution?

2. Another local baseball club, the Manatees, also has 12 players. The batting averages for those players are as follows. 0.275, 0.275, 0.280, 0.280, 0.280, 0.280, 0.285, 0.285, 0.285, 0.290, 0.295, 0.305.
   **a.** Create a dot plot for the batting averages.

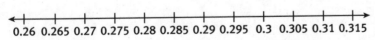

   **b.** Describe the shape of the dot plot.

   **c.** Find the mean and median of the data set. Which is larger?

   **d.** What is the connection between the shape of the distribution and the location of the mean and median in the distribution?

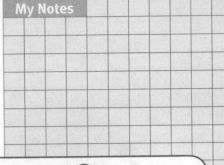

**CONNECT TO SPORTS**

$$\text{Batting Average} = \frac{\text{Number of Hits}}{\text{Number of At-Bats}}$$

For example, if a player gets four hits in ten at-bats, then the batting average is $\frac{4}{10} = 0.400$. (Batting averages are reported rounded to the nearest thousandth.)

**DISCUSSION GROUP TIP**

Reread the problem scenario as needed. Make notes on the information provided in the problem. Respond to questions about the meaning of key information. Summarize or organize the information needed to create reasonable solutions, and describe the mathematical concepts your group will use to create its solutions.

**MATH TIP**

When a graphical representation shows that data has a "tail" in one direction, the data is described as skewed in the direction of the tail (either left or right). With skewed data, the mean is "pulled" away from the median in the direction of the skew. The mean will be close to the median if the data is not skewed and has no outliers.

3. Compare and contrast the shapes of the distributions of batting averages for the Cobras and the Manatees. How are the characteristics of the distributions related to the measures of center, the mean, and the median?

4. Find the standard deviation of the batting averages for the Cobras and the standard deviation of the batting averages for the Manatees. What do these standard deviations measure?

**MATH TIP**

Use technology to determine the standard deviation. On a TI graphing calculator, input the data in a list, and then press STAT, go to CALC, and select *1:1-Var Stats* to calculate the standard deviation (use the *Sx* = value). Alternatively, you can use the formula on page 635.

Three other teams, the Turtles, the Cottonmouths, and the Snappers, have their batting average data displayed in the histograms below.

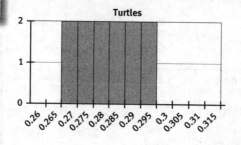

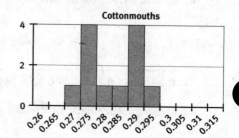

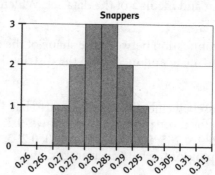

5. Compare and contrast the histograms of these three teams.

**MATH TIP**

Data can be described as unimodal if it has one maximum in a graphical representation. This is true even if the data has two numerical modes as seen here for the Snappers. Data with two local maxima can be described as bimodal.

6. Find the mean and median for each of these distributions. How are your results related to the distributions?

**My Notes**

**7.** Guess which team's distribution of batting averages has the largest standard deviation. Guess which one has the smallest. Use your calculator to find the actual standard deviations and confirm, or revise, your conjectures.

If a distribution follows a well-defined pattern, a smooth curve can be drawn to represent the distribution.

**8.** Below are each of the distributions that we saw in Items 1–7. For each distribution, draw a smooth curve on the distribution that best represents the pattern.

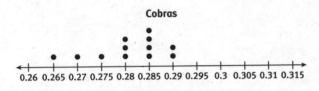

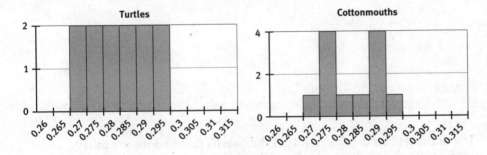

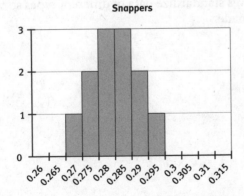

Each of the curves drawn above is called a **density curve**. Density curves have special characteristics:

- Density curves are always drawn above the *x*-axis.
- The area between the density curve and the *x*-axis is always 1.

On the Cobras, the player with the batting average of 0.270 was Walter. One player with a batting average of 0.290 was Leslie. The coach wanted to know how each player compared to the mean batting average.

From your previous work, you discovered that the mean batting average for the Cobras was 0.2808 and that the standard deviation was 0.0076. The coach performed the following calculations:

$$\frac{0.270 - 0.2808}{0.0076} = -1.421; \quad \frac{0.290 - 0.2808}{0.0076} = 1.211$$

**9.** Work with your group on this item and on Item 10. Describe the meaning of each number in the calculations. What do the results of the calculations represent?

**DISCUSSION GROUP TIP**

As you share your ideas for Items 9 and 10, be sure to use mathematical terms and academic vocabulary precisely. Make notes to help you remember the meaning of new words and how they are used to describe mathematical concepts.

**10.** What is the meaning of the positive or negative sign in the result of the calculations?

The numbers that are the results of the coach's calculations are called *z-scores*. Such scores standardize data of different types so that comparisons to a mean can be made.

**MATH TIP**

$$z\text{-score} = \frac{x - \text{mean}}{\text{standard deviation}}$$

### Check Your Understanding

**11.** The grades on a quiz for three of Mr. Dean's classes were analyzed by finding the mean, standard deviation, and shape of the distribution for each class. Mr. Dean dropped his papers after doing this analysis, and the shapes of the distributions were separated from the means and medians. Which shape belongs to which mean and median?

A.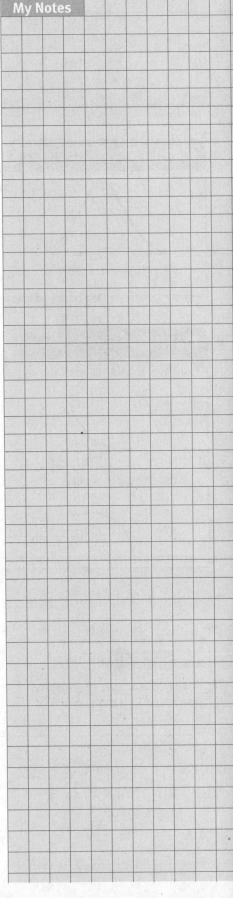

B.

C.

   **a.** Mean: 70      **b.** Mean: 70      **c.** Mean: 70
       Median: 70         Median: 60         Median: 80

**12.** The mean length of a python is 2 m with a standard deviation of 0.3 m. The mean weight of the same species of python is 25 kg with a standard deviation of 5.4 kg. A 2.7 m python weighing 30 kg is captured in a state park. Use $z$-scores to determine which characteristic of the snake is more unusual: its length or its width. Explain your reasoning.

### LESSON 36-1 PRACTICE

Charles has a jar in which he places any pennies that he may obtain during his daily activities. His sister, Oluoma, takes a handful of pennies off the top and records the dates on the pennies:
2013, 2012, 2008, 2012, 2011, 2013, 2012, 2013, 2011, 2011, 2010, 2009, 2012, 2013, 2012, 2010.

**13.** What is the mean date of the pennies? What is the median of the dates?

**14.** Draw a dot plot of the data, and then draw a smooth density curve that represents the data. Describe the shape of the distribution and its relation to your responses in Item 13.

**15.** Find the standard deviation of the penny date data, and determine the $z$-score for the dates of 2012 and 2009. What is the significance of the sign of the $z$-score of each?

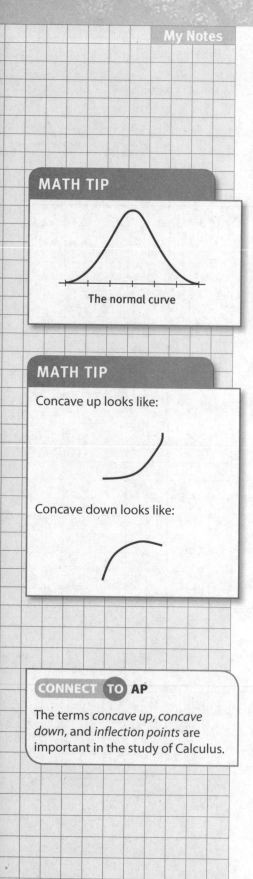

**My Notes**

**MATH TIP**

The normal curve

**MATH TIP**

Concave up looks like:

Concave down looks like:

**CONNECT TO AP**

The terms *concave up, concave down*, and *inflection points* are important in the study of Calculus.

**Learning Targets:**
- Recognize characteristics of a normal distribution.
- Use mean and standard deviation to completely describe a normal distribution.

**SUGGESTED LEARNING STRATEGIES:** Shared Reading, Summarizing, Close Reading, Marking the Text, Activating Prior Knowledge, Interactive Word Wall, Create Representations, Look for a Pattern, Think-Pair-Share, Group Presentations, Jigsaw, Quickwrite, Self Revision/Peer Revision, Create a Plan, Debrief

Consider the distribution of batting averages for the Snappers baseball team. Recall that the distribution is symmetrical, unimodal, and somewhat bell-shaped. Distributions with such characteristics are frequently considered to be **normal distributions**. The density curves for these distributions are called **normal curves**. Normal curves are special, as the mean and standard deviation provide a complete description of the distribution.

The distribution of team batting averages for the St. Louis Cardinals for the 50 years from 1964 to 2013 can be considered approximately normal. The mean batting average for these years is 0.2637, and the standard deviation is 0.0096.

1. What is the median batting average for the St. Louis Cardinals for the years 1964–2013? Explain your reasoning.

To determine a scale when drawing a normal curve, it is important to note that the mean value corresponds to the peak of the curve and that the points at which the curve changes from *concave up* to *concave down* (or vice versa) are approximately one standard deviation from the mean. (These points are called *inflection points*.)

2. Use the mean and standard deviation for the St. Louis Cardinals batting average data from 1964–2013 to label the three middle tic marks on the scale for the normal curve below. Explain how you chose to label the scale.

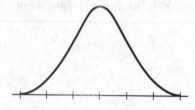

As mentioned previously, normal distributions are completely described by the mean and standard deviation. The *68-95-99.7 rule* further reinforces this fact. This rule states that, in a normal distribution, approximately 68% of the data lies within one standard deviation of the mean, 95% of the data lies within two standard deviations of the mean, and 99.7% of the data lies within three standard deviations of the mean. This powerful fact is illustrated in the diagram below.

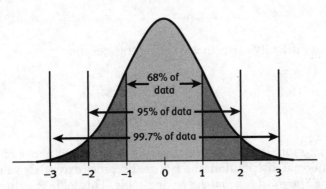

**My Notes**

> **MATH TIP**
>
> In statistics, when talking about a *percent* of a data set, it is customary to use the word *proportion*.
>
> For example: The proportion of data that lies within one standard deviation of the mean is 0.68.

3. Consider your normal curve from Item 2. What percent (proportion) of the data lies between the two data points that were not identified as the mean? Write a sentence about the team batting average of the St. Louis Cardinals that uses the 68-95-99.7 rule and these two data points.

4. Complete the scale for the normal curve in Item 2.

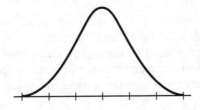

5. Between what two batting averages are 95% of the data? 99.7% of the data? For this 50-year period, in how many years would you expect the team batting average to be outside three standard deviations?

**MATH TIP**

*How to read the Standard Normal Table:* For a given *z*-score, look in the left-hand column to find the row with the appropriate units and tenths digit. On the top row, find the column with the appropriate hundredths digit. Find the cell that is in both the row and column you identified. The four-digit decimal number in this cell represents the proportion of the normal distribution below the *z*-score.

**TECHNOLOGY TIP**

*How to use the normalcdf function on a TI-84 graphing calculator:* Press [2nd] [VARS] for the distribution menu, and then press 2 for *normalcdf*. On your home screen, *normalcdf (* will appear. Enter "−100, z-score, 0, 1)" so that the command looks like *normalcdf (−100, z-score, 0, 1)*, and press [ENTER]. This will yield the proportion of the normal distribution below the *z*-score.

**MATH TIP**

Recall that the area under a density curve is one. Therefore, all numbers on the Standard Normal Table represent areas that are equivalent to the proportion less than a specific *z*-score.

6. Consider the question, "What proportion of the St. Louis team batting averages for the years 1964–2013 is below 0.269?"

   a. Why is 67%, the average of 50% (the mean) and 84% (one standard deviation above), an incorrect response?

   b. What difficulty exists in answering this question?

Recall that a *z*-score is the number of standard deviations above or below the mean. In a normal distribution, the *z*-score becomes extremely valuable thanks to the *Standard Normal Table*, or *z*-table. This table is found at the end of this activity, and it provides the area under the normal curve up to a specified *z*-score. Your graphing calculator can also provide you with results from the Standard Normal Table.

7. Use the Standard Normal Table to answer the following items.

   a. Find the *z*-score for the batting average of 0.269. Round your *z*-score to the nearest hundredth.

   b. Locate the *z*-score on the Standard Normal Table, and write the area that corresponds to the *z*-score.

8. Use the rounded *z*-score you found in 7a and your graphing calculator to find the area and compare it to your result in 7b. Write the calculator syntax of the instruction and the answer, rounded to four decimal places.

## Lesson 36-2
### Characteristics of the Normal Distribution

### Check Your Understanding

Charles and Oluoma took all 900 pennies out of their penny jar and gathered information on their dates. They created a histogram of their data that is displayed below.

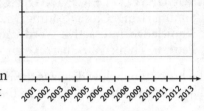

9. Oluoma claimed that the distribution was approximately normal. On what evidence did she base her claim?

10. Charles figured that the mean of the penny date data is 2007, and the standard deviation is 2.5.

   a. What is the median of the data?

   b. How many pennies lie within one standard deviation of the 2007?

   c. The $z$-score for a penny dated 2005 is $-0.7561$. Without computing, find and interpret the $z$-score for a 2009 penny.

### LESSON 36-2 PRACTICE

11. A rock and sand supplier packages all-purpose sand in 60-pound bags. A sample of 200 bags was analyzed, and the distribution of actual weights was approximately normal, with a mean of 61 pounds and a standard deviation of 0.75 pounds. Use the 68-95-99.7 rule to complete the scale on the normal curve shown.

12. Evaluate the $z$-score for a 61.75-pound bag of all-purpose sand, and find the corresponding proportion in the $z$-table. Does this agree with the 68-95-99.7 rule? Explain your reasoning.

13. Evaluate the $z$-score for a bag of sand weighing 59.5 pounds. Using the $z$-table, find the proportion that corresponds to that $z$-score. What does this proportion imply?

14. With the same $z$-score from Item 13, use your graphing calculator to find the proportion for the 59.5-pound bag. Does this agree with your answer from Item 13?

15. Consider a 62-pound bag of all-purpose sand from this sample.

   a. Evaluate the $z$-score for this bag of sand. Using the 68-95-99.7 rule, between which two proportions must this $z$-score correspond?

   b. Use your $z$-score and the $z$-table to find the proportion that corresponds to the $z$-score.

   c. Use your $z$-score and your calculator to find the proportion that corresponds to the $z$-score.

   d. Use the proportions you found in Items 15b and 15c to describe the proportion of bags that weigh less than 62 pounds and the proportion that weighs more than 62 pounds.

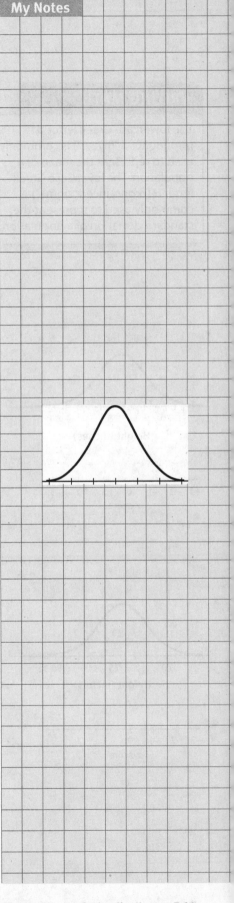

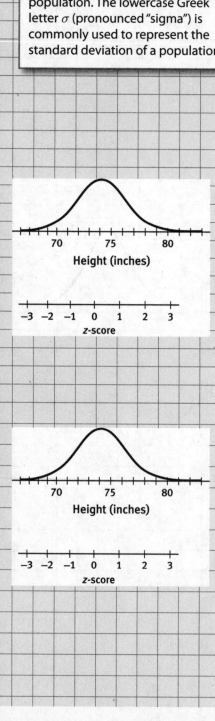

**My Notes**

**WRITING MATH**

The lowercase Greek letter $\mu$ (pronounced "myew") is commonly used to represent the mean of a population. The lowercase Greek letter $\sigma$ (pronounced "sigma") is commonly used to represent the standard deviation of a population.

## Learning Targets:

● Estimate probabilities associated with z-scores using normal curve sketches.
● Determine probabilities for z-scores using a standard normal table.

**SUGGESTED LEARNING STRATEGIES:** Shared Reading, Summarizing, Close Reading, Marking the Text, Activating Prior Knowledge, Interactive Word Wall, Create Representations, Look for a Pattern, Think-Pair-Share, Group Presentation, Identify a Subtask

The histogram below displays the heights, rounded to the nearest inch, of all Major League Baseball players in the year 2012.

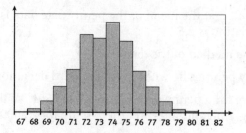

The shape of the graph—symmetric, unimodal, and bell-shaped—indicates that it would be reasonable to model the heights with a normal distribution. The mean and standard deviation of these players' heights are, respectively, $\mu = 73.5$ inches and $\sigma = 2.25$ inches. A picture of a normal density curve having this mean and standard deviation is shown. There are two scales given for the distribution. The upper scale is in inches, and the lower scale is in z-scores. (Remember that a z-score measures the number of standard deviations from a data point above or below the mean.)

1. One baseball player, Kevin Mattison, is 6'0" (72 inches) tall.
   a. Compute and interpret the z-score corresponding to his height.

   b. On the graph shown, draw a vertical line at Kevin Mattison's height, and shade the region under the bell curve and to the left of the vertical line you drew.

   c. The area of the region you shaded, when compared to the area of the entire region underneath the normal curve, corresponds to those players who are as tall as, or shorter than, 72 inches. Just by looking at the picture, estimate what proportion of players satisfies this condition.

2. Another baseball player, Jose Ceda, is 6'4" (76 inches) tall.
   a. What is the z-score corresponding to his height?

**b.** Interpret the meaning of the *z*-score you found in part a.

**c.** On the graph below, draw a vertical line at Jose Ceda's height, and shade lightly the region under the bell curve and to the right of your vertical line.

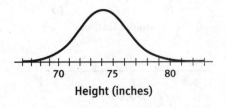

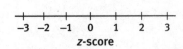

**d.** The region you shaded, when compared to the entire region underneath the bell curve, corresponds to those players who are as tall as, or taller than, 76 inches. Just by looking at the picture, estimate what proportion of players satisfies this condition.

**3.** Suppose you are interested in the proportion of players' heights that, when rounded to the nearest inch, will be 6'3" (75 inches). Those are the players whose heights range from 74.5 inches to 75.5 inches. Compute the *z*-scores for both endpoints of that range. Then draw vertical lines at those locations on the graph, shade the region between the lines, and estimate the proportion of players' heights to which the area of the region corresponds.

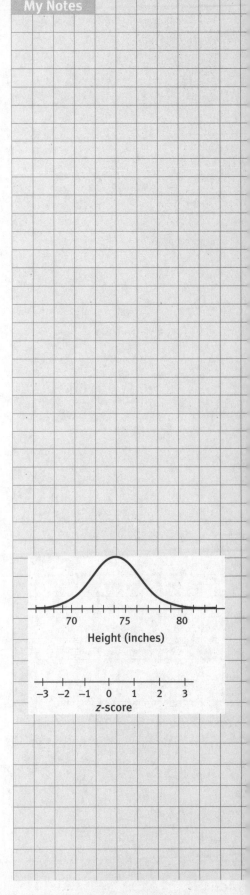

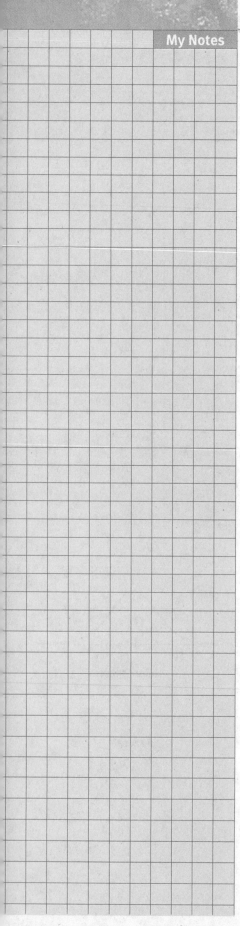

4. One baseball player, Dan Jennings, is taller than 80% of all other players. Draw a vertical line in the graph below at his height, and shade the region that corresponds to the proportion of players who are shorter than Dan. Then estimate Dan Jennings's height and the corresponding z-score.

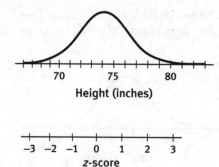

There are four different kinds of estimates you made above, all relative to a distribution of values that is approximately normal:

- Estimating the proportion of the distribution that is less than a given value,
- Estimating the proportion of the distribution that is greater than a given value,
- Estimating the proportion of the distribution that lies between two given values,
- Estimating the value that has a given proportion of the population below it.

There are other variations, but if you master the skills associated with finding good estimates in these four situations, you should be able to handle other similar situations.

You have already seen one way to estimate these values: sketching a normal curve and guessing, just by looking, what proportion of the total area beneath the curve lies in certain regions. Two other methods for making these estimates are more exact: using a Standard Normal Table (*z*-table) and technology. Even when using these two methods, it is always appropriate to sketch a normal curve and shade the region of interest.

**Using the Standard Normal Table (*z*-Table)**

A *z*-table shows the proportion of a standard normal probability distribution that is less than a particular *z*-score for many possible values of *z*. Recall that the area under the normal curve is one, so the values in the *z*-table also refer to the area under the normal curve to the left of a *z*-score as well. Use the *z*-table at the end of this activity.

5. Work with your group on this item and on Items 6–8. In Item 1, you computed the *z*-score corresponding to 72-inch-tall Kevin Mattison. Look in the *z*-table for the *z*-score that you computed and find the proportion of the distribution that is less than that *z*-score. Your answer should be similar to the value that you guessed in Item 1.

6. In Item 2, you computed the *z*-score corresponding to 76-inch-tall Jose Ceda. Look in the *z*-table for the *z*-score you computed and find the proportion of the distribution that is less than that *z*-score. Then use that proportion to address the question, "What proportion of players is *taller* than Jose Ceda?"

**DISCUSSION GROUP TIP**

With your group, reread the problem scenarios as needed. Make notes on the information provided in the problems. Respond to questions about the meaning of key information. Organize the information needed to create reasonable solutions, and describe the mathematical concepts your group uses to create its solutions.

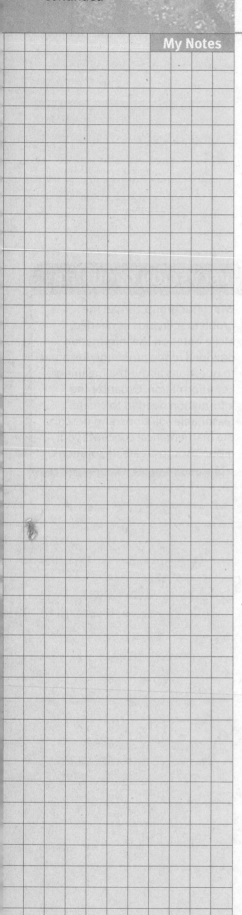

7. In Item 3, you estimated the proportion of players whose heights were between 74.5 and 75.5 inches, and so would round their heights to 75 inches. Use the z-table to estimate that proportion.

8. In Item 4, you estimated the height of Dan Jennings, given that he is taller than 80% of Major League Baseball players. Use the z-table to estimate his z-score, and use this z-score to estimate his height.

### Check Your Understanding

9. If you estimated the proportion of baseball players' heights that, when rounded to the nearest inch, are 80 inches, would you expect that fraction to be larger, smaller, or about the same as the fraction of players whose heights, rounded to the nearest inch, are 73 inches? Explain your answer without doing any computations.

10. In the z-table, if a probability (area) is less than 0.50, what must be true about its corresponding z-score? Why?

11. When using the z-table, sometimes you look up a z-score in the table and then find the corresponding number in the body of the table. At other times, you look up a number in the body of the table and find the corresponding z-score. How do you know which of these is the right thing to do?

## LESSON 36-3 PRACTICE

All members of the junior class at a local high school took the PSAT exam. The distribution of the results of the mathematics section was found to be approximately normal, with a mean score of 52 and a standard deviation of 6.8.

**12.** Andres got a 55 on the mathematics section of the exam.
   **a.** On the normal curve below, shade the proportion of students that scored less than or equal to Andres's score.

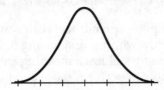

   **b.** Evaluate the *z*-score for Andres's score and use the *z*-table to write the proportion of students that received a score less than or equal to 55.

**13.** Amber got a 60 on the mathematics section of the exam.
   **a.** On the normal curve below, shade the proportion of students that scored greater than or equal to Amber's score.

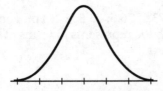

   **b.** Evaluate the *z*-score for Amber's score and use the *z*-table to write the proportion of students that received a score greater than or equal to 60.

**14.** Ms. Diaz, the assistant principal, made a quick review of the scores and commented that, based on her observation, it seemed most students scored between 50 and 56.
   **a.** On the normal curve below, shade the proportion of students that scored between 50 and 56.

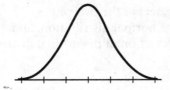

   **b.** Evaluate the *z*-scores for PSAT math scores of 50 and 56, and then use the *z*-table to write the proportion of students that received scores between 50 and 56.

   **c.** Confirm or revise Ms. Diaz's comment regarding the scores of the PSAT math section.

**15.** Stephan claimed that he scored better than 90% of the students in the junior class. Use *z*-scores and your *z*-table to determine what score Stephan must have earned to be correct.

**My Notes**

## Learning Targets:
- Determine probabilities for *z*-scores using technology.
- Use a normal distribution, when appropriate, as a model for a population from which a sample of numeric data has been drawn.

**SUGGESTED LEARNING STRATEGIES:** Summarizing, Marking the Text, Activating Prior Knowledge, Create Representations, Look for a Pattern, Think-Pair-Share, Group Presentation, Jigsaw, Quickwrite, Self Revision/Peer Revision, Create a Plan, Identify a Subtask

Many calculators and computer spreadsheets can compute proportions of normal distributions directly, without first having to compute a *z*-score. (Keep in mind that the *z*-score still has a meaning and is useful in its own right.) Here you will see how to perform those computations using the TI-84.

To find the fraction of a normal distribution lying between any two values, we use this command:

$$normalcdf(L, U, \mu, \sigma),$$

where:
- *L* is the lower (lesser) of the two values,
- *U* is the upper (greater) of the two values,
- $\mu$ is the mean of the normal distribution, and
- $\sigma$ is the standard deviation of the normal distribution.

## Example A
To find the fraction of Major League Baseball players who would round their heights to 75 inches, you would enter:

$$normalcdf(74.5, 75.5, 73.5, 2.25)$$

Answer: 0.1413

## Try These A

**a.** Evaluate *normalcdf*(73.5, 76.5, 73.5, 2.25) on your calculator and interpret what each value represents in terms of the Major League Baseball player context.

**b.** Use your calculator to find the proportion of Major League Baseball players that are between 70 inches and 73 inches tall.

## Lesson 36-4
## Modeling with the Normal Distribution

● If you are interested in an interval of heights that has no lower bound, use the same command but with a very low number for *L*, the lower bound, a number that is well below any reasonable value in the distribution.

### Example B

To find the proportion of players who are shorter than Kevin Mattison, use the following syntax. Notice that *L* is 0 in this example. In the context of heights of baseball players, such a value is unreasonably small, making it an appropriate lower bound.

$$normalcdf(0, 72, 73.5, 2.25)$$

Answer: 0.2525

### Try These B

a. Evaluate *normalcdf*(–100, 76, 73.5, 2.25) on your calculator and interpret what each value represents in terms of Major League Baseball player heights.

b. Use your calculator to find the proportion of these players that are shorter than 72 inches.

● If you are interested in an interval of heights that has no upper bound, use the same command but with a very high number for *U,* the upper bound, a number that is well above any reasonable value in the distribution.

### Example C

To find the proportion of players who are taller than Jose Ceda, use the following syntax. Notice that *U* is 1000 in this example. In the context of heights of baseball players, such a value is unreasonably large, making it an appropriate upper bound.

$$normalcdf(76, 1000, 73.5, 2.25)$$

Answer: 0.1334

### Try These C

a. Evaluate *normalcdf*(75, 200, 73.5, 2.25) on your calculator and interpret what each value represents in terms of Major League Baseball player heights.

b. Use your calculator to find the proportion of these players who are taller than 70 inches.

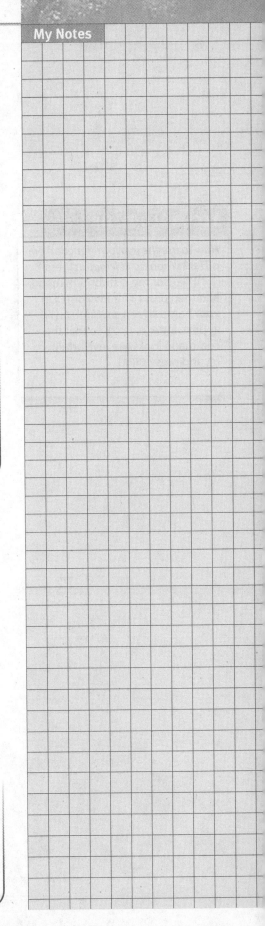

For situations in which you know the proportion of the distribution below an unknown value, the command used to find the unknown value is

$$\text{invNorm}(p, \mu, \sigma) \text{ where:}$$

- $p$ is the fraction of the distribution that is less than the desired value,
- $\mu$ is the mean of the normal distribution, and
- $\sigma$ is the standard deviation of the normal distribution.

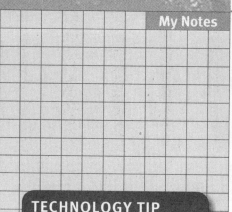

**TECHNOLOGY TIP**

*How to use the invNorm function on a TI-84 graphing calculator:* Press [2nd] [VARS] for the distribution menu, and then press 3 for invNorm. On your home screen, *invNorm (* will appear. Enter *p, μ, σ)"* so that the command looks like invNorm(*p, μ, σ*), and press [ENTER].

### Example D

To find the height of Dan Jennings, who is taller than 80% of the players in Major League Baseball, use the following command.

$$\text{invNorm}(0.8, 73.5, 2.25)$$

Answer: 75.39 inches

### Try These D

a. Evaluate invNorm(0.65, 73.5, 2.25) on your calculator and interpret what each value represents in terms of Major League Baseball player heights.

b. Use your calculator to find the height of a player who is taller than 90% of all Major League Baseball players.

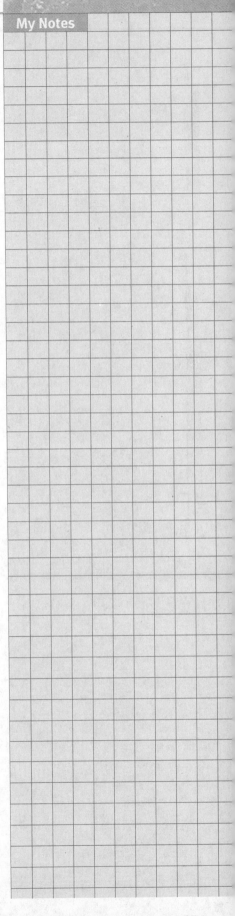

Answer the following questions in two ways. First, use the *z*-table method (include a sketch and shade a normal curve). Second, use technology with your graphing calculator. Recall that answers should agree very closely, but small rounding errors may cause them to be slightly different.

The distribution of batting averages for all Major League Baseball players very closely follows a normal distribution, with a mean of 0.261 and a standard deviation of 0.033.

1. A batting average of 0.300 or higher is considered very good. About what proportion of players have a batting average of at least 0.300?

2. One baseball player, Dewayne Wise, had a batting average that is in the first quartile of the batting average distribution. What was his batting average?

3. What range of batting averages gives the middle 50% of the distribution?

4. Miguel Cabrera of the Detroit Tigers had a batting average during the 2011 season of 0.344. What proportion of players had a batting average as high or higher than Miguel Cabrera during the 2011 season?

### Check Your Understanding

Normal distributions are associated with many populations that are not related to baseball. A wholesale nursery owner has 200 newly sprouted cocoplum plants that she is preparing for eventual sale. After several weeks, she measures each plant and discovers that the distribution of plant heights is approximately normal, with a mean of 8.5 cm and a standard deviation of 1.2 cm.

5. The nursery owner uses her graphing calculator and enters *normalcdf*(8, 9, 8.5, 1.2). What question is she seeking to answer with this calculation?

6. Cocoplum plants that are less than 6 cm tall are discarded, as they are unlikely to be sold. Use your graphing calculator to determine how many plants the nursery owner will discard.

7. Cocoplum plants that are larger than 10 cm are ready to be shipped for sale. Use your graphing calculator to determine how many plants are ready to be shipped.

### LESSON 36-4 PRACTICE

The heights of 2-year-old American girls are distributed in an approximately normal manner. The 5th percentile and the 95th percentile of their heights are about 79 cm and 91 cm, respectively.

8. Estimate the mean and standard deviation of the distribution of 2-year-old girls' heights.

9. Use the mean and standard deviation to estimate the range of heights that would be in the middle 50% for 2-year-old girls.

10. About what proportion of 2-year-old girls are between 32 and 34 inches tall? (There are about 2.54 cm in an inch.)

11. Assume that from age 2 years to 5 years, all American girls grow 9 cm. How would this affect the mean and standard deviation of the population in Items 8–10?

## ACTIVITY 36 PRACTICE

Write your answers on notebook paper.
Show your work.

1. Karen is a high school student doing a statistics project. She was interested in estimating how much money people typically spend on admission, food, drinks, and souvenirs when attending a local minor league baseball game. At one game she attended, she randomly selected 10 people in the audience and then asked them how much money they had spent. The responses are below.

   $8.00   $10.25   $10.00   $9.50   $10.00

   $10.25   $10.25   $12.75   $11.00   $11.25

   a. Make a dot plot of these data.
   b. These data are somewhat dense in the middle and sparser on the tails. Karen thought it would be reasonable to model the data as a normal distribution. She used the mean and standard deviation of her sample to estimate the mean and standard deviation of the amount of money spent by everyone at the ballgame that night. Based on her model, estimate the proportion of people attending the ballgame who spent between $10 and $12.
   c. Again using Karen's model, estimate the amount of money that would complete this sentence: "95% of the people at the ballgame spent at least _____ dollars."

2. When students in Marty's statistics class were asked to collect some data of interest to them, Marty, a player on his school's baseball team, decided to measure the speeds of baseballs pitched by their school's pitching machine. Using a radar gun, he measured 20 pitches. The stem-and-leaf plot below shows the speeds he recorded, in miles per hour.

   ```
   5 | 1 1 3
   4 | 6 6 8 9 9 9
   4 | 1 2 3 3 3 4 4 4
   3 | 6 7 9

   3 | 6 = 36 mph
   ```

   a. Determine the mean and standard deviation of these 20 speeds.
   b. Assuming that the distribution of speeds pitched by this machine is approximately normal, estimate how many pitches out of 100 you would expect to exceed 50 mph.
   c. Assuming that the pitches from this machine are normally distributed, estimate the speed that would be at the 10th percentile of speeds pitched by this machine. What does the 10th percentile imply?

3. The annual salaries of nine randomly sampled professional baseball players, in thousands of dollars, are listed below.

   1680, 316, 440, 316, 800, 347, 600, 16000, 445

   a. If you assume that these come from a normal distribution, what proportion of all players would you expect to make over two million dollars (2000 thousands) per year?
   b. What proportion of the nine players whose salaries are given have salaries over two million dollars per year?
   c. You should have found that there is a pretty big discrepancy between your answers to Items 3a and 3b. Use what you know about normal distributions to explain this discrepancy.
   d. Sketch a drawing of a normal distribution with the mean and standard deviation of these nine salaries. Comment on any features it has that may seem unrealistic.

4. Why is it important to look at a graphical display of a data set before performing probability computations that involve a *z*-table or a normal function on a calculator?

5. Performing normal computations directly on a calculator can be faster than using a *z*-table, but one potentially useful piece of information gets bypassed. What is it?

6. If you are using your calculator's built-in normal functions to answer questions without using the Standard Normal Table, sometimes you have to make up an upper or lower bound that wasn't stated in the question. When and why is that needed?

7. Below is a stem-and-leaf plot showing the distribution of ages, in years, of a random sample of 50 professional baseball players. The mean and standard deviation of the distribution are, respectively, 28.3 years and 5.1 years.

| Stem | Leaf |
|------|------|
| 4 | 2 |
| 4 | 1 |
| 3 | 8 9 |
| 3 | 7 |
| 3 | 5 5 |
| 3 | 2 2 2 3 3 |
| 3 | 0 0 0 0 1 |
| 2 | 8 8 8 8 9 |
| 2 | 6 6 6 6 7 7 7 7 7 |
| 2 | 4 4 4 4 4 4 4 4 5 5 5 5 5 |
| 2 | 2 2 3 3 3 3 |

2|2 represents 22

Would it be reasonable to use a normal distribution model to estimate the proportion of professional players who are 20 years old or younger? Explain your reasoning.

Use the following information for Items 8–10.
A math student who worked part-time at a veterinary clinic was given permission to examine the files of 11 adult cat patients and record their weights in pounds. These are the weights he recorded:

8.5, 9.1, 9.2, 10.2, 10.5, 11.1, 11.9, 11.9, 12.6, 13.6, 14.3.

8. Make a graph of the data to see whether it might be reasonable to believe that the distribution of weights of all cats at this clinic is approximately normally distributed. Comment on what feature(s) of the graph indicate that a normal model is or is not reasonable.

9. Assuming that a normal model is reasonable, about what fraction of cats at this clinic would weigh over 15 pounds?

## MATHEMATICAL PRACTICES
### Attend to Precision

10. Still using a normal model, estimate the range of weights that would be centered on the mean and encompass about 95% of cat weights.

**Table A.  Standard Normal Probabilities**

| z | .00 | .01 | .02 | .03 | .04 | .05 | .06 | .07 | .08 | .09 |
|------|------|------|------|------|------|------|------|------|------|------|
| −3.4 | .0003 | .0003 | .0003 | .0003 | .0003 | .0003 | .0003 | .0003 | .0003 | .0002 |
| −3.3 | .0005 | .0005 | .0005 | .0004 | .0004 | .0004 | .0004 | .0004 | .0004 | .0003 |
| −3.2 | .0007 | .0007 | .0006 | .0006 | .0006 | .0006 | .0006 | .0005 | .0005 | .0005 |
| −3.1 | .0010 | .0009 | .0009 | .0009 | .0008 | .0008 | .0008 | .0008 | .0007 | .0007 |
| −3.0 | .0013 | .0013 | .0013 | .0012 | .0012 | .0011 | .0011 | .0011 | .0010 | .0010 |
| −2.9 | .0019 | .0018 | .0018 | .0017 | .0016 | .0016 | .0015 | .0015 | .0014 | .0014 |
| −2.8 | .0026 | .0025 | .0024 | .0023 | .0023 | .0022 | .0021 | .0021 | .0020 | .0019 |
| −2.7 | .0035 | .0034 | .0033 | .0032 | .0031 | .0030 | .0029 | .0028 | .0027 | .0026 |
| −2.6 | .0047 | .0045 | .0044 | .0043 | .0041 | .0040 | .0039 | .0038 | .0037 | .0036 |
| −2.5 | .0062 | .0060 | .0059 | .0057 | .0055 | .0054 | .0052 | .0051 | .0049 | .0048 |
| −2.4 | .0082 | .0080 | .0078 | .0075 | .0073 | .0071 | .0069 | .0068 | .0066 | .0064 |
| −2.3 | .0107 | .0104 | .0102 | .0099 | .0096 | .0094 | .0091 | .0089 | .0087 | .0084 |
| −2.2 | .0139 | .0136 | .0132 | .0129 | .0125 | .0122 | .0119 | .0116 | .0113 | .0110 |
| −2.1 | .0179 | .0174 | .0170 | .0166 | .0162 | .0158 | .0154 | .0150 | .0146 | .0143 |
| −2.0 | .0228 | .0222 | .0217 | .0212 | .0207 | .0202 | .0197 | .0192 | .0188 | .0183 |
| −1.9 | .0287 | .0281 | .0274 | .0268 | .0262 | .0256 | .0250 | .0244 | .0239 | .0233 |
| −1.8 | .0359 | .0351 | .0344 | .0336 | .0329 | .0322 | .0314 | .0307 | .0301 | .0294 |
| −1.7 | .0446 | .0436 | .0427 | .0418 | .0409 | .0401 | .0392 | .0384 | .0375 | .0367 |
| −1.6 | .0548 | .0537 | .0526 | .0516 | .0505 | .0495 | .0485 | .0475 | .0465 | .0455 |
| −1.5 | .0668 | .0655 | .0643 | .0630 | .0618 | .0606 | .0594 | .0582 | .0571 | .0559 |
| −1.4 | .0808 | .0793 | .0778 | .0764 | .0749 | .0735 | .0721 | .0708 | .0694 | .0681 |
| −1.3 | .0968 | .0951 | .0934 | .0918 | .0901 | .0885 | .0869 | .0853 | .0838 | .0823 |
| −1.2 | .1151 | .1131 | .1112 | .1093 | .1075 | .1056 | .1038 | .1020 | .1003 | .0985 |
| −1.1 | .1357 | .1335 | .1314 | .1292 | .1271 | .1251 | .1230 | .1210 | .1190 | .1170 |
| −1.0 | .1587 | .1562 | .1539 | .1515 | .1492 | .1469 | .1446 | .1423 | .1401 | .1379 |
| −0.9 | .1841 | .1814 | .1788 | .1762 | .1736 | .1711 | .1685 | .1660 | .1635 | .1611 |
| −0.8 | .2119 | .2090 | .2061 | .2033 | .2005 | .1977 | .1949 | .1922 | .1894 | .1867 |
| −0.7 | .2420 | .2389 | .2358 | .2327 | .2296 | .2266 | .2236 | .2206 | .2177 | .2148 |
| −0.6 | .2743 | .2709 | .2676 | .2643 | .2611 | .2578 | .2546 | .2514 | .2483 | .2451 |
| −0.5 | .3085 | .3050 | .3015 | .2981 | .2946 | .2912 | .2877 | .2843 | .2810 | .2776 |
| −0.4 | .3446 | .3409 | .3372 | .3336 | .3300 | .3264 | .3228 | .3192 | .3156 | .3121 |
| −0.3 | .3821 | .3783 | .3745 | .3707 | .3669 | .3632 | .3594 | .3557 | .3520 | .3483 |
| −0.2 | .4207 | .4168 | .4129 | .4090 | .4052 | .4013 | .3974 | .3936 | .3897 | .3859 |
| −0.1 | .4602 | .4562 | .4522 | .4483 | .4443 | .4404 | .4364 | .4325 | .4286 | .4247 |
| −0.0 | .5000 | .4960 | .4920 | .4880 | .4840 | .4801 | .4761 | .4721 | .4681 | .4641 |

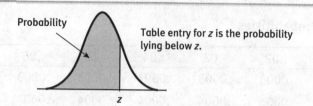

Probability — Table entry for z is the probability lying below z.

## Table A. (*continued*)

| z | .00 | .01 | .02 | .03 | .04 | .05 | .06 | .07 | .08 | .09 |
|-----|-------|-------|-------|-------|-------|-------|-------|-------|-------|-------|
| 0.0 | .5000 | .5040 | .5080 | .5120 | .5160 | .5199 | .5239 | .5279 | .5319 | .5359 |
| 0.1 | .5398 | .5438 | .5478 | .5517 | .5557 | .5596 | .5636 | .5675 | .5714 | .5753 |
| 0.2 | .5793 | .5832 | .5871 | .5910 | .5948 | .5987 | .6026 | .6064 | .6103 | .6141 |
| 0.3 | .6179 | .6217 | .6255 | .6293 | .6331 | .6368 | .6406 | .6443 | .6480 | .6517 |
| 0.4 | .6554 | .6591 | .6628 | .6664 | .6700 | .6736 | .6772 | .6808 | .6844 | .6879 |
| 0.5 | .6915 | .6950 | .6985 | .7019 | .7054 | .7088 | .7123 | .7157 | .7190 | .7224 |
| 0.6 | .7257 | .7291 | .7324 | .7357 | .7389 | .7422 | .7454 | .7486 | .7517 | .7549 |
| 0.7 | .7580 | .7611 | .7642 | .7673 | .7704 | .7734 | .7764 | .7794 | .7823 | .7852 |
| 0.8 | .7881 | .7910 | .7939 | .7967 | .7995 | .8023 | .8051 | .8078 | .8106 | .8133 |
| 0.9 | .8159 | .8186 | .8212 | .8238 | .8264 | .8289 | .8315 | .8340 | .8365 | .8389 |
| 1.0 | .8413 | .8438 | .8461 | .8485 | .8508 | .8531 | .8554 | .8577 | .8599 | .8621 |
| 1.1 | .8643 | .8665 | .8686 | .8708 | .8729 | .8749 | .8770 | .8790 | .8810 | .8830 |
| 1.2 | .8849 | .8869 | .8888 | .8907 | .8925 | .8944 | .8962 | .8980 | .8997 | .9015 |
| 1.3 | .9032 | .9049 | .9066 | .9082 | .9099 | .9115 | .9131 | .9147 | .9162 | .9177 |
| 1.4 | .9192 | .9207 | .9222 | .9236 | .9251 | .9265 | .9279 | .9292 | .9306 | .9319 |
| 1.5 | .9332 | .9345 | .9357 | .9370 | .9382 | .9394 | .9406 | .9418 | .9429 | .9441 |
| 1.6 | .9452 | .9463 | .9474 | .9484 | .9495 | .9505 | .9515 | .9525 | .9535 | .9545 |
| 1.7 | .9554 | .9564 | .9573 | .9582 | .9591 | .9599 | .9608 | .9616 | .9625 | .9633 |
| 1.8 | .9641 | .9649 | .9656 | .9664 | .9671 | .9678 | .9686 | .9693 | .9699 | .9706 |
| 1.9 | .9713 | .9719 | .9726 | .9732 | .9738 | .9744 | .9750 | .9756 | .9761 | .9767 |
| 2.0 | .9772 | .9778 | .9783 | .9788 | .9793 | .9798 | .9803 | .9808 | .9812 | .9817 |
| 2.1 | .9821 | .9826 | .9830 | .9834 | .9838 | .9842 | .9846 | .9850 | .9854 | .9857 |
| 2.2 | .9861 | .9864 | .9868 | .9871 | .9875 | .9878 | .9881 | .9884 | .9887 | .9890 |
| 2.3 | .9893 | .9896 | .9898 | .9901 | .9904 | .9906 | .9909 | .9911 | .9913 | .9916 |
| 2.4 | .9918 | .9920 | .9922 | .9925 | .9927 | .9929 | .9931 | .9932 | .9934 | .9936 |
| 2.5 | .9938 | .9940 | .9941 | .9943 | .9945 | .9946 | .9948 | .9949 | .9951 | .9952 |
| 2.6 | .9953 | .9955 | .9956 | .9957 | .9959 | .9960 | .9961 | .9962 | .9963 | .9964 |
| 2.7 | .9965 | .9966 | .9967 | .9968 | .9969 | .9970 | .9971 | .9972 | .9973 | .9974 |
| 2.8 | .9974 | .9975 | .9976 | .9977 | .9977 | .9978 | .9979 | .9979 | .9980 | .9981 |
| 2.9 | .9981 | .9982 | .9982 | .9983 | .9984 | .9984 | .9985 | .9985 | .9986 | .9986 |
| 3.0 | .9987 | .9987 | .9987 | .9988 | .9988 | .9989 | .9989 | .9989 | .9990 | .9990 |
| 3.1 | .9990 | .9991 | .9991 | .9991 | .9992 | .9992 | .9992 | .9992 | .9993 | .9993 |
| 3.2 | .9993 | .9993 | .9994 | .9994 | .9994 | .9994 | .9994 | .9995 | .9995 | .9995 |
| 3.3 | .9995 | .9995 | .9995 | .9996 | .9996 | .9996 | .9996 | .9996 | .9996 | .9997 |
| 3.4 | .9997 | .9997 | .9997 | .9997 | .9997 | .9997 | .9997 | .9997 | .9997 | .9998 |

# Random Sampling

## Part-Time Jobs
## Lesson 37-1 Surveys

**Learning Target:**
- Explain why random sampling is advantageous when conducting a survey.

> **LEARNING STRATEGIES:** Close Reading, Questioning the Text, Role Play, Summarizing, Paraphrasing, Debriefing, Discussion Groups

Jorge is a member of the student government at a large school with over 2500 students. The student government would like to recommend that students with part-time jobs be permitted to get a class credit in business. Knowing that Jorge is a good statistics student, the student government asked him to estimate the proportion of students at the school who have part-time jobs.

1. What difficulties might Jorge encounter if he tries to ask every student about having a part-time job?

Sometimes you may want to know some characteristic of a large population, such as the median income of households in your state or the proportion of students at a large school who have part-time jobs. Since it is often difficult or impossible to survey everyone in the population, you may wish to *survey* a *sample* of the population and infer conclusions from the sample about the population.

Jorge considers different methods for obtaining a sample.

2. Jorge is thinking about posting the question, "Do you have a part-time job?" on Facebook and collecting *responses* to his post. He knows that not everyone will reply, but he thinks he'll still get a large number of responses. Explain why, even if a large number of people replied (even as much as half of the student body), Jorge would be unwise to suppose that the proportion of people who posted that they have a part-time job is the same as the proportion of all students who have a part-time job.

**MATH TERMS**

A **survey** is a study in which subjects are asked a question or series of questions.

An answer provided by a subject to a survey question is called a **response**.

**MATH TERMS**

A **sample** is part of a population of interest. Data are collected from the individuals in the sample.

**My Notes**

3. Jorge is on the football team at his school and is thinking of asking everyone on the football team if they have a part-time job. Why might this give him a poor estimate of the actual proportion of students at his school with part-time jobs?

4. Jorge is considering standing beside an exit of the school one day after the last class is over and asking every student who passes by if he or she has a part-time job. How might this method produce an inaccurate estimate of the actual proportion of students at his school with part-time jobs?

**MATH TERMS**

A sample shows **bias** if the composition of the sample favors certain outcomes.

**MATH TERMS**

A **simple random sample (SRS)** is a sample in which all members of a population have the same probability of being chosen for the sample.

Sampling can give very good results even if only a small sample of the population is surveyed, but it is critical that the sample be *representative* of the population with respect to the survey question. If the design of a sample favors one outcome over another, the sample is said to be **biased**. Each of Jorge's sampling methods described in Items 2, 3, and 4 display bias, and your responses indicate how this bias was manifested in the results.

How can you be sure that a sample is representative of the population? Many methods of sampling people could produce samples of people that would tend to favor one type of survey response over another.

One way to avoid favoring some types of response over others is to sample people at random, with every person being equally likely to be chosen. Such a sample is called a *simple random sample*, abbreviated **SRS**. A simple random sample is impartial because it does not favor anyone over anyone else. When a simple random sampling process is used to select members from a population, then everyone is as likely to be included in the sample as everyone else, and one person's inclusion in the sample has no effect on anyone else's inclusion in the sample.

**5.** There was bias in each of the sampling methods described in Items 2, 3, and 4 of this activity. Describe how a simple random sample would have avoided such bias.

**6.** Jorge has access to a full roster of all 2500 students at his school. One way to get a simple random sample of students would be for him to write the names of all 2500 students on index cards, put the cards into a large cardboard box and mix them up thoroughly, and then to draw out the desired number of names at random. What difficulties might Jorge encounter in his attempt to take a simple random sample in this way?

Another way to get a simple random sample is to number the list of students from 1 to 2500, and then use technology to randomly generate integers between 1 and 2500 until you have the desired sample size. For example, on TI-84 calculators, the following command generates a random integer between 1 and 2500:

randInt(1,2500)

Use the command to generate random integers that are matched up with the numbered list (ignoring repeated numbers) until you have identified all those names chosen to be in your sample.

**7.** Use your graphing calculator to choose 20 random integers between 1 and 100. Write the calculator syntax and your 20 random integers.

**TECHNOLOGY TIP**

To find the *randInt(* function on a TI-84 calculator, press the MATH button, scroll to *PRB*, and then choose *randInt(*.

**My Notes**

Another method for generating random numbers from 1 to 2500 involves using a random digits table. Since the largest number in this range has four digits, you need to represent all numbers from 1 to 2500 as four-digit numbers. For example, 23 would be represented as 0023, and 798 would be represented as 0798. Then choose a line of the table at random and begin inspecting clusters of four digits. When a four-digit number matches one on Jorge's list, that name is selected as part of the sample. If a number is not on the list, then it is disregarded, as are repeated occurrences of the same number.

| Random digits | | | | | | | |
|---|---|---|---|---|---|---|---|
| **Line** | | | | | | | |
| 101 | 19223 | 95034 | 05756 | 28713 | 96409 | 12531 | 42544 | 82853 |
| 102 | 73676 | 47150 | 99400 | 01927 | 27754 | 42648 | 82425 | 36290 |
| 103 | 45467 | 71709 | 77558 | 00095 | 32863 | 29485 | 82226 | 90056 |
| 104 | 52711 | 38889 | 93074 | 60227 | 40011 | 85848 | 48767 | 52573 |
| 105 | 95592 | 94007 | 69971 | 91481 | 60779 | 53791 | 17297 | 59335 |
| 106 | 68417 | 35013 | 15529 | 72765 | 85089 | 57067 | 50211 | 47487 |
| 107 | 82739 | 57890 | 20807 | 47511 | 81676 | 55300 | 94383 | 14893 |
| 108 | 60940 | 72024 | 17868 | 24943 | 61790 | 90656 | 87964 | 18883 |
| 109 | 36009 | 19365 | 15412 | 39638 | 85453 | 46816 | 83485 | 41979 |
| 110 | 38448 | 48789 | 18338 | 24697 | 39364 | 42006 | 76688 | 08708 |
| 111 | 81486 | 69487 | 60513 | 09297 | 00412 | 71238 | 27649 | 39950 |
| 112 | 59636 | 88804 | 04634 | 71197 | 19352 | 73089 | 84898 | 45785 |
| 113 | 62568 | 70206 | 40325 | 03699 | 71080 | 22553 | 11486 | 11776 |
| 114 | 45149 | 32992 | 75730 | 66280 | 03819 | 56202 | 02938 | 70915 |
| 115 | 61041 | 77684 | 94322 | 24709 | 73698 | 14526 | 31893 | 32592 |
| 116 | 14459 | 26056 | 31424 | 80371 | 65103 | 62253 | 50490 | 61181 |
| 117 | 38167 | 98532 | 62183 | 70632 | 23417 | 26185 | 41448 | 75532 |
| 118 | 73190 | 32533 | 04470 | 29669 | 84407 | 90785 | 65956 | 86382 |
| 119 | 95857 | 07118 | 87664 | 92099 | 58806 | 66979 | 98624 | 84826 |
| 120 | 35476 | 55972 | 39421 | 65850 | 04266 | 35435 | 43742 | 11937 |
| 121 | 71487 | 09984 | 29077 | 14863 | 61683 | 47052 | 62224 | 51025 |
| 122 | 13873 | 81598 | 95052 | 90908 | 73592 | 75186 | 87136 | 95761 |
| 123 | 54580 | 81507 | 27102 | 56027 | 55892 | 33063 | 41842 | 81868 |
| 124 | 71035 | 09001 | 43367 | 49497 | 72719 | 96758 | 27611 | 91596 |
| 125 | 96746 | 12149 | 37823 | 71868 | 18442 | 35119 | 62103 | 39244 |
| 126 | 96927 | 19931 | 36089 | 74192 | 77567 | 88741 | 48409 | 41903 |
| 127 | 43909 | 99477 | 25330 | 64359 | 40085 | 16925 | 85117 | 36071 |
| 128 | 15689 | 14227 | 06565 | 14374 | 13352 | 49367 | 81982 | 87209 |
| 129 | 36759 | 58984 | 68288 | 22913 | 18638 | 54303 | 00795 | 08727 |
| 130 | 69051 | 64817 | 87174 | 09517 | 84534 | 06489 | 87201 | 97245 |

**8.** Beginning at line 122 on the random digit table, identify the first five numbers that would correspond to names on Jorge's list. Compare this method to using the random integer generator on the graphing calculator.

**9.** Suppose that Jorge uses the random number generator on his graphing calculator to choose an SRS of 100 students at his school. He then surveys these students to determine whether they have part-time jobs. He notices that two of the 100 students in his sample are friends who both have part-time jobs working at the local auto garage. Jorge is worried about the over-inclusion of people with part-time jobs in his sample. Should he be concerned?

**Check Your Understanding**

10. Describe a sampling method that Jorge might have thought about using that would have likely *overestimated* the fraction of students at his school who hold part-time jobs.

11. Priscilla is a junior at the same high school. She would like to survey a simple random sample of the 600 juniors in her class to determine preferences for class T-shirt designs. Describe how she could create a SRS of 50 students using a random digits table and using a graphing calculator.

## LESSON 37-1 PRACTICE

Veronica wanted to know how many students in the sophomore class at her school learned a language other than English as their first language. There were 450 sophomores in the sophomore class, too many for Veronica to question each of them, so she prepared 50 questionnaires to distribute to some of the students in the class.

12. In Veronica's survey, what is the population? What is the question of interest? What is the sample?

13. Veronica chooses two classes near her homeroom in which to distribute the questionnaires. One has 25 students and is for first-year Spanish learners, and the other has 25 students and is for ELL (English language learner) students. Why is this selection of students not a simple random sample? What type of bias may exist in this sample?

14. Describe how Veronica could create a simple random sample of 50 students from the sophomore class in two different manners, without using technology.

15. Describe how Veronica could use technology to create a simple random sample.

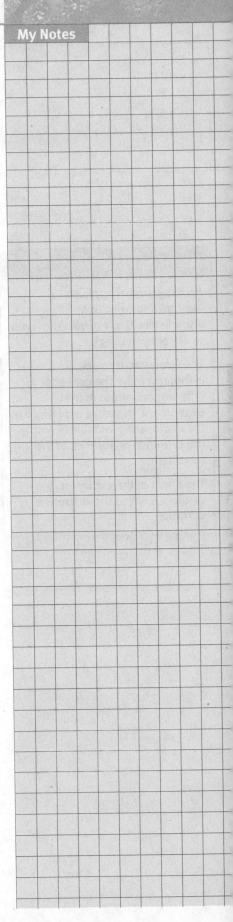

### Learning Target:
- Explain why random allocation of treatments is critical to a good experiment.

**LEARNING STRATEGIES:** Close Reading, Questioning the Text, Role Play, Summarizing, Paraphrasing, Debriefing, Discussion Groups

For a science fair project, Zack and Matt wanted to estimate how the rebound of a tennis ball is changed if it is soaked in water overnight and then allowed to dry out. They would have liked to get a random sample of tennis balls on which to perform an experiment, but they realized such a sample was impossible. Instead, their physical education coach gave them 20 used tennis balls as their sample.

1. Consider the definition of **experiment**. Identify the **explanatory** and **response variables**, the experimental units, and the treatment in Zack and Matt's experiment.

2. Why was it impossible for Zack and Matt to get a random sample of all tennis balls?

3. Zack and Matt decided to perform their rebound experiment on the 20 tennis balls their gym coach gave them. What limits on their conclusions would exist by performing the experiment with these balls?

---

**MATH TERMS**

An **experiment** applies a *treatment* (a condition administered) to *experimental units* to observe an effect.

The **explanatory variable** is what is thought to be the cause of different outcomes in the experiment. In simple experiments, the explanatory variable is simply the presence or absence of the treatment.

The effect of the explanatory variable is called the **response variable**.

---

Zack and Matt planned to take their 20 tennis balls and put them into two groups of ten. The balls in one group would be soaked in water overnight and then allowed to dry out, while the others would just stay dry. They would then measure the rebound of all the tennis balls and compare the data for the two groups.

4. To determine which balls should be soaked and which would remain dry, Matt thought it best to use a *completely randomized design*. Describe a process that would provide a completely randomized design for this experiment.

> **MATH TERMS**
>
> A **completely randomized design** implies that all experimental units have the same probability of being selected for application of the treatment.

5. Zack noticed that ten of the balls their coach gave them were Wilson brand balls, and the other ten were Dunlop brand balls. He thought that they should let the ten Wilson balls be the ones soaked in water and the ten Dunlop balls be the ones that stayed dry. What reasons might Matt have to disagree with Zack?

6. Matt suggested that it would be better to group all the Wilson balls and randomly choose five to be soaked in water. Similarly, he would group all the Dunlop balls and randomly choose five to be soaked in water. Why is this *randomized block design* a good strategy?

> **MATH TERMS**
>
> A **randomized block design** involves first grouping experimental units according to a common characteristic, and then using random assignment within each group.

7. Matt and Zack thought about first measuring the rebound of all 20 dry tennis balls on a tennis court. Then they would soak all of the balls in water overnight and let them dry out. Finally, they would measure the rebound again on the tennis court. They could then see for each individual ball how much its rebound was changed by being soaked in water overnight. This strategy might be effective in accomplishing their research goal, but a critic of their experiment could point out that the change in rebound could be due to something other than having been soaked in water. Can you think of such a possible explanation?

## MATH TERMS

A **matched pairs design** involves creating blocks that are pairs. In each pair, one unit is randomly assigned the treatment. Sometimes, both treatments may be applied, and the order of application is randomly assigned.

8. Describe how a *matched pairs design* may alleviate the potential problems identified in Item 6. Why would it be impossible to have matched pairs in which the order of treatment is randomized?

### Check Your Understanding

**9.** A random process was recommended to Jorge when he wanted to estimate how many students at his school hold part-time jobs. A random process was also recommended to Matt and Zack when they wanted to estimate the effect of waterlogging on tennis ball rebound. Explain how these two random processes are similar and how they are different.

### LESSON 37-2 PRACTICE

A medical researcher wanted to determine the effect of a new drug on a specific type of cancer. He recruited 50 female and 50 male cancer patients, each diagnosed with this specific cancer that had progressed to the same stage. The anticipated effect of the drug was a 50% reduction in the size of the tumor within 4 weeks of treatment. All subjects would receive an injection, but some would receive the drug and others would receive a *placebo*.

**10.** Describe a completely randomized experiment that the researcher could perform with these subjects.

**11.** Describe an experiment that would incorporate a block design and the purpose of the block design.

**12.** Describe an experiment that would incorporate a matched-pairs design and the purpose of the matched-pairs design.

**13.** A *single-blind study* is one in which either the person conducting the experiment or the subjects have knowledge of the treatment, but not both. A *double-blind study* is one in which neither the person conducting the experiment nor the subjects have knowledge of the treatment. Describe an advantage of a double-blind study in the cancer researcher's study.

**ACADEMIC VOCABULARY**

A *placebo* is a treatment applied to an experimental subject that appears to be the experimental treatment, but in fact is a treatment known to have no effect.

**My Notes**

### Learning Target:

- Identify a confounding variable in an observational study.

**LEARNING STRATEGIES:** Close Reading, Questioning the Text, Role Play, Summarizing, Paraphrasing, Debriefing, Discussion Groups

Rebecca read an article online with the headline, "Survey shows that among employed Americans, people who text frequently tend to have lower-paying jobs than those who do not." Rebecca immediately sent a text message to her friend Sissy:

"OMG cc! txting makes u have less $$$! 2 bad 4 us!!!"

1. Why is the study referenced by the article that Rebecca read an *observational study* and not an experiment?

---

**MATH TERMS**

In an **observational study,** a researcher observes and records measurements of variables of interest but does not impose a treatment.

---

**MATH TIP**

The results of an *observational study* can only imply an *association*. The results of an *experiment*, by imposing a condition, can imply *causation*.

---

2. While it is possible that Rebecca is correct, the statement she read didn't say that texting caused people to have lower incomes, only that people who frequently text have lower incomes. Give another possible explanation for why those who text frequently may have lower-paying jobs.

If a study reports an association between two factors, and the researcher merely observed the association between the two variables without applying a treatment, then the researcher cannot determine if one of the factors directly caused the other. A third unmeasured variable that may be associated with both of the measured variables is called a *confounding variable*. This variable is "confounded with" one of the other two, and therefore is a potential explanation of the association.

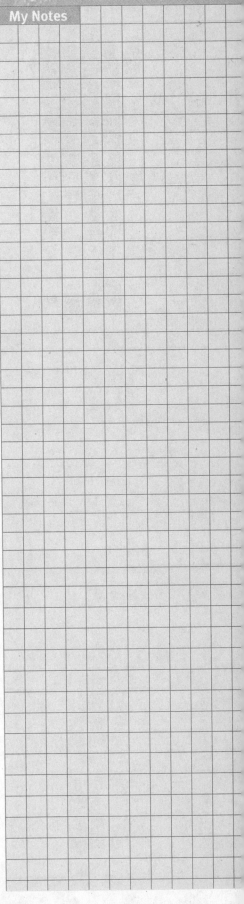

**3.** A 2010 study reported that people who take long vacations tend to live longer than people who do not. One possible explanation is that vacations are good for you, improving your health and increasing your lifespan. Describe another potential explanation for the association, and identify a confounding variable.

A study published in the Journal of the American Medical Association showed that among a group of people who were hospitalized for bicycling accidents, the prevalence of elevated blood alcohol levels was significantly greater than it was among bicyclists who were stopped by the side of the road and who agreed to participate in the study by having their blood alcohol level measured.

**4.** Is there reason to believe that the actual proportion of (non-hospitalized) bicyclists who have elevated blood alcohol levels might be greater than what was estimated by recruiting bicyclists by the side of the road?

My Notes

**5.** The study included a caution about its conclusions, mentioning that the use of bicycle helmets was significantly more common among the people stopped by the side of the road than it was among those who were hospitalized. Why is that relevant to the conclusions one might draw from this study?

## LESSON 37-3 PRACTICE

The crime rate in a small town was shown to be significantly higher whenever ice cream sales were higher. A town councilman was baffled by this, but nevertheless advocated closing down ice cream parlors to lower crime.

**6.** Identify the population and the question of interest in this study.

**7.** Was the ice cream crime rate study an experiment or an observational study? Explain your decision.

**8.** Write a letter to the councilman explaining why his position on closing ice cream parlors may be based on faulty reasoning. Include a potential confounding variable in your letter.

## ACTIVITY 37 PRACTICE
**Write your answers on notebook paper.**
**Show your work.**

### Lesson 37-1

Following an online article about sunbathing posted on a website for teenagers, a poll asked the reader whether he or she regularly sunbathes. 81% of those who responded clicked on "Yes."

1. In this survey, what is question of interest?

2. What is the population that the survey seeks to represent?

3. What is the sample for this survey?

4. Is the sample representative of the population? Is it a simple random sample?

5. What bias may be apparent in the survey?

6. Describe how the bias in this survey may influence the results.

### Lesson 37-2

A study was conducted to see whether drinking eight glasses of water daily would reduce the risk of catching a cold. Forty volunteers who participated in the study were randomly assigned to one of two groups. Those in one group were told not to change any aspect of their daily lives. Those in the other group were instructed to drink at least eight glasses of water daily. At the end of several months, the proportion of people who had caught a cold during that time period was significantly lower among those who drank at least eight glasses of water than among those who didn't. Since this was a randomized experiment, the researchers conducting the experiment thought that the only difference between the two groups of subjects was their water consumption, and, therefore, that drinking eight glasses of water daily can reduce your risk of getting a cold.

7. Why is this study an experiment as opposed to an observational study?

8. Describe a method that the researchers could have used to randomly assign members to each group.

9. What was the treatment in this experiment? What were the explanatory variable and the response variable?

10. Critics of the study identified something other than drinking water that made the two groups of subjects different from one another. What confounding variable may have influenced the results?

11. How could the experiment have been modified to eliminate the problem?

## Lesson 37-3

For many years it was believed that playing classical music for infants was associated with these same people being smarter as older children and adults. Several early studies seemed to support this idea.

**12.** Valentina read one such study that claimed to be an observational study, not an experiment. Explain how such a study would be designed to be an observational study.

**13.** Identify a likely confounding variable in such a study, and explain how it could be responsible for the apparent association between listening to classical music and being smarter.

Bruno considered the classical music theory as well, but thought that an experiment would be better suited to test this theory.

**14.** For such an experiment, identify the question of interest, the experimental units, and the treatment.

**15.** With the help of a local daycare center, Bruno was able to identify 20 parents with infants between the age of 1 month and 2 months. Describe, in detail, an experiment that would test the question of interest.

## MATHEMATICAL PRACTICES
### Reason Abstractly and Quantitatively

**16.** Suppose Bruno's experiment reveals a significant increase in intelligence for those children who listened to classical music. What limitations may exist in the interpretation of the results?

1. A researcher in psychology measured the reading skill, on a scale of 1 to 100, of a random sample of 16 fifth-graders at a school. The skill levels were as follows:

| 51 | 82 | 65 | 69 | 69 | 71 | 58 | 72 |
|----|----|----|----|----|----|----|----|
| 68 | 76 | 56 | 61 | 77 | 64 | 63 | 71 |

Assume that it is reasonable to model the distribution of reading skill levels of all fifth-graders at the school as approximately normal.
   a. Estimate the proportion of fifth-graders at the school with reading skill levels at or below 55.
   b. Estimate the proportion of fifth-graders at the school with reading skill levels between 60 and 70.
   c. Estimate the reading skill level that a fifth-grader would have if his or her score was in the 95th percentile of reading skill levels for fifth-graders at the school.
   d. Create a data display and explain how it supports or conflicts with the assumption of an approximately normal distribution for this data set.

2. A study was done in which volunteer subjects were divided into two groups at random. Subjects in the first group read realistic news stories about fictitious politicians and their political activities. Subjects in the second group read the same stories, but they also read stories about scandals involving the politicians. After several weeks, the subjects were asked to recall information about the politicians. The subjects in the second group recalled more about the activities of the politicians than did the subjects in the first group.
   a. Identify the treatment, explanatory variable, and response variable in this experiment.
   b. What might the researchers conclude as a result of this study?
   c. Suppose that researchers used a block design in the experiment, placing subjects who regularly read news stories in one group and those who did not regularly read news stories in another group. Explain how this may have changed the conclusions that could be drawn from this study.

3. An online survey on a vegetable gardening website found that respondents who planted after April 1 had greater yields than those who planted before April 1.
   a. Describe why this survey is an example of an observational study and not an experiment.
   b. Brianna read the survey results and commented, "Planting after April 1 must cause vegetables yields to be greater." Describe the flaw in her statement.
   c. Why might someone be skeptical about the results of such a survey?

| Scoring Guide | Exemplary | Proficient | Emerging | Incomplete |
|---|---|---|---|---|
| | The solution demonstrates these characteristics: | | | |
| **Mathematics Knowledge and Thinking** (Items 1, 2, 3) | • Clear and accurate understanding of statistical concepts including survey, observational studies, and experimental design, and the impact of randomization on each <br><br> • Clear and accurate understanding of population means and proportions, percentiles, and properties of a normal distribution | • A functional understanding and accurate interpretation of statistical concepts including survey, observational studies, and experimental design, and the impact of randomization on each <br><br> • A functional and mostly accurate understanding of population means and proportions, percentiles, and properties of a normal distribution | • Partial understanding and partially accurate interpretation of statistical concepts including survey, observational studies, and experimental design, and the impact of randomization on each <br><br> • Partial understanding and partially accurate work with population means and proportions, percentiles, and properties of a normal distribution | • Little or no understanding and inaccurate interpretation of statistical concepts including survey, observational studies, and experimental design, and the impact of randomization on each <br><br> • Little or no understanding and inaccurate work with population means and proportions, percentiles, and properties of a normal distribution |
| **Problem Solving** (Items 2, 3) | • An appropriate and efficient strategy that results in a correct answer | • A strategy that may include unnecessary steps but results in a correct answer | • A strategy that results in some incorrect answers | • No clear strategy when solving problems |
| **Mathematical Modeling / Representations** (Item 2) | • Clear and accurate understanding of how to apply experimental design models to a real-world scenario | • Mostly accurate understanding of how to apply experimental design models to a real-world scenario | • Partial understanding of how to apply experimental design models to a real-world scenario | • Inaccurate or incomplete understanding of how to apply experimental design models to a real-world scenario |
| **Reasoning and Communication** (Items 2, 3) | • Precise use of appropriate math terms and language to describe the differences between observational studies and randomized experiments and justify reasoning regarding statistical models <br><br> • Clear and accurate explanation of the effects of changing conditions in a study and why results may not be valid | • Adequate description of differences between observational studies and randomized experiments and justification of reasoning regarding statistical models <br><br> • Adequate explanation of the effects of changing conditions in a study and why results may not be valid | • Misleading or confusing description of differences between observational studies and randomized experiments and justification of reasoning regarding statistical models <br><br> • Misleading or confusing explanation of the effects of changing conditions in a study and why results may not be valid | • Incomplete or inaccurate description of differences between observational studies and randomized experiments and justify reasoning regarding statistical models <br><br> • Incomplete or inadequate explanation of the effects of changing conditions in a study and why results may not be valid |

# Simulations
## Is Martin Improving?
## Lesson 38-1 Devising Simulations

ACTIVITY 38

### Learning Target:
- Devise a simulation that can help determine whether observed data are consistent or inconsistent with a conjecture about how the data were generated.

**SUGGESTED LEARNING STRATEGIES:** Close Reading, Predict and Confirm, Summarizing, Paraphrasing, Think Aloud, Debriefing, Discussion Groups

Martin enjoys playing video games. On his birthday he received "Man vs. Monsters," a game in which the player plays the role of a person who is trying to save the earth from an invasion of alien monsters. At the end of the game, the player either wins or loses. The first three times Martin played the game, he lost. In the next seven games that he played, he won four times, and he felt like his performance was improving. In fact, the sequence of Martin's wins and losses is as follows, where "L" represents losing a game, and "W" represents winning a game.

L, L, L, W, L, L, W, L, W, W

Martin concluded he was getting better at the game the more he played, and he said that this sequence of wins and losses was evidence of his improvement. His sister Hannah, however, was not convinced. She said, "That sequence of wins and losses looks like a random list to me. If you were really getting better, why didn't you lose the first six and then win the last four?"

In this activity, you will use a *simulation* to decide who is correct, Martin or Hannah.

Start by considering that Hannah is correct and that Martin was not really getting better. He had six losses and four wins in a particular order and, if Hannah is correct, those wins and losses could have been arranged in any other order. According to Hannah, Martin's results indicate how good he is at the game—he wins about 40% of the time—but do not indicate whether he is improving.

1. Following this page are ten squares, six of which are marked "Lose" and four of which are marked "Win." These represent the outcomes of the ten games Martin played. Cut out the squares and arrange them *facedown* on your desk.

**MATH TERMS**

A simulation is a process to generate imaginary data, often many times, using a model of a real-world situation.

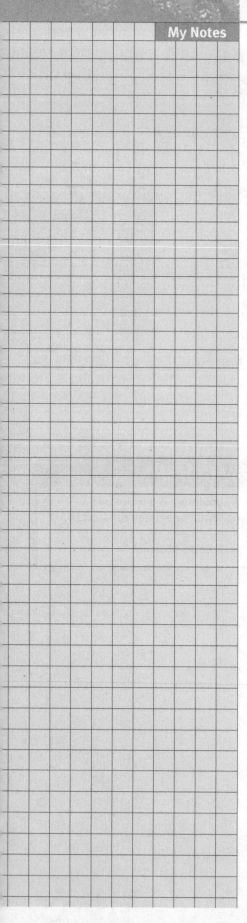

My Notes

2. Once you have placed the cards facedown, mix them up and arrange them in a random sequential order so that you do not know which ones represent wins and which ones represent losses. Then turn them all face up so you can see the L or W, and write down the order of wins and losses here. This is a simulation of Martin's wins and losses.

3. Consider the following two sequences, and write a sentence explaining whether it appears that Martin is improving.

   a. L, L, L, L, W, L, L, W, W, W

   b. W, L, W, W, L, L, L, W, L, L

4. It is desirable to quantify (i.e., measure with a numerical quantity) the extent to which a sequence of wins and losses indicates that a player who achieved it is really improving. Describe a method that may quantify the results of playing ten games such that the number describes the improvement of a player. Be creative!

| | |
|---|---|
| Lose | Lose |
| Lose | Lose |
| Lose | Lose |
| Win | Win |
| Win | Win |

My Notes

This page is intentionally blank.

One way to quantify improvement is to count how many wins occur among the last five games, and subtract the number of wins that occur among the first five games. Call this the "improvement score" for the sequence of results for ten games.

5. Two example sequences are provided below. Find the improvement score for each. Show all work.

L, L, L, L, W, L, L, W, W, W

W, L, L, W, L, L, L, W, L, W

6. Using this method to quantify improvement, what would a negative improvement score imply? What would a positive improvement score imply?

Any number that summarizes data in a meaningful way is called a *statistic*. Your improvement score, a number which is the difference between the number of wins among the last five of ten games and the number of wins among the first five, is a statistic because it summarizes the data with a number that measures improvement.

7. Compute the improvement score for the sequence of wins and losses from your simulation in Item 2 when you mixed up the order of your ten squares.

**MATH TERMS**

A **statistic** is a number that summarizes data in a meaningful way. The mean of a data set is an example of a statistic.

Recall the reason for computing the improvement score. Martin's sister, Hannah, is skeptical that Martin's ability to win the game is improving. She thinks that his particular sequence of wins and losses looks random and does not imply improvement. To address her concern, it is important to determine whether a sequence like Martin's might easily show up if the order of wins and losses really is random. More specifically, it is important to determine if the improvement score that results from Martin's sequence of wins and losses is a number that might easily result from a random arrangement of four wins and six losses.

8. Compute the improvement score for Martin's actual sequence of wins and losses:

$$L, L, L, W, L, L, W, L, W, W$$

### Check Your Understanding

In Item 4, you created a statistic to measure improvement. Below are two other possible "improvement statistics" that Martin might have used to measure his improvement over ten games. For each one, state (a) whether the statistic is actually a measurement of improvement and (b) whether the statistic is likely to provide more information than Martin's improvement score as defined before Item 5. Explain your answers briefly.

9. Count the number of games until Martin achieves his second win. This number of games is the improvement statistic.

10. Identify each win with a "1" and each loss with a "0". Create ordered pairs such that the number of the game (1 through 10) is the $x$-coordinate and the "1" or "0" is the $y$-coordinate. Use technology to make a scatter plot of these ten points and compute the slope of the regression line through the ten points. The slope of the regression line is the improvement statistic. Write the linear equation of the regression line.

## LESSON 38-1 PRACTICE

Teresa conducted a survey of a simple random sample of ten customers shopping in a grocery store. Her survey asked the customers to identify the price of the most expensive item in their basket. The ten responses, rounded to the nearest dollar, are listed below.

12, 8, 3, 2, 9, 25, 14, 8, 4, 5

**11.** Identify two statistics that could be calculated from these data.

**12.** Calculate the statistics that you identified in Item 11, and describe the significance of each statistic.

Steven would like to create simulations that would model the incidence of precipitation in a particular city.

**13.** Consider a fictional city where data indicate that precipitation occurs on 50% of the days in a year. Describe how Steven could perform a simulation to determine the occurrences of precipitation in this city during eight randomly chosen days of the year, using a fair coin.

**14.** Sacramento, California, receives rain on approximately one of every six days during a year. Describe a method by which Steven may simulate precipitation in Sacramento for eight randomly chosen days of the year.

**15.** Vero Beach, Florida, receives rain on approximately one of every three days during a year. Describe a method by which Steven may simulate precipitation in Vero Beach for eight randomly chosen days of the year.

**16.** Hilo, Hawaii receives rain on approximately three of every four days during a year. Describe a method by which Steven may simulate precipitation in Hilo for eight randomly chosen days of the year.

**My Notes**

**Learning Target:**
● Determine if a simulation indicates whether observed data are consistent or inconsistent with a conjecture about the data.

**SUGGESTED LEARNING STRATEGIES:** Close Reading, Predict and Confirm, Summarizing, Paraphrasing, Think Aloud, Debriefing, Discussion Groups

1. In the previous lesson, you carried out a simulation by mixing ten cards representing Martin's wins and losses. Next you created a sequence of the results and then computed the improvement score for the sequence you created. Repeat that process, recording below the improvement score for each randomly ordered sequence of wins and losses that you get. Work with your group and collect your results together until you have collected 40 improvement scores. (Keep all 40 sequences for use later in this activity.)

|  |  |  |  |  |  |  |  |
|---|---|---|---|---|---|---|---|
|  |  |  |  |  |  |  |  |
|  |  |  |  |  |  |  |  |
|  |  |  |  |  |  |  |  |
|  |  |  |  |  |  |  |  |
|  |  |  |  |  |  |  |  |

2. Make a dot plot showing the distribution of the improvement scores that you found in Item 1.

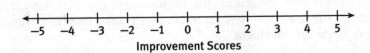

**Improvement Scores**

3. Recall Martin's improvement score that you found in Item 7 of Lesson 1. Describe the column of dots in your dot plot that corresponds to Martin's improvement score.

4. Why are there no improvement scores of $\pm 1$, $\pm 3$, $\pm 5$?

5. Based upon your results, what is the probability of Martin obtaining the improvement score that he received in his initial game? What is the probability of receiving *at least* that score?

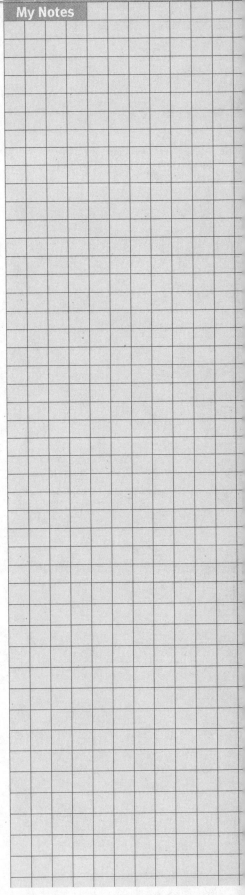

**6.** Is Martin's improvement score one that is likely to occur by chance?

**7.** Consider the event that Martin's sequence of game results was LLLLLLWWWW. Determine his improvement score for this game, and interpret the score with respect to Hannah's claim that his results did not indicate improvement.

## Check Your Understanding

**8.** A physical education class with 15 female students and 10 male students had to select 11 students at random to form a soccer team. Bob was skeptical when the teacher announced that all 11 players selected were female. Describe a simulation that Bob could perform that would determine if such a selection was likely a result of chance or a result of some bias.

**9.** One method of proof in mathematics is known as "proof by contradiction." In such proofs, you begin with a negation of the statement you wish to prove. Then, through logical deduction using known facts, a false statement is concluded. Since the conclusion is false, the original statement must be false, and the statement you want to prove is correct.

Identify one similarity and one difference between a mathematical proof by contradiction and the logical argument that you made in Items 6 and 7.

## Lesson 38-2
**Confirming Data with Simulations**

### LESSON 38-2 PRACTICE

Consider the following alternative statistic to measure improvement: add together the position numbers of all the wins. The larger the total is, the later in the sequence the wins must be. For example:

$$L, L, L, L, W, L, L, W, W, W \rightarrow 5 + 8 + 9 + 10 = \mathbf{32}$$

$$W, L, L, L, L, W, W, W, L, L \rightarrow 1 + 6 + 7 + 8 = \mathbf{22}$$

Call this new statistic the "improvement measure." In the items that follow, use the improvement measure to see whether Martin's particular sequence of wins and losses could easily be explained by his sister Hannah's theory that his wins and losses were really just in a random order.

10. Determine Martin's improvement measure.

11. Describe how you will simulate whether or not Martin's sequence of game outcomes is consistent with Hannah's theory.

12. Show the distribution of the improvement measures that result from many random orderings of Martin's game outcomes. Use the sequences you obtained from the 40 trials in Item 1 of this lesson.

13. State a conclusion about whether Martin's sequence of wins and losses is consistent with Hannah's theory.

14. Explain the logic that led you to your conclusion.

**CONNECT TO AP**

In AP Statistics, it is critical that students be able to write coherent and clear descriptions of simulations that even a non-statistician would be able to follow.

## ACTIVITY 38 PRACTICE

**Write your answers on notebook paper.**
**Show your work.**

Use the following information for Items 1–5.

Jesse, a high school junior, was talking with six of his friends about whom they planned to vote for in the upcoming election of the class president. There were two candidates, Sarah and John. Among Jesse's group of friends there were three girls, and all of them planned to vote for Sarah, a girl. Jesse's three other friends were boys, and two of them planned to vote for John, a boy. Only one friend of Jesse's—a boy—was planning to vote "against gender" and vote for Sarah. Jesse thought that his friends were voting according to their own gender and wondered if this was just a chance occurrence.

1. Jesse wants to perform a simulation to determine if his friends' tendency to vote according to gender was likely a result of random chance. Describe (but do not perform) a simulation that Jesse could perform to accomplish this task.

2. Identify a statistic that Jesse could measure in his simulation.

3. Describe the process for determining the likelihood of the occurrence of the statistic for Jesse's friends.

4. Based on your results from Item 3, assume that the probability of the occurrence of the statistic was 0.40. What conclusion would you make?

5. Based on your results from Item 3, assume that the probability of the occurrence of the statistic was 0.05. What conclusion would you make?

Use the following information for Items 6–9.

For a research project, Tia wanted to see whether people could tell the difference between two brands of cola by taste. She planned an experiment. Volunteer subjects would each be presented with three small identical-looking cups of soda labeled A, B, and C. Two of the cups would contain the same brand of cola while the third cup would contain the other brand. Tia would randomly determine which of the three cups would be the one containing the different brand. She would also randomly determine which cola brand would be in two cups and which would be in one cup.

Each subject would be asked to taste the cola in each cup and then identify which cup contained the different brand. The subjects would not be required to identify the brands, only to tell which cup contained a different brand.

After getting responses from 20 subjects, Tia planned to count how many had identified the correct cup, and then see whether that count was too large to be explainable by just random chance.

6. Identify the statistic that Tia is measuring.

7. Tia is interested in seeing whether her statistic is greater than she would expect by chance alone. What would the value of her statistic be if no one could taste a difference between the two drinks?

Use the following information for Items 8 and 9.

Suppose that 12 of the 20 people in Tia's experiment gave correct cup identifications. Describe a process by which Tia could decide whether 12 correct cup identifications would or would not be surprising if, in fact, everyone was just guessing.

8. Describe such a process using a six-sided number cube. Be sure to identify what each roll of the number cube represents and what the numbers on the number cube represent. You do not have to carry out the process—just describe it clearly.

### MATHEMATICAL PRACTICES
**Make Sense of Problems and Persevere in Solving Them**

9. Describe another such process using only a random number table. Be sure to identify what each digit represents and the meaning of that digit.

# Margin of Error
## Can't Get No Satisfaction
### Lesson 39-1 Introduction to Margin of Error

**Learning Targets:**

- Use margin of error in an estimate of a population proportion.
- Use simulation models for random samples.

**SUGGESTED LEARNING STRATEGIES:** Predict and Confirm, Think Aloud, Debriefing, Discussion Groups

Since 1979, Gallup, a national polling organization, has reported survey results of the question, "In general, are you satisfied or dissatisfied with the way things are going in the United States at this time?"

The results from 1979 to 2012 are displayed on the graph shown.

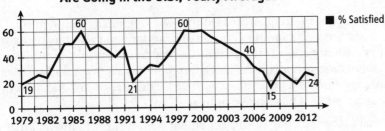

Satisfaction With the Way Things
Are Going in the U.S., Yearly Averages

2013 figure represents yearly average to date.

1. Describe the meaning of the graph and characteristics that may be of interest to a person studying this graph.

2. From 2000 to 2012, there is a steady decline in the satisfaction proportion. What historical events may account for such a decline?

My Notes

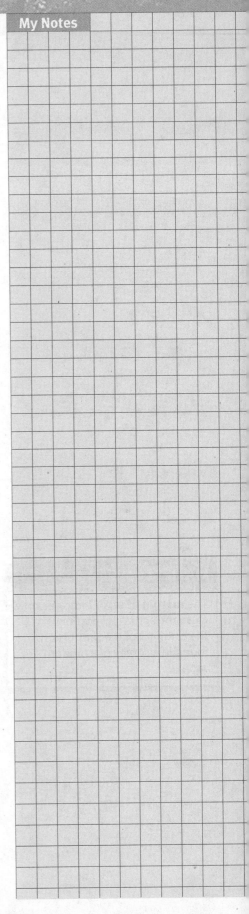

The results of the 2013 Gallup poll asking this question, conducted on November 7–10, 2013, indicated that 20% of Americans are satisfied with the way things are going in the United States. These results were based on telephone interviews with a random sample of 1039 adults, aged 18 and older, living in all 50 U.S. states and the District of Columbia.

3. Why did the Gallup pollsters use a random sample to establish this proportion of satisfied Americans?

Random samples are frequently used to make inferences about entire populations. Since the samples chosen are random and rely on chance, the laws of probability allow us to determine how sample results compare to an actual population proportion. The Gallup poll description continues with the following statement: "One can say with 95% confidence that the margin of sampling error is ±4 percentage points."

4. What is the meaning of this statement with respect to the fact that 20% of the Americans polled stated that they were satisfied with the way things were going in the United States?

MATH TERMS

The **margin of error** indicates how close the actual proportion is to the estimate of the proportion found in a survey of a random sample.

The phrase "±4 percentage points" in the statement is called the *margin of error*. Random samples have characteristics that set bounds on the errors that are likely to exist in the results of that random sample. In this activity, we will investigate these characteristics.

5. The Gallup poll indicated that 20% of the population was satisfied with how things were going in the United States in November 2013. If the actual population proportion is 20%, how many satisfied people would you expect from a random sample of ten people?

**6.** It is possible that your random sample of ten people in Item 5 could yield results that differ from your answer to Item 5. Which results would not be surprising? Which results would be surprising?

**7.** Given the actual population proportion is 20%, how many satisfied people would you expect from a random sample of 100 people? How different from your expected value must a result be for it to be a "surprising" result?

Using your graphing calculator, you can perform a simulation for the situations in Items 5 and 7 to model the selection of a random sample and the number of "successes" in that sample.

**8.** Use the *randBin(* function of your calculator to perform ten different simulations of the survey in Item 5. How many satisfied people exist in a random sample of ten people if the actual proportion is 0.20? Does your result agree with your answer to Item 6?

**9.** Compare the result of your imaginary survey with the ones conducted by the others in your group. Explain why the results are likely different from one another.

**My Notes**

**MATH TIP**

To perform a simulation of a survey, generate imaginary data based on assumptions about actual population characteristics.

**TECHNOLOGY TIP**

To find the *randBin* function on the TI-84, press [MATH] and the arrow keys to select the *PRB* menu, and select *randBin(.* The first entry is the number of subjects in the random sample, followed by a comma, and then the probability of "success" for each subject in that random sample. Press [ENTER] and the result is the number of "successes" for one random sample. If you would like to perform the simulation a number of times, you can follow the probability with a comma, followed by the number of simulations you would like to perform.

For example, to find the number of successes in one random sample of ten people with a probability of success of 0.5, enter *randBin(10, 0.5)* To find the number of successes in eight such random samples, enter *randBin(10, 0.5, 8)*.

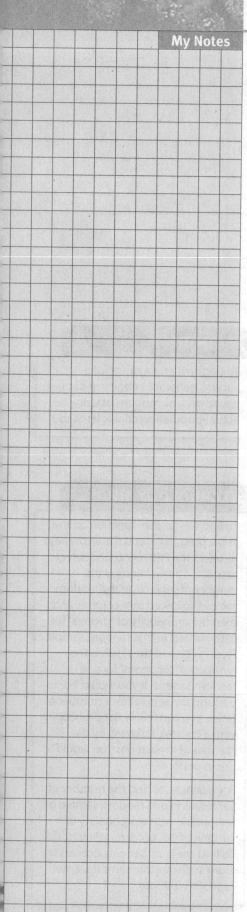

My Notes

**10.** Since the survey results are concerned with the proportion of people who are satisfied, convert each of your results into a *proportion*. The proportion for each result is called the ***sample proportion*** . Combine the proportions from your surveys with the others in your group so that you have 40 survey results.

**a.** Create a histogram to display the distribution of proportions, and comment on the shape of your group's distribution.

**b.** Compute the mean and standard deviation for the 40 survey proportions.

**11.** Use the *randBin(* function of your calculator to perform ten different simulations of the survey in Item 7. How many satisfied people exist in a random sample of 100 people if the actual proportion is 0.20? Does your result agree with your answer to Item 7?

12. Combine the results of your survey with the others in your group so that you have 40 survey results, and find the *proportion* of satisfied subjects for each survey.

   **a.** Create a histogram to display the distribution of proportions, and comment on the shape of your group's distribution.

   **b.** Compute the mean and standard deviation for the 40 survey proportions.

13. Compare and contrast the means and standard deviations for the combined surveys of ten subjects and for the combined surveys of 100 subjects. What conclusion can you infer from these results?

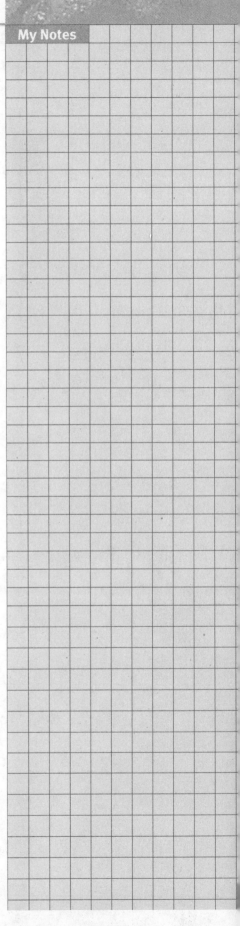

## Check Your Understanding

**14.** In the days prior to a mayoral election, a poll reported, with 90% confidence, that the current mayor had support of 53% of the city's voting population, with a margin of error of 6%. Write a sentence to interpret the results of the survey.

**15.** Describe a procedure that uses a number cube to simulate a population proportion of 33%. How many successes would you expect from 12 trials? Perform the simulation 12 times, record your results, and compare them to your expectations.

## LESSON 39-1 PRACTICE

**16.** Jorge claimed that the results of a survey supported his claim that most of the students in the junior class scored above average on the PSAT test. Valentina read the results of the survey to Jorge: "A survey of a simple random sample of students in the junior class indicated that 48% of them scored above average on the PSAT test. One can say with 95% confidence that the margin of error for this survey is plus or minus 4%." Is Jorge correct that the survey supported his claim?

The Gallup-Healthways Well-Being Index tracks, on a daily basis, the proportion of Americans who say they experienced happiness and enjoyment without stress and worry on the previous day. On one particular day, the survey of 500 people indicated that 54% were happy, with a margin of error of $\pm$ 5%.

**17.** Using technology or a random digits table, describe how you could simulate 20 repetitions of such a survey for a random sample of size 100.

**18.** Perform the simulation that you described in Item 15, and find the mean and standard deviation.

**19.** Change your results to proportions and display them on a histogram. Use an interval width of 0.1.

**20.** Describe the shape of your distribution. Identify proportions that you would expect in such a simulation, and identify proportions that would be surprising in such a simulation.

**My Notes**

## Learning Targets:

- Use margin of error in an estimate of a population proportion.
- Relate margin of error to the population proportion and to the sample size.

> SUGGESTED LEARNING STRATEGIES: Predict and Confirm, Think Aloud, Debriefing, Discussion Groups

"In general, are you satisfied or dissatisfied with the way things are going in the United States at this time?" For this question of interest, recall that the Gallup organization reported that for results based on this sample of 1039 adults, you can say with 95% confidence that the margin of error is $\pm 4$ percentage points.

The distribution of proportions of those who indicate they are satisfied for all possible samples of size $n$ from the population is called the *sampling distribution* of the population for that statistic.

1. What is the population for this question of interest? Why is it not feasible to find the sampling distribution of size $n = 1039$ for this population?

While it is not possible to find the sampling distribution for this statistic, you did generate some ideas by finding a large number of samples using simulations in the previous lesson.

2. In Items 10 and 12 from Lesson 39-1, which distribution was approximately normal? What were the sample sizes in those distributions?

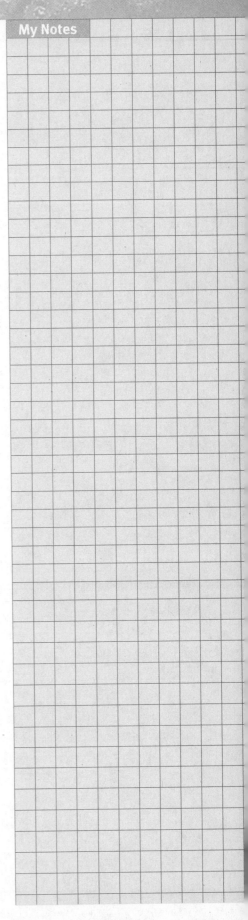

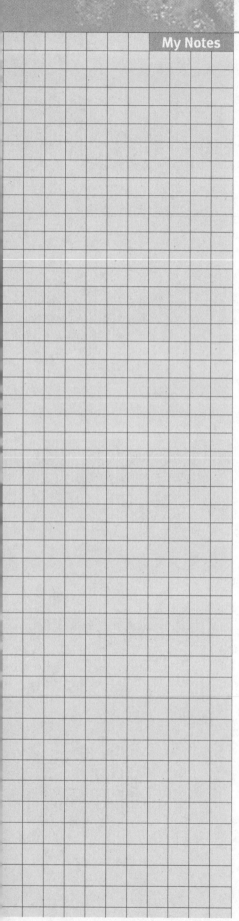

As sample sizes increase, the sampling distribution becomes more and more normal. If a random sample of size $n$ has a proportion of successes $p$, there are two conditions that, if satisfied, allow the distribution to be considered approximately normal. Those two conditions are $n(p) \geq 10$ and $n(1-p) \geq 10$.

**3.** Show that Gallup's survey meets the normal conditions.

**4.** Show that the simulation performed with $n = 10$ *does not meet* the normal condition and that the simulation performed with $n = 100$ *does meet* the normal condition.

In general, when investigating a question of interest, you are not aware of the actual population statistic. However, by taking a simple random sample of an appropriate size, you can make inferences about the entire population. Also recall that normal distributions are completely described by two statistics: the mean and the standard deviation.

The standard deviation for a sampling distribution is given by

$$\sqrt{\frac{p(1-p)}{n}}$$

where $p$ is the sample proportion and $n$ is the sample size.

5. What is the meaning of the standard deviation with respect to a sample proportion?

6. In your simulations, you used $p = 0.20$ and $n = 100$. To be more accurate, would you prefer to use $n = 1000$? Use the formula to evaluate standard deviations to support your answer.

**MATH TIP**

In the previous lesson, you discovered that the mean of the proportions of your sampling distributions was very close to the actual proportion. This is because the mean of the proportions of the entire sampling distribution is equal to the actual proportion. Therefore, *we can consider the proportion p of the random sample as the actual proportion.*

**MATH TERMS**

A **critical value** for an approximately normal distribution is the $z$-score that corresponds to a level of confidence.

The Gallup survey stated that "the margin of error is $\pm 4$ percentage points." The margin of error is the range about the sample proportion in which you would expect to find the actual population proportion. The margin of error is found by multiplying the standard deviation by the **critical value**.

## Example A

A city government said that, based on a survey of a random sample of 800 adults in the city, you can say that 25% of them prefer weekly recycling pickup, with 95% confidence that the margin of error is $\pm 3$ percentage points.

- The sample proportion is 0.25.
- Since $np > 10$, $800(0.25) = 200 > 10$ and $n(1 - p) > 10$, $800(1 - 0.25) = 600 > 10$, we can assume that the sampling distribution is approximately normal.
- You would like to be 95% confident in the statement; this will determine the critical value. Since the distribution is approximately normal, we can use the $z$-table or invNorm function on our calculators. Notice that the 95% interval is evenly divided on either side of our sample proportion (mean).

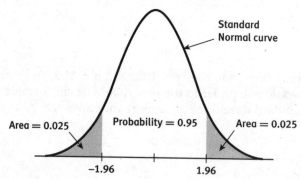

Standard Normal curve

Area = 0.025     Probability = 0.95     Area = 0.025

−1.96          1.96

- Find 0.975 in the body of the $z$-table for the positive critical value (1.96) or 0.025 in the body of the table for the negative critical value ($-1.96$).
- Multiply $\pm 1.96$ by the standard deviation,

$$\pm 1.96 \sqrt{\frac{0.25(1 - 0.25)}{800}} \approx \pm 1.96(0.0153) \approx 0.030$$

- 0.030 is the margin of error.
- Therefore, you are 95% confident that the actual proportion of city residents that prefer weekly recycling pickup is 25% with a margin of error of $\pm 3\%$.

**TECHNOLOGY TIP**

You may also use *invNorm*(0.025,0,1) on the TI-84 to find the critical value. Use the mean 0 and standard deviation of 1 in this function because you are assuming that the values are standardized.

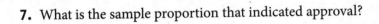

Victor, a member of the Student Government Association at his high school, wanted to know if students approved of the theme of the school's homecoming dance. He polled a simple random sample of 120 subjects from the population of 2000 students at his school, and 72 of the responses indicated approval. Victor would like to report back to the SGA with 90% confidence in the results of his survey.

**7.** What is the sample proportion that indicated approval?

**8.** Victor assumes that the sampling distribution for his poll is approximately normal. Show that he is correct in his assumption.

**9.** Victor wants to report with 90% confidence in his results.
   **a.** On a normal distribution with 90% evenly divided on either side of the sample proportion (mean), what two probability values would you want to identify?

   **b.** What are the critical values associated with these probabilities?

**10.** What is Victor's margin of error?

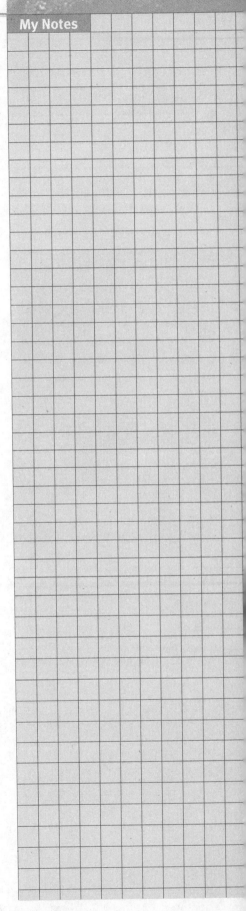

My Notes

**11.** Write a sentence that reports Victor's results to the Student Government Association at his school.

**12.** Without performing the computations, how do you think the margin of error would change if the number of students that Victor polled were 80? How do you think it would change if the number of students were 200?

**13.** Compute the actual margin of error for $n = 80$ and $n = 200$ to confirm or revise your answer to Item 7.

My Notes

### Check Your Understanding

Recall that the standard deviation of a sample proportion is represented by $\sqrt{\dfrac{p(1-p)}{n}}$.

**14.** Describe the meaning of each variable. Explain what happens to the standard deviation when the value of $n$ increases.

**15.** For a fixed value of $n$, what value of $p$ would yield the largest standard deviation?

### LESSON 39-2 PRACTICE

Sofia is a credit card specialist with a large financial institution. She is interested in knowing what proportion of the bank's credit card holders have credit scores in the good or excellent range (scores of 680 and above). Sofia surveyed a simple random sample of 1000 of the bank's credit card customers and found that 750 of them had credit scores of 680 and above.

**16.** For Sofia's survey, identify each of the following.
   **a.** the question of interest
   **b.** the population
   **c.** the sample proportion

**17.** Write the standard deviation for the sample proportion.

**18.** Sofia wants to be 98% confident in her estimate of the actual proportion. What critical values will she use in her determination of the margin of error?

**19.** Compute the margin of error, and write a sentence that describes the results of Sofia's survey.

## ACTIVITY 39 PRACTICE
Write your answers on notebook paper.
Show your work.

### Lesson 39-1

A jar contains 1000 jellybeans that are colored either red or green. 30% of the jellybeans are red, and the remaining jellybeans are green. Assume that the jellybeans are well mixed and that a random sample of 20 jellybeans is chosen from the jar.

1. Would it be unusual to pull out five red jellybeans and 15 green jellybeans? Explain.

2. Would it be unusual to pull out 15 red jellybeans and five green jellybeans? Explain.

3. Describe a simulation that you could perform with a random digits table to model 30 such samples.

4. Describe a simulation that you could perform with a graphing calculator that would model 30 such samples.

5. Perform one of the simulations that you described in Item 3 and Item 4. Convert the number of jellybeans to proportions, and explain how the results of your simulation agree or disagree with your responses to Item 1 and Item 2.

### Lesson 39-2

In late 2011 the Gallup organization surveyed a random sample of 2007 American adults and asked them what they thought about China's relationship with the United States. 76% of those surveyed said that China was either "friendly" or "an ally." Gallup reported the following statement along with the survey results: "For results based on the total sample size of 2007 adults, one can say with 95% confidence that the margin of error attributable to sampling and other random effects is $\pm2.68$ percentage points."

6. What is the population?

7. What is the question of interest?

8. What is the sample proportion?

9. The margin of error reported uses some advanced statistical methods to adjust for sample and population characteristics. Find the "unadjusted" margin of error for this survey.

10. If the sample size for this survey were 1000, what changes would you expect in the margin of error?

11. Compute the margin of error for a sample size of 1000.

### MATHEMATICAL PRACTICES
**Construct Viable Arguments and Critique the Reasoning of Others**

12. In 2011, a New York University professor of journalism, Charles Seife, wrote, "Random events behave predictably in aggregate even if they're not predictable individually." How does that principle relate to the concept of a margin of error in a survey result?

# Designing and Conducting Simulations
## Time Flies When You Are Having Fun
### Lesson 40-1 Random Chance

**Learning Target:**

- Determine whether an apparent treatment effect is too large to be due just to random chance.

> **SUGGESTED LEARNING STRATEGIES:** Activating Prior Knowledge, KWL Chart, Role Play, Summarizing, Paraphrasing, Think Aloud, Debriefing

As you read the scenarios and problems in this activity, mark the text to identify key information and parts of sentences that help you make meaning from the text.

Jamie and Riley wanted to see whether the adage "Time flies when you are having fun!" could be demonstrated scientifically. They decided to conduct a study and recruited 14 classmates to be subjects. Jamie randomly selected seven subjects and assigned them to a group called "Fun." The rest were assigned to a group called "Not Fun." The "Fun" group was given a task of playing a video game enjoyed by all subjects, while the "Not Fun" group was assigned a task of copying code for a programming language with which none were familiar.

1. Is the study described an observational study or an experiment? Explain your reasoning.

Each subject was asked to spend 30 minutes in a quiet room performing their assigned task with no time-keeping capability. At exactly 13.5 minutes into their task, subjects were interrupted and asked to estimate the number of minutes that had passed since the task began.

2. What are the variables in this study?

My Notes

After completing the study for all 14 subjects, Jamie and Riley wanted to analyze the data to determine whether the subjects in the "Fun" group tended to think less time had passed than those in the "Not Fun" group. If they did, then there would be evidence that the expression, "Time flies when you are having fun!" is true.

The table below gives Jamie and Riley's data.

| Group | Perceived Minutes Elapsed | | | | | | |
|---|---|---|---|---|---|---|---|
| Fun | 10 | 11 | 10 | 15 | 9 | 14 | 14 |
| Not Fun | 18 | 17 | 17 | 15 | 10 | 12 | 20 |

**3.** Draw dot plots of the data on the axes below to display the distributions of perceived elapsed times.

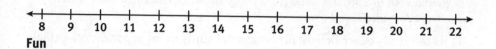

Fun

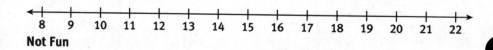

Not Fun

**4.** Compare the two distributions of estimated elapsed times in a way that addresses Jamie and Riley's research question.

Jamie and Riley showed their data to their classmate, Mercedes, who raised an issue they had not considered. She asked, "How do you know that your subjects would not have produced the same results regardless of which group they were in?"

**5.** Suppose that the perception of the passage of time was not affected by the group in which the subjects were placed. Describe how the two distributions would have appeared.

Mercedes suggested that Jamie and Riley consider the difference between medians of the two sets of data—median of the "Not Fun" group minus median of the "Fun" group—to compare the two groups.

**6.** Compute the difference in medians of the two sets. Does this indicate a difference between the two groups?

**7.** How large must the difference between the medians be to show an effect of the task assigned to each group?

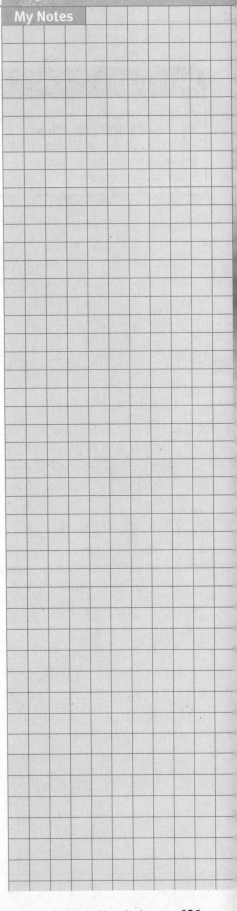

**MATH TERMS**

A statistic computed from a set of data is **statistically significant** if it would have been very unusual for the value of the statistic to be the result of chance alone.

As a result of chance, two data sets cannot be expected to have exactly the same values, even if the treatments really had no effect. However, if the difference in two data sets is so great that it is very unlikely to have occurred by chance, then the results are called ***statistically significant***.

8. Using the data that Jamie and Riley collected, rearrange the "Perceived Minutes Elapsed" values in such a manner that they would be most statistically significant.

| Group | Perceived Minutes Elapsed | | | | | |
|---|---|---|---|---|---|---|
| Fun | | | | | | |
| Not Fun | | | | | | |

9. Create a dot plot for these groups, find the median for each, and compute the difference in medians.

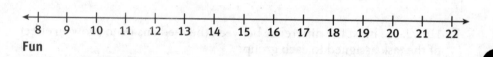

Fun

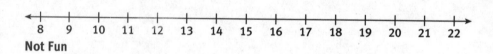

Not Fun

10. Using the data that Jamie and Riley collected, rearrange the "Perceived Minutes Elapsed" values in such a manner that they would **not** be statistically significant.

| Group | Perceived Minutes Elapsed | | | | | |
|---|---|---|---|---|---|---|
| Fun | | | | | | |
| Not Fun | | | | | | |

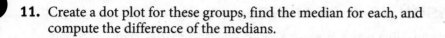

## Lesson 40-1
### Random Chance

**My Notes**

**11.** Create a dot plot for these groups, find the median for each, and compute the difference of the medians.

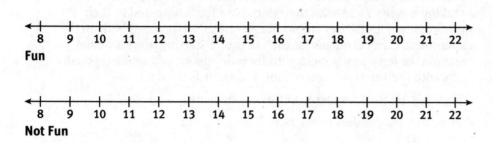

**12.** Explain why the difference in medians may be a good statistic to investigate to determine statistical significance.

### Check Your Understanding

**13.** Find the difference in the mean of the two test groups. Would difference in means be a good statistic for determining statistical significance in this situation?

**14.** Find the difference in the standard deviations of the two test groups. Would difference in standard deviations be a good statistic for determining statistical significance in this situation?

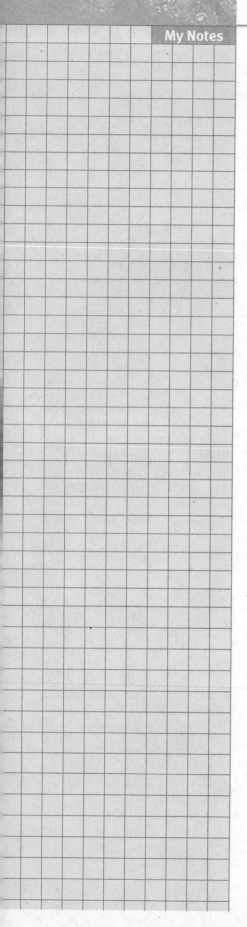

## LESSON 40-1 PRACTICE

Carol and Alina play soccer for a local college team. Based on anecdotal evidence, they think that there is a difference in a player's success rate of taking penalty kicks with their dominant foot compared to their non-dominant foot. They would like to test this hypothesis with an experiment. Carol arranges for each of the 11 starting players on her team to take ten penalty kicks with their dominant foot and ten penalty kicks with their non-dominant foot, and records the data.

**15.** What are the treatments in this experiment?

Alina collected the data in the table below.

| | Number of Successful Penalty Kicks | | | | | | | | | | |
|---|---|---|---|---|---|---|---|---|---|---|---|
| **Dominant Foot** | 8 | 7 | 9 | 9 | 6 | 7 | 7 | 8 | 5 | 9 | 7 |
| **Non-Dominant Foot** | 6 | 7 | 8 | 9 | 5 | 8 | 7 | 6 | 5 | 8 | 8 |

**16.** Draw a dot plot for each distribution. Does it seem that Carol and Alina's hypothesis is supported?

**17.** To test their hypothesis with this data set, which test statistic would be better: difference in medians or difference in means?

**18.** Using the same data values, describe two distributions that would be more supportive of the hypothesis.

**19.** Describe the meaning of statistical significance in this context.

**My Notes**

### Learning Target:
- Design and conduct a simulation to test statistical significance.

**SUGGESTED LEARNING STRATEGIES:** Activating Prior Knowledge, KWL Chart, Role Play, Summarizing, Paraphrasing, Think Aloud, Debriefing

Using the data values from Jamie and Riley's original study, you grouped data values in Lesson 40-1 to create data sets with median differences that were statistically significant and that were not statistically significant. However, the question remains for the original data set collected by Jamie and Riley: Is the difference of medians, 7 minutes, statistically significant in their study?

To investigate this question, create a model to randomly select data values from the original data set. This will represent a situation in which the treatment had no effect on the perception of the passage of time. Recall that the data collected from the study included responses of 9, 10, 10, 10, 11, 12, 14, 14, 15, 15, 17, 17, 18, and 20 minutes.

1. Use the *randInt* function on your calculator to choose random integers from 9 to 20. Repeat the process until you obtain seven of the data values above, without replacement. (Note that 10, 14, 15, and 17 occur multiple times, and therefore can occur the same number of times in your selection.)

   **a.** Write those seven data values as the "Fun" values. The values that remain are the "Not Fun" values. Use the table below to organize your selections.

   | Group | Perceived Minutes Elapsed | | | | | | |
   |-------|---|---|---|---|---|---|---|
   | Fun | | | | | | | |
   | Not Fun | | | | | | | |

   **b.** Find the median of the "Fun" data values and the median of the "Not Fun" data values. Subtract the "Fun" median from the "Not Fun" median.

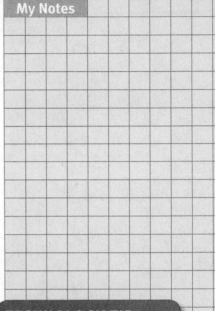

**TECHNOLOGY TIP**

To find the *randInt* function on the TI-84, press [MATH] and the arrow keys to select the *PRB* menu, and select *randInt(*. The first entry is the least integer from the range you would like to sample, followed by a comma, and then the greatest integer from the range. Press [ENTER] and the result is an integer, chosen at random, from the range you indicated.

For example, to choose a random integer between 5 and 15, including 5 and 15, enter *randInt(5,15)*.

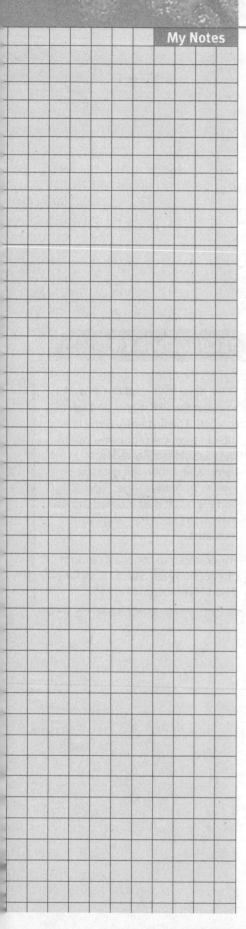

My Notes

2. Repeat the process in Item 1 and record the difference of the medians in the table below.

| Simulation Number | 1 | 2 | 3 | 4 | 5 | 6 | 7 | 8 | 9 | 10 |
|---|---|---|---|---|---|---|---|---|---|---|
| "Fun" Median – "Not Fun" Median | | | | | | | | | | |

3. Combine your list of ten differences with those of your classmates so that you have at least 100 values. (The more values you have, the better your results will be). Write the results in the table below.

| Difference of Medians | Frequency |
|---|---|
| −7 | |
| −6 | |
| −5 | |
| −4 | |
| −3 | |
| −2 | |
| −1 | |
| 0 | |
| 1 | |
| 2 | |
| 3 | |
| 4 | |
| 5 | |
| 6 | |
| 7 | |

**4.** Create a histogram with the combined class values from Item 3, and describe the shape of the distribution.

In Jamie and Riley's real data set, the difference between the median data values of the two groups was 7 minutes. That difference seemed rather large, but it wasn't obvious whether it was so large that it was statistically significant.

**5.** Describe the meaning of *statistically significant* in this context.

**6.** Based on your results, what is the probability of the difference in medians being as great as 7 minutes?

## My Notes

### ACADEMIC VOCABULARY

A **simulation** is a model of a real-world process in which imaginary data are generated, usually many times, to determine what results can be expected from the real-world process.

In AP Statistics, it is important to be able not only to draw an appropriate conclusion from data, but also to articulate a logical argument about how the conclusion follows from the data.

The *simulation* you just conducted is a tool to help determine what values are typical and what values are atypical, assuming that the subjects' responses would have been the same regardless of which treatment group they ended up in.

7. Based on the results of your simulation, is the 7-minute difference in medians statistically significant? Explain.

8. Write a logical argument explaining what Riley and Jamie should conclude from their experiment. Your argument should draw on the assumption behind the simulation, the result of the simulation, and Jamie and Riley's actual data. Review the draft of your argument. Be sure to check that you have described specific details, included the correct mathematical terms to support your reasoning, and that your sentences are complete and grammatically correct. You may want to pair-share with another student to critique each other's drafts and make improvements.

### Check Your Understanding

9. In Jamie and Riley's experiment, are there other possible values that their test statistic might have taken which would have led them to the same conclusion—that "time flies when you are having fun"?

10. Write a conclusion that Jamie and Riley could have drawn if the difference between the medians in their study had been 3 minutes instead of 7 minutes.

## LESSON 40-2 PRACTICE

Use the following for Items 11–13.

In the experiment described in this activity, Jamie and Riley chose to use the difference between the median responses of subjects in the two groups as their test statistic. Suppose instead that they had decided to look at the ratio of the means from the two groups by dividing the mean perceived time in the "Not Fun" group by the mean perceived time in the "Fun" group.

11. Compute the mean perceived times for the "Not Fun" group and the "Fun" group, and then write the ratio.

12. Interpret this ratio in terms of the context of time perception between the "Not Fun" and "Fun" groups.

13. After completing many simulations, what would Jamie and Riley do next to test their hypothesis?

Use the following for Items 14–16.

Recall that in Jamie and Riley's study, they decided to interrupt the subjects' activity at 13.5 minutes. Suppose they had decided instead to interrupt them after 17 minutes.

14. What would have been different about the data?

15. How would the test statistics of difference in medians and ratio of means have changed?

16. Would Jamie and Riley's conclusions be different if the actual time that participants were involved with their activity were increased to 17 minutes? Explain your reasoning.

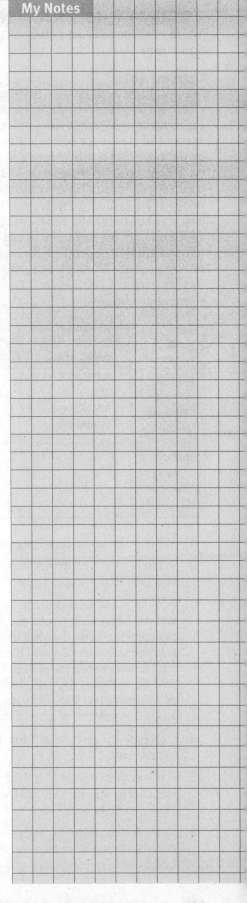

## ACTIVITY 40 PRACTICE
Write your answers on notebook paper.
Show your work.

### Lesson 40-1

Abraham and Luis are interested in conducting an experiment to see whether people's ability to successfully toss a toy ball into a basket is influenced by their belief that others found the task difficult or easy. They position themselves in a central location at their school, place a basket 15 feet away from a spot marked "X," and ask volunteers to try to make the basket. They randomly choose subjects to participate and randomly tell them one of two statements: "So far, only one-fourth of people have made it" or "So far, only one-fourth of people have missed it." They repeat this for a total of 100 subjects. Their data are summarized below.

|  | Number Who Made Shot | Number Who Missed Shot | Total |
|---|---|---|---|
| Told That Most People Made It | 29 | 19 | 48 |
| Told That Most People Missed It | 25 | 27 | 52 |

1. What is the question of interest in this study?

2. What are the treatments imposed by Abraham and Luis in this experiment?

3. Abraham and Luis decided that their test statistic is the difference between the proportion of people who made the shot in the group that was told the task was easy and the proportion of the people who made the shot in the group that was told the task was difficult. Interpret the meaning of a positive test statistic, a negative test statistic, and a test statistic of zero in this context.

4. Compute the test statistic for the results of the experiment.

5. If it was determined that the test statistic was statistically significant, what would Abraham and Luis be able to conclude?

6. If it was determined that the test statistic was not statistically significant, what would Abraham and Luis be able to conclude?

### Lesson 40-2

7. Abraham and Luis's teacher provided them with 200 beads, 100 red and 100 white, of which the only difference was their color. Describe how Abraham and Luis could use those beads to create a simulation to determine whether their test statistic is statistically significant. Be sure to identify what the beads represent.

Use the following for Items 8 and 9.

In a study designed to determine whether babies have an innate sense of morality, babies were shown two puppet shows in a random order: one of them had a puppet being nice, and the other had a different puppet being mean. The babies were then given the opportunity to reach for either the nice puppet or the mean puppet, and the researchers recorded which puppet the babies reached for. Suppose that out of 23 babies in the study, 15 of them reached for the nice puppet.

8. One of the distributions below shows the probability distribution of the number of babies who would reach for the nice puppet if, in fact, babies had no sense of morality and were reaching for a puppet at random. Which distribution is it, and how do you know?

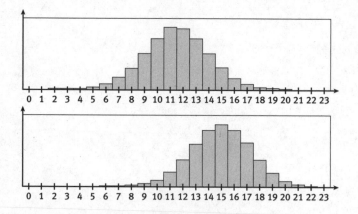

## MATHEMATICAL PRACTICES
**Construct Viable Arguments and Critique the Reasoning of Others**

9. Using the distribution you picked in Item 8 and the observed 15 out of 23 babies reaching for the nice puppet, what conclusion should be drawn, and why?

1. "Zener cards" are used to test whether someone has extrasensory perception (ESP). Each card has one of five distinct images on it:

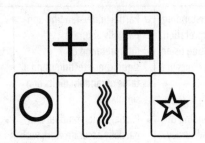

Suppose that a subject is presented with a random assortment of 12 such cards and is asked to identify the images without looking at them. He correctly identifies 6 out of the 12 cards.

a. Given a random card, what is the probability of correctly identifying the image on the card?

b. Use the random digits table below, with 0 and 1 representing correct identifications and digits 2-9 representing incorrect identifications, to perform ten different simulations. Beginning with row 113, record the number of successes for each trial, and make a dot plot of your results.

| 111 | 81486 | 69487 | 60513 | 09297 | 00412 | 71238 | 27649 | 39950 |
|-----|-------|-------|-------|-------|-------|-------|-------|-------|
| 112 | 59636 | 88804 | 04634 | 71197 | 19352 | 73089 | 84898 | 45785 |
| 113 | 62568 | 70206 | 40325 | 03699 | 71080 | 22553 | 11486 | 11776 |
| 114 | 45149 | 32992 | 75730 | 66280 | 03819 | 56202 | 02938 | 70915 |
| 115 | 61041 | 77684 | 94322 | 24709 | 73698 | 14526 | 31893 | 32592 |

c. What conclusion does this data support?

2. An engineer developed a treatment that he hoped would make the fabric of a hot-air balloon last longer. Out of 9 volunteer balloonists with new balloons, he randomly selected 4 to get no special treatment, and 5 to get their fabric treated. The table below shows how many balloon-hours the nine balloons lasted.

| No Special Treatment | 520 | 610 | 435 | 443 | |
|----------------------|-----|-----|-----|-----|-----|
| Received the Special Treatment | 496 | 639 | 550 | 622 | 600 |

a. Find the difference in the means of the two groups.

b. Each balloon-hour total is written on an index card. Describe a simulation using these cards that could help determine the statistical significance of the difference of the means you found in part a.

c. Describe a manner in which the results of the simulation would allow you to reasonably conclude that the difference in the means was not statistically significant.

3. A regular survey asks a random sample of 1070 American adults whether they approve of the job the President of the United States is doing. The margin of error in the proportion of people who say "yes" is stated to be ±3 percentage points.

a. Suppose such a survey yielded a proportion of 0.45. Explain what that means in everyday language.

b. How could the survey be conducted differently to reduce the margin of error?

**Embedded Assessment 2**
*Use after Activity 40*

# Simulations, Margin of Error, and Hypothesis Testing
### PSYCHIC OR JUST HOT AIR?

| Scoring Guide | Exemplary | Proficient | Emerging | Incomplete |
|---|---|---|---|---|
| | The solution demonstrates these characteristics: | | | |
| **Mathematics Knowledge and Thinking** (Items 1, 2, 3) | • Clear and accurate understanding of significance testing using a table of random digits or a simulation<br>• Clear and accurate understanding of margin of error and survey design principles | • A functional understanding and accurate interpretation of significance testing using a table of random digits or a simulation<br>• A functional and mostly accurate understanding of margin of error and survey design principles | • Partial understanding and partially accurate interpretation of significance testing using a table of random digits or a simulation<br>• Partial understanding and partially accurate work with margin of error and survey design principles | • Little or no understanding and inaccurate interpretation of significance testing using a table of random digits or a simulation<br>• Little or no understanding and inaccurate work with margin of error and survey design principles |
| **Problem Solving** (Items 1, 2, 3) | • An appropriate and efficient strategy that results in a correct answer | • A strategy that may include unnecessary steps but results in a correct answer | • A strategy that results in some incorrect answers | • No clear strategy when solving problems |
| **Mathematical Modeling / Representations** (Items 1, 2) | • Clear and accurate understanding of how to apply simulations and random digit tables to analyze real-world scenarios | • Mostly accurate understanding of how to apply simulations and random digit tables to analyze real-world scenarios | • Partial understanding of how to apply simulations and random digit tables to analyze real-world scenarios | • Inaccurate or incomplete understanding of how to apply simulations and random digit tables to analyze real-world scenarios |
| **Reasoning and Communication** (Items 1, 2, 3) | • Precise use of appropriate math terms and language to describe margin of error and how to reduce it in a survey<br>• Clear and accurate explanation of methods to determine statistical significance | • Adequate description of margin of error and how to reduce it in a survey<br>• Adequate explanation of methods to determine statistical significance | • Misleading or confusing description of margin of error and how to reduce it in a survey<br>• Misleading or confusing explanation of methods to determine statistical significance | • Incomplete or inaccurate description of margin of error and how to reduce it in a survey<br>• Incomplete or inadequate explanation of methods to determine statistical significance |

# Symbols

| | |
|---|---|
| $f(x)$ | function |
| $f^{-1}(x)$ | inverse function |
| $a_n$ | the $n$th term of $a$ sequence |
| $|a|$ | absolute value |
| $\sqrt[n]{\phantom{x}}$ | $n$th root |
| $(x, y)$ | ordered pair |
| $(x, y, z)$ | ordered triple |
| $\begin{bmatrix} a & b \\ c & d \end{bmatrix}$ | $2 \times 2$ matrix |
| $I = \begin{pmatrix} 1 & 0 & 0 \\ 0 & 1 & 0 \\ 0 & 0 & 1 \end{pmatrix}$ | $3 \times 3$ identity matrix |
| $a + bi$ | complex number |
| $\sqrt{-1} = i$ | imaginary number |
| $!$ | factorial; $n! = n(n - 1)(n - 2) \ldots \cdot 2 \cdot 1$ |
| $\pi$ | pi; $\pi \approx 3.14$ ; $\pi \approx \frac{22}{7}$ |
| $\sum$ | sigma; sum of terms |
| $e$ | natural base; $e \approx 2.7183$ |
| $\theta$ | theta; angle measure |

# Formulas

| Linear Equations | |
|---|---|
| **Slope** | $m = \dfrac{y_2 - y_1}{x_2 - x_1}$ |
| **Slope-intercept form** | $y = mx + b$ |
| **Point-slope form** | $y - y_1 = m(x - x_1)$ |
| **Standard form** | $Ax + By = C$ |

| Quadratic Equations | |
|---|---|
| **Standard form** | $ax^2 + bx + c = 0$ |
| **Quadratic formula** | $x = \dfrac{-b \pm \sqrt{b^2 - 4ac}}{2a}$ |
| **Vertex form** | $a(x - h)^2 + k = 0$, vertex $= (h, k)$. |

| Sequences and Series | |
|---|---|
| **$n$th term of an arithmetic sequence** | $a_n = a_1 + (n - 1)d$ |
| **Sum of an arithmetic sequence** | $S_n = \dfrac{n}{2}(a_1 + a_n)$<br>$S_n = \dfrac{n}{2}(2a_1 + (n - 1)d)$ |
| **$n$th term of a geometric sequence** | $a_n = a_1 r^{n-1}$ |
| **Sum of a geometric sequence** | $S_n = \dfrac{a_1(1 - r^n)}{1 - r}$ |
| **Sum of the infinite geometric series** | $\displaystyle\sum_{n=0}^{\infty} a_1 r^n$ or $S = \dfrac{a_1}{1 - r}$<br><br>when $|r| < 1$ or $-1 < r < 1$ |

## Other Formulas

**Pythagorean Theorem**    $a^2 + b^2 = c^2$, where $c$ is the hypotenuse of a right triangle

**Distance**    $d = \sqrt{(x_2 - x_1)^2 + (y_2 - y_1)^2}$

**Midpoint**    $m = \left( \dfrac{x_1 + x_2}{2}, \dfrac{y_1 + y_2}{2} \right)$

**Direct variation**    $y = kx$

**Inverse variation**    $y = \dfrac{k}{x}$

**Compound interest**    $A = P\left(1 + \dfrac{r}{n}\right)^{nt}$

## Probability and Statistics

**Permutations**    $_nP_r = \dfrac{n!}{(n-r)!}$

**Combinations**    $_nC_r = \dfrac{n!}{r!(n-r)!}$

**Standard Deviation**    $\sigma = \sqrt{\dfrac{(x_1 - \overline{x})^2 + (x_2 - \overline{x})^2 + \ldots + (x_n - \overline{x})^2}{n}}$

## Trigonometry

For an acute angle $\theta$ in a right triangle:

$$\sin \theta = \frac{\text{opposite}}{\text{hypotenuse}}$$

$$\cos \theta = \frac{\text{adjacent}}{\text{hypotenuse}}$$

$$\tan \theta = \frac{\text{opposite}}{\text{adjacent}}; \tan \theta = \frac{\sin \theta}{\cos \theta}$$

# Properties of Exponents

For any numbers $a$ and $b$ and all integers $m$ and $n$,

$$a^m \cdot a^n = a^{m+n}$$

$$(a^m)^n = a^{mn}$$

$$(ab)^m = a^m b^m$$

$$\frac{a^m}{a^n} = a^{m-n}, a \neq 0$$

$$\left(\frac{a}{b}\right)^m = \frac{a^m}{b^m}, b \neq 0$$

$$a^{-n} = \frac{1}{a^n}, a \neq 0 \text{ and } \frac{1}{a^{-n}} = a^n, a \neq 0$$

$$a^0 = 1, a \neq 0$$

# Properties of Radicals

In the expression $\sqrt[n]{a}$,

$a$ is the radicand, $\sqrt{\phantom{a}}$ is the radical symbol and $n$ is the root index.

$\sqrt[n]{a} = b$, if $b^n = a$      $b$ is the $n$th root of $a$.

$\sqrt[n]{a^m} = a^{\frac{m}{n}}$, where $a > 0$.

$a\sqrt{b} \pm c\sqrt{b} = (a \pm c)\sqrt{b}$, where $b \geq 0$.

$(a\sqrt{b})(c\sqrt{d}) = ac\sqrt{bd}$, where $b \geq 0, d \geq 0$.

$\frac{a\sqrt{b}}{c\sqrt{d}} = \frac{a}{c}\sqrt{\frac{b}{d}}$, where $b \geq 0, d > 0$.

# Properties of Logarithms

For all positive $a, b, p, x,$ and $y$, where $a \neq 1$:

$\log_a b = c$ means that $a^c = b$

$\log_a a^x = x$    and    $a^{\log_a x} = x$

$\log_a(xy) = \log_a x + \log_a y$

$\log_a\left(\frac{x}{y}\right) = \log_a x - \log_a y$

$\log_a(x^p) = p\log_a x$

$\log_a x = \frac{\log_b x}{\log_b a}, b \neq 1$

# Trigonometric Identities

**Reciprocal Identities**

$\sin\theta = \dfrac{1}{\csc\theta}$      $\csc\theta = \dfrac{1}{\sin\theta}$

$\cos\theta = \dfrac{1}{\sec\theta}$      $\sec\theta = \dfrac{1}{\cos\theta}$

$\tan\theta = \dfrac{1}{\cot\theta}$      $\cot\theta = \dfrac{1}{\tan\theta}$

**Pythagorean Identities**

$\sin^2\theta + \cos^2\theta = 1$

$\tan^2\theta + 1 = \sec^2\theta$

$1 + \cot^2\theta = \csc^2\theta$

# SpringBoard Learning Strategies
## READING STRATEGIES

| STRATEGY | DEFINITION | PURPOSE |
|---|---|---|
| Activating Prior Knowledge | Recalling what is known about a concept and using that information to make a connection to a new concept | Helps students establish connections between what they already know and how that knowledge is related to new learning |
| Chunking the Activity | Grouping a set of items/questions for specific purposes | Provides an opportunity to relate concepts and assess student understanding before moving on to a new concept or grouping |
| Close Reading | Reading text word for word, sentence by sentence, and line by line to make a detailed analysis of meaning | Assists in developing a comprehensive understanding of the text |
| Graphic Organizer | Arranging information into maps and charts | Builds comprehension and facilitates discussion by representing information in visual form |
| Interactive Word Wall | Visually displaying vocabulary words to serve as a classroom reference of words and groups of words as they are introduced, used, and mastered over the course of a year | Provides a visual reference for new concepts, aids understanding for reading and writing, and builds word knowledge and awareness |
| KWL Chart (Know, Want to Know, Learn) | Activating prior knowledge by identifying what students know, determining what they want to learn, and having them reflect on what they learned | Assists in organizing information and reflecting on learning to build content knowledge and increase comprehension |
| Marking the Text | Highlighting, underlining, and/or annotating text to focus on key information to help understand the text or solve the problem | Helps the reader identify important information in the text and make notes about the interpretation of tasks required and concepts to apply to reach a solution |
| Predict and Confirm | Making conjectures about what results will develop in an activity; confirming or modifying the conjectures based on outcomes | Stimulates thinking by making, checking, and correcting predictions based on evidence from the outcome |
| Levels of Questions | Developing literal, interpretive, and universal questions about the text while reading the text | Focuses reading, helps in gaining insight into the text by seeking answers, and prepares one for group and class discussions |
| Paraphrasing | Restating in your own words the essential information in a text or problem description | Assists with comprehension, recall of information, and problem solving |
| Role Play | Assuming the role of a character in a scenario | Helps interpret and visualize information in a problem |
| Shared Reading | Reading the text aloud (usually by the teacher) as students follow along silently, or reading a text aloud by the teacher and students | Helps auditory learners do decode, interpret, and analyze challenging text |
| Summarizing | Giving a brief statement of the main points in a text | Assists with comprehension and provides practice with identifying and restating key information |
| Think Aloud | Talking through a difficult text or problem by describing what the text means | Helps in comprehending the text, understanding the components of a problem, and thinking about possible paths to a solution |
| Visualization | Picturing (mentally and/or literally) what is read in the text | Increases reading comprehension and promotes active engagement with the text |
| Vocabulary Organizer | Using a graphic organizer to keep an ongoing record of vocabulary words with definitions, pictures, notes, and connections between words | Supports a systematic process of learning vocabulary |

# SpringBoard Learning Strategies
## COLLABORATIVE STRATEGIES

| STRATEGY | DEFINITION | PURPOSE |
|---|---|---|
| Critique Reasoning | Through collaborative discussion, respond to the arguments of others; question the use of mathematical terminology, assumptions, and conjectures to improve understanding and to justify and communicate conclusions | Helps students learn from each other as they make connections between mathematical concepts and learn to verbalize their understanding and support their arguments with reasoning and data that make sense to peers |
| Debriefing | Discussing the understanding of a concept to lead to consensus on its meaning | Helps clarify misconceptions and deepen understanding of content |
| Discussion Groups | Working within groups to discuss content, to create problem solutions, and to explain and justify a solution | Aids understanding through the sharing of ideas, interpretation of concepts, and analysis of problem scenarios |
| Group Presentation | Presenting information as a collaborative group | Allows opportunities to present collaborative solutions and to share responsibility for delivering information to an audience |
| Jigsaw | Reading different texts or passages, students become "experts" and then move to a new group to share their information; after sharing, students go back to the original group to share new knowledge | Provides opportunities to summarize and present information to others in a way that facilitates understanding of a text or passage (or multiple texts or passages) without having each student read all texts |
| Sharing and Responding | Communicating with another person or a small group of peers who respond to a piece of writing or proposed problem solution | Gives students the opportunity to discuss their work with peers, to make suggestions for improvement to the work of others, and/or to receive appropriate and relevant feedback on their own work |
| Think-Pair-Share | Thinking through a problem alone, pairing with a partner to share ideas, and concluding by sharing results with the class | Enables the development of initial ideas that are then tested with a partner in preparation for revising ideas and sharing them with a larger group |

## WRITING STRATEGIES

| | | |
|---|---|---|
| Drafting | Writing a text in an initial form | Assists in getting first thoughts in written form and ready for revising and refining |
| Note Taking | Creating a record of information while reading a text or listening to a speaker | Helps in organizing ideas and processing information |
| Prewriting | Brainstorming, either alone or in groups, and refining thoughts and organizing ideas prior to writing | Provides a tool for beginning the writing process and determining the focus of the writing |
| Quickwrite | Writing for a short, specific amount of time about a designated topic | Helps generate ideas in a short time |
| RAFT (Role of Writer, Audience, Format, and Topic) | Writing a text by consciously choosing a viewpoint (role of the writer), identifying an audience, choosing a format for the writing, and choosing a topic | Provides a framework for communicating in writing and helps focus the writer's ideas for specific points of communication |
| Self Revision / Peer Revision | Working alone or with a partner to examine a piece of writing for accuracy and clarity | Provides an opportunity to review work and to edit it for clarity of the ideas presented as well as accuracy of grammar, punctuation, and spelling |

# SpringBoard Learning Strategies
## PROBLEM-SOLVING STRATEGIES

| | | |
|---|---|---|
| **Construct an Argument** | Use mathematical reasoning to present assumptions about mathematical situations, support conjectures with mathematically relevant and accurate data, and provide a logical progression of ideas leading to a conclusion that makes sense | Helps develop the process of evaluating mathematical information, developing reasoning skills, and enhancing communication skills in supporting conjectures and conclusions |
| **Create a Plan** | Analyzing the tasks in a problem and creating a process for completing the tasks by finding information needed for the tasks, interpreting data, choosing how to solve a problem, communicating the results, and verifying accuracy | Assists in breaking tasks into smaller parts and identifying the steps needed to complete the entire task |
| **Create Representations** | Creating pictures, tables, graphs, lists, equations, models, and/or verbal expressions to interpret text or data | Helps organize information using multiple ways to present data and to answer a question or show a problem solution |
| **Guess and Check** | Guessing the solution to a problem, and then checking that the guess fits the information in the problem and is an accurate solution | Allows exploration of different ways to solve a problem; guess and check may be used when other strategies for solving are not obvious |
| **Identify a Subtask** | Breaking a problem into smaller pieces whose outcomes lead to a solution | Helps to organize the pieces of a complex problem and reach a complete solution |
| **Look for a Pattern** | Observing information or creating visual representations to find a trend | Helps to identify patterns that may be used to make predictions |
| **Simplify the Problem** | Using "friendlier" numbers to solve a problem | Provides insight into the problem or the strategies needed to solve the problem |
| **Work Backward** | Tracing a possible answer back through the solution process to the starting point | Provides another way to check possible answers for accuracy |
| **Use Manipulatives** | Using objects to examine relationships between the information given | Provides a visual representation of data that supports comprehension of information in a problem |

**68-95-99.7 rule** (p. 559)    In a normal distribution, 68% of the data lies within one standard deviation from the mean, 95% within two standard deviations from the mean, and 99.7% within three standard deviations from the mean.

**regla 68-95-99.7** (pág. 559)    En una distribución normal, el 68% de los datos se encuentra a una desviación estándar de la media, el 95% está a dos desviaciones estándar de la media y el 99.7% está a tres desviaciones estándar de la media.

## A

**absolute value equation** (p. 11)    An equation involving the absolute value of a variable expression.

**ecuación con valor absoluto** (pág. 11)    Ecuación que involucra el valor absoluto de una expresión variable.

**absolute value function** (p. 63)    The function written as $f(x) = |x|$ and defined by $f(x) = \begin{cases} -x & \text{if } x < 0 \\ x & \text{if } x \geq 0 \end{cases}$

**función con valor absoluto** (pág. 63)    Función que se escribe $f(x) = |x|$ y está definida por $f(x) = \begin{cases} -x & \text{if } x < 0 \\ x & \text{if } x \geq 0 \end{cases}$

**absolute value inequality** (p. 13)    An inequality involving the absolute value of a variable expression.

**desigualdad con valor absoluto** (pág. 13)    Desigualdad que involucra el valor absoluto de una expresión variable.

**amplitude** (p. 512)    Half the difference between the minimum and maximum values of a periodic function.

**amplitud** (pág. 512)    La mitad de la diferencia entre el valor mínimo y el valor máximo de una función periódica.

**arc length** (p. 478)    The length of a portion of the circumference of a circle.

**longitud de arco** (pág. 478)    La longitud de una parte de la circunferencia de un círculo.

**arithmetic sequence** (p. 295)    A sequence in which the difference of consecutive terms is constant.

**progresión aritmética** (pág. 295)    Sucesión en la que la diferencia entre términos consecutivos es constante.

**asymptote** (p. 329)    A line that a graph approaches but does not intersect.

**asíntota** (pág. 329)    Recta a la que una gráfica se aproxima, pero no la interseca.

**axis of symmetry of a parabola** (p. 158)    The line that divides a parabola into two congruent halves, passing through the focus.

**eje de simetría de una parábola** (pág. 158)    La línea que divide una parábola en dos mitades congruentes, pasando por el foco.

## B

**bias** (p. 578)    A systemic (not random) inaccuracy in data due to faulty sampling design.

**parcialidad** (pág. 578)    Una sistémica inexactitud (no aleatorio) en datos debido al diseño de muestreo defectuoso.

## C

**Change of Base Formula** (p. 364)    The formula to rewrite a logarithm in a different base: $\log_b x = \dfrac{\log_a x}{\log_a b}; a, b, x > 0; a, b \neq 1$

**fórmula de cambio de base** (pág. 364)    La fórmula para volver a escribir un logaritmo usando una base distinta: $\log_b x = \dfrac{\log_a x}{\log_a b}; a, b, x > 0; a, b \neq 1$

**coefficient matrix** (p. 48)    The matrix formed by the coefficients of a system of equations.

**matriz de coeficientes** (pág. 48)    La matriz formada por los coeficientes de un sistema de ecuaciones.

**combination** (p. 255)    A collection of elements from a set in which order does not matter.

**combinación** (pág. 255)    Una colección de los elementos de un conjunto en el que el orden no importa.

**combined variation** (p. 433)    A relation in which a variable varies directly with one or more variables and inversely with others.

**variación combinada** (pág. 433)    Relación en la que una variable varía directamente con una o más variables e inversamente con otras.

**common difference** (p. 295)    The constant difference between consecutive terms in an arithmetic sequence.

**diferencia común** (pág. 295)    Diferencia constante entre términos consecutivos de una progresión aritmética.

**common logarithm** (p. 348)    A logarithm of the form log $x$, where the base 10 is understood.

**logaritmo común** (pág. 348)    Un logaritmo de la forma log $x$, donde la base 10 se sobreentiende.

**common ratio** (p. 308)    The constant ratio between consecutive terms in a geometric sequence.

**razón común** (pág. 308)    Razón constante entre términos consecutivos de una progresión geométrica.

**completely randomized design** (p. 583)    Implies that all experimental units have the same probability of being selected for application of the treatment.

**diseño completamente al azar** (pág. 583)    Implica que todas las unidades experimentales tienen la misma probabilidad de ser seleccionados para la aplicación del tratamiento.

**completing the square** (p. 139)    Adding a constant to a quadratic expression to transform it into a perfect square trinomial.

**completar el cuadrado** (pág. 139)    Sumar una constante a una expresión cuadrática para transformarla en un trinomio de cuadrado perfecto.

**complex conjugates** (p. 129)    Complex numbers whose product is a real number. $a + bi$ and $a - bi$ are complex conjugates.

**complejos conjugados** (pág. 129)    Números complejos cuyo producto es un número real. $a + bi$ y $a - bi$ son complejos conjugados.

**complex fraction** (p. 451)  A rational expression that contains rational expressions in its numerator and/or denominator.

**fracción compleja** (pág. 451)  Expresión racional que contiene expresiones racionales en su numerador o denominador o en ambos.

**complex number** (p. 124)  A number in the form $a + bi$, where $a$ and $b$ are real numbers and $i = \sqrt{-1}$.

**número complejo** (pág. 124)  Número de la forma $a + bi$, donde $a$ y $b$ son números reales e $i = \sqrt{-1}$.

**complex plane** (p. 124)  A coordinate grid with the horizontal axis representing the real part $a$ of a complex number and the vertical axis representing the imaginary part $b$ of a complex number $a + bi$.

**plano complejo** (pág. 124)  Cuadrícula coordenada en que el eje horizontal representa la parte real $a$ de un número complejo y el eje vertical representa la parte imaginaria $b$ de un número complejo $a + bi$.

**composite function** (p. 81)  A function in which the range of the first function becomes the domain for the second function.

**función compuesta** (pág. 81)  Función en la que el rango de la primera función se convierte en el dominio de la segunda función.

**composition** (p. 81)  A operation on two functions that forms a new function.

**composición** (pág. 81)  Una operación que usa dos funciones para definir una nueva función.

**compound interest** (p. 374)  Interest earned or paid on previously accumulated interest as well as the principal (original amount).

**interés compuesto** (pág. 374)  El interés generado por los intereses previamente acumulados y el capital inicial.

**confounding variable** (p. 586)  An unmeasured variable that may be associated with the measured variables.

**variable de confundir** (pág. 586)  Una variable que puede estar asociada con las variables medidas.

**conjugates** (p. 129)  Two binomial expressions whose product results in the difference of two squares. $a + b$ and $a - b$ are conjugates.

**conjugados** (pág. 129)  Dos expresiones binomiales cuyo producto es la diferencia entre dos cuadrados. $a + b$ y $a - b$ son conjugados.

**consistent system of equations** (p. 30)  A system of equations having at least one solution.

**sistema de ecuaciones consistente** (pág. 30)  Sistema de ecuaciones que tienen al menos una solución.

**constant matrix** (p. 48)  A single-column matrix formed by the constants of a system of equations.

**matriz constante** (pág. 48)  Matriz que contiene solo una columna formada por las constantes de un sistema de ecuaciones.

**constant of variation** (p. 432)  A constant, $k$, multiplied by a variable in the direct variation equation, $y = kx$, or divided by a variable in the indirect variation equation $y = \dfrac{k}{x}$. The constant value in a direct or indirect variation relationship.

**constante de variación** (pág. 432)  Una constante $k$, multiplicada por una variable de la ecuación de variación directa $y = kx$, o dividida entre una variable de la ecuación de variación indirecta $y = \dfrac{k}{x}$. El valor constante en una relación de variación directa o indirecta.

**constraints** (p. 24)  The conditions or inequalities that limit the domain or range of a situation.

**restricciones** (pág. 24)  Las condiciones o disparidades que limitan el dominio o rango de una situación.

**coterminal angles** (p. 488)  Angles that have the same initial and terminal sides but rotations that differ by 360° or $2\pi$ radians.

**ángulos coterminales** (pág. 488)  Ángulos que tienen el mismo lado inicial y el mismo lado terminal pero cuyas rotaciones difieren por 360° o $2\pi$ radianes.

**continuous function** (p. 279)  A function whose graph has no gaps or breaks.

**función continua** (pág. 279)  Función cuya gráfica no tiene espacios vacíos ni quiebres.

**critical value** (p. 614)  The $z$-score that corresponds to a level of confidence for an approximately normal distribution.

**valor crítico** (pág. 614)  El $z$-resultado que corresponde a un nivel de confianza para una distribución aproximadamente normal.

# D

**decreasing function** (p. 329)  A function in which the $y$-values decrease as the $x$-values increase.

**función decreciente** (pág. 329)  Función en la que los valores de $y$ disminuyen a medida que los valores de $x$ aumentan.

**degree of a polynomial** (p. 231)  The highest degree of any term in a polynomial.

**grado de un polinomio** (pág. 231)  El grado mayor entre los términos de un polinomio.

**density curve** (p. 555)  A curve that shows data distribution along the x-axis. The area under the curve is always equal to 1.

**curva de densidad** (pág. 555)  Curva que muestra la distribución de datos a lo largo del eje de las x. El área bajo la curva siempre es igual a 1.

**dependent system of equations** (p. 30)  A system of equations with infinitely many solutions.

**sistema de ecuaciones dependientes** (pág. 30)  Sistema de ecuaciones con infinitas soluciones.

**dimensions of a matrix** (p. 42)  The number of rows and columns in a matrix, indicated by $m \times n$, where $m$ is the number of rows and $n$ is the number of columns; also called the order of a matrix.

**dimensiones de una matriz** (pág. 42)  Número de filas y columnas de una matriz, indicadas por $m \times n$, donde $m$ es el número de filas y $n$ es el número de columnas; también llamada *orden de una matriz*.

**direct variation** (p. 433)  A relationship between two variables, $x$ and $y$, with the form $y = kx$, where $k$ is any constant except zero.

**variación directa** (pág. 433)  Relación entre dos variables, $x$ e $y$, de la forma $y = kx$, donde $k$ es cualquier constante distinta de cero.

**directrix of a parabola** (p. 156)  The fixed line which, along with a fixed point called a focus, defines a parabola.

**directriz de una parábola** (pág. 156)  Recta fija que, conjuntamente con un punto fijo llamado foco, define una parábola.

**discontinuity** (p. 453)  A break in the graph of a function that occurs when certain values of $x$ cause the function to be undefined and are therefore not in the domain of the function.

**discontinuidad** (pág. 453)  Un quiebre en la gráfica de una función que ocurre cuando ciertos valores de $x$ hacen que la función quede indefinida y, por lo tanto, no forman parte del dominio de la función.

**discriminant** (p. 146)  The expression $b^2 - 4ac$ that describes the nature of the solutions of a quadratic equation.

**discriminante** (pág. 146)  Expresión $b^2 - 4ac$ describe la naturaleza de las soluciones de una ecuación cuadrática.

**domain** (p. 59)  A set of input values for which a function is defined.

**dominio** (pág. 59) Conjunto de valores para los cuales la función está definida.

**double-blind study** (p. 585)  Neither the person conducting the experiment nor the subjects have knowledge of the treatment.

**experimento a doble ciego** (pág. 585)  Un estudio en donde ni el investigador ni el participante tiene toda la información sobre el tratamiento.

## E

**elimination method** (p. 34)  An algebraic procedure for solving a system of equations; also called linear combination.

**método de eliminación** (pág. 34)  Procedimiento algebraico para resolver un sistema de ecuaciones; también llamado combinación lineal.

**end behavior** (p. 233)  Describes the $y$-values of a function as $x$-values increase without bound and as $x$-values decrease without bound.

**comportamiento final** (pág. 233)  Describe los valores $y$ de una función a medida que los valores de $x$ aumentan sin límite y a medida que los valores de $x$ disminuyen sin límite.

**entries of a matrix** (p. 42)  The numbers in a matrix that are organized in rows and columns; also called elements of a matrix.

**entradas de una matriz** (pág. 42)  Números de una matriz organizados en filas y columnas; también llamados elementos de una matriz.

**even function** (p. 237)  A function where every power of $x$ is even, $f(-x) = f(x)$, and the graph is symmetrical across the $y$-axis.

**función par** (pág. 237)  Una función donde cada potencia de $x$ es par, $f(-x) = f(x)$, y en donde la gráfica es simétrica a lo largo del eje de las $y$.

**experiment** (p. 582)  A method of data gathering in which a treatment is applied to subjects and the response is observed.

**experimento** (pág. 582)  Método de recolección de datos en que se aplica un tratamiento a los sujetos y se observa la respuesta.

**explanatory variables** (p. 582)  The factors that influence the changes in response variables.

**variables explicativas** (pág. 582)  Factores que influyen sobre los cambios en las variables de respuesta.

**explicit formula** (p. 296)  A formula for a sequence that can be used to calculate any term as long as the first term is known.

**fórmula explícita** (pág.296)  Fórmula que puede servir para calcular cualquier término en una secuencia siempre y cuando el primer término sea conocido.

**exponential decay** (p. 326)  A decrease in a quantity due to multiplying by a factor greater than zero but less than one during each time period.

**disminución exponencial** (pág. 326)  Disminución de una cantidad debido a la multiplicación por un factor mayor que cero pero menor que uno durante cada período de tiempo.

**exponential equation** (p. 372)  An equation in which the variable is in the exponent.

**ecuación exponencial** (pág. 372)  Ecuación en la que la variable está en el exponente.

**exponential function** (p. 326)  A function of the form $f(x) = a \cdot b^x$, where $a$ and $b$ are real numbers, $a \neq 0$, $b > 0$, $b \neq 1$.

**función exponencial** (pág. 326)  Función de la forma $f(x) = a \cdot b^x$, donde $a$ y $b$ son números reales y $a \neq 0$, $b > 0$, $b \neq 1$.

**exponential growth** (p. 326)  A increase in a quantity due to multiplying by a factor greater than 1 during each time period.

**crecimiento exponencial** (pág. 326)  Incremento de una cantidad debido a la multiplicación por un factor mayor que uno durante cada período de tiempo.

**extraneous solution** (p. 376)  A solution that arises from a simplified equation and does not make the original equation true.

**solución extraña** (pág. 376)  Solución que proviene de una ecuación simplificada y no hace verdadera la ecuación original.

**extrema** (p. 279)  The greatest (maximum) and least (minimum) values of a function.

**extremos** (pág. 279)  Valores mayores (máximos) y menores (mínimos) de una función.

## F

**factorial** (p. 255)  The product of a natural number, $n$, and all the natural numbers less than $n$, written as $n!$.

**factorial** (pág. 255)  Producto de un número natural $n$ por todos los números naturales menores que $n$; se escribe $n!$.

**finite series** (p. 312)  A series with a specific number of terms.

**serie finita** (pág. 312)  Serie que tiene un número específico de términos.

**focus of a parabola** (p. 156)  A fixed point, along with a fixed line called a directrix, that is used to define a parabola.

**foco de una parábola** (pág. 156)  Punto fijo que, conjuntamente con una recta fija llamada directriz, se usa para definir una parábola.

**Fundamental Theorem of Algebra** (p. 271)  If $p(x)$ is a polynomial function of degree $n$, where $n > 0$, then $p(x) = 0$ has at least one zero in the complex number system.

**Teorema fundamental del álgebra** (pág. 271)  Si $p(x)$ es una función polinómica de grado $n$, donde $n > 0$, entonces $p(x) = 0$ tiene al menos un cero en el sistema de números complejos.

## G

**Gaussian elimination** (p. 38)  A method of solving a system of linear equations in more than two variables.

**eliminación gaussiana** (pág. 38)  Método para resolver un sistema de ecuaciones lineales con más de dos variables.

**geometric sequence** (p. 308)   A sequence in which the ratio of consecutive terms is a constant.

**progresión geométrica** (pág. 308)   Sucesión en que la razón de los términos consecutivos es constante.

**geometric series** (p. 312)   The sum of the terms of a geometric sequence.

**serie geométrica** (pág. 312)   Suma de los términos de una progresión geométrica.

# H

**horizontal asymptote**   (pp. 329, 426) The line $y = a$ when the end behavior of a function approaches some constant $a$.

**asíntota horizontal** (págs. 329, 426)   Recta $y = a$ cuando el comportamiento final de una función se aproxima a alguna constante $a$.

# I

**imaginary number** (p. 122)   A number of the form $bi$, where $b$ is a real number and $i = \sqrt{-1}$.

**número imaginario** (pág. 122)   Número de la forma $bi$, donde $b$ es un número real e $i = \sqrt{-1}$.

**inconsistent system of equations** (p. 30)   A system of equations with no solutions.

**sistema de ecuaciones inconsistente** (pág. 30)   Sistema de ecuaciones que no tiene ninguna solución.

**increasing function** (p. 329)   A function in which the $y$-values increase as the $x$-values increase.

**función creciente** (pág. 329)   Función en la que los valores de $y$ aumentan a medida que aumentan los valores de $x$.

**independent system of equations** (p. 30)   A system of equations with exactly one solution.

**sistema de ecuaciones independientes** (pág. 30)   Sistema de ecuaciones que tiene exactamente una solución.

**infinite series** (p. 312)   A series that continues without end.

**serie infinita** (pág. 312)   Serie que continúa indefinidamente.

**initial side** (p. 487)   For an angle on the coordinate plane in standard position, the initial side is the positive $x$-axis.

**lado inicial** (pág. 487)   En el caso de un ángulo en un plano de coordenadas en posición estándar, el lado inicial es el eje positivo de las $x$.

**inverse functions** (p. 91)   Functions $f$ and $g$ are inverse functions if and only if $f(g(x)) = x$ for all $x$ in the domain of $g$ and $g(f(x)) = x$ for all $x$ in the domain of $f$.

**funciones inversas** (pág. 91)   Las funciones $f$ y $g$ son funciones inversas si y sólo si $f(g(x)) = x$ para todo $x$ en el dominio de $g$ y $g(f(x)) = x$ para todo $x$ en el dominio de $f$.

**inverse variation** (p. 432)   A relationship between two variables, $x$ and $y$, with the form $xy = k$ or $y = \frac{k}{x}$, where $x \neq 0$, $y \neq 0$, and $k$ is any constant other than zero.

**variación inversa** (pág. 432)   Relación entre dos variables, $x$ e $y$, de la forma $xy = k$ o $y = \frac{k}{x}$, donde $x \neq 0$, $y \neq 0$ y $k$ es cualquier constante distinta de cero.

# J

**joint variation** (p. 433)   When one variable varies directly with the product of two or more other variables.

**variación conjunta** (pág. 433)   Cuando una variable varía directamente con el producto de otras dos o más variables.

# L

**linear inequality** (p. 21)   An inequality that can be written in the form $Ax + By < C$, $Ax + By > C$, $Ax + By \leq C$, $Ax + By \geq C$, where $A \neq 0$ and $B \neq 0$.

**desigualdad lineal** (pág. 21)   Una desigualdad que puede escribirse en la forma $Ax + By < C$, $Ax + By > C$, $Ax + By \leq C$, $Ax + By \geq C$, donde $A \neq 0$ y $B \neq 0$.

**logarithm** (p. 348)   The power to which a base, $b$, must be raised in order to equal a number $y$. $\log_b y = x$ if and only if $y = b^x$, where $y > 0$, $b > 0$, and $b \neq 1$.

**logaritmo** (pág. 348)   Potencia a la que debe elevarse una base $b$ para igualar un número $y$. $\log_b y = x$ si y sólo si $y = b^x$, donde $y > 0$, $b > 0$ y $b \neq 1$.

**logarithmic equation** (p. 376)   An equation that involves logarithms of expressions containing variables.

**ecuación logarítmica** (pág. 376)   Una ecuación que implica logaritmos de expresiones con variables.

**logarithmic function** (p. 348)   A function of the form $f(x) = a\log_b x$, where $a$ and $b$ are real numbers, $a \neq 0$, $b > 0$, $b \neq 1$.

**función logarítmica** (pág. 248)   Una función de la forma $f(x) = a\log_b x$, donde $a$ y $b$ son números reales, $a \neq 0$, $b > 0$, $b \neq 1$.

# M

**margin of error** (p. 606)   Indicates how close the actual proportion is to the estimate of the proportion found in a survey of a random sample.

**margen de error** (pág. 606)   Indica cuán cerca está la proporción real a la estimación de la proporción en una encuesta sobre una muestra aleatoria.

**matched pairs design** (p. 584)   Involves creating blocks that are pairs in which one unit is randomly assigned the treatment; sometimes, both treatments may be applied, and the order of application is randomly assigned.

**pares con diseño** (pág. 584)   Consiste en la creación de pares en los que una unidad se asignó aleatoriamente el tratamiento; a veces, ambas pueden aplicarse tratamientos, y el orden de aplicación es asignado aleatoriamente.

**matrix (plural: matrices)** (p. 42)   A rectangular arrangement of numbers in rows and columns written inside brackets.

**matriz (plural: matrices)** (pág. 42)   Arreglo rectangular de números escritos entre corchetes. Los números están organizados en filas y columnas. Los números se llaman elementos o entradas de la matriz.

**matrix equation** (p. 48)   A system of linear equations written with matrices in the form $AX = B$ where $A$ is the coefficient matrix, $X$ is the variable matrix, and $B$ is the constant matrix.

**ecuación matriz** (pág. 48)   Un sistema de ecuaciones lineales escritas con matrices en la forma $AX = B$, donde $A$ es la matriz de coeficientes, $X$ es la matriz variable y $B$ es la matriz constante.

**midline** (p. 512)   A horizontal axis that is used as the reference line about which the graph of a periodic function oscillates.

**línea de equilibrio** (pág. 512)   Eje horizontal que sirve como referencia en torno a la cual oscila la gráfica de una función periódica.

**multiplicative identity matrix** (p. 47)   A square matrix, $I$, in which all entries are 0, except entries along the main diagonal, which are all 1.

**matriz de identidad multiplicativa** (pág. 47)   Una matriz cuadrada, $I$, donde todas las entradas son 0, excepto las entradas sobre la diagonal principal, las cuales llevan un valor de 1.

**multiplicative inverse matrix** (p. 47)   A matrix $A^{-1}$ is the multiplicative inverse of matrix $A$, if $A \cdot A^{-1} = I$, the identity matrix.

**matriz inversa multiplicativa** (pág. 47)   Una matriz $A^{-1}$ es el multiplicativo inverso de la matriz $A$, si $A \cdot A^{-1} = I$, la matriz de identidad.

# N

**natural logarithm** (p. 360)   A logarithm with a base of $e$, written $\ln x$.

**logaritmo natural** (pág. 360)   Un logaritmo con base $e$, escrito $\ln x$.

**normal curve** (p. 558)   The density curve of a normal distribution.

**curva normal** (pág. 558)   La curva de densidad de una distribución normal.

**normal distribution** (p. 558)   A set of data with a symmetrical, unimodal, bell-shaped graph.

**distribución normal** (pág. 558)   Conjunto de datos con una gráfica simétrica, unimodal, y forma de campana.

# O

**observational study** (p. 586)   A method of data gathering in which subjects are watched and variables of interest are measured without trying to influence their responses in any way.

**estudio observacional** (pág. 586)   Método de recolección de datos en que los sujetos son observados y las variables de interés son medidas sin intentar influir de manera alguna sobre sus respuestas.

**odd function** (p. 237)   A function where every power of $x$ is odd, $f(-x) = -f(x)$, and the graph is symmetrical around the origin.

**función impar** (pág. 237)   Una función donde cada potencia de $x$ es impar, $f(-x) = -f(x)$, y en donde la gráfica es simétrica en torno al origen.

**one-to-one function** (p. 408)   A function such that for each number in the range of the function, there is exactly one corresponding number in the domain of the function.

**función uno a uno** (pág. 408)   Función tal que para cada número del rango de la función, hay exactamente un número correspondiente en el dominio de la función.

**ordered triple** (p. 36)   A solution of a system in three variables, written $(x, y, z)$.

**trío ordenado** (pág. 36)   Una solución para un sistema con tres variables, escrito $(x, y, z)$.

# P

**parabola** (p. 156)   The set of points in a plane that are equidistant from a fixed point (focus) and a fixed line (directrix).

**parábola** (pág. 156)   Conjunto de puntos de un plano que son equidistantes de un punto fijo (foco) y una recta fija (directriz).

**parent function** (p. 65)   The most basic function of a particular type, such as $f(x) = x$ (linear); $f(x) = x^2$ (quadratic); $f(x) = x^3$ (cubic); $f(x) = |x|$ (absolute value); $f(x) = b^x$ (exponential), $f(x) = \frac{1}{x}$ (rational), $f(x) = \sqrt{x}$ (square root), and $f(x) = \sqrt[3]{x}$ (cube root).

**función básica** (pág. 65)   La función más básica de un tipo en particular, como $f(x) = x$ (lineal); $f(x) = x^2$ (cuadrática); $f(x) = x^3$ (cúbica); $f(x) = |x|$ (valor absoluto), $f(x) = b^x$ (exponencial), $f(x) = \frac{1}{x}$ (racional), $f(x) = \sqrt{x}$ (raíz cuadrada), y $f(x) = \sqrt[3]{x}$ (raíz cúbica).

**partial sum** (p. 299)   The sum of the first $n$ terms of a series.

**suma parcial** (pág. 299)   Suma de los $n$ primeros términos de una serie.

**period** (p. 512)   The horizontal distance required for the graph of a periodic function to complete one repetition or cycle.

**periodo** (pág. 512)   La distancia horizontal requerida para que la gráfica de una función periódica complete una repetición o ciclo.

**periodic function** (p. 511)   A function that repeats its values in regular intervals called periods.

**función periódica** (pág. 511)   Una función cuyos valores se repiten en intervalos regulares llamados periodos.

**permutation**   An ordered arrangement from a set of elements.

**permutación**   Arreglo ordenado de un conjunto de elementos.

**phase shift** (p. 535)   The distance a periodic function is translated horizontally from its parent function.

**desplazamiento de fase** (pág. 535)   La distancia que una función periódica es transferida horizontalmente desde su función madre.

**piecewise-defined function** (p. 58)   A function defined by different rules for different non-overlapping intervals of its domain.

**función por tramos** (pág. 58)   Función que se define usando reglas diferentes para intervalos diferentes no traslapados de su dominio.

**placebo** (p. 585)   A treatment applied to an experimental subject that appears to be the experimental treatment, but in fact is a treatment known to have no effect.

**placebo** (pág. 585)   Un tratamiento se aplicó a un sujeto experimental que parece ser el tratamiento experimental, pero en realidad es un tratamiento que no tienen ningún efecto.

**polynomial function** (p. 231)   A function that can be written in the form $f(x) = a_n x^n + a_{n-1} x^{n-1} + \ldots + a_1 x + a_0$, where $n$ is a nonnegative integer and $a_0, a_1, \ldots a_n$ are real numbers.

**función polinómica** (pág. 231)   Función que puede escribirse en la forma $f(x) = a_n x^n + a_{n-1} x^{n-1} + \ldots + a_1 x + a_0$, donde $n$ es un entero no negativo y $a_0, a_1, \ldots a_n$ son números reales.

**power function** (p. 404)   A function of the form $f(x) = ax^b$ where $a$ and $b$ are real numbers, $a \neq 0$.

**función potencia** (pág. 404)   Función de la forma $f(x) = ax^b$ donde $a$ y $b$ son números reales $a \neq 0$.

**power regression** (p. 404)   A method to determine a power function that best fits a set of data.

**regresión de poder** (pág. 404)   Un método para determinar la función potencia que mejor se ajuste a un conjunto de datos.

**probability distribution** (p. 565)   The probabilities of each possible outcome of a random experiment or survey.

**distribución de probabilidades** (pág. 565)   Las probabilidades de cada resultado posible de un experimento aleatorio o encuesta.

# Q

**quadratic equation** (p. 107)   An equation of the form $ax^2 + bx + c = 0$, where $a \neq 0$.

**ecuación cuadrática** (pág. 107)   Ecuación de la forma $ax^2 + bx + c = 0$, donde $a \neq 0$.

**quadratic function** (p. 104)   A function of the form $f(x) = ax^2 + bx + c$, where $a$, $b$, and $c$ are real numbers and $a \neq 0$.

**función cuadrática** (pág. 104)   Función de la forma $f(x) = ax^2 + bx + c$, donde $a$, $b$ y $c$ son números reales y $a \neq 0$.

**quadratic regression** (p. 169)   A method to determine a quadratic function that best fits a set of data.

**regresión cuadrática** (pág. 169)   Un método para determinar la función cuadrática que mejor se ajuste a un conjunto de datos.

**question of interest** (p. 581)   The topic for which information is to be collected in a survey or a careful study.

**pregunta de interés** (pág. 581)   Tema para el cual se recolectará información en una encuesta o un estudio minucioso.

# R

**radian** (p. 480)   An angular measure equal to the length of a corresponding arc on the unit circle. $360° = 2\pi$ radians.

**radián** (pág. 480)   Una medida angular igual a la longitud de un arco correspondiente en un círculo unidad. $360° = 2\pi$ radianes.

**randomized block design** (p. 583)   Involves first grouping experimental units according to a common characteristic, and then using random assignment within each group.

**diseño del bloque aleatorio** (pág. 583)   Implica primero agrupar unidades experimentales según una característica común, y luego usar la asignación arbitraria dentro de cada grupo.

**range** (p. 59)   The set of all possible output values for a function.

**rango** (pág. 59)   El conjunto de todos los valores de salida posibles para una función.

**rational function** (p. 425)   A function that is the quotient of two polynomials.

**función racional** (pág. 425)   Función que es el cociente de dos polinomios.

**recursive formula** (p. 296)   A formula for a sequence that can be used to calculate any term if the preceding term is known.

**fórmula de recursión** (pág. 296)   Una fórmula para una secuencia que se puede usar para calcular cualquier término si el término anterior es conocido.

**reference angle** (p. 490)   The acute angle formed by the terminal side of an angle and the $x$-axis.

**ángulo de referencia** (pág. 490)   El ángulo agudo formado por el lado terminal de un ángulo y el eje de las $x$.

**relative extrema** (p. 279)   Maximum or minimum points that occur at a point within a given interval of a function.

**extremos relativos** (pág. 279)   Puntos máximos o mínimos que ocurren en un punto ubicado en un intervalo de una función.

**relative maximum** (p. 232)   The greatest value of a function over an interval.

**máximo relativo** (pág. 232)   El valor mayor de una función en un intervalo.

**relative minimum** (p. 232)   The least value of a function over an interval.

**mínimo relativo** (pág. 232)   El valor menor de una función en un intervalo.

**removable point of discontinuity** (p. 453)   A domain value that would cause the original function, but not the simplified function, to be undefined. Also called a "hole" in the graph of the function.

**punto de discontinuidad removible** (pág. 453)   Un valor de dominio que causaría que la función original, pero no la función simplificada, estuviera indefinida. También se le conoce como un "agujero" en la gráfica de la función.

**response** (p. 577)   An answer provided by a subject to a survey question.

**respuesta** (pág. 577)   Contestación de un sujeto a una pregunta de la encuesta.

**response variables** (p. 582)   The outcomes of an experiment.

**variables de respuesta** (pág. 582)   Resultados de un experimento.

**root of an equation** (p. 146)   A solution of an equation.

**raíz de una ecuación** (pág. 146)   Solución de una ecuación.

# S

**sample** (p. 577)   A portion of the population.

**muestra** (pág. 577)   Porción de la población.

**sample proportion** (p. 608)   The proportion of each result of a survey.

**proporción de la muestra** (pág. 608)   La proporción de cada resultado de una encuesta.

**sampling distribution** (p. 611)   The distribution of proportions of a given statistic based on a random sample.

**distribución de muestreo** (pág. 611)   La distribución de proporciones de una estadística dada basada en una muestra aleatoria.

**sequence** (p. 295)   An ordered list of items or numbers.

**sucesión** (pág. 295)   Lista de elementos o números.

**series** (p. 299)   The sum of the terms in a sequence.

**serie** (pág. 299)   Suma de los términos de una sucesión.

**sigma notation** (p. 303)   Notation using the Greek letter sigma ($\Sigma$) to express the sum of a series. Also called summation notation.

**notación sigma** (pág. 303)   Notación usando la letra griega sigma ($\Sigma$) para expresar la suma de una serie. También se le llama *notación de sumatoria*.

**simple random sample (SRS)** (p. 578)   A sample for which all members of a population are equally likely to be chosen.

**muestra aleatoria simple (MAS)** (pág. 578)   Muestra de que todos los miembros de una población tienen la misma probabilidad de ser escogido.

**simulation** (p. 607, 629)   A process in which imaginary data are generated, usually many times, to determine typical results.

**simulación** (pág. 607, 629)   Un proceso en el cual los datos imaginarios se generan, por lo general muchas veces, para determinar resultados típicos.

**single-blind study** (p. 585)   A study in which either the person conducting the experiment or the subjects have knowledge of the treatment, but not both.

**estudio ciego solo** (pág. 585)   Un estudio en el cual la persona que conduce el experimento o los sujetos tienen el conocimiento del tratamiento, pero no ambos.

**solution of a system of equations** (p. 29)   A point, or set of points, whose coordinates make the equations of the system true.

**solución de un sistema de ecuaciones** (pág. 29)   Un punto o el juego de puntos, cuyas coordenadas hacen verdaderas las ecuaciones del sistema.

**square matrix** (p. 47)   A matrix in which the number of rows equals the number of columns.

**matriz cuadrada** (pág. 47)   Una matriz donde el número de filas es igual al número de columnas.

**square root regression** (p. 403)   A method to determine a square root function that best fits a set of data.

**regresión cuadrática** (pág. 403) Un método para determinar la función cuadrática que mejor se ajuste a un conjunto de datos.

**standard deviation** (p. 553)   A measure of the amount of spread or variation of a set of data from its mean.

**desviación estándar** (pág. 553)   Medida de la cantidad de dispersión o variación de un conjunto de datos con respecto a su media.

**standard form of a polynomial** (p. 231)   A simplified form of a polynomial with the terms in descending order by exponent.

**forma estándar de un polinomio** (pág. 231)   Una forma simplificada de un polinomio con los términos en orden descendiente según el exponente.

**standard form of a quadratic equation** (p. 113)   A quadratic equation written in the form $ax^2 + bx + c = 0, a \neq 0$.

**forma estándar de una ecuación cuadrática** (pág. 113)   Una ecuación cuadrática escrita en la forma $ax^2 + bx + c = 0, a \neq 0$.

**standard position** (p. 487)   An angle on the coordinate plane with the vertex at the origin and the initial side on the positive $x$-axis.

**posición estándar** (pág. 487)   Un ángulo en el plano de coordenadas cuyo vértice está en el origen y cuyo lado inicial está en el eje positivo de las $x$.

**statistic** (p. 597)   A number that summarizes data in a meaningful way, e.g., the mean.

**estadística** (pág. 597)   Un número que resume los datos de una manera significativa, por ejemplo, la media.

**statistical significance** (page. 622)   A number that expresses the probability that the result of a given experiment or study could have occurred purely by chance.

**significación estadística** (pág. 622)   Un número que expresa la probabilidad de que el resultado de un estudio o experimento dado podría haber ocurrido por casualidad.

**step function** (p. 61)   A piecewise-defined function with constant values throughout each interval of its domain.

**función escalonada** (pág. 61)   Una función por partes con valores constantes a lo largo de cada intervalo en su dominio.

**substitution method** (p. 33)   An algebraic method of solving a system of equations by solving one equation for one variable in terms of the others.

**método de la substitución** (pág. 33)   un método algebraico para resolver un sistema de ecuaciones mediante la solución de una ecuación para una variable en cuanto a los demás.

**sum of the infinite geometric series** (p. 313)   The limiting value of the partial sums of an infinite geometric series whose terms approach zero.

**suma de las series geométricas infinitas** (pág. 313)   El valor limitante de las sumas parciales de una serie geométrica infinita cuyos términos se aproximan a cero.

**summation notation** (p. 259)   Notation used to represent the sum of a number of terms. Also called sigma notation.

**notación de sumatoria** (pág. 259)   Notación usada para representar la suma de una cantidad de términos. También se le conoce como notación sigma.

**survey** (p. 577)   A study in which subjects are asked a question or a series of questions.

**encuesta** (pág. 577)   Un estudio en el que los sujetos se les pide una pregunta o una serie de preguntas.

**synthetic division** (p. 250)   A method of polynomial division.

**división sintética** (pág. 250)   Método de división polinomial.

# T

**terminal side** (p. 487)   The ray that forms an angle with the initial side, or $x$-axis, for an angle on the coordinate plane.

**lado terminal** (pág. 487)   El rayo que forma un ángulo con el lado inicial, o eje de las $x$, para un ángulo en el plano de coordenadas.

**treatment** (p. 582)   The method in an experiment that is used to try to influence the subjects' responses.

**tratamiento** (pág. 582)   Método en un experimento, usado para intentar influir sobre las respuestas de los sujetos.

**trigonometric function** (p. 491)   Periodic functions that describe the relationships between sides and angles in a triangle.

**función trigonométrica** (pág. 491)   Funciones periódicas que describen las relaciones entre lados y ángulos en un triángulo.

# U

**unit circle** (p. 480)   A circle with a radius of 1 unit.

**círculo unidad** (pág. 480)   Un círculo con un radio de 1 unidad.

# V

**variable matrix** (p. 48)   A single-column matrix formed by all of the variables of a system of equations.

**matriz variable** (pág. 48)   Una matriz que contiene solo una columna formada por todas las variables de un sistema de ecuaciones.

**vertex form of a quadratic function** (p. 186)   A quadratic function written in the form $f(x) = a(x - h)^2 + k$, where the vertex of the function is $(h, k)$.

**forma vértice de una función cuadrática** (pág. 186)   Una función cuadrática escrita en la forma $f(x) = a(x - h)^2 + k$, donde el vértice de la función es $(h, k)$.

**vertex of a parabola** (p. 158)   The point that represents the maximum or minimum value of the function.

**vértice de una parábola** (pág. 158)   Punto que representa el valor máximo o mínimo de la función.

**vertical asymptote** (p. 426)   The line $x = b$ if the absolute value of function $f$ increases without bound as $x$ approaches some number $b$.

**asíntota vertical** (pág. 426)   Recta $x = b$ si el valor absoluto de la función $f$ aumenta sin límite a medida que $x$ se aproxima al número $b$.

## X

**x-intercept** (p. 279)   The value(s) $x$ for which $f(x) = 0$.

**intercepto en x** (pág. 279)   Valores de $x$ para los cuales $f(x) = 0$.

## Y

**y-intercept** (p. 9)   The value of a function for $f(0)$.

**intercepto en y** (pág. 9)   Valor de una función para $f(0)$.

## Z

**z-score** (p. 556)   A measure that quantifies the distance a data point is from the mean of a set of data.

**z-resultado** (pág. 556)   Una medida que cuantifica la distancia un punto de datos es de la media de un conjunto de datos.

**zero of a function** (p. 146)   For a function $f(x)$, any value $x$ such that $f(x) = 0$.

**cero de una función** (pág. 146)   Para una función $f(x)$, cualquier valor de $x$ tal que $f(x) = 0$.

# Verbal & Visual Word Association

| Definition in Your Own Words | Important Elements |
|---|---|
| | |

| Visual Representation | Academic Vocabulary Word | Personal Association |
|---|---|---|
| | | |

# Word Map

Definition

Visual

Academic Vocabulary Word

Example

Example

Example

# Eight Circle Spider

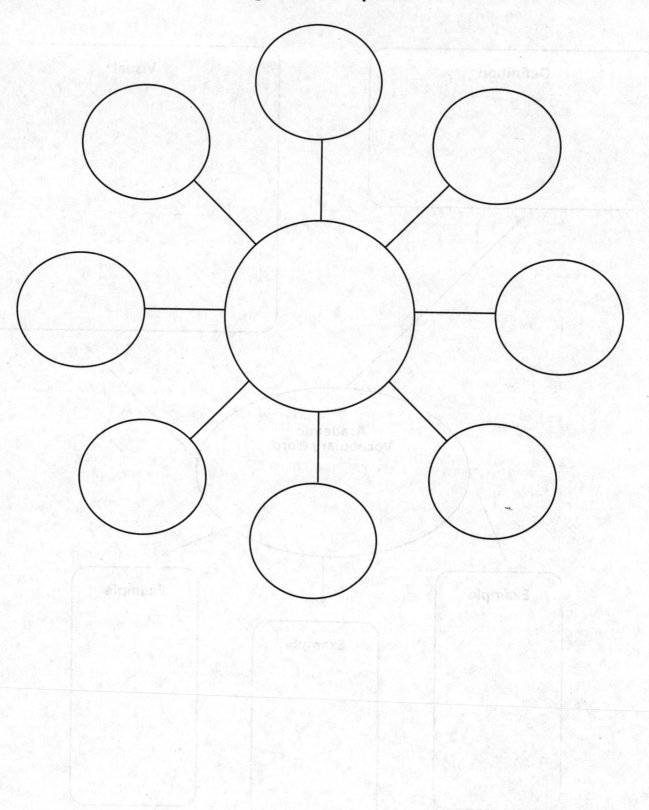

# Venn Diagram

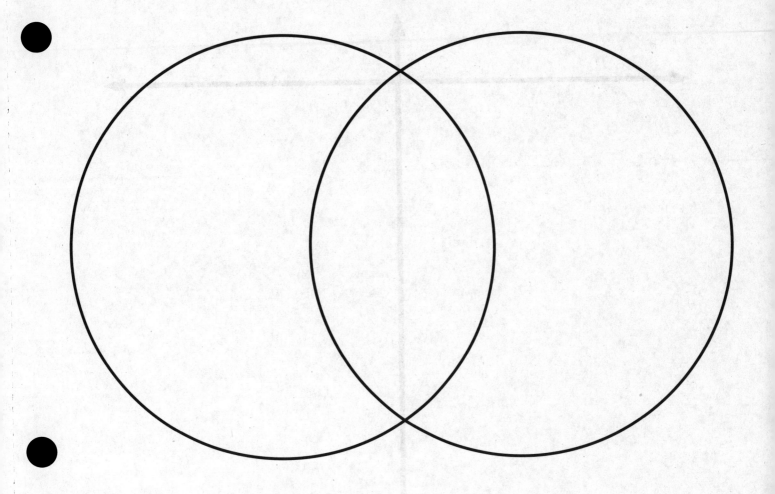

# Vertical/Horizontal T-Table

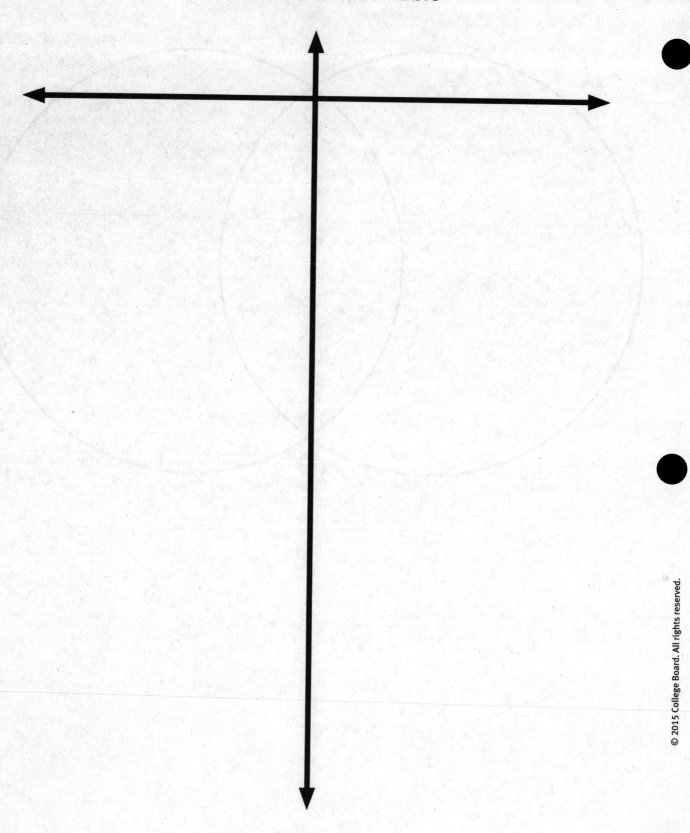

# Number Lines

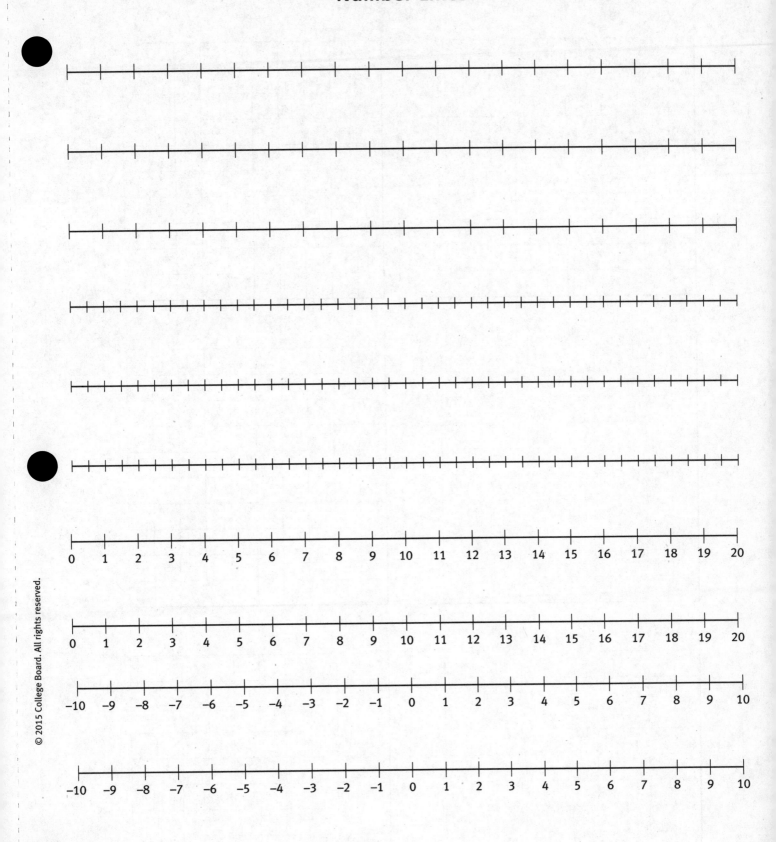

# 1<sup>st</sup> Quadrant Grids

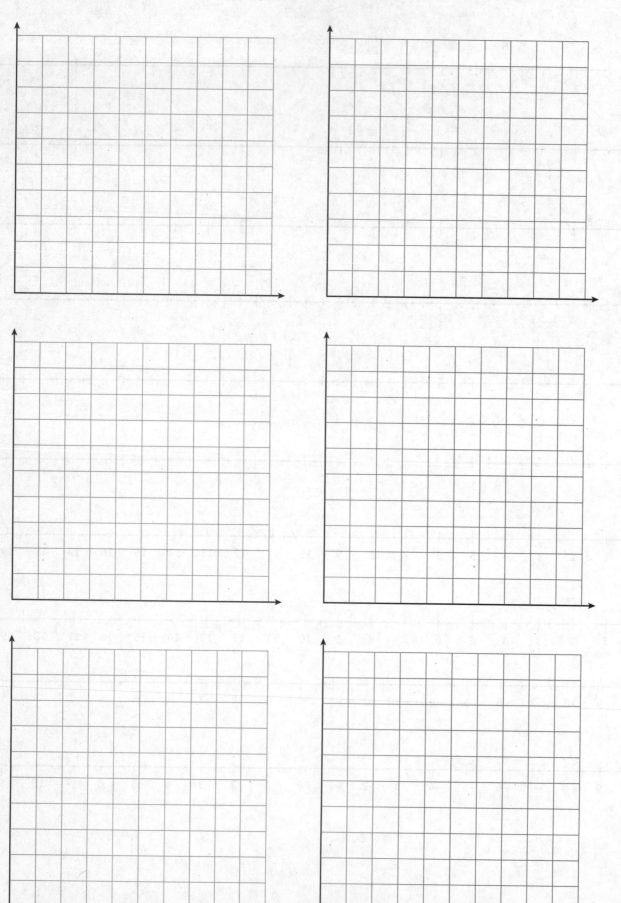

# 5 by 5 Coordinate Grids

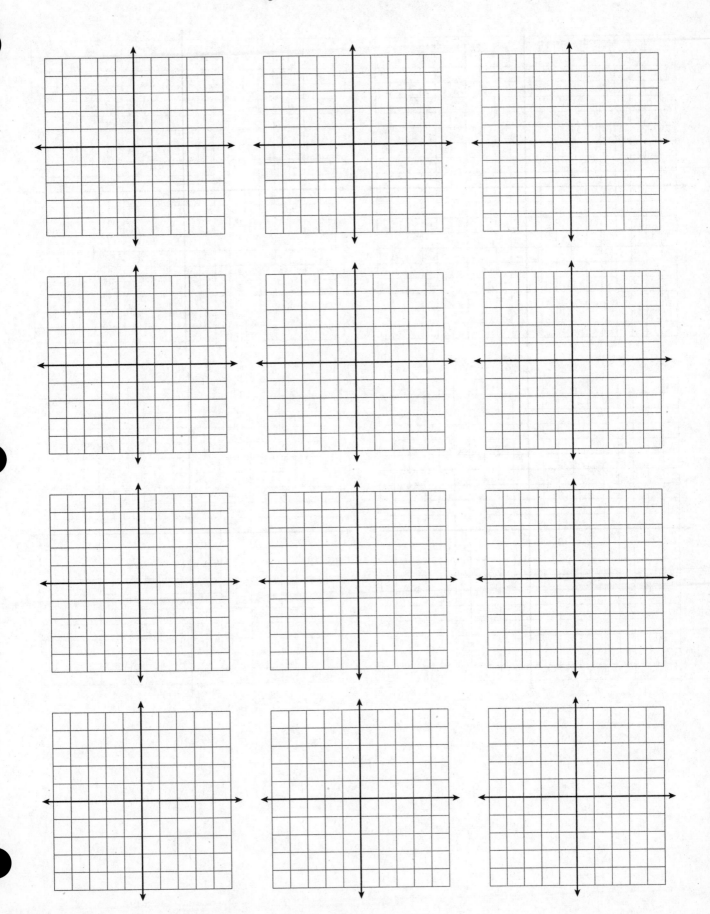

# 20 × 20 Grids

# Tables and Graphs

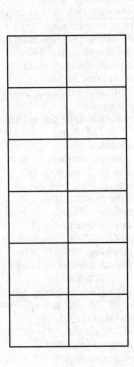

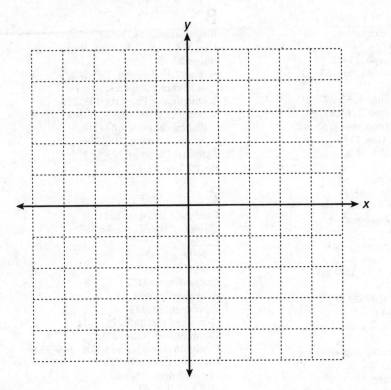

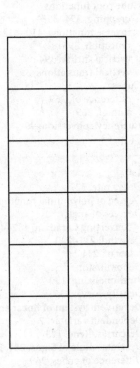

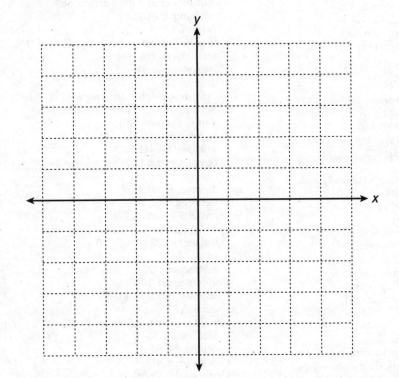

# Index

## A

Absolute value equations
  defined, 11
  solve and graph, 11–12
Absolute value function, 63–70
  defined, 63
  horizontal shrink, 65, 67–68
  horizontal stretch, 65, 67–68
  horizontal translations, 65–66
  parent function, 173
  reflection, 65
  vertex, 63
  vertical shrink, 65, 67
  vertical stretch, 65, 67
  vertical translations, 65–66
Absolute value inequalities
  defined, 13
  solve and graph, 13–14
Addition
  complex number, 126–127
  functions, 73–74
  logarithm, 350–352
  matrix, 43–44
  polynomials, 241–245
  properties
    Commutative Property of, 44
    of Equality, 4
    of Inequality, 13
  rational expressions, 449–450
Addition-elimination method, 34
Algebraic expression, 3
Alkanes, 295–297
Alternative notation, 255
Amplitude of periodic function, 512
Angles
  coterminal, 488
  initial side, 487
  in radian measure converted to degree,
    482–483
  reference, 490
  in standard position, 487–490
  terminal side, 487
Arc length
  constant of proportionality and,
    479–480
  defined, 478
  radians, 480
Arithmetic sequence, 295–304
  common difference, 295
  defined, 295
  explicit formula, 296–297
  partial sum, 299–301
  recursive formula, 296
  series, 299
Asymptote
  defined, 329
  of exponential function, 329–335
  of logarithmic functions, 365–368
  of rational function, 426–428
  of tangent function, 523, 527
Axis of symmetry
  graph of parabola, 158
  graph of quadratic function, 198

## B

Batting average, 553–557
Bias, 578
Binomials
  Binomial Theorem, 259–262
  difference of squares, 108–110
  Distributive Property, 108, 109
  factoring trinomials into, 267
  multiplication of, 108–110
  Pascal's Triangle, 256–258
Binomial Theorem, 259–262
Boyle's Law, 433

## C

Cardano, Girolamo, 121
Change of Base Formula, 364
Circle
  arc length, 478
  unit circle, 480
Circumference, 477
Coefficient matrix, 48
Combinations, 255
Combined variation, 433–434
Common difference, 295
Common logarithm function, 348–354
Common ratio, 308–310
Commutative Property
  of Addition, 44
  polynomials, 246
Completely randomized design, 583
Completing the square
  defined, 139
  to solve quadratic equations, 139–140
  vertex form, 186–188
Complex conjugate
  defined, 129
  to factor quadratic expressions, 132
Complex Conjugate Root Theorem, 273
Complex fractions, 451
Complex number, 124–134
  addition, 126–127
  complex plane, 124
  defined, 124
  division, 129–130
  factoring with, 132–134
  imaginary part of, 124
  multiplication, 127–128
  real part of, 124
  set of, 124
  subtraction, 127
Complex plane, 124
Composite function, 81–86
  defined, 81
  inner and outer functions, 84–86
  notation for, 85
  writing, 84–85
Composition, 81
Compound interest
  defined, 374
  formula for, 374–375
Concave down, 558
Concave up, 558

Confounding variable, 586–588
Consistent system of linear equations, 30
Constant matrix, 48
Constant of proportionality, 323
  arc length and, 479–480
Constant of variation, 432
Constraints, 24, 541
Continuous functions, 279
Convergence
  sum of infinite geometric series, 314,
    317–318
Coordinate plane
  angle in standard position, 487–490
  unit circle on, 491–493
Cosecant (csc), 504
Cosine (cos) function
  defined, 491
  as even function, 521
  of 45°-45°-90° triangles, 494–496
  graphing, 521–526
  period, midline and amplitude,
    521–526
  Pythagorean identity, 501–503
  of 30°-60°-90° triangles, 494–496
  translating, 533–538
  unit circle and, 491–492, 494–497
Cotangent (cot), 504
Coterminal angles, 488
Counterexample, 216
Critical value, 614
Cube root equation, 397–398
Cube root functions
  graphing, 394–396
  inverse functions, 410–412
  reflection, 395
  vertical shrink, 394
  vertical translations, 395
Cubes
  difference of, 269
  sum of, 269
Currency conversion, 99
Cusp, 63

## D

Decay rate, 327
Degree of polynomial function, 231
Degrees of angle
  converting to radian, 482–483
Demand, 211–220
  law of, 211
Denominator
  rationalizing, 137
Density curve, 555
Dependent system of linear equations, 30
Dependent variable, 7
Descartes, René, 123
Descrates' Rule of Signs, 281, 282–283
Difference of cubes, 269
Difference of squares, 108–110
  difference of cubes, 269
  sum of cubes, 269
Directrix, 156–158
Direct variation, 433

graphic organizer, 108–110
   perfect square trinomial, 108–110
   Zero Product Property, 111–114
graphing, 153–163
   axis of symmetry, 158
   as minimum/maximum, 155
   opening down, 155
   opening up, 155
   vertex, 155
roots of, 146, 204–205
solving
   completing the square, 139–140
   factoring, 107–115
   Quadratic Formula, 122, 144–145
   square root of both sides, 137–138
solving systems of equations with linear
   equations, 211–220
standard form, 113–114, 139
   completing square to derive
     Quadratic Formula, 141–142
writing, 107
   in standard form with solutions,
     113–114
Quadratic Formula
   completing the square to derive,
     141–142
   defined, 122
   deriving, 141–142
   solving quadratic equations, 122, 201
Quadratic function
   application of, 103–106
   domain and range of, 198
   graphing, 104–106, 200–205
     axis of symmetry, 198, 200
     discriminants and nature of solution,
       204–205
     minimum/maximum of, 200
     opening down, 200
     opening up, 200
     vertex, 195, 200
     $x$-intercept, 197, 200
     $y$-intercept, 197, 200
   introduction, 103–106
   inverse functions, 407–410
   inverse relations, 406–408
   parent function
     defined, 173
     horizontal stretch or shrink, 180–184
     reflection, 178–179
     transformation of, 173–184
     translations, 173–177
     vertex form, 186–188
     vertical stretch or shrink, 178–184
   quadratic regression, 167–170
   standard form, 194
   vertex form of, 186–188
   write
     given three points, 163–166
     from verbal description, 193–194
   zeros of, 146, 204–205, 271
Quadratic inequalities
   factoring, 116–118
   graphing, 206–208
Quadratic regression, 167–170
Quotient identity, 504–506
Quotient Property of Logarithm,
   350–353, 362–363

## R

Radians
   converting to degrees, 482–483
   defined, 480
Radical functions
   cube root functions, 394–396
   graphing
     steps in, 455
   horizontal asymptote, 426–427
   square root functions, 387–390
Radicand, 143
Random chance, 619–622
Random digit table, 580
Randomized block design, 583–584
Random sampling
   completely randomized design, 583
   in experiments, 582–585
   graphing calculator for, 579
   margin of error and, 606–609
   matched pairs design, 584
   random digit table, 580
   randomized block design, 583–584
   simple random sample, 578
   surveys, 577–581
Range
   inverse functions, 91, 407
   logarithmic functions, 365–368
   piecewise-defined functions, 59–60
   quadratic function, 198
Rate of change, 463
   of function, 19
Rational equations, 463–466
   extraneous solutions, 464
Rational expressions
   addition, 449–450
   complex fractions, 451
   division, 447
   multiplication, 446
   simplifying, 445–460
   subtraction, 449–450
Rational function
   defined, 425
   discontinuity, 453
   finding horizontal asymptotes, 453–456
   finding vertical asymptotes, 453–456
   graphing, 457–460
   horizontal translation, 437
   introduction to, 417–424
   as inverse variation, 431–434
   parent function, 425
   transformation, 435–440
   vertical asymptote, 426–428
   vertical reflection, 437
   vertical stretch, 436–437
   vertical translations, 437
Rational inequality, 467–469
Rationalize numerator, 138
Rationalize the denominator, 137
Rational Root Theorem, 281–282
Reciprocal function, 435
Reciprocal identity, 504–506
Recursive formula
   arithmetic sequence, 296
   defined, 296
   geometric sequence, 309
Reference angle, 490
Reflection

absolute value functions, 65
cube root function, 395
defined, 389
parabola, 178–184
parent function, 178–184
square root function, 389
Relative extrema, 279
Relative maximum of functions, 232–233
Relative minimum of function, 232–233
Remainder Theorem, 281, 284
Removable points of discontinuity, 453
Response, in survey, 577
Response variable, 582
Richter scale, 343–347
Right triangles
   45°-45°-90° triangles
     cosine of, 494–496
     sine of, 494–496
   30°-60°-90° triangles
     cosine of, 494–496
     sine of, 494–496
     tangent of, 495–496
   unit circle and, 494–497
Rigid transformation, 174
Roots
   of polynomial function, 281–286
   solving quadratic equations by factoring
     with complex, 133
Roots of equation, 146, 204

## S

68-95-99.7 Rule, 559–561
Sample proportion, 608
Sampling
   bias, 578
   survey, 577
Sampling distribution, 611–613
Scale factor, 323
Secant (sec), 504
Sequence
   arithmetic, 295–304
   defined, 166, 295
   geometric, 307–318
   terms of, 295
   writing terms of, 312
Series
   convergence of, 317–318
   defined, 299
   finite, 312
   geometric, 312–318
   infinite, 312
   notation for, 303
   partial sum, 299–301
   writing terms of, 312
Set notation, 59, 60
Sigma notation
   defined, 259
   elements of, 303
   sum of infinite series, 315
Simple random sample, 578–579, 628
Simulations
   confirming data with, 600–602
   design and conduct, to test statistical
     significance, 625–628
   devising, 593–598
   of survey, 607
Sine (sin) function
   defined, 491

45°-45°-90° triangles, 494–496
graphing, 515–520
as odd function, 515
period, midline and amplitude of, 515–520
Pythagorean identity, 501–503
30°-60°-90° triangles, 494–496
translating, 533–538
unit circle and, 491–492, 494–497
Single-blind study, 585
68-95-99.7 rule, 559
Slope, 9
Slope-intercept form, 20
Square matrix, 47
Square prism, 208
Square root equations, 391–393
Square root functions
extraneous solutions, 391
graphing, 387–388
horizontal translation, 388
inverse function, 401–403, 406–408
reflection, 389
square root regression, 403–404
transformations, 387–390
vertical stretch, 388
Square root regression, 403
Standard deviation
normal distribution, 559
symbol for, 562
Standard form
of linear equation, 9
of polynomials, 231, 246
of quadratic equation, 113–114
Standard Normal Table
defined, 560
determine probabilities using, 565–566
example of, 575–576
reading, 560
Standard position for angle, 487–490
Statistic, 597. *See also* Probability and statistics
Statistically significant, 622–628
defined, 622
design/conduct simulation to test, 625–628
Step function
defined, 61
graphing, 61–62
Substitution method
defined, 33
with three variables, 37–38
with two variables, 33–34
Subtraction
complex number, 127
functions, 74
logarithm, 350–352
matrix, 43–44
polynomials, 241–245
rational expressions, 449–450
Subtraction Property
of Equality, 4
of Inequality, 13
Summation notation, 259, 303
Sum of cubes, 269
Sum of finite geometric series, 312–313
Sum of infinite geometric series, 313–315
convergence, 314, 317–318
notation for, 315
Supply and demand, 29, 211–220
law of, 211

Surveys, 577–581
defined, 577
simulation of, 607
Synthetic division of polynomials, 250–251
Systems of equations
linear and nonlinear, 211–220
Systems of linear equations, 29–52
classification
consistent, 30
dependent, 30
inconsistent, 30
independent, 30
solution of, 29
solving
elimination method, 34–35
Gaussian elimination, 38–40
graphing, 29–32
with matrices, 48–52
substitution method, 33–34, 37–38
with three variables, 36–41
with two variables, 29–35
solving with nonlinear equations, 211–220

**T**

Tangent (tan) function
asymptote of, 523, 527
defined, 495
graphing, 527–532
as odd function, 527
period and midline of, 527–532
Pythagorean identity, 501–503
30°-60°-90° triangles, 495–496
translating, 533–538
unit circle, 495–497
Terminal side of angle, 487
Terms, of sequence, 295
Theorems
Binomial Theorem, 259–262
Complex Conjugate Root Theorem, 273
Factor Theorem, 281, 284–285
Fundamental Theorem of Algebra, 271
Pythagorean Theorem, 501
Rational Root Theorem, 281–282
Remainder Theorem, 281, 284
30°-60°-90° triangles
cosine of, 494–496
ratio of side lengths, 494–496
sine of, 494–496
tangent, 495–496
Torr, 433
Transformations
absolute value functions, 65–70
cube root functions, 394–395
defined, 65, 173
of exponential function, 331–335
horizontal stretch or shrink, 65
absolute value function, 67–68
of parent quadratic function, 180–184
horizontal translations
absolute value function, 65–66
logarithmic functions, 365–368
natural base exponential functions, 336–339
order for multiple, 180–184
of parent function, 65–70, 173–184
rational function, 435–440
reflection

absolute value function, 65
parent function, 178–184
rigid, 174
square root functions, 387–390
translation
absolute value function, 65–66
of parent quadratic function, 174–177
vertex form and, 186–188
vertical stretch or shrink
absolute value function, 65, 67
of parent quadratic function, 178–184
Translation
absolute value functions, 65–66
parent quadratic function, 174–177
trigonometric functions, 533–538
Triangles
right
45°-45°-90°, 494–496
30°-60°-90° triangles, 494–496
unit circle and, 494–497
Trigonometric functions, 511–538
cosecant, 504
cosine
graphing, 521–526
Pythagorean identity, 501–503
unit circle and, 494–496
cotangent, 504
defined, 491
periodic, 511–514
reciprocal and quotient identities, 504–505
secant, 504
sine
graphing, 515–520
Pythagorean identity, 501–503
unit circle and, 494–496
tangent
graphing, 527–532
Pythagorean identity, 501–503
unit circle and, 495–496
translating, 533–538
Trigonometry
angles in standard position, 487–490
Pythagorean identity, 501–503
radian measure, 477–484
reciprocal and quotient identities, 504–506
special right triangles and unit circle, 494–497
trigonometric functions, 511–538
unit circle on coordinate plane, 491–493
Trinomials
factoring, 108–110
into binomials, 267
perfect square trinomial, 108–110, 139
Two-variable equations, 7–10
graphing, 17–20

**U**

Unit circle
on coordinate plane, 491–493
cosine and, 491–492
defined, 480
sine and, 491–492
special right triangles and, 494–497
tangent and, 495–497

## V

Variable matrix, 48
Variables
   confounding variable, 586–588
   dependent, 7
   explanatory, 582
   independent, 7
   response, 582
Variation
   combined, 433–434
   constant of variation, 432
   direct, 433
   joint, 433
Vertex
   absolute value functions, 63
   of parabola, 158, 195
      as minimum/maximum, 155
      as minimum/maximum of function, 200
Vertex form of quadratic function, 186–188
Vertical asymptote
   defined, 426, 453
   finding, 453–456
   rational function, 426
Vertical reflection
   rational function, 437

Vertical shrink
   absolute value functions, 65, 67
   cube root function, 394
   defined, 388
   exponential function, 331, 334
   natural base exponential functions, 337, 338
   parabola, 178–184
   parent function, 178–184
Vertical stretch
   absolute value functions, 65, 67
   defined, 388
   exponential function, 331, 333, 334
   logarithmic functions, 367–368
   natural base exponential functions, 338
   parabola, 178–184
   parent function, 178–184
   rational function, 436–437
   square root function, 388
Vertical translations
   absolute value functions, 65–66
   cube root function, 394
   defined, 388
   exponential function, 332
   logarithmic functions, 367–368
   rational function, 437

## W

Writing Math, 60, 73, 74, 75, 77, 85, 91, 99, 123, 198, 295, 315, 562

## X

$x$-intercept
   of parabolas, 197, 200

## Y

$y$-intercept
   defined, 9
   of parabolas, 197, 200

## Z

Zero Product Property, 111–114, 271
Zeros of quadratic function, 146, 204, 271
$z$-score
   using graphing calculator, 568–571
   using normal curve to estimate, 562–564
   using Standard Normal Table, 565–566, 575–576